BASIC
REFRIGERATION

Principles • **Practice** • **Operation**

A SIMPLIFIED PRESENTATION OF THE FUNDAMENTALS
OF REFRIGERATION GIVING EQUAL TREATMENT
TO ALL COMMON REFRIGERANTS, DESIGN,
OPERATION, AND SERVICING OF THE
APPARATUS AND SYSTEM

BY

GUY R. KING

Santa Monica City College

SECOND EDITION

PUBLISHERS
NICKERSON & COLLINS CO.
CHICAGO 44

PREFACE

DURING many years of teaching refrigeration to practical men, the writer has failed to find a text which he considered wholly suitable. For practical men, such a text must be written in every day English, and not presuppose a college course in thermodynamics. Yet it must not be over-simplified by leaving out basic theory. This book is an attempt to answer such requirements.

A brief review is first given of those basic physical principles necessary to understand refrigeration cycles. Then the student is introduced to a detailed physical description of compression refrigeration. Each piece of equipment used is then described, stressing its part in the complete refrigeration cycle. Illustrations are drawn from all branches of equipment: domestic, commercial and industrial. Where there are differences in these branches, they are pointed out. But no attempt is made to separate them into separate subjects. Pictures and diagrams are used wherever possible to help give a picture of the processes explained.

After the student thoroughly understands the physical process of refrigeration, calculations are given to show how to choose the proper size equipment. These calculations are kept as simple as possible so that anyone who can solve a simple formula should be able to master them. Yet, simplification has been done, not by omissions, but by using every day terms and illustrations.

Many tables and charts were prepared to compare conditions, and to give short cuts in calculations. Useful tables and similar data are put together in the appendix so they may be easily found when wanted for reference. Questions are given at the end of each chapter to bring out the key points in the chapter, and to give the student practice in solving problems. Answers to all numerical problems are given in the appendix.

In this second edition, the changes made are only those necessary to bring the material up-to-date. Descriptions of obsolete refrigerants were dropped, and more information given on the fluorocarbon group. More attention was given to larger hermetic compressors, and to developments in synthetic insulations. Data was added on brine and water absorption systems.

This work is a compilation of much the author has collected both from practical experience, and from the association and help of other men. It is impossible to acknowledge all the sources of information here collected, or to give credit to all men, books, notes, magazines, etc., which have supplied information which has gone into this book. But particular thanks should be given to the late Emerson Brandt of Nickerson & Collins Co., for his advice and encouragement, and his help in collecting illustrations.

It is hoped this book will be of value to the beginners and students of refrigeration, and to practical men in the field, whether selling, installing, servicing or operating large or small equipment.

GUY R. KING

Santa Monica, California
February, 1961

CONTENTS

CHAPTER 1—FUNDAMENTALS 5
Introduction. Heat and temperature. Specific heat. Latent heat. Change of state. Vapor. Gas and vapor. Energy. Pressure. Partial pressure. Heat Transfer. Scope of refrigeration.

CHAPTER 2—COMPRESSION SYSTEM OF REFRIGERATION 18
Evaporation. Pressure cycle. Temperature cycle. Heat cycle. Liquid-vapor cycle. Standard ton conditions.

CHAPTER 3—REFRIGERANTS 31
Requirements. Analysis. Physical properties. Development of refrigerants. Water. Sulphur dioxide (R 764). Methyl chloride (R 40). Ammonia (R 717). Carbon dioxide. "Carrene 1" (R 30). Fluorinated Hydrocarbons or Fluorocarbons (R 11, R 12, R 13, R 22, R 113, R 114). Other conditions than standard ton. Changing refrigerants. Handling refrigerants.

CHAPTER 4—EXPANSION VALVES 53
General. Function of expansion valve. Hand expansion valve. Low side float valve. High side float valve. Capillary tube. Automatic expansion valve. Thermostatic or Thermal expansion valve.

CHAPTER 5—EVAPORATORS 73
Requirements for evaporators. Types of evaporators. Flooded evaporators. Dry evaporator. Improved Designs. Convection and forced draft evaporators. Evaporator feeds.

CHAPTER 6—COMPRESSORS 87
General. How a compressor works. Historic. Compressor sizes. Construction details. Suction valves. Discharge valves. Gas passages. Shaft seals. Stuffing boxes. Lubrication, Cooling. Service valves. Capacity control. Dual effect. Compressor speeds—piston speeds. Horizontal double acting compressors. Hermetically sealed units. Rotary compressors. Centrifugal compressors. Steam jets.

CHAPTER 7—CONDENSERS 119
Requirements. Operation. Air cooled condensers. Air vs. water cooled condensers. Double pipe condensers. Atmospheric condensers. Shell-and-tube condensers. Shell-and-coil condensers. Water supply. Cooling towers. Evaporative condensers.

CHAPTER 8—FLOW EQUIPMENT 133
Liquid receiver. Pipes and piping. Hand valves. Filters and strainers. Driers or dehydrators. Oil traps. Automatic purgers. Sight glasses. Heat exchangers.

CONTENTS

CHAPTER 9—ELECTRIC CONTROLS AND
            CONTROL VALVES 148
General. Back pressure control. Temperature control. High
pressure; high temperature cutouts. Low oil cutout. Low water
cutout. Float switch. Control applications. Solenoid valves.
Constant pressure valve. Check valve. Water regulating valves.
Pressure relief devices.

CHAPTER 10—LUBRICATION 161
Requirements. Oil foaming. Oil selection.

CHAPTER 11—DEFROSTING METHODS 167
General. Defrost cycle. Periodic removal. Hot gas defrosting.
Thermobank system. Water spray defrost. Heater defrost.
Brine spray.

CHAPTER 12—COMPRESSOR DRIVES 174
Requirements. Electric drives. Steam drive. Diesel. Gas engines.

CHAPTER 13—FOOD PRESERVATION 184
General. Natural ripening and enzymic action. Bacteria and
molds. Other changes. Cold storage. Freezing.

CHAPTER 14—OPERATING 190
General. Maintain temperatures. Economy. Safety. Automatic
refrigeration. General maintenance.

CHAPTER 15—SERVICING 210
General. Variations from refrigeration requirements. Food
storage troubles.

CHAPTER 16—REFRIGERATED ENCLOSURES 222
Requirements. Insulation. Cork. Vegetable fiber. Mineral; Glass
insulations. Plastic insulations. Reflective insulations. Other
insulations. Moisture proofing. Openings and doors. Cabinet
construction. Tank and pipe insulations. Excessive heat.

CHAPTER 17—INSTRUMENTS AND METERS 235
General. Stem thermometers. Dial thermometers. Recording
thermometers. Pressure gages. Electric instruments.

CHAPTER 18—HEAT CALCULATIONS 248
General. Design temperature. K factors. Usage factors. Con-
densing unit size. Evaporator sizing. Boxes over 1500 cubic feet.
Thickness of insulation. Condensers.

CHAPTER 19—HUMIDITY IN REFRIGERATION 274
Relative and absolute humidity. Humidity measurement. Effect of evaporator temperature.

CONTENTS

CHAPTER 20—COMPRESSOR CALCULATIONS—I 283
General. Refrigerant tables. Compressor size. Compressor horse-power. Complete analysis of expansion valve and evaporator. Mollier or pressure-heat diagram. Sizing compressors. Compressor indicator diagrams.

CHAPTER 21—COMPRESSOR CALCULATIONS—II 310
Capacity variations. Effect of changing suction pressure. Effect of changing condensing temperature. Detailed standard ton conditions. Effect of subcooling. Effect of superheated suction vapor. Wet compression. Changing refrigerants. Heat exchangers. Two stage systems. Booster systems. Cascade system. Dual effect.

CHAPTER 22—REFRIGERANT LINES—PRESSURE DROPS ... 339
General. Effect of pressure drops. Figuring velocities and pressure drops. Effect of changing conditions of flow.

CHAPTER 23—BRINE IN REFRIGERATION 348
General. Brine chemistry. Corrosion control. Brine concentrations. Congealing tanks. Eutectic plates.

CHAPTER 24—LIQUID COOLING 362
Beverage cooling requirements. Water coolers. Beer coolers. Charged or soda water. Milk coolers. Brewery refrigeration. Refrigeration in wine making.

CHAPTER 25—COMPLETE SYSTEMS 376
Commercial multiplexing. Cold storage. Locker plants. Air conditioning. Ice making. Faster ice freezing methods.

CHAPTER 26—CARBON DIOXIDE—DRY ICE 409
Carbon dioxide refrigeration. Manufacture of dry ice. Advantages and disadvantages. Use of dry ice.

CHAPTER 27—ALTITUDE AND ITS EFFECT 416

CHAPTER 28—ABSORPTION SYSTEMS 421
Simple intermittent system. Continuous ammonia system. Water absorption system. Diffusion-absorption system. Electrolux system.

CHAPTER 29—THE REFRIGERATION CODE 428
General. American Standard Association safety code for mechanical refrigeration.

APPENDIX

Table A-1—Weights and Specific Heats of Various Substances....431
Table A-2—Properties of Food Products_____432
Table A-3—Sizes and Weights of Food Containers_____436
Table A-4—Energy Conversion Equivalents_____439
Table A-5—Pressure Ratios_____439
Table A-6—Weights and Measures_____440
Table A-7—Dimensions of Soft Drawn Copper Tubing_____442
Table A-8—Dimensions of Standard Weight Iron Pipe_____444
Table A-9—Thermal Conductivity of Various Materials_____445
Table A-10—Other Heat Loads_____446
Table A-11—Cooler Usage Factors_____446
Table A-12—Heat Transfer in Refrigeration Equipment_____447
Table A-13—Refrigerant Required to Charge a System_____448
Table A-14—Log. Mean Temperature Difference_____449
Table A-15—Refrigerant Tables_____450
Table A-16—Heat Loss from Bare and Insulated Pipe_____487
Calculating Overall Heat Leakage Factors_____489
Answers To Problems In Questions_____493

CHAPTER 1

FUNDAMENTALS

Introduction.—To know the principles of refrigeration it is necessary to understand the following:

1. The mechanical equipment used to produce refrigeration.
2. The physical laws operating within this mechanical equipment.
3. How this mechanical equipment controls the operation of these physical laws.

Therefore, to get a full understanding of our subject, let us review the important physical laws involved.

Heat and Temperature.—The first and most important subject to take up is heat and its effects. The question may come up, why study heat when we are interested in refrigeration or cold? But cold is relatively less heat. If we remove heat from a substance we cool it. So we must know something of heat change and heat transfer.

We must understand the difference between heat and temperature. *Temperature is the intensity of heat,* or how strong the heat is; how hot it is, as we say. Fahrenheit temperatures abbreviated F are used entirely in practical refrigeration. Temperature scales other than Fahrenheit and their relationships are shown in Fig. 1—1.

Consider two containers on the stove, one with one pint of water and the other with 8 pints or a gallon. Let these containers be the same size so they absorb the same amount of heat in the same length of time. Suppose conditions are such that the pint comes to a boil in 5 minutes. We will find that the 8 pint kettle will take 8 times as long or 40 minutes to come to a boil[1]. If both pots are boiling, they will be at the same temperature. The boiling temperature of water is 212 F[2]. It has taken 8 times as much heat from the stove to heat the gallon to the boiling temperature.

---

[1] This assumes no variations in losses. Such losses would change these figures slightly.
[2] At atmospheric pressure at sea level.

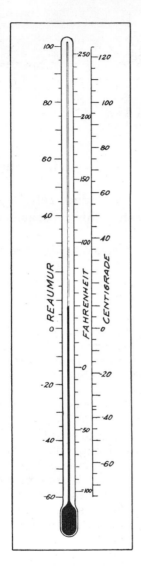
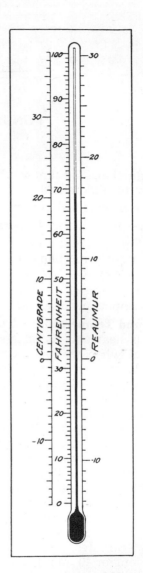

TEMPERATURE   FORMULAS

$F = \frac{9}{5}C + 32$; $C = \frac{5}{9}(F-32)$; $R = \frac{4}{9}(F-32)$;

$F = \frac{9}{4}R + 32$; $C = \frac{5}{4}R$; $R = \frac{4}{5}C$.

Fig. 1-1. Various temperature scales.

If the gallon is heated for 20 minutes instead of 40, it would not be heated to the boiling temperature. A thermometer would show the pint much hotter than the gallon. But the gallon would have 4 times as much heat because it absorbed heat from the fire 4 times as long. If the gallon heated 20 minutes was removed from the fire, it would stay warm longer than the pint heated to the boiling point. If each was put in separate hot water bottles, the gallon would stay warm longer and, therefore, keep one warm longer. The gallon would give up more heat to warm something (or someone) even though it was not as hot to start with. That is why the measurement of temperature is not enough. We must be able to measure the quantity of heat. This depends on the temperature, the quantity of substance and the type of substance involved.

Heat is a form of energy. For engineering work including refrigeration, it is measured in British Thermal Units, better known by its abbreviation of Btu. *The Btu is the amount of heat necessary to raise the temperature of one pound of water 1 degree F.*

In the previous problem let us take one pound of water instead of one pint[1]. Let us assume the water is at 60 F. To raise its temperature to 212 F, it must be heated:

212 — 60 = 152 degrees F.

Since it takes one Btu to heat one pound of water 1 degree, it will take 152 Btu to heat the pound 152 degrees or to the boiling point. If the other container had 8 pounds[2], each pound would require 152 Btu to heat it to the boiling point. Therefore 8 pounds would require:

8 × 152 = 1216 Btu.

The water heated only 20 minutes would absorb half as much heat or:

½ × 1216 = 608 Btu.

This would raise its temperature half of the 152 degrees necessary to raise it to 'the boiling point. Its final temperature would therefore be:

(½ × 152) + 60 = 136 F.

Therefore the kettle with one pound of water heated to 212 F had 152 Btu of heat added to it, and the larger kettle, which was heated to 136 F, had 608 Btu added.

Specific Heat.—If we put one pound of iron on the stove and checked its temperature with a thermometer, we would find it would reach 212 F in less than a minute. But if removed from the stove, it would cool off more quickly than our water did. It takes much less heat to raise the temperature of iron than to raise the

---

[1] One pound of water would be almost a pint.
[2] Eight pounds of water would be 0.96 gallons.

temperature of water a given amount. Also, we need remove less heat to reduce its temperature. Experiment shows it only takes 0.118 Btu of heat to raise the temperature of one pound of iron 1 degree F. This is called the specific heat of iron. *The specific heat of a substance is the amount of heat necessary to raise the temperature of one pound of that substance 1 degree F.* Since it took one Btu to raise the temperature of one pound of water 1 degree, the specific heat of water is 1.

TABLE 1-1. SPECIFIC HEAT OF FOODS ABRIDGED TABLE
(For complete table see Appendix, Table A-2)

Food	Specific Heat Btu per lb.
FRUITS AND VEGETABLES	
Most fruits, berries, vegetables	0.92
MEAT	
Beef	0.77
Fish, Poultry	0.82
Veal	0.70
Lamb, Pork	0.66
DAIRY PRODUCTS	
Butter, Cheese	0.64
Eggs	0.76
Milk, Cream	0.92

Table 1-1 and Tables A-1 and A-2 in the Appendix give some useful specific heats. To find the total heat necessary to raise the temperature of any substance, multiply its weight times its specific heat times the temperature change, or:

$$H = WS(t_2 - t_1)$$

where

H = heat in Btu
W = weight in lbs.
S = specific heat, from Tables 1-1, A-1 or A-2
t_1 = original temperature in degrees F.
t_2 = final temperature in degrees F.

Example 1-1.—How much heat is required to heat 25 lbs. of lead from 70 to 200 F?

$$H = WS(t_2 - t_1)$$
$$= 25 \times .030 \ (200 - 70)$$
$$= 97.5 \text{ Btu of heat.}$$

Also, if 97.5 Btu of heat were removed from 25 lb. of 200 F lead, it would reduce its temperature to 70 F. That is, the formula will work for heating or for cooling.

Example 1-2.—How much refrigeration is required to cool 400 lb of beef at 85 F to 36 F?

$$H = WS(t_2 - t_1)$$
$$= 400 \times .77 \ (36 - 85)$$
$$= -15,100 \ Btu$$

The (—) sign can be taken as requiring cooling instead of heating, that is, removing heat instead of adding it.

Latent Heat.—Let us go back to our pint of water. If it was left on the stove after it came to a boil, its temperature would remain the same. But it would gradually boil away; that is, it would slowly change from water to steam. But if it was taken from the stove, it would stop boiling. That is, it requires heat to boil water, to change water to steam. If the water came to a boil in 5 minutes, it would take about 38 minutes to boil dry. So it takes much more heat to evaporate a pound of water already at the boiling temperature than to heat it to that temperature. Experiment shows it takes 970 Btu of heat to evaporate one pound of water already at 212 F into steam. This is known as the latent heat of evaporation or the latent heat of vaporization. Latent means hidden. This is hidden as far as the temperature is concerned because the steam is still at 212 F. Thus, *The latent heat of vaporization is the amount of heat necessary to change a liquid to a vapor with no change in temperature.*

If this vapor was collected in a coil or steam radiator instead of boiled off into the room, it would give 970 Btu of heat back to the room as it condensed. Thus, this latent heat is available to be used for heating if the steam was condensed back to water.

If we put a pound of ice on the stove and melt it, we would find it would take almost as long to completely melt the ice as to heat the pound of water from 60 F to 212 F. Furthermore, the water around the ice would not heat up as long as it was in contact with unmelted ice. A thermometer would show both the ice and water to be 32 F during the entire melting period. Thus, we have another hidden or latent heat. Experiment shows it takes 144 Btu[1] of heat to melt a pound of ice. This is the latent heat of fusion. Thus, *the latent heat of fusion is the heat necessary to change a solid to a liquid without a change in temperature.*

Since ice must absorb heat to melt, this heat must be supplied by some other source. As previously stated, to remove heat from something is to cool it. Therefore the melting ice will cool whatever supplies this heat.

---

[1] 143.33 Btu have been established as a more accurate value, but the whole number of 144 Btu has been adopted by the trade. Practical figures as commonly used are given throughout this book.

Example 1-3.—In Example 1-2, we figured it took 15,100 Btu to cool 400 lb. of beef from 85 to 36 F. How much ice would be required to do this cooling?

Each pound of ice would absorb 144 Btu. Thus it would take $\frac{15,100}{144}$ =104.9 lb of ice to do the job, neglecting losses. This is a typical refrigeration problem. The refrigeration can be by ice or mechanical means.

In fact, mechanical refrigerators are usually compared to ice to describe the amount of cooling they are capable of doing. Small machines are now rated directly in Btu per hour cooling capacity. At one time, they were rated in "Ice Melting Equivalent," better known as IME.

Example 1-4.—How many Btu per hour of refrigeration would a machine rated at 10 IME's be able to produce?

Since 1 lb of ice absorbs 144 Btu, 10 IME are equivalent to:

$$10 \times 144 = 1440 \text{ Btu per hr}$$

Larger sized machines are rated in tons of refrigeration. *A ton of refrigeration is the same amount of refrigeration as is produced by one ton of ice melted each 24 hours.* Since one pound of ice has a latent heat of 144 Btu, one ton will have a latent heat of $2000 \times 144 =$ 288,000 Btu. That is, it will take 288,000 Btu of heat to melt one ton of ice. Since a one ton machine will absorb 288,000 Btu in 24 hours, it will absorb $\frac{288,000}{24} = 12,000$ Btu per hour, or $\frac{12,000}{60} = \frac{200 \text{ Btu}}{\text{per minute}}$.

Example 1-5.—One ton of refrigeration is equivalent to how many IME per hr?

One ton of refrigeration is equivalent to 12,000 Btu per hr. Therefore: $\frac{12,000}{144} = 83.3 \text{ IME}$

Beside latent heat of evaporation and latent heat of fusion, latent heat of sublimation is another term which may be encountered. Certain substances such as dry ice, which is ice made of carbon dioxide gas, evaporate directly from the solid or ice form to a vapor. Such evaporation from the solid form is known as sublimation. Evaporation by any other name, such as sublimation, still requires heat. Thus, *latent heat of sublimation is the heat necessary to change a solid to a vapor.* It may be considered as the sum of the latent heat of fusion and the latent heat of evaporation. For dry ice this latent heat is 246 Btu per pound. Its sublimation point is —109 F.

Example 1-6—How much dry ice would be required to cool the beef in Example 1-2?

Since 15,100 Btu of cooling was required, it would take:
$$\frac{15,100}{246} = 61.3 \text{ lb of dry ice.}$$

It will be noted in Example 1-3, it took 105 lb of water ice to do this same job. However, other factors such as cost and required temperatures are more important than weight alone. This will be covered in more detail in Chapter 26.

Change of State.—In the above cases, we have mentioned water in the form of a solid (ice), liquid, and a vapor (steam). Many other substances can be changed from solid to liquid or liquid to vapor by applying heat. A latent heat must be added to change a solid to a liquid or a liquid to a vapor. Heat must be absorbed, or taken away, to change a vapor to a liquid or a liquid to a solid. The amounts of heat will vary greatly with different substances. They will also vary with different pressures on the same substance. We also note with dry ice, changes directly from a solid to a vapor are possible. Any such *change of a substance from solid, liquid or vapor form to any of these other forms is known as a change of state.*

Vapor.—*Whenever steam or vapor is in contact with the liquid from which it is evaporated or whenever it is at its evaporating temperature, it is known as saturated vapor.* If it is boiling quietly so that only vapor, no liquid, is present, it is known as dry saturated. But if it is boiling violently so it spatters droplets of liquid into the vapor, or if an attempt is made to cool the vapor so that some of it will recondense, it is known as wet vapor. Wet vapor may be droplets of liquid carried through a pipe with a flow of vapor, or it may form as a fog in the vapor.

If more heat is applied to a boiling liquid, the liquid merely boils faster. The temperature of a vapor from this liquid cannot be raised above the boiling point as long as liquid is present. But if the vapor is carried away from the liquid in a pipe or otherwise and then heated, nothing prevents a rise in temperature. A vapor so heated above its boiling temperature is known as superheated vapor.

Thus, vapor may be wet, dry saturated, or superheated. *A wet vapor contains some unevaporated liquid. A dry saturated vapor has no liquid mixed with it, but is exactly at evaporating temperature. A superheated vapor has been heated above its boiling temperature.*

Gas and Vapor.—We have spoken of evaporated liquid as a vapor. This is the correct term for it. Many times, we hear such a substance incorrectly called a gas. A gas is actually a highly superheated vapor. The principle difference is that a gas will follow the "gas law". The volume of a gas varies inversely with the absolute pressure and directly with the absolute temperature. Any such change can be calculated by formulas[1]. But as a gas approaches its condensing temperature, errors are found in the use of these formulas. The closer the temperature of the gas is to the condensing temperature, the greater these errors become. *Vapor is the gaseous substance on which the "gas formulas" will not work.* Such information, when desired, must be taken from tables which are records of tests. No exact dividing line can be given between a vapor and a gas. *For refrigeration purposes such a substance is a vapor, and tables must be used to find its properties.*

Energy.—Heat is a form of energy. *Energy is ability to do work.* It may be in the form of mechanical energy, such as delivered by a steam engine or electric motor. It may be chemical energy, as the energy in gasoline or gun powder. It may be electrical energy, as delivered by a generator or battery. Or it may be heat energy, which may be used to drive internal combustion engines or steam engines.

Notice that heat energy is changed to mechanical energy in the last mentioned case. Chemical energy may be changed to heat energy by combustion. Electric energy may be converted to mechanical energy in an electric motor, or to heat energy in an electric heater. These are but a few possible changes of the form of energy. But energy can neither be created or destroyed. We can only convert it from one form to another.

Since energy is neither made nor destroyed, there is always the same relationships between the units of the different forms of energy. That is, 746 watts of electric energy equals one horsepower of mechanical energy. One horsepower of mechanical energy equals 2545 Btu per hour, or 42.42 Btu per minute of heat energy. A complete table of energy conversion equivalents is given in Table A-4 (Appendix).

Pressure.—All refrigeration systems contain a pressure which must be controlled. Most of this is a vapor pressure. Any gas or vapor enclosed in a container will press or push out equally in all directions. This pressure may be greater or less than atmospheric pressure. If it is greater than atmospheric pressure, it is measured by the amount of pressure or push on each square inch of surface. The unit used is pounds per square inch, abbreviated lbs. per sq in or psi. The pressure usually indicated is gage pressure, abbreviated psig. This is the pressure shown on an ordinary pressure gage. It is important to remember such a gage measures the difference between the pressure in the system and atmospheric pressure. Thus, a change

---

[1] Given in any elementary book of physics or chemistry.

in atmospheric pressure without a change in the system would give a different gage reading. Normally the variation in atmospheric pressure at any one place would be so small that it could not be detected on the gage. But a pressure specified for sea level would give a different condition at an altitude, because altitude affects atmospheric pressure.

The average atmospheric pressure at sea level is 14.7 psi[1]. Therefore we can get the total pressure in any system at sea level by adding 14.7 to the gage pressure. Such a pressure is called the absolute pressure, abbreviated psia. It would be the pressure in the system measured above a perfect vacuum, that is, measured above no pressure at all. The same results will always be obtained at the same absolute pressures. This is why absolute pressures are used so much. If a gage pressure is specified, it is assumed to be at sea level unless otherwise stated. A more complete description of this with the variations to be expected at different altitudes will be given in Chapter 27.

If the pressure in the system is less than atmospheric, it is usually measured in inches of vacuum (pressure of a column of mercury so many inches high). Here again gage pressure is compared to atmospheric pressure. A 30 inch[2] vacuum would be a perfect vacuum at sea level; where the barometric pressure is 30 inches. A 10 inch vacuum would be 10 inches below atmospheric pressure, or one third of a perfect vacuum. This is sometimes called a gage pressure of 10 inches of vacuum, despite the contradiction of the terms pressure and vacuum. But it should be remembered that any partial vacuum has some absolute pressure.

If it is necessary to change a vacuum to an absolute pressure, it is subtracted from 30 inches. Thus, our 10 inch vacuum would be an absolute pressure of:

$$30 - 10 = 20 \text{ inches absolute pressure.}$$

But absolute pressures are nearly always given in lbs per sq in, so it is necessary to convert our inches to lb per sq in. If it is remembered that atmospheric pressure is 14.7 psi and also 30 inches, then 14.7 psi equals 30 inches. From this we can set up a proportion of:

$$\frac{\text{Pounds}}{\text{Inches}} = \frac{14.7}{30}$$

Thus to convert our 20 inch absolute pressure to lb per sq in:

$$\frac{\text{Pounds}}{20} = \frac{14.7}{30}$$

---

[1] This varies as the barometer changes; 14.696 psi is the accurate mean pressure.

[2] 29.92 inches is the accurate mean.

$$\text{Pounds} = \frac{20 \times 14.7}{30} = 9.8 \text{ psia pressure.}$$

or the direct ratio of lb per sq in to inches as given in Table A-5 in the Appendix may be used.

.49 × 20 = 9.8 psia

A rough approximation of a conversion can be obtained by remembering 2 inches equals 1 psi. This will usually give an answer as near as can be read on a gage. For instance, our 20 inch absolute pressure would then become 10 psi absolute. This is very close to the 9.8 psia obtained above.

Partial Pressure.—Consider two containers of equal volumes connected by a line and a pump, Fig. 1-2. Let container A be filled with a light gas X to a pressure of 50 psia. Let container B be filled with a heavy gas Y to a pressure of 25 psia. Now if the pump is operated to force all of gas Y into container A with gas X, the result will be a pressure of 75 psia. That is, X still exerts its 50 psia and Y adds its 25 psia to this. Furthermore, despite the fact that Y is heavier than X, it will be found that there is no tendency for it to fall to the bottom, or for X to rise to the top. *Each gas fills the entire container and exerts its individual pressure on all inside surfaces of the container.* This is known as *Dalton's Law of Partial Pressures.*

Heat Transfer.—Heat may be transferred or moved from one point to another by three methods: conduction, convection and radiation.

Conduction is heat transfer by contact. If one end of a metal bar is heated, the other end soon warms up. Each atom or particle warmer than its neighbor passes some of its heat to this neighbor by contact or conduction. Heat is transferred from the warm to the cold side of a wall by conduction. Heat gets through the walls of a metal pipe by conduction.

Convection is heat transfer by the movement of a fluid, usually water or air. Air blowing over a product and back to cooling coils picks up heat from the product by conduction. This heat is carried to the coils by convection. Air convection may be natural (by gravity circulation) or forced (by a blower). In other cases water or brine may be used to convect heat from a product to cooling coils.

Radiation is heat movement through space by shining, just as light is radiated. The sun radiates heat to the earth. A person near a fire feels warmth from the fire. One near a cold surface feels chilled as heat from his warm body is radiated to the colder surface. A product near a coil in a room above 32 F may be frozen as it radiates its heat directly to the colder coil. Radiant heat can be blocked just as light can be blocked by anything that forms a shadow.

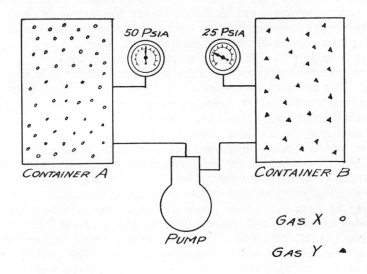

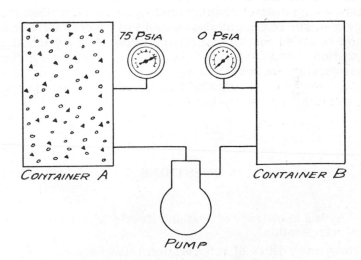

Fig. 1-2. Dalton's Law of partial pressure.

Scope of Refrigeration.—Refrigeration equipment can be roughly divided into three general classifications; domestic, commercial and industrial. *Domestic refrigeration is for the home kitchen.* It is nearly always a cooling cabinet with its mechanical equipment built in to give a completely self contained unit. The cabinets may vary in size from 2 or 3 cubic feet up to 10 or 12 cubic feet.

Commercial refrigeration is for holding food for sale in a retail store. This includes the general run of grocery refrigerators, meat boxes, refrigerated show cases, ice cream cabinets, beverage coolers and small sized air conditioning equipment. The refrigerated compartment may be a cabinet similar to a domestic box, but usually larger, called a reach-in cabinet; or it may be a walk-in cooler. It may be self contained, or the mechanical equipment may be in a basement or other convenient place.

Industrial refrigeration is that used in the manufacturing or processing of foods or other products requiring refrigeration. This includes ice plants, cold storage plants, dairies, food freezing, meat packing plants, breweries, large air conditioning equipment, etc. The amount of refrigeration required is large. The cooling may be done in refrigerated rooms, or in insulated warehouses which are entirely refrigerated. The required mechanical equipment is usually grouped in a central engine room.

There are no distinct dividing lines between these classifications. A large domestic box might also be sold to a grocery store or restaurant and be called commercial refrigeration. A dairy might supply refrigeration to retail cabinets from the same engine room that suplies refrigeration for milk cooling or ice cream freezing. But such a classification gives us a general idea whether we are working with small, medium, or large equipment.

QUESTIONS

1-1. Why is a knowledge of heat and its effects necessary in a study of refrigeration?

1-2. How many Btu's of refrigeration must be used to cool 1 gal. of milk from 80 F to 45 F?

1-3. A 1 qt glass milk bottle weighs 1.44 lb. How much refrigeration per gallon of milk is required to cool the milk bottles from 80 F to 45 F?

1-4. A qt cardboard milk carton weighs 3 oz. How much refrigeration per gallon of milk is required to cool the cartons from 80 F to 45F?

1-5. If the cooling of Questions 1-2, 3 and 4 was done with ice, how much ice would be required per gallon of milk, neglecting other losses?

1-6. Repeat Question 1-5 with dry ice.

1-7. Explain where conduction is an aid in a refrigeration system.

1-8. Explain where conduction should be reduced as much as possible in a refrigeration system.

1-9. Explain where convection is an aid in a refrigeration system.

1-10. Explain where radiation is an aid in a refrigeration system.

1-11. Explain where radiation should be reduced as much as possible in a refrigeration system.

1-12. What is the difference between a wet vapor and a super-heated vapor?

1-13. Are formulas or tables best for finding the properties of refrigerant vapors?

1-14. A gage pressure of 25 psi is how much absolute pressure?

1-15. What is the difference between domestic, commercial, and industrial refrigeration?

CHAPTER 2

THE COMPRESSION SYSTEM OF REFRIGERATION

Evaporation.—Let us go back to our illustration of water boiling on the stove. As long as it was boiling, it was absorbing heat. But to absorb heat, something else must supply that heat. To supply or give up heat is to cool. Therefore, as long as heat is absorbed by the boiling water, whatever gives up that heat is cooled off. In our illustration, the flame is cooled. The double boiler, Fig. 2-1, uses this fact. As long as water is in the lower container, anything in the upper container will not be heated above 212 F. This, in spite of a flame that may be 2000 F. More fire or a hotter flame causes more rapid boiling, or the evaporation of a greater quantity of liquid, but no rise in temperature. Put the other way around, the more evaporation, the more the cooling effect on the flame.

Fig. 2-1. The double boiler.

Heretofore we have always spoken of the boiling temperature of water as 212 F. But if we were to boil our water on the top of a mountain 10,000 feet high, we would find our water would boil at 193 F. Again, nothing we could do in applying more heat would cause the water to get hotter than 193 F. Perhaps you have heard of a camping trip in the mountains where eggs could not be hard boiled, or beans could not be cooked. The reason is that boiling water at such elevations is not hot enough to do the required cooking.

This is because atmospheric pressure is less at higher altitudes. At 10,000 feet the pressure is only 10 psi instead of 14.7 psi. A barometer would read 20.4 inches instead of 30 inches. A 20.4 inch vacuum would be a perfect vacuum at this elevation. The lower the pressure, the lower the boiling temperature. If we check the effect of a greater pressure, we find the boiling temperature higher. In a steam boiler with the pressure at 100 psig, the temperature of the boiling water is 338 F. So, *a change of pressure will change the boiling temperature.*

Fig. 2-2 gives the boiling temperature of water at different pressures. From this or tables, we find at a pressure of 0.178 psia, or a gage pressure of 29.56 inches of mercury, water could be boiled at 50 F. As long as this vacuum could be maintained, the water temperature could not be raised above 50 F. The boiling would absorb heat, which would remove heat from, or cool the heat source. As long as there was air or anything else warmer than 50 F around the water, boiling or evaporation would continue. The only difficulty with this idea is maintaining the required vacuum. As the water boils, the steam or vapor formed must be removed by a pump or other device to prevent the pressure from rising. Such a pump must have an enormous capacity, because at these very low pressures the vapor has expanded to an enormous volume. However, such a system is used in certain refrigeration applications.

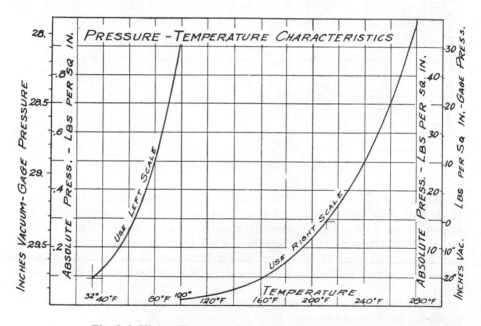

Fig. 2-2. Water: Pressure-Temperature characteristics.

To eliminate some of the difficulties of using water for refrigeration, we need a liquid which evaporates more easily. If we spill a little ether on our hand, it gets quite cool. There is enough evaporation without boiling to absorb considerable heat. In this case, the heat absorbed from the hand cools the hand. If we boil the ether at atmospheric pressure, we find it boils at 94.3 F. Fig. 2-3 gives the boiling temperature of ether for different pressures. From this we find we could boil ether at 15 F if we maintain a 25.5 inch vacuum on it.

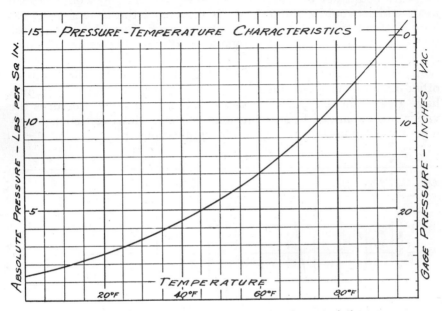

Fig. 2-3. Ether: Pressure-Temperature characteristics.

Again, anything warmer than 15 F would supply heat and cause it to boil. Whatever supplies this heat is cooled to a temperature approaching 15 F. This makes it possible to produce satisfactory refrigerating temperatures without such extreme vacuums. Ether has been tried, and at one time had a limited use in refrigeration. However, other fluids have been found which produce better results.

One of the oldest and best known of these is ammonia. Fig. 2-4 gives its pressure-temperature characteristics. At atmospheric pressure, it boils at 28 F below 0 F. A cylinder of the liquid at room temperature, say 85 F, would be under a pressure of 152 psig. The liquid in the cylinder always maintains the pressure corresponding to the temperature found on the chart.

If the cylinder valve was opened to allow vapor to escape, the liquid would evaporate or boil off more vapor to replace it. But evaporation requires heat which is drawn from the liquid itself,

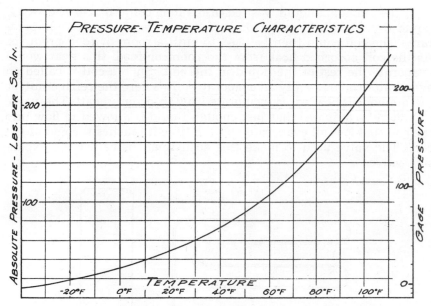

Fig. 2-4. Ammonia: Pressure-Temperature characteristics.

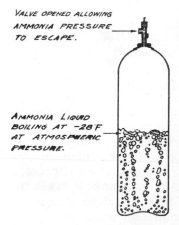

VALVE OPENED ALLOWING AMMONIA PRESSURE TO ESCAPE.

AMMONIA LIQUID BOILING AT −28 F AT ATMOSPHERIC PRESSURE.

Fig. 2-5. Boiling liquid ammonia.

so it is left a little cooler. Therefore the pressure in the cylinder becomes slightly lower. This action could be continued by leaving the valve open until the pressure dropped to atmospheric. The temperature would then be reduced to −28 F, Fig. 2-5. At any time before the pressure reached atmospheric, the pressure-temperature relationship would be that shown on Fig. 2-4.

If the cylinder was turned upside down and the valve opened, liquid would come out of the valve. But the boiling temperature of the liquid at atmospheric pressure is −28 F. Therefore, as it emerges from the valve, part of it will evaporate instantly, or flash into vapor. Heat to evaporate this liquid is taken from itself, so the unevaporated liquid is immediately chilled to −28 F. If the liquid in the cylinder was 85 F, about 21 percent of it must evaporate to cool the rest to −28 F. The rest of the liquid would then be available for refrigeration.

If the ammonia liquid was fed into a long coil, Fig. 2-6, the —28 F liquid would chill the metal walls of the coil to nearly that temperature. The coil could then be used to chill a room or food products. As the coil absorbed heat from the room or food, this heat would evaporate the rest of the liquid in the coil. Such a coil is called an evaporator coil or simply an evaporator. It is here the refrigerant, as the ammonia is called, is evaporated by absorbing heat. The valve should be so adjusted that just enough liquid is allowed to flow into the coil that it is all evaporated by the time it reaches the end of the coil. The valve used to make this adjustment is called the expansion valve.

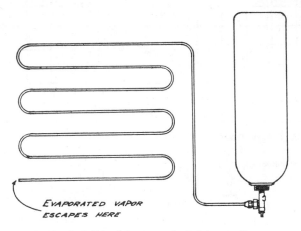

EVAPORATED VAPOR
ESCAPES HERE

Fig. 2-6. Liquid ammonia fed to a coil.

Such a system would produce refrigeration as long as ammonia was present in the cylinder. But if allowed to escape to the air, it would be a public nuisance, not to mention costly to replenish. The rest of the equipment in the refrigerating plant, the compressor, condenser, and motor drive is just a reclaiming plant. It takes the evaporated vapor and converts it back to a liquid so it may be reused. This should be stressed. The compressor and its motor in no way directly produces cold.

The compressor is used to remove the vapor from the coil as fast as it is evaporated. It then compresses this vapor back to 152 psig. The mechanical energy used in this compression ends up as heat energy in the vapor. This heats the vapor to 290 F as it leaves the compressor. This hot, high pressure vapor then goes to a condenser. This is an assembly of pipes having water or air, or both, flowing over them. The air or water absorbs heat from the pipes, which first cools the vapor to 85 F. The vapor cannot be cooled below this temperature and remain a vapor at that pressure. So further cooling condenses it back to a liquid. From here it drains back to a cylinder where it is ready to be used again. This storage cylinder is called the liquid receiver. The complete cycle is shown schematically in Fig. 2-7.

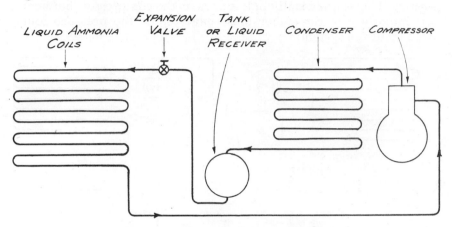

Fig. 2-7. Schematic refrigeration system.

Pressure Cycle.—From the above, we see the refrigerant circulates round and round in the system. From the expansion valve it travels through the evaporator, then back the suction line to the compressor. This much of the system is at the low pressure required by the evaporator. This low pressure will vary, depending on the temperature required. It can be found opposite the required evaporator temperature in Fig. 2-4. It is important to recognize the fact that the pressure will be the same from the expansion valve through to the compressor. This is called the low pressure side, or more simply, the low side, of the system. Since the evaporator itself is the most important part of the low side, the term low side is often used to mean an evaporator coil. The pressure in the low side is sometimes called the back pressure. That is, it is the pressure on the back side of the compressor. It is also sometimes called suction pressure.

The compressor takes the low pressure vapor and builds it up to a pressure high enough to condense. The compressor discharge line, the condenser, the liquid receiver, and the liquid line are all at this high pressure. This part of the system is called the high side. Actually the compressor crankcase usually contains low pressure vapor. But for practical purposes, the entire compressor is considered part of the high side.

Thus the complete system is divided into a high and a low side, Fig. 2-8. The expansion valve and the compressor are the division points. A pressure gage anywhere in the high side will give the high pressure. A gage anywhere in the low side will give the low pressure. Gages are usually put at or near the compressor, but again, it is important to remember these gages show the pressure found throughout the system.

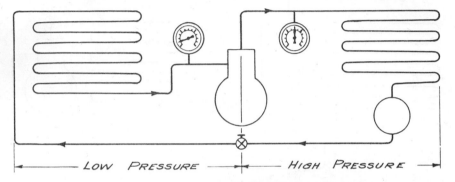

Fig. 2-8. High and low sides.

In the above illustrations we have spoken of ammonia evaporating at atmospheric pressure, which is —28 F. Temperatures this cold are sometimes used, but higher temperatures are more commonly encountered. A 15 F temperature coil would be more common. From Fig. 2-4, or from tables, we find we must maintain a 28.4 psig pressure on the low side to allow the ammonia to boil at 15 F. As in the above case, we still have an identical pressure throughout the low side, but now 28.4 psig. This need not change the condensing pressure which remains at 152 psig. These latter pressures are shown graphically in Fig. 2-9.

Temperature Cycle.—The temperature cycle is shown graphically in Fig. 2-10. If the pressure in the evaporator is such that the refrigerant boils at 15 F, any part of the evaporator in which liquid is present will be at this temperature. It is important to remember that as the end of the coil is approached, its temperature does not gradually rise as the coil absorbs heat. The heat boils the liquid within the coil. This liquid boils at the same temperature in all parts of the coil, since it is all at the same pressure. The end of the coil, after the last bit of liquid is evaporated contains only vapor.

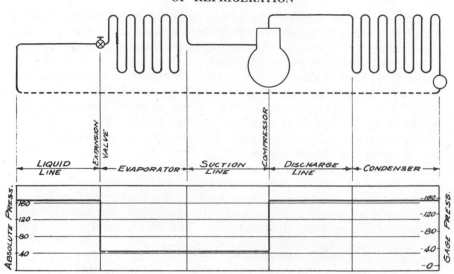

Fig. 2-9. Pressure cycle of refrigerating system.

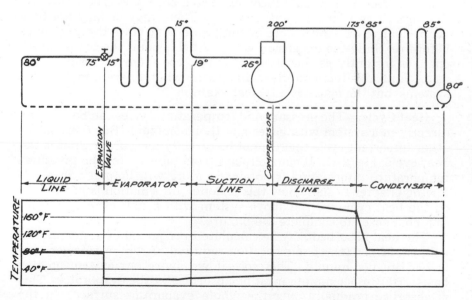

Fig. 2-10. Temperature cycle of refrigerating system.

With no liquid present, the vapor can and does become heated above its boiling temperature. Therefore superheated vapor, that is, vapor heated above its boiling temperature, usually leaves the coil. It may pick up 4 F of superheat, heating it from 15 F to 19 F. As the vapor flows back the suction line to the compressor, additional superheat will be absorbed. If the line is well insulated, this may not be over 7 F more, heating it up to 26 F. Thus, entering the compressor we have a 26 F vapor at a pressure of 28.4 psig. The compressor builds this up to 152 psig. At these conditions the heat of compression would heat this vapor up to 200 F. Thus, the vapor leaving the compressor is at 152 psig pressure and 200 F temperature.

At this high temperature some cooling will be encountered in the discharge line, the amount depending on the length of the line. If we assume it cools to 175 F going to the condenser, we have 152 psig vapor at 175 F entering the condenser. The first few coils of the condenser cool the vapor to 85 F, the condensing temperature. Then any further heat removal condenses the vapor to a liquid. But as long as a vapor is present, the liquid cannot be cooled below 85 F. If sufficient liquid collects in the lower coils so it does not contact vapor, it may be sub-cooled below 85 F.

Let us assume it is subcooled 5 degrees. This would reduce its temperature to 80 F. Thus an 80 F liquid, still at 152 psig pressure would collect in the liquid receiver. From here it will flow through the liquid line to the expansion valve. There may or may not be a slight change of temperature of the liquid as it flows through pipes before reaching the expansion valve. At this point the temperature changes instantly as the pressure is reduced from 152 psig to 28.4 psig. Naturally, temperatures will be somewhat different in different systems, but the above is a typical example.

Heat Cycle.—The pressure and temperature cycles can be checked directly in a system with gages and thermometers. But there is another important cycle that cannot be directly measured. That is the heat cycle, Fig. 2-11. It can be found from tables after the pressure-temperature information is obtained. More will be given in a following chapter to show how this is done. Information is given here on the heat cycle for the above system with a 15 F evaporator and 85 F condenser to complete the picture.

The heat absorbed may be calculated per pound of ammonia circulated, or per ton of refrigeration required. A ton of refrigeration is 200 Btu per minute. Therefore if we figure our system on this basis, 200 Btu per minute must be absorbed by the evaporator. This is absorbed gradually over the whole evaporator surface. In the suction line, 2.5 Btu more are picked up.

The vapor is then drawn to the compressor where work is done on it, compressing it from 28.4 psig to 152 psig. The mechanical energy used in this compression is converted to heat energy in the vapor itself. This adds 33.2 Btu of heat to the vapor. Thus we now have a total of 235.7 Btu in the vapor leaving the compressor. This vapor goes to the condenser. Here the 235.7 Btu must be removed to liquify it and make it ready for use in the evaporator again.

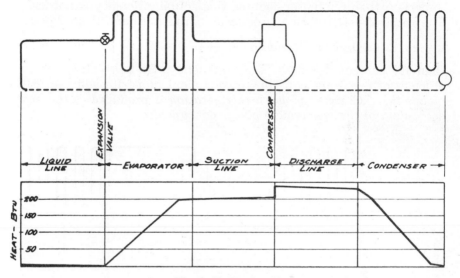

Fig. 2-11. Heat cycle

Notice the evaporator and compressor add heat to the fluid. The condenser takes heat from it. The total heat taken from the fluid by the condenser must equal all the heat absorbed from the evaporator and from the compressor. Thus the entire system is nothing more than a heat pump. Heat is pumped from the evaporator at a low temperature level (15 F) to the condenser at a high temperature level (85 F). At the higher temperature level it may be disposed of by air or water cooling. The air or water used to cool the condenser extracts or absorbs all the heat from the evaporator and the compressor.

Also notice, to absorb 200 Btu of heat in the evaporator only 33.2 Btu of mechanical power are necessary. More refrigeration is produced than mechanical power is involved. This is not a form of perpetual motion, or getting something for nothing. The refrigeration is produced by the evaporating liquid, not by direct action of mechanical power. The mechanical power is used to "pump" the heat to a higher level so it may be absorbed by water or air at ordinary temperatures. If the term efficiency is considered, we must handle a total of 235.7 Btu in the condenser to obtain 200 Btu of refrigeration in the evaporator. Thus the efficiency would be $\frac{200}{235.7}$ = .85 or 85%. Thus 85 percent of the total heat handled is utilized directly in cooling. But since mechanical power is more costly, and therefore more important than condenser cooling, this actual efficiency is not used. The ratio of refrigeration produced to the mechanical energy required, is used. Here it would be $\frac{200}{33.2}$ = 6.02. Since this is more than 100 percent it cannot be an efficiency. So it is called the coefficient of performance. Thus *a coefficient of performance of 6.02 means that 6.02 times as much refrigeration is produced as the heat equivalent of the mechanical power consumed.*

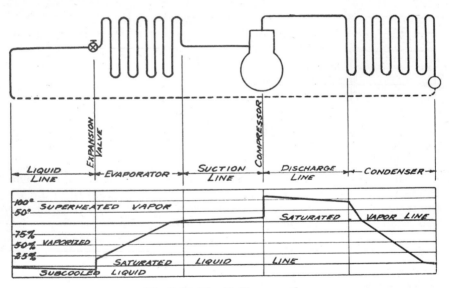

Fig. 2-12. Liquid-Vapor cycle.

Liquid-Vapor Cycle.—The liquid-vapor cycle, Fig. 2-12, was described at the beginning of the chapter, but should be reviewed here. The liquid in the receiver, usually sub-cooled, is fed to the expansion valve. Here its pressure is reduced. This evaporates some of it, 13 percent in this case, to chill the other 87 percent of the remaining liquid to 15 F. This 13 percent of evaporated vapor is called flash gas.

The heat in the evaporator gradually evaporates the rest of the saturated liquid to a saturated vapor. At or near the end of the evaporator the last of the liquid is evaporated. Any additional heat absorbed superheats the vapor. Only vapor should return to the com-

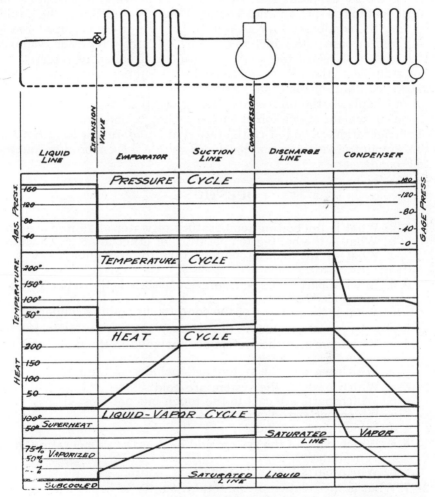

Fig. 2-13 Refrigerating cycles: standard ton conditions, ammonia.

pressor. The compressor raises the pressure and superheat of the vapor. From here it goes to the condenser where, first the superheat is removed to form a saturated vapor, then this saturated vapor is condensed to a saturated liquid.

Standard Ton Conditions.—The above charts apply only to an ammonia system operating at the above temperatures. Fig. 2-13 combines a similar set of data for a slightly different condition. Here we have a 5 F evaporator, no superheat in the evaporator, and 9 F of superheat in the suction line. The condenser is at 86 F, and the liquid leaving the condenser subcooled 9 F. This condition is considered a standard or base with which to compare other conditions or systems. It is called standard ton conditions, and is frequently referred to. For simplicity, the 9 F of superheat in the suction line, and the 9 F subcooled liquid is sometimes omitted.

In Chapter 1, the information was given that 200 Btu per minute is the equivalent of one ton of ice per 24 hours, and is called one ton of refrigeration. A ton of refrigeration at *standard ton conditions is this amount of refrigeration produced with a 5 F evaporator and an 86 F condenser.*

QUESTIONS

2– 1. a. What is the boiling temperature of water at 29 in. vacuum?
    b. What is the boiling temperature of ether at 16 in. vacuum?
    c. What is the boiling temperature of ammonia at 20 psig pressure?

2– 2. a. In what part of the refrigeration system is the actual cooling produced?·
    b. What is the purpose of the compressor and the condenser?

2– 3. Draw a schematic picture of the complete refrigeration system.

2– 4. a. Which parts of the system are included in the high pressure side?
    b. Which parts of the system are included in the low side?

2– 5. a. Which parts of the system are cold?
    b. Which parts are cool to the touch but not frosted?
    c. Which parts are warm to the touch?
    d. Which parts are hot?

2– 6. a. Which parts of the system add heat to the refrigerating fluid circulated?
    b. Which parts take heat from this fluid?

2– 7. What is the relation of the total quantity of heat picked up by the refrigerating fluid to that lost from this fluid?

2– 8. What is the meaning of the term *coefficient of performance?*

2– 9. a. In what parts of the system is there only liquid?
    b. In what parts is there only vapor?
    c. In what parts is there both liquid and vapor?

2–10. What is the complete definition of a ton of refrigeration at standard ton conditions?

CHAPTER 3

REFRIGERANTS—THEIR PHYSICAL AND REFRIGERATING PROPERTIES

W E HAVE mentioned that the evaporation of water, ether and ammonia have been used to produce cooling, or refrigeration. Each of these and many other fluids may be used for the same purpose. But some give better results than others. What is required of a good refrigerant? Why are some refrigerants used for certain applications, and other refrigerants used elsewhere? No one refrigerant has all the desirable qualities. So one must be chosen having the best balance between desirable qualities and undesirable qualities 1or the required application.

Requirements.—Following is a list of qualities desired in a good refrigerant:

1. It should produce maximum refrigeration per cubic foot of vapor pumped.
2. It should have a reasonable condensing pressure.
3. It should have a reasonable evaporating pressure.
4. It should be stable.
5. It should have no effect on metal.
6. It should have no effect on oil.
7. Its critical temperature should be well above the condensing temperature.
8. It should be non-poisonous and non-irritating.
9. It should be non-inflammable.
10. It should be available at reasonable prices.
11. It should be easy to find leaks.
12. A minimum of power should be required to compress it.
13. Its freezing point should be well below the evaporator temperature.

Analysis.—1. *It should produce maximum refrigeration per cubic foot of vapor pumped.* A refrigerant is wanted which will give the maximum amount of refrigeration for a given size or investment in

31

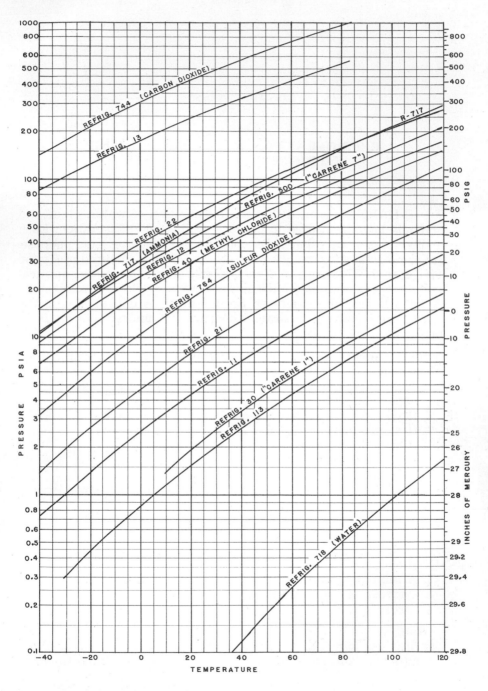

Fig. 3-1. Temperature-Pressure relationships—common refrigerants.

equipment. Evaporators and condensers will change in size but little for different refrigerants, because their effect is produced mainly by the area involved. But a compressor of given size can pump only a given volume of refrigerant vapor. When the proper amount of refrigerant is evaporated to do the required amount of cooling, the vapor has a certain volume. This will vary considerably with different refrigerants. It is actually made up of two factors, the latent heat of the refrigerant (the amount of heat necessary to evaporate one pound of it) and its volume per pound.

2. *It should have a reasonable condensing pressure.* The condensing pressure depends on the saturation pressure of the refrigerant at ordinary condensing temperatures. This should not be too high. Excessive pressures require heavy (which means expensive) equipment and piping.

Centrifugal compressors cannot build up a large pressure without an excessive number of stages. Therefore, they require a very low condensing pressure. Most centrifugal compressors use a refrigerant with a condensing pressure between zero and 10 psig. At low condensing temperatures, the condenser may operate under a slight vacuum.

Fig. 3-1 gives the temperature-pressure relationships of the common refrigerants. These are given to a logarithmic scale so both high and low values can be shown. Or pressures as well as other values can be taken from refrigerant tables, given in the Appendix.

3. *It should have a reasonable evaporating pressure.* For all but hermetic compressors, it is desirable to have an evaporator pressure very near atmospheric, but slightly above it. The rotating shaft of the compressor must come out through the crankcase wall with a packing or seal to prevent leakage of refrigerant out, or air in, Fig. 3-2.

But this seal cannot always be made leak-proof. If it has about the same pressure on each side of it, the leakage will be a minimum. Since air or moisture entering the system will cause a great deal of difficulty, it would be more desirable to lose a small amount of refrigerant than to allow air to leak into the system. Therefore the crankcase pressure, which is usually the suction pressure, should be slightly above atmospheric. Since different jobs require different

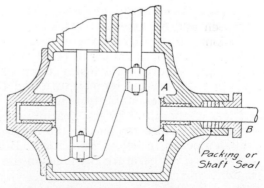

If crankcase pressure A equals atmospheric pressure B, there will be no leakage through the packing. If pressure A is greater than B, any leakage present will be from A to B.

Fig. 3-2. Why low pressure but not a vacuum is wanted.

evaporator temperatures, this leads to the use of different refrigerants to approach the ideal of a suction pressure near atmospheric but above it.

Hermetically sealed compressors do not have a shaft seal. Therefore they can be operated at a vacuum with no trouble.

Suction pressures for any given temperature can be found on Fig. 3-1, or from the refrigerant tables in the Appendix.

4. *It must be stable.* Stability means the refrigerant must remain in its original chemical form. For instance, ammonia is a chemical combination of nitrogen and hydrogen. If it should separate into these gases, neither would make a good refrigerant. Many vapors or gases which are not made of a single chemical element have a breakdown temperature above which they are not stable. That is, they are apt to separate into the elements of which they are made. It is necessary that this breakdown temperature for the refrigerant selected be well above the operating temperatures of the system.

5. *It should have no effect on metal.* A refrigerant must be chosen which will not corrode or otherwise react with the metals normally used in a refrigeration system. An absorption system using sulphuric acid as an absorber was once tried. Some of the problems introduced by such a fluid can easily be imagined.

6. *It should have no effect on oil.* A refrigerant must be chosen which has no harmful effect on properly selected lubricating oils. There is danger of chemical reactions which cause gumming, sludging or varnish formation. There is also trouble with some refrigerants mixing with and thinning the oil to where it makes a poor lubricant. Ethyl chloride, which once was used as a refrigerant, thinned the oil like mixing it with solvent. It gave so much trouble one manufacturer tried glycerine instead of oil as a lubricant.

7. *Its critical temperature should be well above its condensing temperature.* All vapors or gases have a temperature above which it is impossible to liquefy them, regardless of the pressure applied. This is the critical temperature. It is important that this be higher than any required condensing temperature. Notice the difference between the critical temperature and the breakdown temperature mentioned under stability. The vapor may be heated above the critical temperature by the heat of compression. If it can be cooled below this before condensing, no harm is done. It will condense at any temperature below its critical. But if it is heated above the breakdown temperature any place in the system, irreparable damage is done.

8. *It should be non-poisonous and non-irritating.* It must be handled by operators and service men. Also if poisonous or highly irritating, a hazard is created in case of leakage or breakage of equipment. Imagine the panic if ammonia or were to break out in an auditorium or other crowded location.

9. *It should be non-inflammable.* An inflamable refrigerant would also create a hazard both when handled by operators, and in case of leakage.

10. *It should be available at reasonable prices.* Sufficient quantities of the refrigerant should be available in ordinary markets at a reasonable cost. At this cost it must be of sufficient purity to cause no refrigeration difficulties.

11. *It should be easy to find leaks.* Some simple means of determining whether leaks are present in the system, and of finding exactly where those leaks are located should be possible.

12. *A mimimum of power should be required to compress it.* The different refrigerants may require different amounts of power to compress them. Obviously, the less the power required the cheaper are the operating costs of the refrigeration plant.

13. *Its freezing point should be well below the evaporator temperature.* If flow is to be maintained in the system, a refrigerant which freezes at temperatures encountered in the evaporator cannot be used. Except where water is used as a refrigerant, this did not have to be considered a few years ago, and still does not on ordinary jobs. But on those special jobs which go down to 100 F or more below 0 F, this must be considered.

Physical Properties of Common Refrigerants.— Table 3-1 lists some important physical properties of the most common refrigerants. Table 3-2 gives the same data for some of the less common refrigerants. Table 3-1 (and 3-2) gives first, the name by which the refrigerant is most commonly known, then its chemical name, then its chemical formula. Some refrigerants are commonly known by their chemical name, and some by a number. All are occasionally referred to by their formula.

Item 4 gives the boiling point at atmospheric pressure. This alone gives some indication of the pressure characteristics. A low boiling temperature would mean such a temperature can be obtained in the evaporator without a vacuum. But a pressure would be necessary to condense the refrigerant. A very low boiling temperature, such as 50 to 100 F below zero would indicate considerable pressure was necessary in the evaporator for ordinary refrigerating temperatures. An excessively high condensing pressure would probably be required. On the other hand, a boiling point of 50 to 100 F above zero would indicate a vacuum was needed in the evaporator, and the condensing pressure would be near atmospheric. Boiling temperatures like that of water (212 F) indicate an exceedingly high vacuum in the evaporator, and some vacuum in the condenser.

Table 3-1—Physical Properties of Common Refrigerants

	Refrigerant 718	Refrigerant 11	Refrigerant 40	Refrigerant 12	Refrigerant 22	Refrigerant 717	Refrigerant 744
1. Common Name	Water	"Carrene 2"	Methyl Chloride			Ammonia	Carbon Dioxide
2. Chemical Name	Water	Trichloro-monofluoro-methane	Methyl Chloride	Dichloro-difluoro-methane	Monochloro-difluoro-methane	Ammonia	Carbon Dioxide
3. Chemical Symbol	H_2O	CCl_3F	CH_3Cl	CCl_2F_2	$CHClF_2$	NH_3	CO_2
4. Boiling Temp. at Atmospheric	212F	74.7F	-10.8F	-21.6F	-41.4F	-28.0F	-109.3F
5. Cond. Press. at 86F	28.67"	3.6 psig	80.0 psig	93.2 psig	159.8 psig	154.5 psig	1024 psig
6. Evap. Press. at 5F	29.67"[1]	24.0"	6.5 psig	11.8 psig	28.3 psig	19.6 psig	319.7 psig
7. Latent Heat at 5F, in Btu/lb.	1071[1]	84.0	180.8	69.5	93.6	565	115.3
8. Volume at 5F, in cu ft/lb.	2444[1]	12.3	4.66	1.48	1.25	8.15	0.267
9. Displacement 5F, 86F, in cfm/ton			6.09	5.81	3.60	3.44	0.943
10. Critical Temp.	477[1]	388.4F	315F	332.7F	204.8F	271.4F	87.8F
11. Freezing Temp.	32.0F	-168F	-103.9F	-252F	-256F	-107.9F	-69.9F
12. Least Detect. Odor	None	20%	None	20%	20%	53 ppm	None
13. Irritability	None	None	None	None	None	700 ppm	None
14. Toxicity	None	10% 2 hr.	2% 2 hrs.	20% 2 hr.	10% 2 hr.	0.5% 30 min.	30% 1 hr.
15. Flammability	None	None	8.1-17.2% 69 psig	None	None	13.1 to 26.8% 54 psig	None
16. Toxic in Flame	None	Yes	Yes	Yes	Yes	No Additional	None
17. Sp. Gr. Liquid 5F, Water=1.	1.00[1]	1.57	0.99	1.44	1.34	0.66	0.985
18. Sp. Gr. Vapor at Atm. Air=1.		4.85	2.04	5.20	4.00	0.74	2.35
19. Power 5F, 86F	——[2]	0.983	0.96	1.00	1.01	0.99	1.78
20. Compression Temp. 5F, 86F	——[2]	113F	156F	102F	131F	210F	160F

[1] For 40F instead of 5F.

[2] Compressed by steam jet; mechanical power and compression temperature have no meaning.

[3] At single stage comparable with other refrigerants. Usually compressed two stage with power of 0.93 HP.

Table 3-2—Physical Properties of Some Other Refrigerants

	Refrigerant 113	Refrigerant 30	Refrigerant 21	Refrigerant 114	Refrigerant 764	Refrigerant 500	Refrigerant 13
1. Common Name		"Carrene 1"			Sulphur Dioxide	"Carrene 7"	
2. Chemical Name	Trichlorotri-fluoroethane	Methylene Chloride	Dichloromono-fluoromethane	Dichlorotetra-fluoroethane	Sulphur Dioxide	(Note 4)	Monochlorotri-fluoromethane
3. Chemical Symbol	$C_2Cl_3F_3$	CH_2Cl_2	$CHCl_2F$	$CClF_2CClF_2$	SO_2	(Note 4)	$CClF_3$
4. Boiling Temp. at Atmospheric	117.6F	105.2F	48.0F	38.4F	14F	-28F	-114.5F
5. Cond. Press. at 86F	13.9"	9.5"	16.5 psig	22.0 psig	51.7 psig	113.4	(Note 5)
6. Evap. Press. at 5F	27.9"	27.6"	19.2"	16.1"	5.9"	16.4 psig	177.1 psig
7. Latent Heat at 5F, in Btu/lb.	70.6	163	109	62.0	169.4	84.2	45.6
8. Volume at 5F in cu ft/lb.	27.04	49.9	9.13	4.22	6.42	1.52	0.190
9. Displacement 5F, 86F, in cfm/ton	100.8	74.3	20.4	19.6	9.08	4.97	1.56[6]
10. Critical Temp.	417	480F	353F	294F	315F	221F	83.9
11. Freezing Temp.	-31.0	-142	-211	-137	-103.9	-254F	-296
12. Least Detect. Odor	20%	20%	20%	20%	3 to 5 ppm	20%	None
13. Irritability	None	None	None	None	8 to 12 ppm	None	None
14. Toxicity	5% 1 hr.	5% 30 Min.	10% 30 Min.	20% 2 hr.	0.7% 5 min.	20% 2 hr.	None
15. Flammability	None	None	None	None	None	None	None
16. Toxic in Flame	Yes	Yes	Yes	Yes	No Additional	Yes	None
17. Sp. Gr. Liquid 5F, Water=1.	1.66	1.34	1.46	1.46	1.47	1.29	1.18
18. Sp. Gr. Vapor at Atm. Air=1.	6.5	2.95	3.75	3.75	2.56	4.4	5.7
19. Power 5F, 86F	0.96	0.96	0.94	1.02	0.97	1.02	1.35[6]
20. Compression Temp. 5F, 86F	87F	205F	142F	87F	191F	105F	100F

4. Azeotropic mixture of 73.8% CCl_2F_2 plus 26.2% CH_3CHF_2.

5. Above critical temperature.

6. at 5F and 70F.

Items 5 and 6 give the condensing pressure and evaporator pressure for standard ton conditions, that is, 86 F condenser and 5 F evaporator.

Item 7 gives the latent heat per pound of refrigerant at 5 F. This is the amount of heat necessary to evaporate one pound of the refrigerant. *Item 8* gives the volume, or actual cubic feet of space which would be filled by the vapor from one pound of refrigerant evaporated at the pressure shown in item 6. *Item 9* combines items 7 and 8 (with a correction for flash gas) to show the actual amount of vapor that must be pumped per minute to produce one ton of refrigeration, or 200 Btu per minute. These figures give a direct comparison of the sizes of compressors necessary to produce the same amount of of refrigeration. Fig. 3-3 graphically shows this information for the different refrigerants.

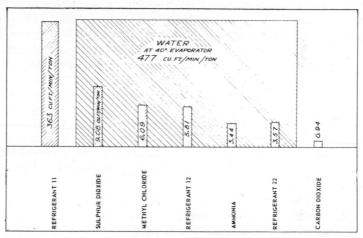

Fig. 3-3. Graphic displacements of common refrigerants.

Item 10 gives the critical temperature, and *Item 11* gives the freezing point. The condensing temperature must always be below the critical temperature and the evaporator temperature must always be above the freezing point.

Item 12 gives the least amount of the refrigerant mixed with air that is detectable by odor. This may be given in per cent or in parts per million (ppm). Note it takes 10,000 ppm to make 1 per cent. *Item 13* gives the per cent usually found to be irritating. *Item 14* gives the per cent and time of exposure necessary for a fatal dose. The actual hazard of a refrigerant is usually a combination of these. A refrigerant which is easily detected by smell, and particularly one which is irritating, may not be as hazardous as a less toxic one which gives no particular warning of its presence.

If a vapor can reach 10 percent concentration before it creates dangerous properties, it can be considered as relatively non-toxic. At this or greater concentrations, enough air is displaced that normal breathing does not supply sufficient oxygen. Therefore any gas, toxic or not, would cause discomfort. Water is not a poison, but if one were shut up in a room filled with it, he would not live long. Similarly, this could be true of any substance other than air. One other thing to consider with respect to hazards is the weight of the refrigerant vapor. This is shown in item 18. If the vapor is heavier than air, any leakage could very easily collect in large concentrations in low places such as basements or holds of ships. Once in such a hollow, positive ventilation is necessary to eliminate it.

Item 15 gives some information regarding the flammability and explosion hazards. Interstate Commerce regulations recognize it only as inflammable or non-inflammable. But there is some variation in the hazards involved. Inflammable vapors will burn with more or less limited mixtures of air. This mixture must not be too rich or too lean. Naturally, the narrower the limits of the mixture that will burn, the less chance of having exactly that mixture. After being ignited, some vapors burn much more rapidly than others. Also, the burning increases the temperature which increases the pressure. High speed burning plus the pressure increase is what causes explosive violence. Item 15 gives the limiting proportions of inflammable mixtures, and the maximum pressures built up by ignition.

Item 16 gives information regarding another hazard. Some refrigerants which are non-poisonous and non-inflammable break down to poisonous compounds when exposed to high temperatures. Thus, such a refrigerant leaking into a room with any high temperature source could be hazardous. Unvented gas stoves or electric heating elements could cause such a breakdown. But the toxic products are very irritating so will tend to drive occupants out of a room before dangerous amounts can be breathed. This breakdown would also be a definite hazard to fire department personnel in case of fire in the building.

Item 17 gives the specific gravity of the liquid at 5 F compared to water, that is, the ratio of its weight to the weight of the same volume of water. There is some variation in the weight of the liquid with temperature, but for most refrigerants this will not run over 10 per cent for a change from 0 F to 100 F. *Item 18* gives the specific gravity of the vapor at atmospheric pressure compared to the weight of air. This is the condition of the vapor when it escapes from a system. The weight of the vapor varies almost directly with absolute pressure.

Item 19 gives the horsepower required to produce one ton of refrigeration at standard ton conditions. This is the power required to actually compress the vapor without including any of the losses involved. Actual power including losses will run up to 50 per cent higher than these figures. But for the same size jobs, the power losses will run approximately the same for the different refrigerants.

Item 20 gives the compression temperature reached by the vapor at standard ton conditions. That is the temperature of the compressor discharge. High temperatures require water jacketed cylinders, and give rise to lubrication troubles due to oil breakdown.

Tables 3-3 and 3-4 combine the factors discussed before in an overall comparison of the various refrigerants.

TABLE 3-3—REFRIGERATING PROPERTIES OF COMMON REFRIGERANTS

	Refrigerant 718 Water	Refrigerant 11 "Carrene 2"	Refrigerant 40 Methyl Chloride	Refrigerant 12	Refrigerant 717 Ammonia	Refrigerant 22	Refrigerant 744 Carbon Dioxide
1. Maximum Refrigeration per cu. ft.	Poor[1]	Poor[1]	Fair	Good	Good	Good	Good
2. Reasonable Condensing Pressure	Poor	Good	Good	Good	Good	Good	Good
3. Reasonable Evaporating Pressure	Poor	Poor	Good	Good	Good	Good	Poor
4. Stability	Good	Good	Good	Good	Good	Good	Good
5. No Effect on Metals	Good	Fair	Fair	Fair	Good	Fair	Good
6. No Effect on Oil	Good	Good	Good	Good	Good	Good	Good
7. High Critical Temperature	Good	Good	Good	Good	Good	Good	Poor
8. Non-Poisonous; Non-Irritating	Good	Good	Poor	Good	Poor	Good	Good
9. Non-Inflammable	Good	Good	Poor	Good	Poor	Good	Good
10. Availability: Cost	Good	Fair	Fair	Fair	Good	Fair	Good
11. Ease of Finding Leaks	Poor	Fair	Fair	Fair	Good	Fair	Poor
12. Power Required	Good	Good	Good	Good	Good	Good	Poor
13. Freezing Point	Poor	Good	Good	Good	Good	Good	Fair

[1] Good for Centrifugal Compressors or Steam Jet

TABLE 3-4—REFRIGERATING PROPERTIES OF SOME OTHER REFRIGERANTS

	Refrigerant 113	Refrigerant 30 "Carrene 1"	Refrigerant 21	Refrigerant 114	Refrigerant 764 Sulphur Dioxide	Refrigerant 500 "Carrene 7"	Refrigerant 13
1. Maximum Refrigeration per cu. ft.	Fair[2]	Fair[2]	Good[2]	Good[2]	Poor	Good	Good
2. Reasonable Condensing Pressure	Fair[2]	Fair[2]	Fair[2]	Fair[2]	Good	Good	Poor
3. Reasonable Evaporating Pressure	Fair[2]	Fair[2]	Good[2]	Good[2]	Fair	Good	Fair[3]
4. Stability	Good	Good	Good	Good	Good	Good	Good
5. No Effect on Metals	Good	Good	Good	Good	Good[4]	Good	Good
6. No Effect on Oil	Fair	Fair	Fair	Fair	Good	Fair	Fair
7. High Critical Temperature	Good	Good	Good	Good	Good	Good	Poor
8. Non-Poisonous; Non-Irritating	Good	Good	Good	Good	Poor	Good	Good
9. Non-Inflammable	Good	Good	Good	Good	Good	Good	Good
10. Availability: Cost	Fair	Fair	Fair	Fair	Fair	Fair	Fair
11. Ease of Finding Leaks	Fair	Fair	Fair	Fair	Good	Fair	Fair
12. Power Required	Good	Good	Good	Good	Good	Good	Poor[3]
13. Freezing Point	Fair	Good	Good	Good	Good	Good	Good

[2] Good for Centrifugal Compressors   [3] Good for Low Temperature Applications   [3] Good Only if Dry

Historic Development of Refrigerants.—The first refrigerants used were known chemicals which could be easily liquefied and evaporated. Ammonia was the first chemical used extensively for refrigeration. It proved so successful that it has been the most important industrial refrigerant ever since. It was also used in the first commercial butcher shops, retail dairies, etc.

The hazards of ammonia led to the search for something safer for certain applications. Carbon dioxide became the accepted refrigerant for hospitals, prisons and passenger ships. But its excessive pressure prevented its general adoption.

Even ammonia operated at too high a pressure, and required too cumbersome equipment to be applied to anything approaching domestic applications. So other chemicals were investigated by those experimenting with a "mechanical ice box." Many substances were tried, but sulfur dioxide became the favorite, closely followed by methyl chloride. These were successful enough to be applied to early commercial equipment.

Both these refrigerants had hazards which, some designers felt, held back the full development of domestic and commercial refrigeration and air-conditioning. So a study was made to find a refrigerant that had all the advantages desired of a good refrigerant. A whole new series of chemicals were discovered and developed, the fluoriated hydrocarbons or fluorocarbons, which contained most of these advantages. Different members of the series had boiling points from 100 F or more below zero to over 200 F above zero. Therefore, one could be found with pressure characteristics that would fit almost any refrigeration application.

Such refrigerants were first called by their trade name "Freon," followed by a designating number. As other manufacturers began to supply these chemicals, they called them by their own trade names. Much confusion resulted.

Headed by the American Society of Refrigeration Engineers (now called American Society of Heating, Refrigeration and Air Conditioning), it was finally decided to call them all "Refrigerant," followed by a number. The "Freon" numbering system was adopted for the fluorocarbons. But this numbering system was expanded to cover all refrigerants.

This is why we may see two, or sometimes more different names for the same chemical. It is perfectly proper to call the fluorocarbons by their trade name, or simply call them "Refrigerant" followed by their proper number. The older refrigerants are, at the present, still most commonly called by their chemical names.

Old names and numbers are still to be found on the nameplates of installed equipment. Therefore, some of the more common old names are listed together with the new numerical designation.

INDIVIDUAL REFRIGERANTS:

Water.—To compare the list of requirements of a good refrigerant with the properties of water would seem to make a very poor refrigerant of this common fluid. The enormous volume of its vapor is such that the use of an ordinary compressor is impossible. High vacuums are required in both the low and high pressure sides of the system. The required vacuum on the low side is so high that it is difficult to maintain. Leaks are difficult to find. Their only evidence is when air leaking into the system prevents proper operation. To check for a suspected leak the system must be charged with compressed air and all joints tried with soap suds. The 32 F freezing point makes it impossible to use for ordinary applications.

However, for certain applications above 32 F such as chilling large quantities of water and for air conditioning, it has satisfactorily filled some very rigid requirements. First, it is absolutely safe. It has no odor or poisonous properties, and it is not inflammable. If any amount of it were accidentally released in a crowded building, it would not cause panic. It is cheap and can be obtained anywhere.

The problem of handling the excessive volume of the low pressure vapor has been solved by the use of steam ejectors. The steam jet system using water as a refrigerant has been used extensively in air conditioning.

Refrigerant 764 or Sulfur Dioxide.—This is the gas obtained by burning sulfur, easily recognized by its sharp, irritating odor. It is highly toxic. If perfectly dry, it has no effect on metals. But it will combine with moisture to form sulfurous and sulphuric acids. Just the moisture that has been introduced with air entering a system, or moisture absorbed by oil left open to the air has corroded valves, and even stuck pistons.

Outside of this trouble, which could be avoided by proper installation and service procedures, this made a very successful refrigerant for small systems. At one time it was used for the majority of domestic systems, and had considerable use in early commercial work.

Refrigerant 40 or Methyl Chloride:—The use of methyl chloride as a refrigerant was tried and adopted by some manufacturers as soon as some of the difficulties of sulfur dioxide began to show. Colder temperatures than with sulfur dioxide are possible without a vacuum. Its volume is smaller, so it can be handled by a smaller compressor. Its condensing pressure is low enough to be easily handled.

In its pure state methyl chloride has no effect on most metals of compressor construction. *But it must never be used in contact with zinc or aluminum.* In contact with these metals, it breaks down to form spontaneously combustible gas. If contaminated with moisture, it will cause electrolytic action which will dissolve copper from tubing and deposit it on wearing steel parts. Methyl chloride will dissolve natural rubber, so this must not be used in gaskets or packing.

In common with other halides, it will mix in any proportion with oil and thin the oil. This has caused some trouble, but better compressor design plus the use of a heavier oil has largely eliminated troub'e from this source.

It is toxic and slightly asphyxiating. It has a rather sickly sweet ether odor, but small amounts cannot be detected by smell. Small quantities can be breathed with no ill effects. Greater amounts will cause drowsiness, mental confusion, and nausea. It has about the same effect as too much alcoholic stimulant without the stimulation, and has been called a "methyl drunk." Greater concentrations can cause asphyxiation and even death.

Because of the toxic and fire hazards of methyl chloride, it is no longer used in new equipment. But much of it is still found in older systems.

Refrigerant 717 or Ammonia.—This is the first refrigerant to be successfully used for mechanical refrigeration, and still is one of the leading refrigerants as to quantity produced and sold, and as to the tonnage of refrigeration produced by it. It used to be produced from nitrates, but since World War I, the bulk of it has been produced by chemically combining nitrogen from the air with hydrogen taken from water.

It is colorless in both liquid and vapor form. It has its so well known strong irritating odor. It boils at —28 F at atmospheric pressure. It is very highly soluble in water. Household ammonia is 2 or 3 percent of it dissolved in water. Commercial aqua ammonia is 28 percent ammonia dissolved in water. The specific gravity of the pure liquid ammonia is 0.66, and that of the vapor is 0.74. Thus, the liquid is lighter than water, and the vapor is lighter than air.

The very high latent heat of ammonia more than offsets its light weight. It gives 1.69 times the refrigeration of Refrigerant 12 for the same displacement. Its low boiling point requires a pressure on the low side for ordinary evaporator temperatures, 19.6 psig at 5 F, but makes ordinary freezer work possible without vacuums. Its condensing pressure gets high enough, 154.5 psig at 86 F, that proper care must be taken in designing equipment to hold it. Extra heavy pipe is usually used on the high side to give sufficient factor of safety.

Pure ammonia has been proven stable at the pressures and temperatures existing in a refrigeration system. But there seems to be some catalytic action in the presence of oil and other impurities. This causes some breakdown at compressor discharge temperatures and pressures. This forms non-condensable gases which must be purged off.

Below 200 F there seems to be very little of this action. Between 250 F and 300 F the increase in non-condensable gas becomes very great. Exact temperatures at which this happens cannot be specified because it varies for different systems, probably due to varying amounts of oil carry-over, carbon present, moisture and other impurities.

Some of the non-condensable gas may also come from oil breakdown or cracking occurring at discharge conditions. But regardless of where it comes from, it indicates discharge temperatures should not go above 250 F if such a limit is possible.

It has no effect on metals if dry, but will attack and destroy any copper or copper alloy if wet. Since it combines so quickly and completely with any moisture present, even moisture in the air, it has proven very difficult to keep dry in systems the size of the usual ammonia job. Parts of the system must periodically be opened to the air for inspection or maintenance. This difficulty has led to the design of systems containing no copper alloys. Developments have shown that special bronzes can be made which are corrosion proof against ammonia and water. These bronzes have been introduced into ammonia equipment in a limited way.

Pure ammonia will not have any effect on a properly refined lubricating oil. But with any moisture or acid oil, it may sludge badly. Although the ammonia has no effect on a good oil, compression temperatures must be watched. Ammonia gives a higher compression temperature than other refrigerants, 210 F at standard ton conditions. This, and the higher temperatures of higher compression ratios, will cause the oil to break down, which means carbonization, sludge and varnish formation. Ammonia compressors must be water jacketed to limit high discharge temperature, but this will not wholly prevent it.

The critical temperature and freezing points impose no limitations on ordinary systems. But in special applications where temperatures of 100 below 0 F or lower are required, some other refrigerant must be used because of ammonia's freezing point, —107.9 F.

The irritating and toxic properties of ammonia are another feature against it. When it combines with moisture, which it does so readily, it forms a powerful caustic. This, when in contact with human flesh can cause first, second, or third degree burns according to the concentration and length of exposure. This is especially true of the moist surfaces of the eyes, nose, mouth and lungs. Any moist part of the body is instantly irritated, and with increased exposure, burned by it. It even takes place to a lesser degree on the outside skin since the skin contains moisture. Any sweaty surface of the body can be badly burned. However, the per cent that is irritating is much smaller than the per cent that can burn or be fatal, so it is its own warning agent.

Its irritating odor gives instant warning of a leak. For a positive leak test, the white smoke from a mixture of ammonia and sulfur dioxide, is used. The sulfur dioxide is supplied by burning sulfur sticks. These are made up by dipping long slivers of wood in melted sulfur. A previously prepared supply is usually kept on hand. Or sulfur sticks can be obtained from suppliers of ammonia.

Ammonia is inflammable, but within rather narrow limits of concentration in air. It is one of the cheapest of the refrigerants, and it has been so well established that it can be obtained all over the civilized world. The power required to produce refrigeration with ammonia is about average. It is not over two percent higher than the lowest powered refrigerant at standard ton conditions.

Although it is not as safe as some of the other refrigerants, in large plants it is common to have it under the supervision of engineers. Small leaks can be immediately repaired. In case of a bad leak, the engineer is present. He knows immediately how to isolate the leaking part, and make the necessary repairs.

From the standpoint of refrigeration produced, ammonia is one of the best refrigerants on the list. Its hazardous features are the only thing against it. We find it predominating in industrial plants where the capacity is large. The average ice plant, cold storage plant, ice cream factory, wholesale creamery, or any other application of similar refrigeration requirements would not, in the past, consider any other refrigerant.

Carbon Dioxide.—Traces of this gas are present in the atmosphere. It is found dissolved in the water of some wells. It is formed by burning any fuel containing carbon, as do most fuels. It is the gaseous product given off during fermentation; it is a byproduct of many chemical processes. Most of that produced commercially comes from fermentation or chemical byproducts. Charged water for drinks is ordinary water with this gas dissolved in it, either naturally or artificially. It is what gives the bite or tang to soda pop. Dry ice is frozen carbon dioxide.

This gas is colorless, odorless and non-toxic except in high concentrations. The liquid is colorless, but since the triple point is 69.9 psig, no liquid can exist at atmospheric pressure. As shipped in steel drums, it may be either a liquid or gas depending on whether it is below its critical temperature of 87.8 F or not.

It has the lowest volume but the highest pressure and highest power requirement of any refrigerant. Its critical temperature is 87.8 F, which causes condensing problems at high ambients. It is stable, has no effect on oil or metal, and is not irritating or inflammable.

Carbon dioxide has so many faults and limitations as a good refrigerant that it might seem surprising that it has been used to any great extent. But it is safe. Before the introduction of fluoronated hydrocarbon refrigerants it was the only safe refrigerant. Therefore, in applications where safety was of greater importance than whether it was the most economical or most convenient, it found widespread use. Due to the heavy compression equipment, and the power necessary to handle it, it has never been used in commercial sizes. But in industrial sizes it was at one time used almost exclusively in passenger ships, hospitals, around prisons and similar institutions, and in early air conditioning applications. Since 1935 such jobs have used one of the synthetic refrigerants which combine safety with better refrigeration properties.

It should not be forgotten that carbon dioxide compression equipment is required for the manufacture of dry ice. So new equipment is still required for this special application.

Halides; Refrigerant 30 or "Carrene 1."—Many synthetic refrigerants have been developed, largely from methanes and ethanes. They are called halides because of the presence of the halogen elements chlorine or fluorine or both. Various combinations of these elements with carbon and sometimes hydrogen give different characteristics, many of which have exactly fit certain refrigeration requirements.

They are all somewhat similar to ether (also a halide) having a sweet, ethereal odor. Most of them have such a slight odor that it is only noticeable in a large concentration. Both the liquid and vapor are clear and colorless. The liquid is quite heavy, usually about one and one half times as heavy as water. The vapors will run from three to six times the weight of air. With such a heavy, dense liquid and vapor, pipe lines, passages in compressors, and valve openings must be of liberal size, and have a minimum of bends or other restrictions. Otherwise excessive pressure drops would occur.

All halides will mix with oil. At ordinary temperatures they will mix in any proportion. A few separate out, as oil separates from water, at low temperatures encountered in the evaporator. All halides thin the oil as they mix. Most compression equipment is now designed with this in mind to keep this mixing at a minimum.

It will dissolve any natural rubber material, so this must be kept in mind when selecting gaskets or packing. Synthetic, oil resisting rubber of the neoprene or chloroprene types will hold it.

Leaks may be checked with a halide torch. For systems which operate at a vacuum, a charge of air must be added to bring the pressure above atmospheric. A mixture of air and refrigerant escaping from a leak will still be indicated on the halide torch.

Refrigerant 30 (Carrene 1) was one of the first synthetic halides developed exclusively for refrigeration purposes. It was developed for centrifugal compressors, and used exclusively in this country for the first centrifugal refrigeration systems. These were applied entirely to air conditioning work.

These early centrifugal compressors are now considered obsolete. But there are many of them still in operation which require this refrigerant.

Fluorinated Hydrocarbons or fluorocarbons:—The addition of fluorine to the halides brought about the development of the new series of refrigerants previously mentioned. This has produced a group of refrigerants which are relatively non-toxic and non-inflammable, besides having the above mentioned halide properties. They will all break down to irritating and toxic gases when in contact with flame or hot surfaces. They are all quite similar in their properties except for boiling temperatures.

The following list covers those most commonly used and a few of the less commonly used ones. There are many more available for experimental work. A complete list of all refrigerants that have been used, or are in experimental development can be found in the lastest edition of the "Air Conditioning and Refrigerating Data Book, Design Volume", published by the American Society of Heating, Refrigerating and Air Conditioning Engineers.

Refrigerant 11.—A low pressure refrigerant suitable for either low or high temperature applications in a centrifugal compressor. It is the commonest refrigerant used in centrifugals at the present time.

Refrigerant 12.—A moderate pressure refrigerant suitable for reciprocating compressors. This was the first of the fluorocarbons which began to replace other refrigerants such as sulfur dioxide and methyl chloride. It is the commonest refrigerant found in domestic and commercial refrigeration and small air conditioning systems at the present time.

Refrigerant 13.—A high pressure refrigerant with a very low boiling point. Its high pressure and low critical temperature make this unsuitable for ordinary applications. But it is an excellent refrigerant in the low temperature end of a cascade system producing refrigeration at 100 F or more below zero.

Refrigerant 22.—A refrigerant quite similar to Refrigerant 12, but with a higher pressure. Its pressure characteristics are somewhat similar to ammonia. It is used in commercial, small industrial, and some air conditioning. A smaller compressor can be used with this refrigerant than with Refrigerant 12. But this must be balanced against higher condensing pressures; as high as 300 psig and sometimes more with air cooled condensers.

Refrigerant 113.—A low pressure (high vaccum) refrigerant suitable only for centrifugal compressors at air conditioning temperatures.

Refrigerant 114.—A low pressure refrigerant which has been used in centrifugal compressors in large size applications, and in rotary compressors for domestic sizes. Its pressure is a little higher than most centrifugal refrigerants. Its volume is too great to be suitable for a reciprocating compressor.

Other Conditions Than Standard Ton.—Standard ton conditions have been used for all comparisons which would be changed by a change of temperature. This is to give a fair comparison of each refrigerant with the others. On the whole the different refrigerants will change about the same for changing temperatures. There are a few cases where some properties which are nearly the same will change relative positions for higher or lower evaporator temperatures. Also note that conditions such as condenser and evaporator pressures, displacements, horsepower and compression temperatures will change greatly with changing temperatures. So what is marked good or fair for standard ton conditions might be poor for other widely varying conditions. And some items marked poor could be good at other conditions. Any more complete comparison would have to be worked out for the exact conditions prevailing. But the data given will still serve as a good comparison of systems operating under average conditions.

Changing Refrigerants.—The question is sometimes asked, can the refrigerant in a system be changed without affecting the operation of that system? Can obsolete refrigerants be changed to something more modern?

Before making any such changes, it is best to consult the manufacturer of the refrigeration system. He is best qualified to pass judgment on any changes contemplated. If manufacturers' recommendations are lacking, the following points should be kept in mind.

1. The system will probably give maximum efficiency with the refrigerant for which it was designed. Sizes of lines, ports and passages in the compressor, valve clearances, the pressure applied to the valve springs, are all designed to give the best possible results based on the volume and density of the fluid handled. A different refrigerant would have a different volume and density, so all the conditions so carefully designed for would be changed. It would be like having a suit tailored to an individual, then selling it to someone else. Even though it might fit approximately, it could never fit another person as well as the one it was tailored for.

The result in the case of the refrigerant is that the losses in the system, particularly in the compressor, are apt to be greater. In some cases they will be considerably greater. Sometimes manufacturers do design a compressor which they adapt to two or more refrigerants, with or without minor changes such as valve clearance and valve springs. Such compressors could be changed over with no ill effect if other factors are considered.

2. All refrigerants have different refrigerating effects for a given displacement. Therefore, if no other changes are made, there will be a variation in refrigerating capacity. This variation, neglecting losses mentioned above, will be proportional to the data given under item 9 of Table 3-1 and of the graphic illustration in Fig. 3-3. If a change such as from Refrigerant 22 to Refrigerant 12 was made, the capacity would be reduced. This would reduce the load on the condenser and driving motor. But a change in the opposite direction would increase the capacity. This would overload the motor and the condenser. The overloaded condenser would raise the head pressure which would further overload the motor.

In open type, belt driven compressors this variation in capacity is usually compensated for by changing the operating speed of the compressor. This is done by changing the size of the motor pulley. When the unit is to be slowed down, a smaller motor pulley is required. This sometimes leads to a pulley so small that the driving belts are flexed excessively around the smaller pulley, and their life is materially reduced.

3. Any change in refrigerant should naturally require the entire system be thoroughly cleaned. This includes draining and flushing out the compressor oil. The new oil must be suitable for the new refrigerant to be used.

4. Expansion valves or float valves should be exchanged or recalibrated for the new refrigerant. A thermostatic expansion valve is always made for a specific refrigerant, and will give best operating characteristics with this refrigerant. All pressure regulating valves

or pressure switches must be readjusted to the new pressure conditions imposed by the new refrigerant.

5. Ammonia should not be used in a system designed for any low pressure refrigerant. Copper tubing, brass and bronze fittings, and bronze bearings are used extensively in low pressure design. This will give trouble with ammonia. Also, ammonia operates at a higher pressure than the low pressure refrigerants, and may prove harder to hold with the lighter design. Due to high discharge temperatures, ammonia compressor cylinders are water jacketed. Some low pressure compressors have a water passage in the head, but it would be entirely inadequate for ammonia cooling. Most halocarbon refrigerant compressors use only air cooling on the cylinder and head.

Some Refrigerant 12 compressors have been used for ammonia booster compressors, that is, for the first stage of two stage compression. But the entire system is designed for ammonia, and a compressor of suitable design is chosen. In fact, some manufacturers have found it expedient to build a compressor suitable for either low pressure ammonia work or standard Refrigerant 12 work.

6. Refrigerant 12 or Refrigerant 22 are the only common refrigerants with characteristics near enough to those of ammonia to be considered as possible substitutes for the latter. But it is not good policy to change an ammonia system without a complete change of all equipment. The Freons are such excellent solvents they will loosen gums, sludges and scales that ordinary cleaning processes will not touch. Therefore such a change would lead to a constant repetition of plugged valve orifices, filters, and screens. Also, the fluorocarbons are so much heavier that excessive pressure drops could be expected in the piping, ports and passages designed for the much lighter ammonia.

7. Carbon dioxide is in such a pressure class by itself that it could not be substituted in a system designed for any other refrigerant. And it would be illogical to try to use another refrigerant in the cumbersome, heavy equipment designed specifically for carbon dioxide. Where such a change is desired, all equipment is changed with a great savings in weight, space and power requirements.

Handling Refrigerants.—The high vacuum refrigerants, that is, those with boiling points at or near atmospheric temperatures, or with condensing pressures near atmospheric are stored, handled and shipped in drums similar to oil drums. It should be remembered that the pressure of any refrigerant rises rapidly with a rise in temperature. Such refrigerants should not be stored near heat sources, such as a heater or boiler. Also there is always some expansion of the liquid with a temperature rise. Therefore the drum should not be filled completely full, since any rise in temperature will expand the refrigerant and cause it to bulge or even burst the drum.

All higher pressure refrigerants are handled in special steel cylinders that are made to conform with Interstate Commerce Commission regulations. This makes it possible to ship the refrigerant in the same container in which it is stored or sold.

In all but the smallest sizes, there is a fusible plug in the cylinder to protect it from the excessive pressure that would be present in case of fire or other excessive heat. Again it is of utmost importance that these cylinders not be overfilled. The fusible plug is to protect them against excessive vapor pressure, and will only fail due to heat. But the liquid in a cylinder filled nearly full would expand to fill the cylinder with a small rise in temperature. Then even a slight

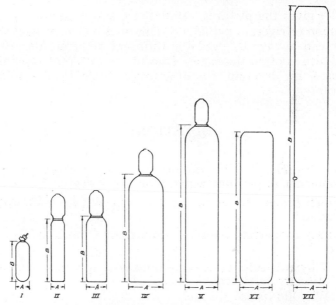

Fig. 3-4. Dimensions and capacities of refrigerant cylinders.

Shape	Dia. "A"	Height "B"	Approx.[1] Tare Weights	Capacity in Lbs.			
				CH_3Cl	R-12	R-22	NH_3
I	4″	12″	4 to 10 lbs.	3	4	3.5	
II	4	19	10 to 15	6	10	9	
III	6	20	17 to 23	15	25	22	
IV	10	33	50 to 90	60	100		
V	10	48	70 to 120	90	145	125	
IV[2]	12	33	60 to 120	90	145		
V[2]	10	44	73				50
V[2]	12	58	132 to 141				100
V[2]	14½	60	192				150
VI	10	46	105				50
VII	10	84	169 to 175				100
VII[2]	12	84	204 to 257				150

NOTES—
[1]These weights will differ somewhat for cylinders supplied by different manufacturers.
[2]Same approximate shape but different dimensions.

additional rise would exert a hydrostatic pressure in the cylinder that no steel would hold. The result would be an explosion. And you cannot explode a steel cylinder without considerable violence. No drum should ever be filled without first determining that it is empty. Then it should be weighed both before and after filling to insure that its capacity is not exceeded.

The men who handle different sized cylinders soon get to know the amount of the different refrigerants for which each one is safely rated. But for a new refrigerant, a new sized cylinder, or for a new person, the amount should be checked from the supplier or other source.

Fig. 3-4 gives the pictures, dimensions, and capacities of some of the common refrigerant cylinders. This does not mean that the same cylinder can always be used for different refrigerants. But their external size is often the same. Due to the different thicknesses of metal used by different manufacturers, their tare weights vary considerably.

QUESTIONS

3-1. Which properties that are desirable in a refrigerant, are most important to produce dependable refrigeration?

3-2. Which properties are important to produce economical refrigeration?

3-3. Which properties are most important from a safety point of view?

3-4. a. Why was sulphur dioxide once so commonly used as a low pressure refrigerant?
b. Why did its use die out?

3-5. Why is Refrigerant 12 so popular in domestic and commercial applications?

3-6. a. Which refrigerants are most commonly used for air conditioning applications?
b. Why?

3-7. Why has Refrigerant 12 or 22 not displaced ammonia in most industrial plants?

3-8. In what types of installations is Refrigerant 11 to be found?

3-9. List some of the problems involved when the refrigerant in the system is replaced with another.

3-10. Why is it important to weigh the refrigerant being transferred to any refrigerant drum?

CHAPTER 4

LIQUID FEED DEVICES OR
EXPANSION VALVES

General.—The refrigeration trade has commonly called the valve or device feeding refrigerant to the evaporator an expansion valve. Many technical men object to this term "expansion valve." True, some of the liquid changes to vapor at this point, and expands in volume as it does so. But as pointed out in Chapter 2, only a small part of the liquid changes to vapor as it goes through this valve. The remaining liquid contracts as it chills. Also with float valves and capillary tubes used for this purpose, the term "expansion valve" becomes a poorer description yet. For these reasons, it is sometimes called an evaporator feed device, refrigerant feed device, liquid feed device, or refrigerant control device.

Function of Expansion Valve.—To better understand the function of an expansion valve, let us first consider an analogy. A tank supplies water to a coil which is placed inside the firebox of a furnace, Fig. 4-1A. The flow of water from the tank to the coil is regulated by a control valve. This valve is so set that water from the tank flows into the coil at exactly the same rate it is evaporated, or boiled away, by the furnace. It should be so adjusted that some water will run all the way through the coil, but the last drop of water should be evaporated to steam before rolling out of the end of the coil. If the valve is not open wide enough, all the water is evaporated before reaching the end of the coil. The last few lengths of pipe are then useless in that they evaporate no water. If the valve is opened too wide, unevaporated water leaves the coil. This would waste the water, and if dry steam was required, the excess water might cause damage.

Fig. 4-1B shows how this analogy fits a refrigeration system. The liquid receiver corresponds to the water tank, and the liquid refrigerant, to the water. The regulating valve is the expansion valve. The evaporator coil corresponds to the pipe coil in the furnace. The liquid receiver does not have to be as high as the evaporator coil because the pressure of the high side will push the liquid through the expansion valve to this low pressure coil. The box at 40 F will be hot compared to the boiling temperature of the refrigerant. Therefore, it will evaporate the liquid refrigerant in the coil just as the water was boiled in the analogy. The expansion valve must be so regulated that some liquid refrigerant will reach the last pipe before evaporating. Too little refrigerant will not use the entire coil. Too much will return liquid to the compressor where it may do damage.

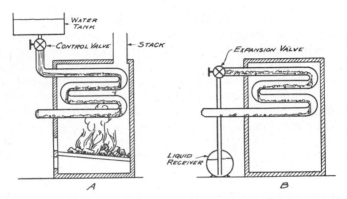

Fig. 4-1. Evaporator analogy.

If warm air or warm food enters the box, the greater amount of heat will evaporate all the refrigerant before it reaches the end of the coil. Therefore, the expansion valve will have to be opened wider if the entire coil is to be used. This will more rapidly remove the extra heat than if only a part of the coil is effective. As the heat is extracted from the warmer goods, less heat will be left to evaporate the refrigerant. Therefore, the valve will have to be gradually closed to compensate for this decrease in heat load. That is, *the expansion valve must regulate the flow of refrigerant according to the heat load.* The expansion valve does not control temperature.

Referring back to the refrigeration cycle charts, Fig. 2-13, page 29 we note the following conditions at the expansion valve.

1. The pressure instantly drops from high pressure to low pressure at the expansion valve needle.

2. The temperature instantly drops from the condensing temperature to the evaporating temperature at the valve needle.

3. There is no change in the heat content of the refrigerant as it passes through the expansion valve.

4. The refrigerant approaches the expansion valve as a liquid. Part of it, 14 per cent at the conditions illustrated, instantly changes to a vapor at the needle.

Hand Expansion Valve.—The hand expansion valve, Fig. 4-2, is nothing more than a needle valve, or in large sizes a plug valve, which makes fine adjustments or fine control of the flow possible. Obviously an attendant or engineer must always be present to make what adjustments are necessary with this type of valve.

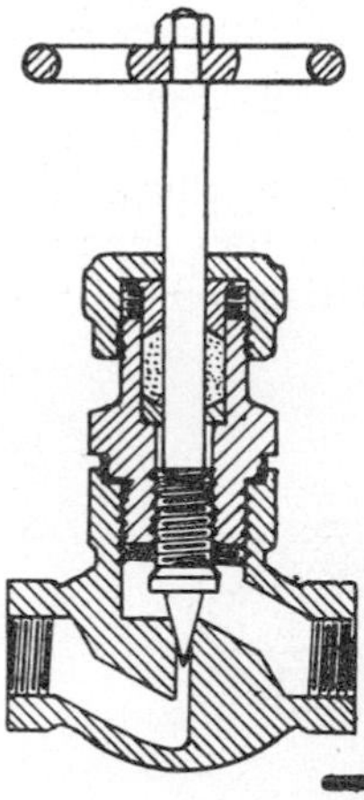

At one time the hand expansion valve was all that was available for refrigeration plants. It was the only expansion valve available with the early ammonia and carbon dioxide systems. Now, some form of automatic valve is standard. But a hand expansion valve is usually bypassed around the automatic valve to make operation possible in case of failure or repairs to the automatic valve, as shown in diagram, Fig. 4-3.

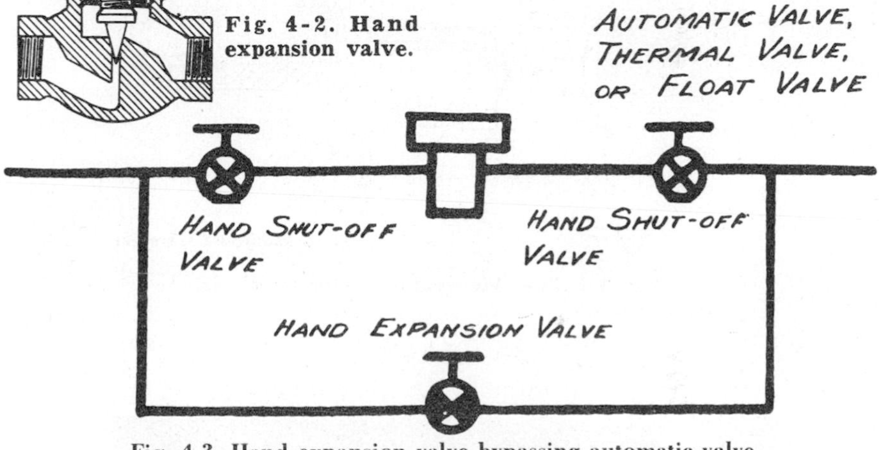

Fig. 4-2. Hand expansion valve.

Fig. 4-3. Hand expansion valve bypassing automatic valve.

Low Side Float Valve.—One of the easiest of the automatic feed devices to understand is the low side float valve. This, at one time, was widely used in both domestic and small commercial systems. Now their only common use is in large commercial and industrial systems. Fig. 4-4 shows the float mechanism itself. Fig. 4-5 shows how it may be connected inside the liquid header of an ammonia evaporator. Fig. 4-6 shows how it can be mounted outside the accumulator in a separate chamber. The latter method of installation is more common, as it can be more easily serviced.

In all these cases, the liquid refrigerant level is maintained at the float level. As liquid is evaporated, the level drops and the connecting linkage opens the valve to admit more liquid. As the entering liquid raises the level to the required point, the float is lifted and this closes the valve. Shut-off is complete and positive when there is no evaporation of refrigerant, as during the off cycle. It is called a low side float valve because the float ball and mechanism is in the low pressure side of the system.

Its principal advantages are as follows. It gives excellent automatic control. It maintains the proper refrigerant level regardless of load conditions, load changes, off cycles of the compressor, or any other such operating variables. Another advantage is that any number of evaporators can be operated in the same system. Each float valve will only pass the refrigerant required for its evaporator, no more and no less, regardless of conditions. Therefore, there is no limit to the number of low side float operated evaporators that may be properly operated in the same system. Each will draw only its required refrigerant.

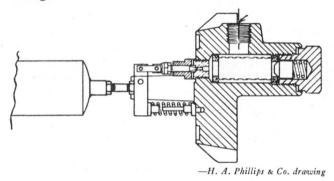

—*H. A. Phillips & Co. drawing*

Fig. 4-4. Low side float valve for ammonia.

—*York Corp. photo*

Fig. 4-5. Low side float valve inside liquid heater.

Its principal disadvantage is that it will not work satisfactorily in a dry expansion coil, see Chapter 5. Or if improperly applied to a flooded evaporator, it will give erratic operation. The chamber containing the float must be so located that the boiling action will not bobble the float up and down, and interfere with smooth operation.

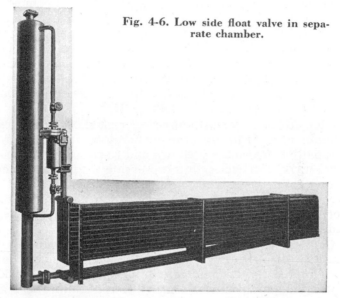

Fig. 4-6. Low side float valve in separate chamber.

—*H. A. Phillips & Co. photo*

Following are some of the difficulties that have been encountered with a low side float valve. The ball may spring a leak from corrosion, from cracks, or from solder joints. The obvious result of such a defect would be that the float would sink and open the valve. This would flood the coil and allow refrigerant to flood back the suction line.

The needle or seat or both may wear. They may wear smoothly so they will still hold refrigerant when shut off tight. But to compensate for the wear, the float must rise higher to push the needle further into the seat. The higher float means a higher liquid level. This may cause floodbacks (liquid refrigerant carried to the compressor) under the more violent boiling caused by heavy loads. Or the needle and seat may wear unevenly or even become pitted by the wire drawing[1] of the refrigerant. Then it will leak continuously.

---

[1]Wire drawing is a flow of high velocity through a nearly closed valve. The velocity becomes so great through the small orifice under pressure that it may actually erode or cut the metal.

Too much refrigerant can have no effect on an evaporator with a low side float valve. This is because the refrigerant is admitted only as required. But if there is insufficient refrigerant, the liquid level in the evaporator cannot be maintained high enough to close the valve completely. During the running cycle, bubbles of warm, high pressure vapor will be admitted to the evaporator. This must be removed by the compressor. This uses up part of the useful compressor capacity, yet still consumes power. The compressor operating on this excess warm vapor may run hot. If the refrigerant shortage is acute enough that a lot of warm vapor enters the evaporator with what liquid can be condensed, the evaporator itself will begin to warm up. Such a condition can increase to where the compressor will only recirculate vapor with a negligible cooling effect.

With automatic operation, slight refrigerant shortages allow high pressure liquid or vapor to enter the evaporator during the off-cycle. This will rapidly increase the pressure and warm up the evaporator. This makes for short off cycles, thus increasing the running time, and the cost of operating the system. Under a slight shortage with back pressure controls, such short cycling has been known to make an evaporator too cold by operating the compressor when refrigeration is not needed.

Since the float of a low side float valve system must have the proper buoyancy to operate the needle at the proper level, the floats must be calibrated for the refrigerant used. Floats for halocarbon refrigerants and for ammonia have such different calibrations, as well as being made of different materials, that they could not be interchanged.

High Side Float Valve.—Another form of float valve control is the high side float valve. This differs from the low side float valve in that the float chamber is on the high pressure side of the valve needle, in that a rising float opens the valve, Fig. 4-7. Thus, this valve dumps the liquid to the evaporator as rapidly as it is condensed, but does not allow any uncondensed vapor to pass through the valve. Such a system makes the evaporator instead of the liquid receiver the refrigerant storage part of the system. It is sometimes used without a liquid receiver.

One trouble peculiar to early designs of high side float valves was that they sometimes became air bound. If air or other non-condensable gas was in the system, the liquid flowing to the float valve chamber carried this gas with it. Since the valve would pass only liquid, the gas collected. As the valve chamber filled with gas, it prevented more liquid from flowing into it. If no liquid entered, the float valve would not open, and the system failed to function. The remedy was to "purge" the valve; that is, open a plug provided in the top of the chamber and let the air or gas blow out. Once all the air was eliminated from the system, the trouble would not recur. With ammonia valves, a bleeder tube is inserted in the valve to allow any non-condensable gas to bleed off to the evaporator, Fig. 4-7.

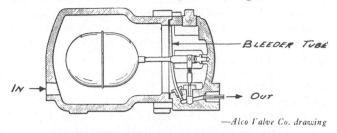

—Alco Valve Co. drawing

Fig. 4-7. High side float valve for ammonia.

Since the evaporator was the storage chamber for the refrigerant, this valve was very sensitive to high or low refrigerant charges. Too much refrigerant in the system would flood the evaporator (fill it to overflowing). With too little refrigerant, the valve would work satisfactorily, but the refrigeration and the frost level on the evaporator would be low. Some evaporators with high side float valves became very erratic with low refrigerant charges.

The greatest use of the high side float valve was in early domestic units. It has been used in some self contained commercial applications, both with low pressure refrigerants and with ammonia. But its use is very restricted here.

Capillary Tube.—The capillary tube is not a valve at all, but answers the purpose of an expansion valve in domestic systems and some small commercial systems. This shows more than ever that the purpose of the expansion valve is to divide the high and low pressure sides of the system while permitting a flow to the low side. The capillary tube is nothing more than a coil of several feet of very fine tubing, usually having an orifice of about 0.03 to 0.06 in. The pressure of the high side of the system is used up in forcing the liquid through the long restricted passage. It has been called a restrictor tube. The length of tube used gives just the right restriction to allow the proper amount of liquid to trickle through to the evaporator. The only adjustment possible is the length of tube used, and once this is installed, it is fixed.

However, the proper size capillary tube with the proper refrigerant charge is somewhat self regulating, or self adjusting. It is usually installed without a liquid receiver. If insufficient refrigerant passes through, the liquid refrigerant backs up into the condenser. This restricts the inside volume of the condenser available for the gas discharged from the compressor. The head pressure rises and forces a greater flow through the capillary tube. If all the liquid is drained from the condenser, there is still sufficient restriction to give a separation between the high and low pressure.

Naturally, such a system as this is not as efficient in operation as an expansion valve that adjusts itself to the refrigerant flow required. But on domestic and small, self contained commercial jobs, the operating cost is comparatively small. Therefore, the savings possible with a better device are insignificant. The capillary tube is cheaper than any other evaporator feed device, and has nothing to wear out. It is now used in all domestic systems. It is being applied to more and more hermetically sealed commercial equipment.

In many ways the capillary tube works like the high side float valve. It passes condensed refrigerant to the evaporator. Thus, the liquid storage is in the evaporator. One essential difference between its operation and that of the above mentioned valve, is that the pressure balances on the off cycle. That is, the high pressure in the high side bleeds through the tube until the pressures on the high side and the low side are the same. After all the condensed liquid has passed, the warm vapor goes over. This warm vapor is then chilled and condensed by the cold liquid in the evaporator. To prevent too large a loss from this, the volume of the evaporator is usually large compared to the volume of the high side of the system. This is another reason for omitting the receiver from this type of system. Then there is not enough of this warm vapor compared to the cold liquid to make any appreciable difference in the evaporator temperature during the normal off cycle.

The principal trouble to be expected with such a small tube would be that it would become plugged with dirt. In earlier construction this difficulty was experienced. Also moisture in the refrigerant plugged it with ice. But to manufacture a successful refrigeration unit, ultra cleanliness has been found to be absolutely essential, regardless of the type of expansion valve. And this is the obvious answer to the difficulties once encountered with the capillary tube.

Like the high side float valve, it is critical to the amount of refrigerant charged. Too much will fill the evaporator and flood back to the compressor. Too little will improperly fill the evaporator, lead to oil logging and erratic operation.

A change of refrigerant very probably will not work properly. The length and diameter of the tube chosen must balance the pressure forcing the refrigerant through, the quantity of refrigerant required, and the viscosity of the refrigerant. Any change will upset this balance.

Automatic Expansion Valve.—The automatic expansion valve is nothing more than a pressure reducing valve, Fig. 4-8. The sensitive element, the flexible diaphragm, has the evaporator pressure on the lower side of it, and atmospheric pressure above it. These pressures are balanced and adjusted with springs. For a given pressure setting, the valve opens just enough that the flow through it balances the vapor removed by the compressor. If the evaporator pressure starts to decrease, the pressure below the diaphragm is reduced, and the adjusting spring pushes down. This motion is transferred to the cage and needle by push rods to open the needle wider. This allows more high pressure refrigerant to flow into the evaporator, thus raising the pressure back to that required.

Any increase in pressure similarly raises the diaphragm, and the closing spring closes the valve. When the compressor stops for an off cycle, there is an immediate rise in pressure since the compressor is no longer removing the evaporating vapor. This rise in pressure closes the valve during the off cycle.

Fig. 4-9 shows an automatic expansion valve using a metallic bellows instead of a diaphragm.

Sometimes this constant pressure type of control is an advantage, and sometimes a disadvantage. It is an advantage where it is desired to maintain a constant evaporator temperature. But it does not respond well to varying loads. When the temperature surrounding

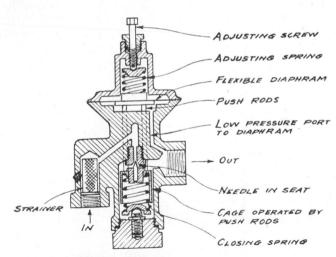

Fig. 4-8. Automatic expansion valve.

the evaporator coil rises due to a greater heat load, the liquid refrigerant in the coil is all evaporated before any of it reaches the end of the coil. Thus, the last coils of the evaporator are useless as far as extracting heat from the room.

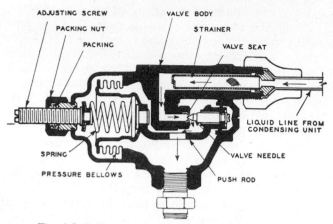

Fig. 4-9. Bellows type automatic expansion valve.

Yet when the temperature has risen, this is just the time when all of the coil is most needed. Under such conditions, the room is much slower in coming down to the proper temperature than if the entire coil were actively refrigerated. On the other hand, if there is insufficient heat in the room to evaporate all the refrigerant entering the coil, there is nothing to prevent the unevaporated liquid from flooding back the suction line to the compressor.

Its complete action can best be illustrated by following through what happens when refrigeration is started on a warm coil fed with this valve, Fig. 4-10. During the off cycle, the valve will remain closed as previously explained. As the compressor is started, the reduction in pressure opens the valve enough to let only a limited amount of refrigerant to flow. This small quantity is all evaporated by the first section of warm evaporator tubing it hits, "A-B". But this refrigerates or cools this section of tubing so the liquid following can flow through

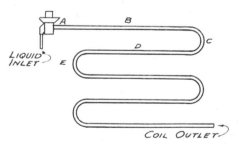

Fig. 4-10. Action of automatic expansion valve on evaporator.

without all evaporating. The following liquid then strikes the warm section "B-C" and is evaporated, chilling "B-C" while it does so. Thus, the liquid will gradually work its way toward the end of the coil. But there will be some heat from the room passing through the refrigerated section of the coil at all times. This also evaporates some of the liquid refrigerant. If the coil is long enough, or the heat passage through it great enough, a point will be reached where the heat flow through the coil is sufficient to evaporate all of the liquid refrigerant. If this happens, liquid never reaches the end of the coil.

On the other hand, if the heat in the room is insufficient to evaporate all the liquid refrigerant, it will gradually work its way back to the suction line. In so doing, it actually makes an evaporator out of the suction line, and produces refrigeration where it is not needed, but which must be paid for in power bills. If the suction line is short, the liquid may reach the compressor and cause damage. Of course, such conditions could be corrected by readjusting the valve. But it is expected to work automatically, so in practice an average setting must be found which uses as much of the coil as possible under heavy loads, but does not flood back under light loads. A thermostat is used and so adjusted on low pressure work that the machine turns off before it floods back.

Besides not responding well to a varying refrigeration load, it has one other disadvantage. It does not work well with more than one evaporator in a system. Fig. 4-11 shows why. If evaporator "A" is operated at a higher temperature which means a higher pressure than "C", the higher pressure vapor from "B" will back up through "D" to "C" and close the other valve. Thus, coil "C" will get no refrigerant and will not refrigerate. Under limited conditions both coils could be operated at exactly the same pressure, but if one valve had its operated at exactly the same pressure, but if one valve had its pressure set just a little too high, or if due to a slight change in adjustment due to wear, stickiness, change of temperature of valve parts, etc., the other coils will be starved. Such applications have been made, but they must be accurately adjusted and closely watched, and are not to be recommended.

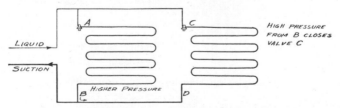

Fig. 4-11. Why automatic expansion valve will not multiplex well.

Because of its constant temperature characteristics, the automatic expansion valve is much used in certain applications, particularly in liquid cooling jobs where it is important to maintain a liquid bath at a constant temperature. The valve is also simpler, which means cheaper, and possibly a little more trouble-free than valves which are more responsive to the load.

Due to its relative simplicity, there is little to go wrong with this valve. Needles and seats may erode so they leak during the off cycle. But the use of present day materials has largely eliminated this trouble. Also, the gradual wear will necessitate the valve moving further into the seat to shut off. This will raise the evaporator pressure and tend to flood back if uncorrected, but may be corrected by readjustment. Diaphragms or bellows have been known to crack or corrode through, but again, modern valves have largely eliminated this trouble.

An excessive refrigerant charge will have no effect on this valve. A low charge will allow some high pressure vapor to enter the evaporator. Peculiarly, this will sometimes cause a slug of liquid back to the compressor because a large bubble of high pressure vapor can sweep everything before it as it travels through the evaporator to the compressor.

Each valve usually has considerable range of pressure through which it can be adjusted. Its operation is usually equally satisfactory at any required evaporator temperature. For very cold temperatures, below -20 F, the manufacturer should be consulted for recommendations.

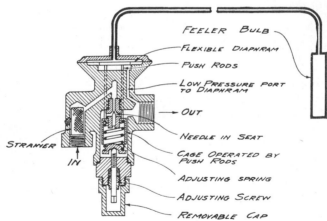

Fig. 4-12. Thermostatic expansion valve.

Thermostatic or Thermal Expansion Valve.—This valve is also sometimes called a DX or a TX valve. It is an automatic expansion valve with an additional device to correct the adjustment for the load on the evaporator, Fig. 4-12. It is actually more automatic in its operation than the so-called automatic expansion valve. To understand how the thermostatic expansion valve works, refer to the temperature cycle of Fig. 2-13. The expansion valve and evaporator section of this is reproduced to a larger scale in Fig. 4-13 under three different conditions.

At "A" is the condition to be found with a starved evaporator, at "B" with an evaporator operating nearly flooded, and at "C" with it full flooded. There are two important differences in the different conditions illustrated. The first and most important is that in "A", only about 60 percent of the evaporator surface is wet on the inside. Since the part that is dry does practically no work, only about 60 percent of the evaporator is doing useful work, that is, cooling the room. About 95 percent of the evaporator is used in "B", which only makes a 5 percent loss in the full usage of the evaporator. Condition "C" gives fullest use of the evaporator surface. But if there is liquid at the end of the coil, as in this case, any sudden surge in evaporation might push some of the liquid on through to the compressor. Therefore, it is too critical a point at which to attempt to operate this type of evaporator[2]. Condition "B" causes relatively little loss in capacity, so for safety sake is used.

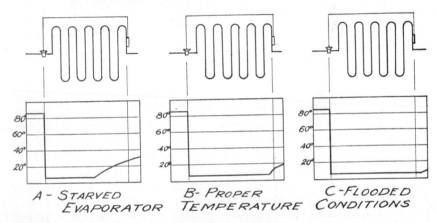

A - STARVED EVAPORATOR   B- PROPER TEMPERATURE   C -FLOODED CONDITIONS

Fig. 4-13. Comparison of suction temperature under various evaporator conditions.

The second difference to be noted in Fig. 4-13 is the difference in the temperature of the vapor leaving the evaporator. At "A" there is 20 F of superheat picked up in the dry section of the coil. At "B" there is 10 degrees of superheat, and at "C" there is none. Notice this is a difference in temperature between the active part of the coil and the end of the coil. Differences such as these will exist regardless of the temperature at which the coils operate. This fact is made use of to adjust the expansion valve to operate the coil at condition "B".

Fig. 4-12 shows that the thermostatic expansion valve is an automatic expansion valve with a temperature sensitive element attached. The feeler bulb is attached to the last coil of the evaporator to "feel" the temperature change of Fig. 4-13. The bulb is nearly

[2]See Chapter 5 for a more complete discussion of evaporator types.

always charged with the same refrigerant as is used in the system. The pressure created by the refrigerant in the bulb is transmitted to the top of the flexible diaphragm. An adjusting spring and screw are provided to balance the valve to the evaporator. Once this is set, changes in the load on the coil are automatically adjusted for by the changing pressure on top of the diaphragm. The preliminary adjustment should be such that approximately 10 degrees of superheat balance the coil.

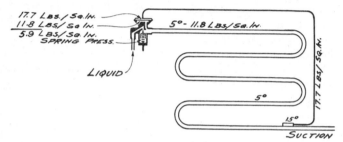

Fig. 4-14. Pressures and temperatures in thermostatic expansion valve and evaporator.

Fig. 4-14 shows how this 10 degrees gives a pressure difference which actuates the valve. The conditions given are for Refrigerant 12. The 5 F evaporator has a pressure of 11.8 psig. This pressure is applied to the under side of the diaphragm, and remains constant as long as the evaporator temperature does not change. The 10 F superheat in the suction line heats the feeler bulb to 15 F. This causes a pressure of 17.7 psig which is applied to the top of the diaphragm. The difference of 5.9 psi is balanced by the adjusting spring. When there is 5.9 psi more pressure on top of the diaphragm than on the bottom, the flow of the refrigerant through the valve is just sufficient to maintain condition "B" of Fig. 4-13. The valve is properly adjusted to allow the right amount of refrigerant into the coil to balance the load.

Condition "A" Fig. 4-13 is an extreme condition, but if it did occur, the 20 F of superheat would heat the feeler bulb to 25 F. This would cause a pressure of 26.1 psig on top of the diaphragm. The pressure below would remain at 11.8 psig. Thus there is 26.1— 11.8 = 14.3 psi greater pressure above the diaphragm. This would hold the valve wide open to permit the flow of a maximum amount of refrigerant.

A less extreme case would be where sufficient heat around the coil would evaporate all the liquid, and 15 F of superheat was picked up by the time the refrigerant reached the bulb. A 20 F bulb would cause a pressure difference of 9.2 psi on the diaphragm and open it wider. If this wider opening allowed the refrigerant to reach the point of Fig. 4-13-"B" which would give 10 F of superheat, the valve will balance and stay at this new position. If not, the valve will readjust itself again.

If the heat load drops so unevaporated refrigerant approaches the end of the coil, the superheat drops. If the superheat dropped to 5 degrees, this would heat the bulb to 10 F which gives a pressure of 14.6 psig or a difference of 2.8 psi on the diaphragm. Thus, the spring would close the valve a little further, which would reduce the flow of refrigerant.

If the liquid refrigerant reached the coil end, the temperature would be 5 F, and the pressure would be the same on both sides of the diaphragm. The spring would then close the valve completely and hold it closed until the pressure on top of the diaphragm increased again.

It might seem the valve should be operated with much less than 10 F of superheat to better use the entire coil. Some superheat is obviously necessary, because if the liquid reached the control bulb, there would be no way of telling whether it just reached it, or flooded clear back to the compressor. The reason one F or two F of superheat is not used is because this would mean a difference of less than one psi between normal operation and a completely closed valve. It is practically impossible to make a valve which is sensitive enough to react to such a small change, but which will not fluctuate too widely under changing load conditions. That is, it would be either completely closed or wide open most of the time, instead of following the load smoothly. The manual adjustment makes it possible to change the superheat setting at which the valve will operate. About 10 F of superheat has been found to work out best in practice for natural convection coils. As little as three to five degrees must be used on some blower coils and some freezer coils.

A variation in the construction of this valve is the external equalizer. This is recommended for large evaporators where there is considerable pressure drop through the evaporator. Any such pressure drop will be maximum for heavy loads, and will be little or nothing for light loads. Fig. 4-15 illustrates extreme conditions under heavy loads. The maximum pressure drop in this case is 4 psi. Assume the valve is set for an average superheat of 10 F under a light load as in Fig. 4-14. The pressure below the diaphragm is 11.8 psig and above is 17.7 psig giving a difference of 5.9 psig. Under a heavy load, Fig. 4-15, the pressure at the end of the coil is 11.8 $-4 =$ 7.8 psi. This gives an evaporating temperature of -2.8 F[3]. But 15 F at the end of the coil is necesary to get the 5.9 psi difference. Thus, to balance the valve, the total superheat setting is actually 15—

(—2.8) = 17.8 F. This will starve the coil. But a heavy load condition is just the time when maximum flooding is required.

The external equalizer takes the pressure that is applied under the diaphragm from the same point the temperature of the superheat bulb is taken, Fig. 4-16. Therefore any change in the pressure in the coil is compensated for. The 10 F superheat is added to the temperature of the evaporating liquid at the end of the coil. It is always constant, regardless of any change of pressure through the coil.

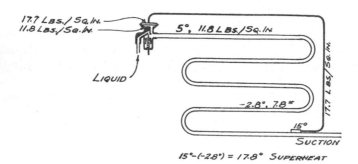

Fig. 4-15. Pressure drop in large coil.

Since active refrigeration is not produced during the off cycle, the high conductivity of the metal evaporator tube tends to equalize the temperature throughout the coil. This keeps the difference in temperature between the active section of the coil containing liquid, and the bulb less than 10 F which closes the valve. This shuts it off tight during the off cycle so it will not flood the evaporator.

The big advantage of the thermostatic expansion valve when it is properly used is that it gives completely automatic evaporator flow control. It responds readily to variation in load, and balances the entire coil without allowing any floodbacks.

Its principal disadvantage is its complexity. This not only means a more costly valve, but a valve with more parts to go wrong.

If this valve is properly selected for the job, and properly installed, it gives very little trouble. But the right valve must be chosen for the job. It must be of the proper size. Too small a valve will not allow enough refrigerant to pass to fill the entire coil on heavy loads. Too large a valve will cause hunting. That is, it opens too wide when an increasing load calls for more refrigerant. This

[3]It has been stated that the evaporator temperature is constant through the entire evaporator. Normally it is. But here are special cases where there may be sufficient variation to somewhat alter operating conditions. In this case, note that the temperature gets colder as the end of the coil is approached.

allows flooding. This flooding then closes the valve. Thus, the valve alternately opens too wide, then closes too much, and does not readily settle down to a proper balance.

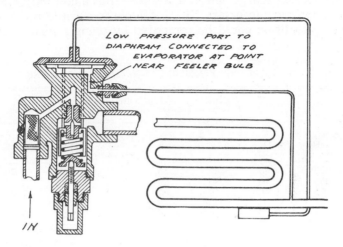

Fig. 4-16. Thermostatic expansion valve with external equalizer.

Some valve manufacturers supply different sized orifices for different loads on valves to give different ratings between the different sizes manufactured. Table 4-1 shows how one manufacturer rates one of his valves with different orifice assemblies. It is the difference in pressure between the high and low side that actually determines how much refrigerant is forced through a given sized orifice. Note that with this valve and a given orifice size, extreme pressure changes may reduce capacities 30 percent or increase them 20 percent from average conditions.

Some manufacturers supply an orifice that goes in the outlet of the valve. This orifice is small enough that at anywhere near full load, most of the pressure drop is across this orifice instead of at the needle and seat. In this way, any erosion due to wire drawing will take place in this secondary orifice instead of on the needle or seat. In some cases, valve capacities are more easily changed by changing this orifice than by changing a needle and seat assembly.

One manufacturer has adapted the thermostatic expansion valve to flooded operation. The feeler bulb has a built-in electric heater. Its design is such that when submerged in liquid the heat does not reach the bulb, so the valve remains closed. When the liquid level drops below the bulb-heater assembly, the heat reaches the bulb and the valve opens.

A trouble sometimes experienced with some applications of this
valve is found where there is not enough difference in temperature
between the room and the coil to supply the required superheat. If
there was an extra large coil in a room so that a coil only 8 F colder
than the room was necessary, 10 F of superheat could not be picked
up. Such a condition could be remedied by using a heat exchanger,

TABLE 4-1—CAPACITIES OF ONE SIZE OF THERMOSTATIC EXPANSION VALVE FOR
REFRIGERANT 12 AT DIFFERENT PRESSURES, WITH DIFFERENT ORIFICE ASSEMBLIES

Valve No.	Orifice Assembly No.	Capacity in Tons of Refrigeration Under Pressure Differences Between Valve Inlet and Outlet as Follows:						
		30 Lb.	40 Lb.	50 Lb.	Design Pressure Difference 60 Lb.	70 Lb.	80 Lb.	90 Lb.
TCL	000F	.35	.45	.55	.60	.65	.70	.75
TCL	00F	.70	.80	.90	1.00	1.10	1.10	1.20
TCL	0F	1.40	1.60	1.80	2.00	2.20	2.30	2.40
TCL	1F	2.50	2.90	3.30	3.60	3.90	4.20	4.40
TCL	2F	3.40	3.90	4.40	4.80	5.20	5.60	5.90

Courtesy Alco Valve Co.

Fig. 4-17. Here the extra heat is supplied by the warm liquid from
the condenser which feeds the expansion valve.

This same condition could also occur at very cold temperatures
for a little different reason. It has been shown how 10 F of superheat at 5 F evaporator gives 5.9 psi pressure difference across the
diaphragm. But at a -40 F evaporator, the pressure with Refrigerant 12
would be 9.3. This plus 5.9 lbs. would give 15.2 psia pressure on top

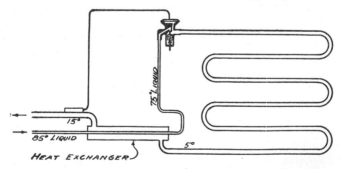

Fig. 4-17. Heat exchanger to supply expansion valve superheat.

of the diaphragm necessary to balance the valve. But the temperature for 15.2 psia is -20 F, or 20 degrees of superheat. Thus if no
heat exchanger was used, the valve would not work in a room
colder than -20 F. Such a wide split in temperature between the
coil and the room is very uneconomical.

The fact is too often overlooked that 10 F. of superheat at zero degree evaporator does not mean exactly 10 degrees at any other temperature. On ordinary jobs, the variation is so little that it could be compensated for by readjusting the valve. But extreme variations are apt to lead to trouble. Table 4-2 shows variations in

TABLE 4-2—THERMOSTATIC EXPANSION VALVE SUPERHEAT VARIATIONS WHEN SET FOR 10 F ON ZERO DEGREE EVAPORATOR

Evaporator Temperature	Methyl Chloride	Superheat temperature to operate valve		
		Refrig. 12	Refrig. 22	Ammonia
40	5.3	5.7	5.8	5.2
20	7.4	7.3	7.5	7.2
0	10.0	10.0	10.0	10.0
—20	14.2	13.3	13.6	14.2
—40	20.7	18.3	18.5	20.4

superheat temperature necessary to operate thermostatic expansion valves at different evaporator temperatures, when set for 10 F of superheat at zero deg. evaporator temperature. Some manufacturers have special valves made for evaporator temperatures below zero degrees F. It is always safest to depend on manufacturer's recommendations in such applications. The above data shows why a heat exchanger is standard practice on such cold installations operated by thermostatic expansion valves.

Each valve is made specifically for the refrigerant it is to be used with, as well as the sized job. The bulb is usually charged with the same refrigerant with which it is to be used. Occasionally, because the wrong valve is available, someone tries to use it and compensate for the difference by readjustment. Such adjustments of a misapplied valve will never give satisfactory results.

In commercial applications, more thermostatic expansion valves are used at the present time than all other types of refrigerant controls put together. Its fully automatic characteristics under all load conditions make it excellently suited for the attention-free automatic requirements of commercial operation. Its adoption in industrial applications was slower than in commercial, but it is now being applied in ever increasing numbers. It does have limitations on full flooded evaporators, and on very cold temperature work.

QUESTIONS

4–1. What is the principal purpose of the expansion valve?

4–2. Can the expansion valve normally be used to control temperature?

4–3. What are the principal differences between the high side float valve and the low side float valve?

4–4. a. How is the operation of the high side float valve similar to the operation of the capillary tube?

b. How does it differ?

4–5. What are the operating characteristics of the automatic expansion valve?

4–6. What are the advantages of the low side float valve?

4–7. What are the advantages of the thermostatic expansion valve?

4–8. The thermostatic expansion valve is sometimes called a superheat valve. Why?

4–9. Can a single model thermostatic expansion valve be applied to all refrigerants?

4–10. What are some of the problems of operating a thermostatic expansion valve at -30 F?

CHAPTER 5

EVAPORATORS

THE evaporator, as the name implies, is that part of the system in which the liquid refrigerant is evaporated. It is variously called the chilling coil, freezing coil, evaporator or low side. The evaporating process, that is, the heat absorbed in evaporating the liquid refrigerant is the purpose of the entire refrigerating system. It is the absorption of this heat that we call cooling. Due to the relative simplicity of the evaporator, its importance is often overlooked. But the whole system depends on the proper operation of the evaporator.

Requirements for Evaporators.—There are three principle requirements of good evaporator design:

1. It must supply sufficient cold surface to absorb the required heat.

2. It must have a chamber to hold the liquid refrigerant to be evaporated, and room for the evaporated vapor to separate from the liquid.

3. It must provide circulation without excessive pressure drop in the evaporator.

1. *It must supply sufficient cold surface.* The total surface must be proportional to the required load. The refrigerant could be boiled in a tank. But this would be uneconomical because of the large volume of refrigerant required to fill it, and the small exterior surface it offers to absorb heat. The usual way of obtaining the required surface is to make the evaporator in the form of pipe coils, Fig. 5-1. With fluorocarbon refrigerants, copper tubing is usually used. Its surface is often extended, usually by sheet metal fins, Fig. 5-2. Other methods have also been used. Fig. 5-3 shows the use of plate surface evaporators. In this case, plates are set vertically for ceiling coils and set horizontally for shelf coils. Refrigerant channels in the plates may be formed by soldering or welding tubing between the two surface plates. Or they may be formed by grooves pressed in a second plate which is welded to the first. Iron pipe is used for ammonia. Finned surfaces or other such surface extensions are less often used in this case.

The use of extended surfaces such as fins is limited to applications where the evaporator coils are used to chill air. Where water or other liquids are cooled by evaporators, fins are not needed. Heat transfer from a liquid is much more rapid than from a gas, such as air. Note how much more rapidly cold water will chill us (remove heat from us) than will cold air.

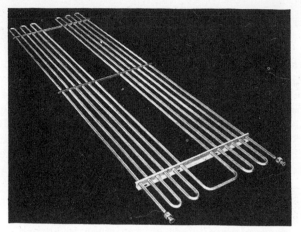

—*Rempe Co. photo*

Fig. 5-1. Simple pipe coil evaporator.

2. *It must have a chamber to hold the liquid and allow the vapor to separate.* This separation must be complete in order that vapor

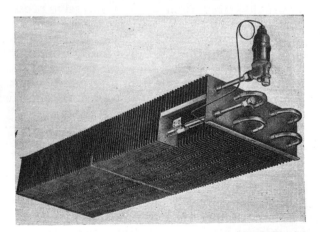

—*Rempe Co. photo*

Fig. 5-2. Finned coil evaporator.

can be removed by the compressor without drawing slugs of liquid with it. In other words, under heavy loads (lots of heat) it must not boil over. A slight amount of liquid returned to the suction line cuts the efficiency of the compressor. A large amount may damage the compressor.

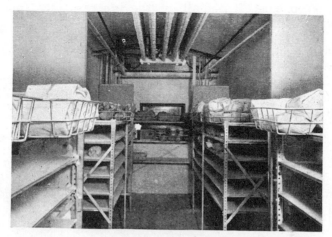

—*Dole Refrigerating Co. photo*

Fig. 5-3. Plate evaporators used as ceiling and shelf coils.

3. *It must provide circulation without excessive pressure drop.*
Circulation is essential to maximum heat transfer. If one watches
water come to a boil, there is a period where bubbles begin to form
on the inside surface of the pot and cling there. These insulate the
liquid from the metal at such points. As stated above, liquid transfers heat better than gas (bubbles). If these bubbles were swept
from the surface, actual boiling would commence sooner. The same
is true inside an evaporator. The only sure way of knowing bubbles
are not insulating the pipe from the liquid, is to have a circulation
which sweeps these bubbles from the surface as fast as they are
formed. The circulating force is usually provided by the flow of refrigerant through the coils.

An excessive pressure drop through the coil affects proper expansion valve operation, penalizes the compressor capacity, and
under heavy loads may cause coil starving (not enough refrigerant).
So, although flow or circulation of refrigerant is necessary, it must
not be such that friction will be excessive.

Types of Evaporators.—Evaporators have been divided into
either "flooded" or "dry" types. *A flooded evaporator has some form
of tank or header which keeps the inside evaporator surface full or
flooded with liquid.* A higher heat transfer rate per square foot of
evaporator surface is usually attained with flooded systems. But
they require a larger charge of liquid refrigerant to keep them full.
*A dry expansion system is not "dry," but contains relatively less
liquid than a flooded system.* The inside of the evaporator is only
about one fourth or one third full of liquid. But the boiling action

serves to keep most, if not all, of the inner surface splashed or wetted with liquid refrigerant.

Flooded Evaporators.—Figs. 5-4 and 5-5 show domestic evaporators that are fed with capillary tubes. Notice in each case, the presence of a header or accumulator in the outlet to keep the evaporator flooded. This header also acts as a liquid equalizer. It makes some variation possible in the refrigerant level on the low side without either starving the evaporator or flooding the compressor. Such a header is essential to the proper operation of an evaporator fed by a capillary tube.

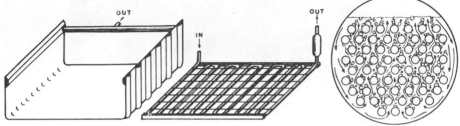

Fig. 5-4. Freezer compartment evaporator.

Fig. 5-5. Shelf type evaporator.

Fig. 5-7. Liquid circulation in boiler type evaporator.

An evaporator similar to Fig. 5-4 can be used in a single compartment domestic refrigerator. Or it could be used in the freezer compartment of a dual temperature cabinet. An evaporator the shape of Fig. 5-5 can be used in the top of the cooler compartment of a dual temperature cabinet. Or several of them can be used as shelves in a freezer cabinet. In the latter case, the inlet is to the bottom shelf. The outlet of this feeds the next higher shelf. This type of feed continues through each shelf to the top. The header is on the outlet of the top shelf.

Typical industrial flooded evaporators fed with low side float valves are shown in Figs. 4-5 and 4-6, pages 56 and 57. Such evaporators could be used for cooling either liquid or air.

Fig. 5-6 shows a liquid or brine cooler similar to a horizontal return tube boiler. But it provides for several passes of the brine back and forth in these tubes. The refrigerant is in the tank or boiler. The heat flows from the brine or water through the tube walls to the refrigerant. The tubes give the surface necessary to transfer the heat. The top surface of the refrigerant is adequate to allow the bubbles formed by boiling, to break through to give proper vapor separation. The bubbles rising from the tubes induce a circulation of the liquid refrigerant up through the tube bundles and back down the sides of the evaporator, Fig. 5-7.

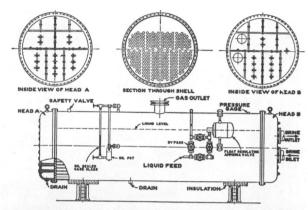

Fig. 5-6. Multipass brine cooler. —*Henry Vogt Machine Co. drawing*

Fig. 5-8. Single pass brine cooler. —*Henry Vogt Machine Co. photo*

Fig. 5-8 shows a similar evaporator designed for use in the brine tank of an ice plant. Here the brine only makes one pass through the tubes. It is forced through by the action of an agitator in the brine. Fig. 5-9 shows an ice maker of similar construction, but set vertically. Fig. 5-10 shows an industrial ice cream freezer operated as a flooded evaporator. The enlarged header on top is to give the required room for vapor separation.

Many designs have been evolved to make a trombone or hairpin type of coil like Fig. 5-1 operate fully flooded. Fig. 5-11 shows a method commonly used at one time and still found in many plants. An accumulator is made use of to keep the coil flooded and to separate the evaporated liquid from the vapor. These early forms were usually fed by a hand expansion valve, but more recently by low side float valves.

The best industrial evaporators of modern design combine an accumulator with headering, Fig. 4-9, page 62. Shorter lengths of pipe are used for the evaporator surface. These shorter lengths are connected with headers or feeders, which in turn are supplied with liquid from an accumulator. Return headers carry a mixture of liquid and vapor back to the accumulator. In this design, the mixture

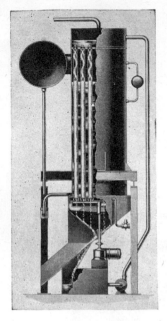

—*Henry Vogt Co. photo*

Fig. 5-9. Tube ice maker.

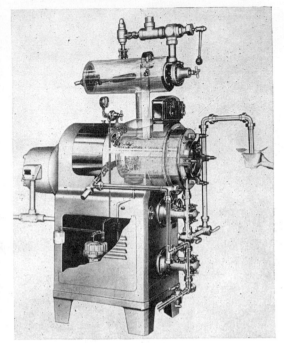

—*Creamery Package Mfg. Co. photo*

Fig. 5-10. Phantom view of continuous ice cream freezer.

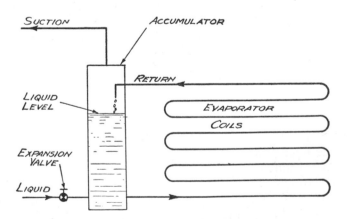

Fig. 5-11. Accumulator used on flooded evaporator.

of liquid and vapor in the tubes is lighter than the liquid in the accumulator. This induces a rapid flow through the tubes from the bottom to the top to give the circulation required for good heat transfer. Yet the headers and tubes are short enough that this good circulation does not set up an excessive pressure drop. Accumulators must be of adequate size or surging is caused, that is, they become filled to overflowing by the "boiling over" action in the tubes when a sudden heat load is applied.

One design makes use of a liquid ammonia pump to give forced circulation from an accumulator. Fig. 5-12 shows the details of such a system.

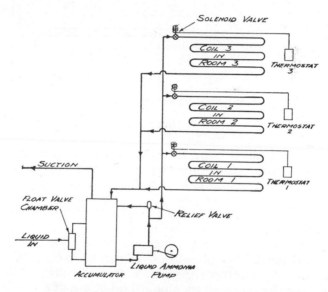

Fig. 5-12. Liquid ammonia circulating system.

Dry Evaporator.—In Fig. 4-1, page 54, an analogy was given between an evaporator and a water pipe in a furnace. Such a coil is typical of a dry expansion evaporator, although far from "dry." There are actually two different ways such a coil may operate. Some vapor (flash gas) is formed as the liquid goes through the expansion valve Fig. 2-12, page 28. Fig. 5-13 shows how this vapor forms bubbles in the pipe. As more evaporation takes place, these bubbles increase in size until they fill the tube. From here on, the evaporator is a series of sections filled with liquid alternated with vapor. The sections of liquid decrease in length and the sections of vapor increase in length. These sections travel rapidly from the point of formation to the end of the coil. The coil can still be adjusted so the last section of liquid entirely evaporates at the approximate end of the coil. But any in-

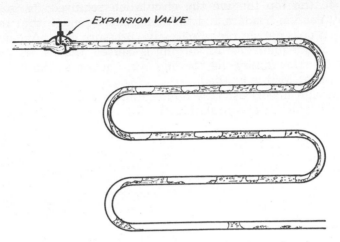

Fig. 5-13. Evaporation in small tube evaporator.

crease in load will immediately increase the size of the bubbles and push the liquid ahead faster. Some of this liquid may be pushed out so fast that it is pushed clear through to the compressor before it has time to evaporate. Also, superheating of the bubble takes place between the slugs of liquid. This dries off the inner surface between the liquid slugs so there are actually "dry" sections of the evaporator. And any dry section of evaporator is an inactive one, that is, it will absorb almost no heat. The circulation in such an evaporator is good, but the separation of liquid and vapor is poor. And if the evaporator is of any great length, the pressure drop can be excessive.

To correct this condition, the coil diameter could be increased, Fig. 5-14. Here the liquid flows along the bottom of the tube, while the vapor separates from it and flows through the top of the tube. There should be enough splashing or agitation to keep the entire inner wall of the tube wet, but not enough to throw the liquid together in a slug which completely shuts off the gas passage. Here the liquid flow in the bottom, and the vapor flow through the top of the tube gives circulation, but there is enough room for a separation of the vapor and liquid. Such an evaporator would be ideal, and could be obtained by proportioning the tube size to the amount of refrigerant circulated, and the speed of flow. But too slow a speed is possible too. With the low pressure refrigerants there is always some oil carried to the evaporator which must be swept through to the suction line. A pipe that is too large will slow the circulation down to the point where this oil is not carried along, and it will

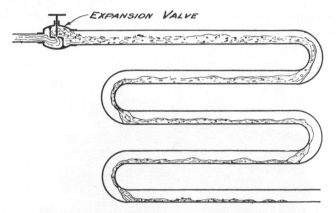

Fig. 5-14. Evaporation in large tube evaporator.

trap in any low points in the coil. And what would be the right sized evaporator coil for a light load would not be the correct one for a heavy load. Actually, a dry expansion evaporator of about the right size will probably operate as in Fig 5-14 on light loads, and as Fig. 5-13 on heavy loads. It may even act as in Fig. 5-13 for part of its length and as in Fig. 5-14 for the rest.

Both of the foregoing illustrations are with top feed. That is, the liquid is fed into the coil at the top, allowed to flow to the bottom by gravity, and the vapor pumped out the bottom. Sometimes an up feed is used. With coils of small pipe size, these will operate similar to Fig. 5-13. With larger pipe sizes they will operate more as in Fig. 5-14 on the horizontal runs, but as in Fig. 5-13 in the vertical lifts from coil to coil. Such operation is necessary to get the liquid up hill against gravity. More liquid must be present in the coil to make such operation possible, and to get liquid up the coil high enough to reach the expansion valve bulb. This makes the coil operate more nearly flooded than with a down feed, with the advantages of higher heat transfer. But it is also more apt to flood back and give erratic operation under varying load conditions. It does not operate as completely flooded as a true flooded evaporator. And if not operated sufficiently flooded it will trap oil badly.

Improved Designs.—The first coils designed for dry expansion were entirely of the "trombone" type, Fig. 5-1. Such coils are still used to a limited extent in all branches of refrigeration. But a study of their operation showed that for a coil of any size the difficulties explained in Fig. 5-13 were encountered.

One of the first methods used to offset these difficulties was to use an accumulator as mentioned with flooded evaporators. Accumulators were hooked up in many ways, but always with the same purpose; to keep the coil more nearly flooded, to separate the un-evaporated liquid from the vapor, return the liquid to the coil and the vapor to the suction line.

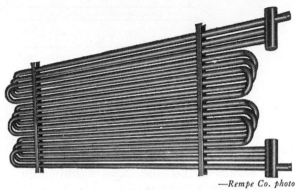

—*Rempe Co. photo*

Fig. 5-15. Headered pipe coil.

A second method of giving better operation is headering, Fig. 5-15. The circuits are divided so all the liquid does not have to be fed through one pipe. Therefore, the smaller amount of liquid per coil will operate more nearly like Fig. 5-14. Notice the flooded evaporators of Figs. 4-5 and 4-6, pages 56 and 57 and the domestic evaporator of Fig. 5-4 are all headered. In Fig. 5-4 the same header serves both as a liquid header and a suction header. Both commercial and industrial evaporators make extensive use of headers.

Convection and Forced Draft Evaporators.—Evaporators used for cooling air may be divided into two general types, convection or natural draft evaporators, and forced draft evaporators. To cool an entire room satisfactorily, air must be made to flow from the evaporator to all parts of the room. If natural convection is used, circulation is supplied by the tendency of cold air to drop and warm air to rise. If a bare coil is used, there is considerable interference between the cold air falling and the warm air rising, Fig. 5-16. However, radiation as well as convection is effective in cooling the room with a bare coil. But radiation is not so effective in a crowded room because the heat from the goods in the room must "shine" directly to the coil. If these goods are "shaded" by other goods, they will be very slow in coming down to temperature if air circulation is poor.

One method of increasing this circulation is to use baffles. These are insulated pans, sometimes with vertical flues, so placed as to separate the chilled, falling air from the warm, rising air. This gives a more positive circulation, Fig. 5-17. Note that air from the room is guided up, then through the entire coil, then back down to the room. If coil temperatures get too low, goods directly under the baffle outlet can be damaged by

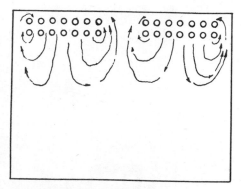

Fig. 5-16. Air circulation from coils.

freezing. But because these goods are shielded (shaded) from the coils by the baffles, lower coil temperatures can be carried than without baffles before there is danger of freezing.

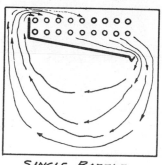

SINGLE BAFFLE

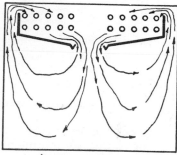

DOUBLE BAFFLE

Fig. 5-17. Baffles to direct air circulation from coils.

The most effective method of obtaining rapid, positive air circulation is with a forced draft evaporator. Fig. 5-18 to 5-20 show common forms of blower coils. Many other designs are also used. Blower coils will give more even temperatures in all parts of the room than other common evaporator systems. Also, it is possible to get a closer control of humidity with such coils. Ammonia coils like Fig. 5-20 may either be headered or operated flooded from an accumulator. The latter system is most common.

Evaporator Feeds.—One very important thing that should be understood about different types of evaporators is the type of expansion valve suitable to feed each. A capillary tube or high side float valve is only suitable for a flooded evaporator such as Figs. 5-4 or 5-5.

—*Marlo Coil Co. photo*

Fig. 5-18. Blower type evaporator coil.

The header, or miniature accumulator takes up any variation in quantity or change in volume of the refrigerant. If such a feed was applied to an ordinary trombone coil, the refrigerant charge of the system would be so critical that a few ounces too much or too little would flood or starve the coil. Also, the proper charge for a heavy load would not be proper for a light load.

The low side float valve is used in industrial evaporators similar to Fig. 4-5, Fig. 4-6, pages 56 and 57 or Fig. 5-6 to 5-10. If applied to a trombone coil as in Fig. 5-11, an accumulator is necessary as a surge chamber. It has the same purpose as the header in the high side float evaporator. A low side float valve cannot be used on a dry expansion coil without some form of header or accumulator.

On the other hand, an automatic expansion valve cannot be used on any of the above mentioned flooded coils. It will not work because the pressure in no way determines how full of refrigerant is the coil or header. It would starve under heavy loads and flood under light loads. Neither will the thermostatic expansion valve work

—*Peerless of America, Inc. photo*

Fig. 5-19. Left. Wall type
blower coil.

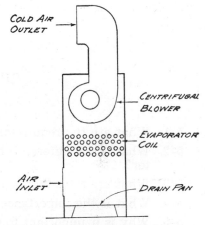

Fig. 5-20. Industrial blower coil.

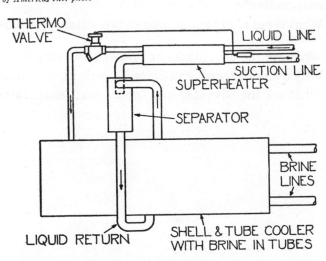

—*Alco Valve Co. drawing*

Fig. 5-21. Heat exchanger to supply superheat to flooded coil.

directly on a flooded coil. The vapor leaves the flooded coil with little or no superheat. This is an advantage to compressor operation, but superheat is necessary to operate this valve. Some flooded coils similar to Fig. 5-6, particularly with Freon-12 as a refrigerant, have been fed by a thermostatic expansion valve by using a heat exchanger to supply the necessary superheat, Fig. 5-2. The necessary heat is supplied by the warm liquid from the liquid line. A more detailed discussion of the use of heat exchangers is given in Chapter 8.

QUESTIONS

5-1. What are the requirements of a good evaporator?

5-2. What is the difference between a dry and a flooded evaporator?

5-3. What are the advantages of a flooded evaporator?

5-4. What is the importance of sufficient evaporator surface?

5-5. Why is it important to separate the vapor from the liquid in the evaporator?

5-6. What types of expansion valves are suitable for dry expansion evaporators?

5-7. What types of expansion valves are suitable for flooded evaporators?

5-8. What are the advantages of proper headering of evaporators?

5-9. Why cannot excessive velocity be permitted in an evaporator?

5-10. What are the advantages of forced draft evaporators?

CHAPTER 6

COMPRESSORS

General.—The refrigeration compressor is the heart of the refrigeration system. It removes the vapor from the evaporator, and supplies liquid to it. It maintains the low side pressure at which the refrigerant evaporates, and the high side pressure at which it condenses. In brief, it supplies the forces necessary to keep the system operating. Many different types of compressors have been used to do this, and many different details tried with individual types of compressors.

Fig. 6-1 shows a cross section of a typical industrial compressor, the details of which will be considered later.

How a Compressor Works—Fig. 2-9 page 25 shows the pressure as being instantly raised from the low pressure to the high pressure by the compressor. Fig. 6-2 shows this drawn out over the stroke of the compressor to show exactly how the pressure is built up. But this only shows what happens on the compression stroke of the compressor. A complete analysis of the suction and discharge strokes follows.

Both the suction and discharge valves are held closed by a combination of spring pressure and vapor pressure. On the down stroke with both these valves closed, the pressure in the cylinder will be lowered as the volume increases. When this pressure in the cylinder becomes less than the pressure below the suction valves, the difference in pressure opens these valves. On the rest of the down or suction stroke, the vapor from the evaporator and suction line flows into this constantly increasing volume.

At the bottom of the stroke there is no longer an increase in volume to keep the vapor flowing. Therefore, there is no pressure difference, and the springs close the suction valve, trapping the cylinder full of vapor. On the rising stroke this vapor is compressed from its low pressure to a pressure greater than the discharge pressure on top of the discharge valve. This greater pressure forces the discharge valve open. The rest of the rising or compression stroke forces this compressed vapor out through this valve. At the end

Fig. 6-1. Sectional view of a two cylinder vertical single acting compressor.

of the stroke, there is no longer a difference of pressure to hold the valve open, so the spring closes it. There is still a small amount of high pressure vapor trapped in the clearance space between the piston and the valve plate. This must be re-expanded to a pressure slightly lower than the suction pressure by the down-going piston before the suction valve opens again.

This is well shown on a compressor indicator diagram. Such a diagram can be made by an instrument called an indicator which can be connected to a compressor in operation.

With older, slower machines, indicators were common engine room test devices to check compressor operation. They will not react fast enough to keep up with modern high speed compressors, so are not as common as they once were. However, they illustrate the principles of compressor operation, and the pressure changes that take place in the cylinder.

An indicator is actually nothing more than a recording pressure gage. The fundamentals of an indicator are shown in Fig. 6-3. The pressure in the compressor cylinder is applied to the indicator piston. The greater the pressure, the higher the piston is forced up against

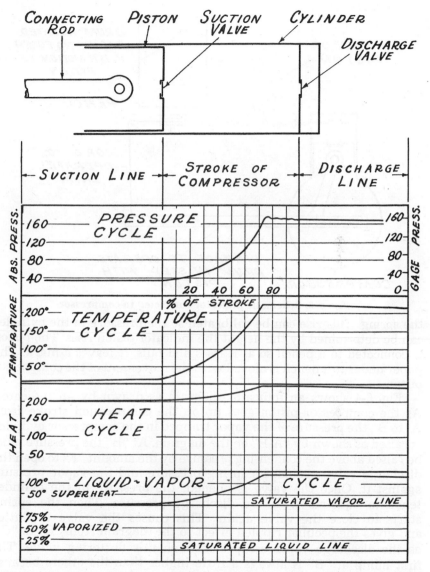

Fig. 6-2. Refrigeration cycles detailed at the compressor. Ammonia at standard
ton conditions.

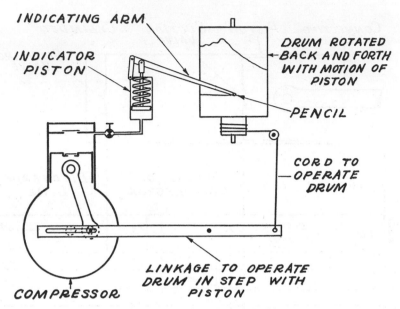

INDICATING ARM

INDICATOR
PISTON

DRUM ROTATED
BACK AND FORTH
WITH MOTION OF
PISTON

PENCIL

CORD TO
OPERATE
DRUM

LINKAGE TO OPERATE
DRUM IN STEP WITH
PISTON

COMPRESSOR

Fig. 6-3. Schematic indicator connected to compressor.

the spring. This rise can be calibrated so the pressure in the cylinder can be determined by the height the indicator piston rises. The piston is connected to a pencil so as it rises and falls, it leaves a mark. The paper under this pencil is moved with the movement of the compressor piston.

Fig. 6-4 shows an indicator diagram as drawn by an indicator. As the compressor piston goes up on the compression stroke from A' to B', the pressure of the vapor trapped in the compressor cylinder is raised as shown by "A-B" on the diagram. At "B" the pressure must be raised above the condensing pressure by the amount "F" to open the discharge valve against its spring pressure and the vapor pressure against it. Once the valve is opened, the pressure in the cylinder tends to equalize with the discharge pressure. Then the spring starts to close the valve again. This causes the valve to flutter and gives the peculiar rippled effect to the diagram from "B" to "C," as the discharge vapor escapes through this fluttering valve. The first hump at "B" is always a little higher than the others because it has to supply the initial push to open the discharge valve. At C' the end of the stroke is reached. This shows on the diagram at "C". Since the stroke is finished there is no more flow through the valve. The pressures in the cylinder and cylinder head equalize, and the spring closes the valve.

There is still a small amount of high pressure vapor trapped in the cylinder represented by "E". At the beginning of the suction stroke,

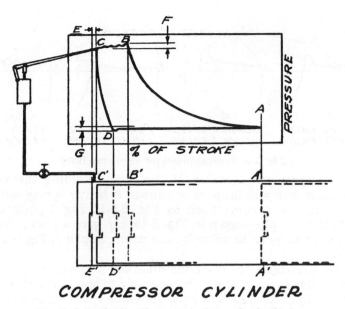

COMPRESSOR CYLINDER

Fig. 6-4. Indicator diagram as drawn by indicator.

this high pressure vapor must be expanded down to the low pressure before any new low pressure vapor can enter the cylinder. C'-D' of the stroke accomplishes this. It is shown on the diagram by the line "C-D". At "D" the pressure must be brought below the suction pressure by the amount "G" to open the suction valve. There is not the heavy head pressure against this valve, so a lighter spring can be used to make it hold. With the lighter spring and smaller vapor pressure, there is practically no fluttering as with the discharge valve. Once the valve opens, the flow of vapor through it is enough to hold it open, and the suction line "D-A" is steady. .

Fig. 6-4 is for a hypothetical compressor using ammonia as the refrigerant. However, except for the pressures involved, it is practically the same shape diagram as would be found for any refrigerant. But these diagrams will vary considerably for different operating conditions. They will even be changed by the mechanical condition of the compressor. The actual shape of the curve "A-B" will tell whether there is leakage within the cylinder, such as past valves, rings, etc. Detailed information on analyzing this line will be given in Chapter 20.

Several possible discharge lines are shown in Fig. 6-5. This line will always be above the discharge vapor pressure. The higher the line is, the more power is required to compress against this higher pressure. A heavy discharge valve such as a poppet valve, Fig. 6-15 will give a diagram as in Fig. 6-5-A. It takes considerable extra

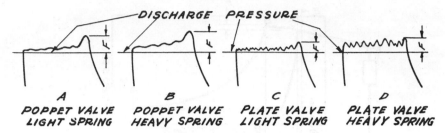

Fig. 6-5. Typical indicator discharge lines.

pressure to open such a valve. If the spring holding the valve is
light, the pressure will drop off as shown. A heavy spring with such
a valve will give a curve such as Fig. 6-5-B. Light plate or disk
valves, which are also shown in Fig. 6-15, can give a lower discharge
line, although this can be offset by too strong a spring, Fig. 6-5-C and
Fig. 6-5-D.

Fig. 6-6 illustrates the complete diagram. The extra dip at "D" in
the suction line is the extra push necessary to open the suction valve.
A heavy suction valve such as a poppet valve could cause a larger dip
than a plate or feather valve if actuated by spring pressure alone.
However, some poppet valves have been so balanced that the inertia of
the rising and falling piston helps to snap them open and closed. This
should give a curve with almost no dip at the heel. This distance "G"
is caused by the pressure necessary to hold the valve open against the
spring. This will be large with a heavy spring, or small with a light
one.

The length of the line "H-J" is actually the length of the effective
stroke of the compressor figured at the suction pressure. This, in
spite of the fact the line "K-L" represents the total actual stroke of
the piston. That is, a piston traveling the distance "H-J" with no leakage, loss of pressure, or other losses would do as much work as the
actual piston traveling the distance "K-L". The length of the line "H-J"
divided by the length of the line "K-L" is the volumetric efficiency of
the compressor. Thus, as shown in Fig. 6-7, a heavy suction valve
spring can materially reduce the effective stroke and the volumetric
efficiency. Note how an increase in "G" shortens the distance "H-J".
Fig. 6-8 shows how excessive clearance reduces the effective stroke.
That is why the clearance between the piston head and the valve
plate is made as small as possible.

Fig. 6-9 compares the diagrams made by a high suction pressure
and a low suction pressure. For constant discharge pressures, as
shown here, the length of the discharge line "B-C" is an excellent
comparison of the amount of vapor pumped. At high suction pressures a much greater amount of vapor is pumped as shown by these
lines. This is caused by the fact that there is actually more vapor

forced into the cylinder by the higher suction pressure. It should also be noted that the volumetric efficiency is higher at the higher suction pressure.

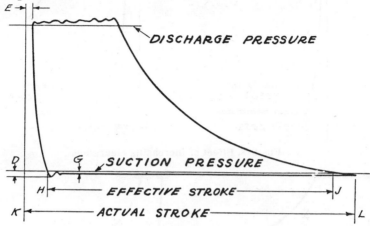

Fig. 6-6. A complete indicator diagram showing difference between effective stroke and actual stroke.

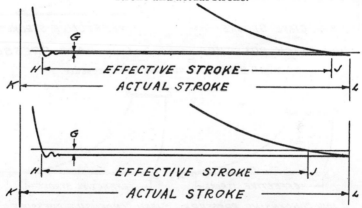

Fig. 6-7. Effect of heavy suction valve spring.

Fig. 6-10 compares the diagrams made by high and low discharge pressures. The size of the diagram is a measure of the power required to compress the vapor. The lower discharge pressure requires less power (makes a smaller diagram), and also gives a better volumetric efficiency.

A thorough understanding of the indicator diagram is the best way of understanding exactly what goes on inside the compressor cylinder. As mentioned above, the size of the diagram indicates the power necessary to compress the vapor. The shape of the diagram tells much about the actual operation of the compressor. In fact, it

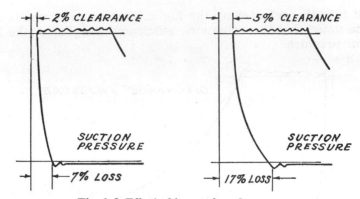

Fig. 6-8. Effect of increasing clearance.

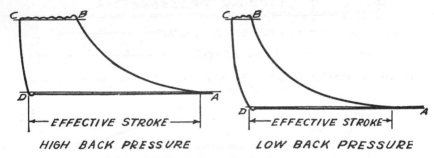

Fig. 6-9. Effect of varying back pressure.

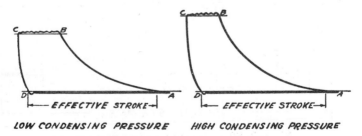

Fig. 6-10. Effect of varying condensing pressure.

is commonly used on large sized equipment to determine whether it is operating properly, whether valves and rings are tight, etc. It is helpful to remember that anything that increases the size of the diagram increases the horsepower required. Anything that decreases the length of the discharge line at a constant discharge pressure decreases the capacity of the compressor.

It should also be remembered as previously stated that the compressor does not refrigerate or cause refrigeration. It is the evaporation of the liquid in the cooling coils that does this. But the amount of vapor removed from these coils determines the speed at which this liquid can evaporate. Therefore the quantity of vapor removed from the coils indirectly determines the amount of refrigeration that can be produced at a continuous rate. So, although we sometimes speak of the amount of refrigeration produced by a given sized compressor, it should be remembered that it is only indirectly this is done.

Historic.—The earliest refrigeration compressors were designed after the general style of steam engines built at that time, that is, the horizontal double acting pattern, Fig. 6-31. Many of these old machines are still found in use. Although they have the advantage of being near the floor and accessible, they require a great deal of floor space. Also the weight is such that cylinders and sometimes shafts wear out of round. The first attempt to remedy these faults was to stand the double acting compressor on end in a pair of "A" frames, Fig. 6-11. Due to top heaviness, inaccessibility, etc., this was not very satisfactory. The vertical single acting compressor was the next step. These were first built in two cylinder designs, and many are so built today, Figs. 6-1 and 6-24.

Fig. 6-11. An A-frame compressor.

Present trends are to smaller, higher speed multi-cylinder compressors, sometimes called "VW" compressors, Fig. 6-12. Capacities are varied by using a different number of cylinders instead of building a different sized machine. From three to twelve cylinders may be used. Direct drives to 1200 rpm or even 1800 rpm motors are common. With mass production methods, and better standardization of cylinder sizes, both the size and the cost of a given capacity machine has been reduced. Replacement parts for repairs are also more readily available.

The centrifugal compressor, Figs. 6-37 and 6-38, was first introduced into this country for large air conditioning applications. But by the time of World War II, they began to be used for large, lower temperature jobs. They are now being applied to an increasing number of large industrial applications.

The centrifugal compressor is beginning to do to the refrigeration field what the steam turbine has done to the steam power field. The steam turbine has made larger powered steam driving equipment possible with much smaller dimensions than could be done with reciprocating steam engines. It has also made it possible to build more powerful engines than would be possible with a reciprocating engine. Similarly the centrifugal compressor makes it possible to build large tonnage refrigeration equipment in a much smaller size than with reciprocating compressors. And a much larger tonnage centrifugal compressor can be built than would be possible to build a reciprocating compressor. On the other hand, due to the large capacity obtained from a relatively small piece of equipment, and due to the precision work required, centrifugal compressors in small capacities cannot be built in competition with reciprocating compressors. It is particularly above 100 ton capacity that they show their advantages over reciprocating compressors.

Original experimentation on small equipment came after large equipment was well developed. Low pressure refrigerants were adopted and many types of compressors tried. But before the advent of hermetically sealed equipment, most manufacturers came to a miniature vertical single acting compressor, Fig. 6-13, with from one to four cylinders. Speeds were stepped up. Later, much that was learned on these low pressure, small compressors was applied to ammonia equipment.

Fig. 6-12. A modern VW type compressor.

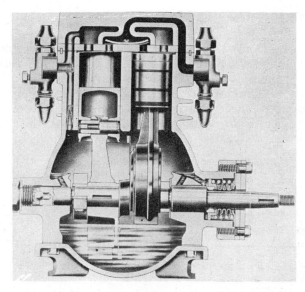

—*General Electric Co. photo*

Fig. 6-13. Low pressure refrigerating compressor with suction direct to valve plate.

Much early trouble in attempts to produce trouble-free, automatic refrigeration centered around the shaft seal. It allowed refrigerant to leak out, and air and moisture to leak into the system. Before 1930, one domestic manufacturer introduced the hermetically sealed compressor to eliminate this trouble. By 1940, all manufacturers of domestic compressors used hermetic designs, Figs. 6-32 and 6-33. Some were using it for fractional horse power commercial equipment.

At the present time, fractional horse power, open type, belt driven units are practically obsolete. Many manufacturers build hermetic compressors up to five or ten horsepower, some much higher.

Compressor Sizes.—Many different methods of rating compressors are used. Small machines, such as are used on domestic or commercial boxes may be rated in Btu per hour, or by the horse power used to drive them. The latter is commonest. Intermediate sizes, such as large commercial or small industrial machines may be rated in horse power or in tons of refrigeration. Most industrial compressors, and nearly all ammonia compressors are rated in tons of refrigeration, or by their bore and stroke. Thus a 6x6 means, unless otherwise stated, a 2 cylinder compressor with a 6 inch bore and a 6 inch stroke. Such sizes usually range from 3x3 to a 10x10 or 12x12 for most manufacturers.

CONSTRUCTION DETAILS

Valves.—Domestic and small commercial compressors usually have all valves in a valve plate, Fig. 6-13. The suction valves are on the bottom of the plate, and the discharge valves on top. For commercial servicing, this makes valve replacement easier and quicker. A new valve plate replaces all valves and valve seats. Discharge valve construction details are shown in Fig. 6-14. Suction valves may be either a leaf or ring valve.

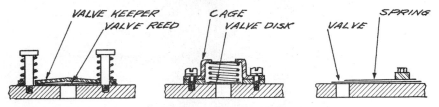

Fig. 6-14. Low pressure discharge valves.

Fig. 6-15 shows a few typical valves of the type used for large fluorocarbon or ammonia compressors. Valves of the same shape but with different spring pressures are often used for both suction and

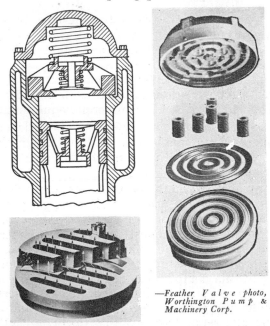

—*Feather Valve photo, Worthington Pump & Machinery Corp.*

Fig. 6-15. Typical ammonia compressor valves: upper left, poppet valve; right, ring valve; lower left, feather valve.

discharge. A trunk type piston with suction valves in the piston head, Fig. 6-1, is used almost exclusively in such machines. Early design depended entirely on the poppet type valve. Lighter valves, such as disk valves or leaf valves have become more common because they usually give higher volumetric efficiencies and work better at higher speeds. However, especially with higher compressor ratios, the thinner valves have been known to heat and warp sufficiently to cause leakage. The use of high grade Swedish steel or modern alloy steel has largely eliminated this trouble.

In an ammonia compressor, the discharge valve is set in a plate which is held down by a heavy spring, Fig. 6-1 and Fig. 6-15. Such a plate is known as a safety head. This is used on large sized equipment, because with more powerful driving motors as well as larger investments, liquid slugging could be disastrous with a solid head. The safety head can lift against its spring, then reseat itself, so no damage is done. A safety head is also incorporated in fluorocarbon machines in sizes comparable to ammonia machines.

Gas Passages.—In the early design of small refrigeration compressors, the suction vapor was introduced directly into the crankcase. But it gave considerable trouble with oil slugging. Any sudden decrease in pressure on the oil, such as happens when starting the compressor after an off cycle, would cause the oil to foam up. This foam, similar to the foam on beer, rises up and is swept through the suction valve into the cylinder by the suction vapor, Fig. 6-17. Oil is non-compressible, and cannot change direction to flow out the discharge valve as rapidly as the piston moves. This causes a severe knocking which strains all parts of the compressor.

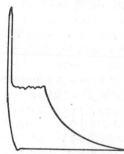

Fig. 6-17 lists some of the possible results of oil slugging. It has exactly the same effect as water in a steam engine cylinder. Liquid refrigerant has the same effect as oil in slugging the compressor. That is why expansion valves and evaporators must be so designed and installed that no liquid is returned in the suction line. Fig. 6-16 shows a hypothetical indicator diagram showing the effect of a slug of oil or refrigerant. Such a diagram could only be drawn theoretically, as stops on the indicator would prevent the indicator piston and pencil rising to the peak of the slug pressure.

Fig. 6-16. Indicator diagram of oil slugging.

Present design of open type fluorocarbon compressors brings the suction vapor in through ports cored in the cylinder wall castings, as in Fig. 6-13. A breather line extends from this to the crankcase. This is necessary to balance the crankcase pressure, and to give oil from the suction line a means of returning to the crankcase. A check valve or screen is in this breather line to stop or break up any foam that might rise up in the crankcase and enter this breather.

Most hermetic compressors bring the suction vapor into the hermetic case in such a way that this vapor flows over the electric motor winding windings. This helps give some cooling effect to the windings, and would help evaporate liquid refrigerant that might return from faulty evaporator operation. The suction into the cylinder is taken from a point inside the case high enough that the entire case would have to be filled with oil foam to get oil into the cylinder.

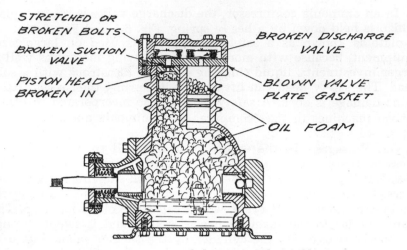

Fig. 6-17. Oil foaming and slugging, and possible results.

The trunk type piston as illustrated in Fig. 6-1 is used almost entirely on large sized machines, whether for ammonia or the fluorocarbons. It effectively separates the suction vapor from the oil. It also has the breather and oil return back to the crankcase. A modified form of the trunk piston has been used on some smaller designs. But it is too large and bulky to fit well into such small design.

Fig. 6-18 shows a method used by some manufacturers to increase the volumetric efficiency on the suction side. Ports are cut in the side of the cylinder walls at such a location that they are uncovered at the bottom of the stroke. These are used in addition to some other form of suction valve. If of ample size, they can increase the volume of vapor flowing into the cylinder. The adjacent indicator diagram shows how this takes place.

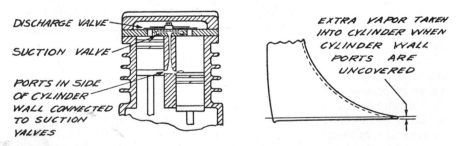

Fig. 6-18. Ports in cylinder walls to increase volumetric efficiency, and resulting indicator card.

Stuffing Boxes; Shaft Seals.—Regardless of the method used to bring the suction vapor into the compressor, it has proved next to impossible to keep the refrigerant vapor out of the crankcase. There is some leakage past the rings. The oil lubricating the cylinder walls dissolves some refrigerant, then carries it back to the crankcase. This is the reason an equalizer line to the crankcase is essential. The crankcase pressure is then maintained at suction pressure.

With refrigerant in the crankcase, leakage past the revolving shaft must be prevented. In older ammonia machines, this was done with some form of packing. This might be a flexible packing, Fig. 6-19, or a metallic packing, Fig. 6-20. The flexible packing is similar to a common stem packing except for the oil lantern. Lubricating oil is fed to this, usually under pressure, to keep the shaft and packing lubricated. The metallic packing is a series of sectional Babbitt or other bearing metal rings made to hug the shaft tightly with springs or with synthetic rubber. This, and the oil seal between the shaft and contact rings prevents leakage past the shaft. Synthetic rubber packing, or gaskets prevent leakage around the packing assembly.

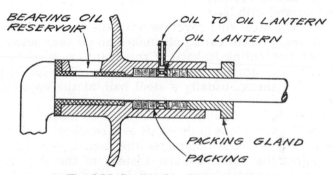

Fig. 6-19. Stuffing box for ammonia.

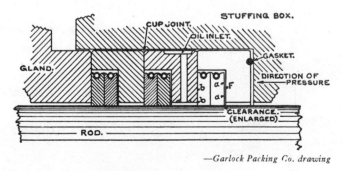

—*Garlock Packing Co. drawing*

Fig. 6-20. Metal rod packing.

On all fluorocarbon compressors, and most modern ammonia compressors, the seal is some form of metallic one. This is a flat metal or carbon face rotating under oil against a similar flat stationary face. The accurately matched flat faces under oil seal off any leakage.

Fig. 6-21 shows a bellows type shaft seal. This usually bears against a hardened steel ring on the shaft as shown. A synthetic rubber ring forms a seal between the shaft and steel ring. The seal nose is a special alloy of soft bronze, or a bronze mixed with lead or graphite. The steel ring revolves with the shaft, but the bronze nose is stationary. Lubricating oil makes an oil seal between these two surfaces, preventing leakage at this point. A spring maintains the necessary pressure between the two faces. This spring pressure is opposed by a thrust, usually a steel ball, at the opposite end of the shaft.

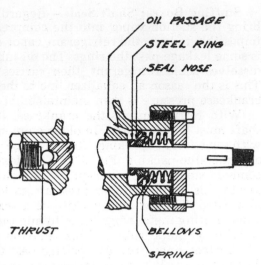

Fig. 6-21. Bellows type shaft seal.

The flexible bellows allows the seal nose to move sufficiently to follow the slight variations in the shaft as it revolves. A gasket under the outside ring or collar completes the seal. Older seals pressed directly against the shaft shoulder instead of the steel ring. But if this shoulder should become scored by long wear, or by grit or dirt, it is difficult to refinish and expensive to replace.

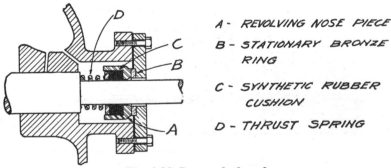

A - REVOLVING NOSE PIECE

B - STATIONARY BRONZE RING

C - SYNTHETIC RUBBER CUSHION

D - THRUST SPRING

Fig. 6-23. Rotary shaft seal.

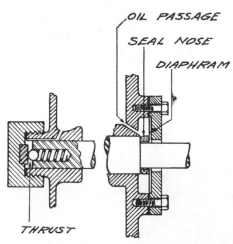

Fig. 6-22. Diaphragm type shaft seal.

Fig. 6-22 shows a similar type seal using a diaphram for flexibility instead of a bellows. With this type, the thrust spring is put on the other end of the shaft. It takes less room than a bellows seal, but does not have as great a flexibility.

Another type of shaft seal is the rotary seal, Fig. 6-23. The collar "A" revolves with the shaft. The spring back of it serves to keep it against the stationary bronze nose piece "B", so there is no leakage past this face. The spring also bulges the synthetic rubber cushion "C" so it will ride the shaft with sufficient pressure to prevent any leakage along the shaft.

Lubrication.—Lubrication of vertical single acting machines may be taken care of by splash or by force feed. Occasionally lubricators are used to supply oil to some parts. Fig. 6-13 shows a typical compressor which uses splash feed lubrication. The cranks dip into the oil as they revolve. This forces oil to the crank bearing, and also splashes a fog of oil throughout the crankcase. Some of this oil fog lubricates the cylinder walls. That which collects on the under side of the piston head drips down to the funnel shaped opening at the top of the connecting rod. This feeds oil to the wrist pin. Oil running down the end of the crankcase collects in reservoirs, and feed the main bearings and the shaft seal.

All lubricated bearings are so designed that some oil continually leaks from them. This makes room for a constant flow of fresh oil flowing through these points to carry away frictional heat, as well as lubricate the bearings. Splash lubrication is used on smaller units. Some sealed compressors depend on splash feed. Splash may be used on ammonia compressors up to a 5x5 size.

Fig. 6-1 shows a compressor with force feed lubrication. The oil sump is low enough that oil is not touched by the cranks or rods. An oil pump driven by the main shaft picks up oil from this sump and feeds it to the oil system. This carries oil under pressure to all moving parts. Cylinders may be lubricated by oil escaping from wrist pins, or they may be supplied with oil by separate lubricators. Force feed is used on many hermetic compressors regardless of size, and on nearly all machines above a 5x5 size.

Fig. 6-24 shows a lubricator such as mentioned above. It is sometimes used to augment force feed lubrication, and with horizontal machines sometimes is the only means of lubrication. A lubricator is nothing more than an oil pump which can be adjusted to give the proper flow of oil to each of the required parts.

—Vilter Manufacturing Co. photo

Fig. 6-24. Ammonia compressor with force feed lubricating unit.

Cooling.—As pointed out in Chapter 2, compressing the refrigerant vapor generates heat. This raises the temperature of the vapor, which in turn heats the cylinder walls, valves, etc. that it touches. On compressors of any size, some cooling is necessary. This does not effectively cool the discharge vapor. But without cooling, the cylinder walls would become so hot they would be difficult to lubricate. There would be trouble due to oil breakdown.

Tables 3-1 and 3-2 gave the discharge temperatures for different refrigerants at standard ton conditions. Figs. 14-9 to 14-11 show the discharge temperatures for different operating conditions. Notice the fluorocarbon refrigerants do not heat up as much as ammonia. Air cooling has proved sufficient for most refrigerants other than ammonia.

The compression temperature of ammonia is such that water cooling is necessary. Therefore a water jacket on the upper part of the cylinders and in some cases over the cylinder head is used.

There are cases where air cooled ammonia compressors are used as booster compressors[1]. But this is with a combination of low compression ratios and very cold entering vapor. Under such conditions, the discharge temperature does not become excessive. Lately some booster compressors on quite low temperature are cooled by liquid refrigerant in the jacket.

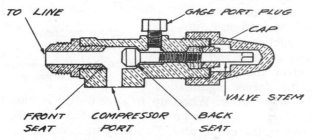

Fig. 6-25. Compressor service valve.

Service Valves.—Except for sealed domestic and small commercial equipment most refrigeration compressors have valves at the inlet and the outlet of the compressor, Figs. 6-13 and 6-24. The valve on the inlet or suction side is called the suction service valve. The valve on the outlet or discharge is the discharge service valve. The only difference between them is usually the size. The suction valve is larger because the low pressure suction vapor has a larger volume than the high pressure discharge vapor.

Fig. 6-25 shows the construction of valves used with fluorocarbon refrigerants. When the valve stem is screwed all the way forward, front seated as it is called, the valve is closed. But the passsage to the service plug is open. If a gage is installed in place of this plug, the gage will indicate the pressure in the compressor. If the valve is screwed all the way back, back seated, the port to the service plug is closed, and the main passage is opened. Thus, the valve may be back seated to remove the plug and install the gage. Then if the valve is turned one or two turns forward, the compressor will function normally, and the pressure in the system will be indicated on the gage. These ports are also useful for special operations such as charging and discharging the system.

---

[1] See Chapter 21.

An ammonia compressor usually has valves plus a by-pass, Fig. 6-26. The valves are used for closing the lines when necessary. The bypass may be used for starting unloaded (with the pressures equalized) or for special pumpout operations. With the valves "A" and "C" open and "B" and "D" closed the compressor can be started with no load on it, unloaded. The suction pressure is on both the suction and discharge side of the piston, so there are no forces against

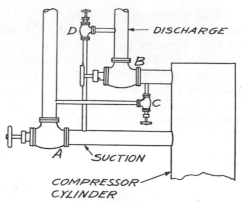

Fig. 6-26. Ammonia compressor valves and bypasses.

turning the compressor. When up to speed, "C" is closed and "B" opened. The bypass can also be used to suck from the discharge line and discharge to the evaporator. This may be necessary in case work must be done on the condenser or receiver. The refrigerant pumped from the high side is discharged through the other bypass to the evaporator. In this case the evaporator becomes the condenser and receiver temporarily.

Many modern compressors combine the bypass and valves in a manifold, Fig. 6-27. Normal operation is with the discharge bypass valve closed, the suction valve open, the discharge valve open, and the suction bypass valve closed. With the discharge bypass and the suction valve open and the other two valves closed, the machine can be started up unloaded. The discharge vapor passes back to the suction line. After the machine is up to speed, closing the discharge bypass and opening the discharge valve puts the machine in normal operation.

Capacity Control.—One problem of operating refrigeration compressors is to balance the compressor capacity against the refrigeration requirements. That is, the vapor should be removed from the suction line at exactly the same rate it is produced by evaporation in the evaporator. This should hold true whether a large or small amount of liquid is evaporated.

If the compressor removes the vapor faster than it is produced, the pressure is gradually lowered. This reduces the evaporator temperature. If the compressor cannot remove the vapor as rapidly as it is formed, the pressure, and consequently the temperature of the evaporator rises. With most automatic systems, particularly domestic and commercial, a compressor which is large enough for the worst conditions required is usually selected.

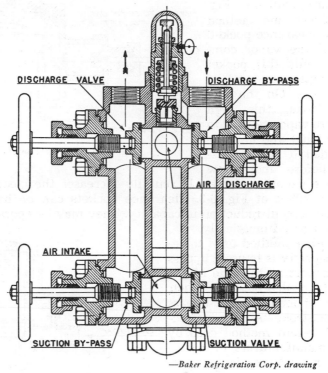

—*Baker Refrigeration Corp. drawing*

Fig. 6-27. Ammonia compressor manifold.

A control is installed to shut off the compressor when it reduces the pressure below a predetermined point. Then as the pressure rises, the compressor is turned on again. With ammonia systems, this cycling is done more or less by hand. On large industrial
systems several compressors may be used. If one is not enough,
two are put in operation, if two are not enough three are used, etc.
It is the duty of the operator to watch the pressure and use the
proper number and size of compressors to hold this constant.

With large sized compressors, one compressor more makes quite
a large step in operating capacity. In the old days with steam drives,
this could be balanced by varying the speed. But with the present
electric drives this is not so simple. So other devices have been devised to control the capacity of a single compressor. These capacity
control devices are only occasionally used as they increase the cost

of the compressor. But when they are required they are available. Fig. 6-28 shows one method used, a clearance pocket. Part of the vapor compressed fills this pocket on the pressure end of the stroke. On the suction stroke, this high pressure vapor returns to the cylinder and must be expanded to the low pressure before more low

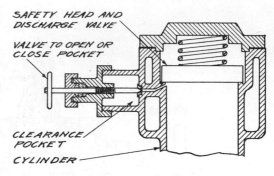

Fig. 6-28. Clearance pocket.

pressure vapor can enter. It acutally increases the clearance, and has the effect of Fig. 6-8. Clearance pockets can be had to give 25 or 50 percent reduction in capacity. They may be operated either by hand or automatically.

Another method used to reduce capacity is to use a bypass suction port in the side of the cylinder wall, Fig. 6-29. When a valve is opened in the bypass line, the stroke "A-B" is ineffective. A recent method used by some manufacturers of multicylinder machines is to make inoperative one or more cylinders. This may be done by holding the suction valves open

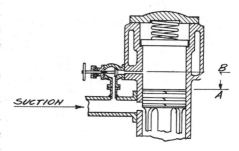

Fig. 6-29. Bypass capacity control.

when capacity reduction is required, or by valving off these cylinders so the suction vapor cannot enter them. All the above capacity reduction methods also reduce the power required to turn the compressor. Therefore, they are an economical way of balancing the capacity to the requirements.

Dual Effect.—Many methods have been used to operate two evaporators at different pressures from one compressor. The most common way of doing this is with special valves. (To be discussed in Chapter 9.) But one method available with some manufacturers of industrial equipment is shown in Fig. 6-30. Beside the standard suction valves, there are ports in the side of the cylinder wall at the bottom of the stroke. These ports connect to a separate suction line. The low pressure or cold suction connects to the usual suction intake. The high pressure or warm suction connects to the cylinder wall ports. The cylinder is filled with low pressure vapor on the suction stroke. As the wall ports are uncovered, the high pressure suction vapor rushes in, compresses the low pressure suction vapor to the high pressure, and fills the remaining space.

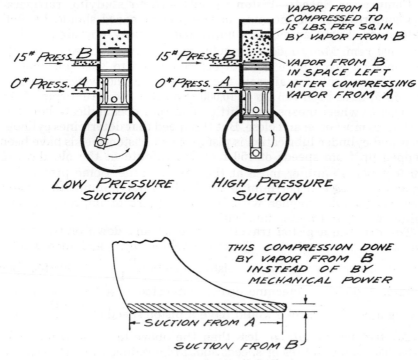

Fig. 6-30. Dual effect compressor.

The gain in capacity is proportional to the absolute suction pressure. For a zero psig and a 15 psig suction pressure, these are approximately 15 psia and 30 psia. The total refrigeration produced would be 30/15 or 2 times that produced in the low pressure suction alone. Thus, for every 2 tons of refrigeration, one ton is produced at the low pressure and one ton at the high pressure suction. For a 10 psig and a 20 psig, the total refrigeration would be 35/25 or 1.4 times the refrigeration produced in the low pressure alone. For every 1.4 tons, one ton is at the low pressure and 0.4 tons at the high pressure. If there was no difference between the two pressures, no refrigeration would be produced in the evaporator connected to the second suction line. The power required in the above cases would be only the power necessary to produce the total refrigeration at the highest pressure. It should be remembered, the higher the suction pressure, the less power is required. In the first example given, the power required would be the same as the power necessary to produce 2 tons of refrigeration at 15 psig.

Compressor Speeds—Piston Speeds.—When studying refrigeration compressors, the meaning of compressor speed should be well understood. Early ammonia compressors usually operated at less than 100 rpm. Many modern machines are direct connected to 1725 rpm motors. Some have been direct connected to 3450 rpm motors. Compressors built for aircraft use, where size and weight are at a premium, have been run up to 10,000 rpm. But the actual rpm of the shaft or flywheel means very little. The rpm does indicate how fast the valves must open and close. But the speed that determines cylinder wear and cylinder lubrication is piston speed. Piston speeds have been stepped up from speeds of 150 feet per minute in the old days to 600 feet per minute or more at the present time. Some present designers feel 600 feet per minute should be a maximum. Others have gone considerably higher with the proper use of improved alloys, lighter parts, and better lubrication.

The distance a piston travels is once up and down or two times the stroke per revolution. Thus a machine with a 6 inch stroke turning 400 rpm would have a piston speed of $\dfrac{6 \times 2}{12} \times 400$ feet per minute. A domestic machine direct connected to a 1725 rpm motor having a one inch stroke would have a piston speed of $\dfrac{1 \times 2}{12} \times 1725$ = 287 feet per minute, or less than the above machine which only turns 400 rpm. Compressor speeds should be reduced to piston speeds before any attempt is made to compare the speeds of any two machines.

COMPRESSOR TYPES

Horizontal Double Acting Compressors.—The horizontal double acting compressor, abbreviated "HDA," as previously mentioned was the first type to be commonly built. It is still favored by a few engineers, because with a large diameter cylinder and a long stroke, it can be made in larger capacities than other common forms of reciprocating compressors. Fig. 6-31 shows the fundamentals of its design. It is usually direct connected to an electric motor.

Suction and discharge valves are placed in each end of the cylinder, so pumping is done on each stroke instead of each revolution, as with the "VSA." Poppet valves, plate valves, and ring valves have all been used. Safety heads are not used because in this position, they could not be depended on to reseat properly.

Since the pressure on the stuffing box alternates between high and low pressure, and since the rod slides back and forth through it instead of rotating, the service against it is much more severe than in a vertical compressor. The oil lantern is connected to the suction line so any high pressure vapor that has leaked past the packing this far, will be carried back the suction to the cylinder. Oil is also carried back in this line to help cylinder lubrication. The extra friction on the packing generates considerable heat. The oil removes some of this, but sometimes not enough. In such cases a small amount of liquid refrigerant is piped through a small hand expansion valve to a passage around the stuffing box, then to the suction. Thus, actual refrigeration is used to control the packing temperature.

Lubrication of this type of machine may be with an oil pump, lubricator, or with a combination of both. Oil is fed to the various bearings at a low pressure. Oil to the shaft packing may be at a higher pressure. Some oil is supplied directly to the cylinder walls to augment that leaking through the stuffing box.

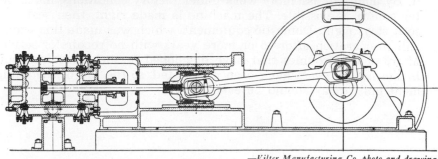

—*Vilter Manufacturing Co. photo and drawing*

Fig. 6-31. Horizontal double acting compressor.

Vertical Single Acting Compressor.—A very common type of compressor used at the present time is the vertical single acting, sometimes abbreviated "VSA" compressor. Fig. 6-1 and 6-24 show typical examples of this compressor used on ammonia. The crankcase acts as a base. It supports the cylinders and main bearings, and acts as an oil reservoir.

The crankshaft converts the rotary motion of the flywheel to a reciprocating motion to operate the pistons. The stuffing box prevents leakage past the shaft, either of refrigerant out, or air into the system. The pistons in the cylinders draw in the refrigerant vapor on the suction stroke, and compress and discharge it on the compression stroke. Suction valves in the piston head, and discharge valves in the safety head allow flow in the proper direction, but act as check valves against any reverse flow. A water jacket surrounds the upper part of the cylinder and the head to keep the cylinder walls cool.

Hermetically Sealed Units.—To build a fully automatic, trouble-free, long lived compressor such as was needed for the maximum development of domestic and small commercial equipment, early designs had several weak points. One of the greatest of these was the shaft seal. A slight oil leakage was necessary to keep the face lubricated. Over a period of years, this could drain the compressor of oil. Sooner or later the seal would pick up some dirt or grit which would cause it to wear, and eventually leak refrigerant. Another weakness was the belt drive. Belt tension had to be adjusted to take up stretch. Belts would wear, become frayed, and sometimes break. Oversized motors to take care of varying belt frictions as well as other variables were common.

The most successful method found to eliminate all these troubles was to direct connect the motor and compressor, and enclose them both in a gas tight housing. Such a compressor is called hermetically sealed. Not only has it solved the above mentioned problems, but further advantages have been found, or have been developed into it. By doing all assembly work under factory conditions, much better control is possible. The machine is made right, then sealed up so it stays right. Domestic equipment, which was made this way, is still in operation after 15 or more years with no repairs or service. Many of the troubles that have developed in such machines built in the last 15 years have been eliminated, so the life of the equipment built today should be even greater.

Such design has been so successful that it has entirely dominated the domestic field. It is being applied by an increasing number of manufacturers to self contained commercial equipment such as reach in cabinets, ice cream cabinets, frozen food cabinets, water coolers, etc. Manufacturers are also supplying such equipment for remote installation in the field. One manufacturer builds a line of sealed reciprocating units up to 100 hp., Fig. 6-34.

Many different shapes and designs have been used. Most of the domestic sealed units are built with a vertical shaft, Fig. 6-32. Some use a reciprocating compressor as shown. Others use a rotary compressor, Fig. 6-33.

Commercial compressors are usually built on a horizontal shaft as in Fig. 6-34. They may have anything from two to twelve cylinders. One manufacturer makes a hermetically sealed centrifugal compressor.

Rotary Compressors.—Another common type used for certain applications is the rotary compressor. This is made in two general

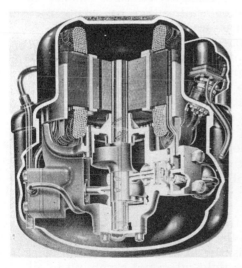

—Universal Cooler Corp photo
Fig. 6-32. Hermetically sealed reciprocating compressor.

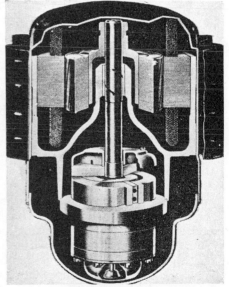

—Frigidaire Division photo
Fig. 6-33. Hermetically sealed rotary compressor.

—*Westinghouse Electric Corp. photo*

Fig. 6-34. Examples from a complete line of hermetically sealed compressors.

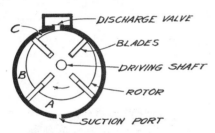

Fig. 6-35. Rotary compressor — blades in rotor.

types. The first is illustrated in Fig. 6-35. The rotor, containing four or more blades, revolves off center in the cylinder or housing. The blades are constantly held out against the outer wall, either by spring pressure or by centrifugal force. As space "A" moves past the suction port, the trapped volume is at its largest. As this space moves around to "B" and "C", this trapped volume is decreased to the point where it becomes practically nothing. This compresses the vapor, then forces it out the discharge valve.

Fig. 6-36 illustrates the second type of rotary compressor. Here the shaft is in the center of the housing, but the rotor is on an eccentric. The blade is in the outer housing and is held against the rotor by spring pressure. The chamber "A" is at its maximum in Fig. 6-36-1, and gradually decreases to nothing as the rotor revolves to the point shown in Fig. 6-36-3.

One large difference between the action of the rotary and the reciprocating compressor is that in the former, the pressure balances when the compressor stops. That is, the fit around the rotor, blades and end plates cannot be made gas tight when not revolving in oil. Therefore a check valve is often used in the suction line to prevent the high pressure discharge gas from leaking through the compressor back to the evaporator. Others allow this leakage to balance the pressure during the off cycle so the compressor can start unloaded.

Another difference between rotary and reciprocating compressors is that the rotary will draw a much better vacuum. Against a closed valve, it will instantly pull down to within a small fraction of an inch of a perfect vacuum. A reciprocating compressor may only be able to pull down to a 25 inch to a 28 inch vacuum. On the other hand, the rotary compressor has not been so successful pumping against heavy discharge pressures. Another feature of the rotary is, that it is easy to design to handle a large volume of refrigerant. The displacement per revolution is the difference in volume between the inner rotor and the outer cylinder. If made as large as the crankcase of a reciprocating compressor, it will handle a much larger volume of vapor than the cylinders of a reciprocating compressor.

All these factors add up to the fact that the rotary compressor is well suited to the use of a very low pressure refrigerant, such as Refrigerant 114. It easily handles the large volume of such a refrigerant at the low back pressure required to produce suitable evaporator temperatures. It also has been used successfully with Refrigerant 12. It is used at the present time by two manufacturers of domestic units.

Another common use of the rotary compressor is as a booster compressor for very low temperature jobs, both for fluorocarbons and ammonia. Again, its high vacuum, high volume characteristics at low discharge pressures fit it perfectly to this type of application.

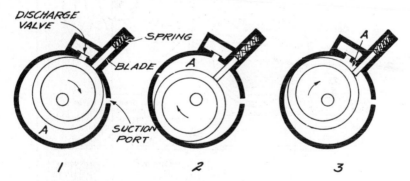

Fig. 6-36. Rotary compressor—blade in outer cylinder.

Centrifugal Compressors.—The centrifugal compressor, Figs. 6.37, and 6.38 is fundamentally a centrifugal blower. In a few cases, it is only single stage, but usually it is more, up to five stages. The discharge of the first wheel is fed to the inlet of the second, etc. By building them to operate at very high speeds, 5000 to 8000 rpm, they will build up about 15 psi pressure difference with a dense gas, between the inlet and the discharge. The centrifugal forces set up by such speeds handle a very large volume of vapor. Thus, a very low pressure refrigerant such as Refrigerant 11 well fits into the requirements of this compressor.

Due to the high speeds used, the rotor of this compressor must be built with the same care as a steam turbine rotor, with its special alloys, accurate balancing, etc. It is built into a packaged unit with its own condenser and evaporator. Water or brine is circulated wherever refrigeration is required. Since there is apt to be a certain amount of air leakage into the system through the shaft seal, an automatic purge device is used to separate the refrigerant from the air and eliminate the air[2].

[2]To be covered in Chapter 8.

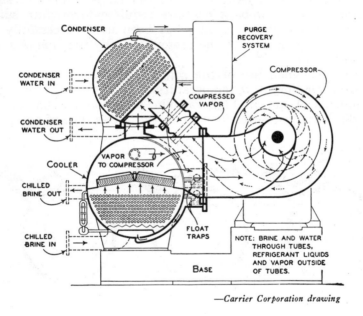

—*Carrier Corporation drawing*

Fig. 6-37. Centrifugal compression system.

—*Carrier Corporation photo*

Fig. 6-38. A centrifugal compressor.

Steam Jets.—Another device used instead of a compressor is the steam jet. It is only used with water as a refrigerant. Fig. 6-39 shows the fundamentals of such a system. A steam jet blasts through the

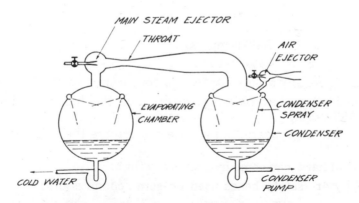

Fig. 6-39. Steam jet refrigeration system.

throat. In so doing it draws a high vacuum on the evaporating chamber, a sufficiently high vacuum to bring the evaporating temperature of water down to 40 F. The jet carries the low pressure water vapor with it over to the condenser where both are condensed by contact with condensing water. The water and condensate is drawn from the condenser by some form of pump. A second steam jet on the condenser is necessary to remove air which may be drawn in through possible leaks, or which is brought in dissolved in the water. This is fundamentally a purge device. Notice the vapor condensed in the condenser is discarded with the condenser water. But the main advantage of water as a refrigerant is that it is cheap enough that there is no need to be economical with it.

The water chilled by evaporation is pumped to where it is needed to absorb heat. It is then returned to the evaporating chamber in a spray to give a maximum of surface from which evaporation may take place. This makes evaporative cooling possible whether the water is actually boiled or not.

Water cannot be run much below 40 F without approaching the danger range of freezing. Therefore such a system is only suitable where 40 F is the minimum temperature required. The biggest application of such relatively warm evaporator temperatures is in air conditioning work. Therefore this is the commonest use of steam jet refrigeration. Since it uses steam instead of mechanical power for the driving force, its biggest advantage is in areas of cheap fuel.

QUESTIONS

6-1. What is a "VSA" compressor?

6-2. What is an indicator card?

6-3. Are there any disadvantages of strong compressor valve springs?

6-4. Do high or low back pressures have the highest volumetric efficiencies?

6-5. Does a large clearance increase or decrease the volumetric efficiency?

6-6. What harm can come from oil slugging?

6-7. Why are safety heads used on some compressors?

6-8. Name four different methods of capacity control.

6-9. What are some of the advantages of hermetically sealed compressors? Disadvantages?

6-10. What factor is most important in considering compressor speeds?

CHAPTER 7

CONDENSERS

Requirement.—The condenser must take the superheated vapor from the compressor, cool it to its condensing temperature, then condense it. Review the condenser section of the Cycle Chart, Fig. 2-13. The action in the condenser is just the opposite to the action in the evaporator. Where the evaporator absorbs heat to change a liquid to a vapor, the condenser gives off heat to change the vapor back to a liquid. However, the requirements of a condenser are similar to those of an evaporator. The condenser must have the required heat transfer surface. It must provide sufficient volume for the vapor delivered to it. It must allow the condensed liquid to separate from the uncondensed vapor.

The condenser must have the required heat transfer surface. All the heat picked up in the evaporator, and the heat of compression added in the compressor must be removed from the vapor by the condenser. The total heat which must be removed will vary according to conditions, but roughly will be about 1.25 times the heat picked up in the evaporator.

The condenser must provide sufficient volume for the vapor pumped to it by the compressor. Before this vapor condenses, it has a definite volume. This volume can be decreased by increasing the pressure. But any increase in pressure increases the work done by the compressor, and therefore, the cost of driving the compressor. Normally any condenser which provides sufficient surface would give sufficient volume.

The condenser must allow the condensed liquid to separate from the uncondensed vapor. One reason for the above mentioned point of sufficient volume, is for the purpose of supplying room for this separation. If the liquid does not separate from the vapor and flow out, the condenser fills with liquid. This leaves insufficient volume for the additional vapor pumped to it. A second reason for adequate separation of liquid and vapor is that too much liquid between the vapor and the metal walls of the condenser can act as a partial insulator. This will retard heat transfer from the vapor to the condenser surface.

Operation.—Fig. 7-1 shows an air cooled condenser in it's simplest form. The hot vapor from the compressor enters the top. In the first small section this vapor is cooled to the condensing temperature for the pressure prevailing in condenser, 90 F at 100 psig for Refrigerant 12 in this case. From here on, as heat is extracted, the vapor is condensed. Droplets form on the inside surface of the tube and flow down toward the outlet similar to the way drops of water form on a

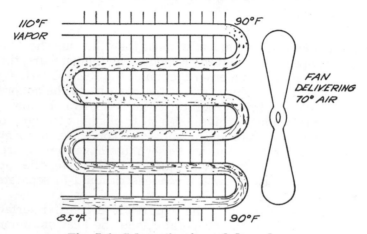

Fig. 7-1. Schematic air cooled condenser.

window in a steaming room. These droplets collect and run together until they fill the entire tube. From here down any further extraction of heat results in subcooling the liquid, that is, cooling it below 90 F. But its pressure still stays at 100 psig because of the pressure on it from the vapor above it. To keep this heat extraction going on, a fan forces a blast of air over the outside of the condenser. This air cools, or extracts heat from the condenser. The air in turn is heated as it does this.

When the compressor starts, the vapor pumped into the condenser raises the pressure. The heat of compression raises the temperature to a point warmer than the air flowing over the outside of the condenser. This allows the air to cool or extract heat from this vapor. The pressure is raised to the condensing pressure corresponding to the temperature to which the vapor is cooled. Finally an equilibrium is established at a constant condition. The supply of vapor and the heat it carries, balances the heat extracted by the air and the vapor removed by condensation.

The cooler the liquid can be made in the condenser, the better. Less liquid will have to be used (and pumped by the compressor) to do a given job, see Fig. 22-2. Also the lower the condenser pressure, the less work for the compressor, and the less power required to drive it. The lower the condensing temperature, the lower will be the condensing pressure. In Fig. 7-1, 90 F is the actual condensing temperature, although the liquid is afterwards cooled to 85 F. If this cooling was done in a different manner, the pressure could be brought down to 91 psig, the condensing pressure for 85 F. The pressure of the vapor will be the pressure corresponding to the temperature of the liquid it contacts. Thus, since the liquid at the

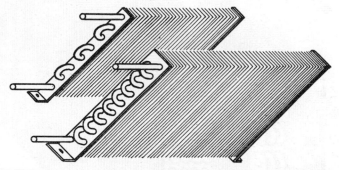

Fig. 7-2. Single row single pass and double row single pass air cooled condensers.

point it completely closes the tube is at 90 F this establishes the pressure at 100 psig. Any further cooling of the liquid will have no effect on the pressure. The same amount of cooling with better separation would reduce the pressure to 91 psig. This is another reason it is desirable to get a good separation of the liquid from the vapor in the condenser.

Air Cooled Condensers.—Fig. 7-1 is typical of small air cooled condenser design. It would be known as a single row, single pass condenser. Fig. 7-2 shows such a condenser with a double row single pass condenser. The double row single pass has two rows of tubes to give greater surface, but all the refrigerant must pass through all the tubing before escaping. Such condensers are commonly used on domestic jobs and on commercial jobs up to ⅓ or ½ h.p. Such condensers are suitable for small jobs, but are open to the above mentioned objections that they do not satisfactorily separate the condensed liquid from the vapor. And the larger the condenser, the worse this condition becomes.

Fig. 7-3 shows how this can be improved by headering each row so that the refrigerant is divided. In the case of the double row double pass, half the refrigerant goes through each coil. Since half the liquid is then condensed in each coil, the liquid will not fill the coil so quickly. Also shown is a triple row triple pass and a 4 row 4 pass condenser. Such designs are used on the larger sized air cooled condensers.

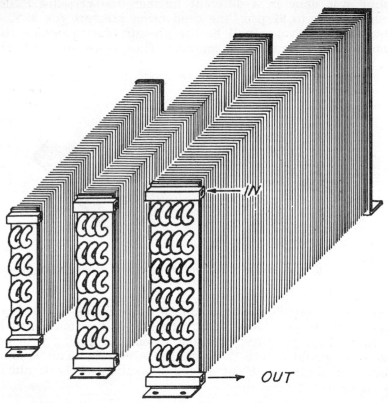

Fig. 7-3. Double row double pass, three row three pass and four row four pass air cooled condensers.

Some domestic air cooled condensers do not depend on a fan for air circulation, but on the fact that warm air rises and creates some air flow. Larger areas are required in such cases. Such a condenser may cover most of the bottom of a cabinet or it may cover the back.

Air circulation over the coils can be obtained in different ways. Most domestic units depend on natural convection. Flues are usually arranged to aid this convection. The condenser may be a coil similar to Fig. 7-2 mounted under the cabinet. Or it may be expanded to cover a part of the back cabinet wall. Occasionally it is clipped or soldered to the inside of the outer shell of the cabinet. In this way the cabinet shell itself forms the heat transfer surface of the condenser.

Most small commercial hermetic machines with air cooled condensers include a fan, driven by a small shaded pole motor. Above three horsepower, it is difficult to get enough condenser surface in front of a fan of this type. Therefore three horsepower is about as large a completely self contained air cooled condensing unit as is available.

If air cooling is wanted above three horsepower, a separate condenser, usually mounted on the roof is used. This is properly designed to give sufficient surface and the proper fan for forced convection. These remote air cooled condensers are commonly available up to 50 tons capacity. Some manufacturers make larger sizes. For requirements above these sizes, several units can be combined to give the required capacity.

Air vs. Water Cooled Condensers.—Air cooled condensers make a much simpler installation than water cooled condensers. There is no need to pipe water or provide a drain from an air cooled job. No water regulating valve or cooling tower is needed. There are no problems from water scale or corrosion. Restrictive legislation on the use or drainage of water is of no consequence.

But water cooling has advantages too. Particularly in the summer when loads are already heaviest, cooler water is available than air. Also water gives better heat transfer, so it is possible to get a condensing temperature nearer to water temperature than to air temperature. And the lower the condensing temperature, the lower the pressure and the cheaper the operating costs.

In small sized units, the saving is not enough to pay for the added cost of the installation of a water cooled condenser. But as sizes go up, the savings become greater, while the cost of piping is little more. Up to three horsepower air cooled self-contained condensing units are available. If air cooling is wanted above three horsepower, a remote air cooled condenser is needed.

Condensing units with water cooled condensers are available from about one third horsepower up. But below three to five horsepower their use is decreasing because of greater complications and restrictions on the use of water. As sizes get larger, however, the advantages of water cooling begins to overbalance their disadvantages and they are more often chosen.

Double Pipe Water Cooled Condensers.—A simple and commonly used water cooled condenser is shown in Fig. 7-4. This is a double pipe condenser, formed by placing one copper tube inside the other, then bending to the required form. The refrigerant is run in the outside space and the water in the center. This puts water on one side of the refrigerant and air on the other. Notice the water flows in the opposite direction to the refrigerant. This is known as counterflow and is commonly used wherever possible in all heat transfer equipment. In this way, the coolest water is used for the final cooling on

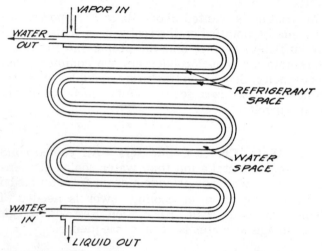

Fig. 7-4. Schematic double pipe water cooled condenser.

the liquid refrigerant. This gets the liquid refrigerant as cool as possible. The warmest water strikes the hottest refrigerant vapor. This makes it possible for the water to pick up more heat. In this way less water is used and a lower condensing temperature and pressure possible. The diagrams, Fig. 7-5, show comparable results that can be obtained with a given condenser with counterflow and parallel flow.

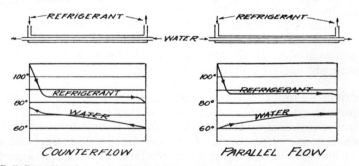

Fig. 7-5. Results of counterflow and parallel flow in double pipe condenser.

The bent copper tubing condenser is a simple, cheap form used where water cooling is wanted on small systems. But the water side of any water cooled condenser usually requires cleaning sooner or later. And the bent tubing cannot be cleaned except chemically. There is one type of double pipe condenser on the market with headers at the ends. These headers can be opened to mechanically clean the water tubes.

Fig. 7-6 shows a double pipe condenser used with ammonia. Since copper tubing can not be used with ammonia, this condenser is made up of pipe and fittings. This was a favorite type of condenser for many years. But the multiplicity of joints necessary at the end of each pipe were difficult to prevent from leaking.

A further disadvantage of the double pipe condenser, whether the fluorocarbon or ammonia type, is the same trouble encountered in single pass air cooled condensers. It will not give good separation of liquid and vapor.

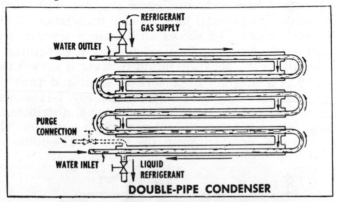

Fig. 7-6. Ammonia double pipe condenser.

Shell and Tube Condensers.—The shell type condenser effectively eliminates the biggest disadvantage of the above mentioned condensers, poor separation of liquid and vapor. Fig. 7-7 shows a cross section of a horizontal shell and tube condenser. It could be made almost identical to the brine cooler of Fig. 5-6. The water is introduced into the bottom tubes and it passes back and forth through the condenser several times. The larger liquid surface at the bottom of the condenser gives good contact to the vapor to maintain a pressure corresponding to the liquid temperature. If the lower tubes cool the liquid, the entire volume including its surface is cooled. This liquid surface is in direct contact with vapor, so it reduces the condensing pressure. The pressure drop on the refrigerant side is negligible. The heads are removable for cleaning the water sides of the tubes without disturbing any refrigerant connections.

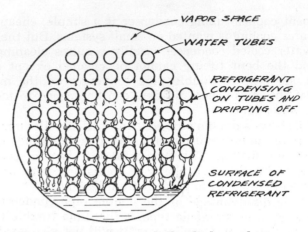

Fig. 7-7. Cross section of shell and tube condenser.

Fig. 7-8 shows how such condensers are used with complete condensing units on commercial jobs. In such installations it also acts as a liquid receiver. Fig. 7-9 shows an ammonia installation. Two or more such condensers may be used to give the required capacity. With industrial jobs a separate liquid receiver is always used.

Fig. 7-10 is a diagram of a vertical shell and tube condenser. Such condensers are only used on ammonia. Fig. 7-11 shows the construction of the head of one of these. Water is distributed over the entire head where it enters the tubes through a swirler. This causes the water to spin or swirl down the sides of the tubes instead of

—*Brunner Manufacturing Co. photo*

Fig. 7-8. Condensing unit with shell and tube condenser.

Fig. 7-9. Ammonia horizontal shell and tube condensers with receiver below.

dropping through the center where much of it would be away from the walls. Only a single pass of water is used through this type of condenser.

This condenser is not considered quite as efficient as the horizontal shell and tube if they are both kept clean. Notice the lack of good counterflow. But the vertical condenser does not foul up as rapidly as a horizontal condenser, particularly in bad water areas.

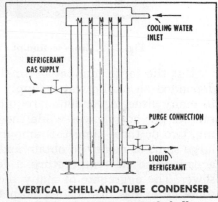

Fig. 7-10. Ammonia vertical shell and tube condenser.

The once through pass of water, plus the effect of gravity helps carry sediment and scale through the tubes instead of depositing it.

Shell and Coil Condensers.—Fig. 7-12 shows a shell and coil condenser used on commercial units. The results obtained here would be about the same as with a shell and tube. The only way to clean the water side of the coils would be chemically. Since there are less joints here than in a shell and tube, there is less danger of developing leaks.

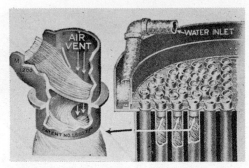

Fig. 7-11. Condenser water distributor.

Water Supply; Cooling Towers.—Any water cooled condenser must have a supply of water. On small commercial jobs city water is used. A water valve[1] is used to allow water to flow only when needed.

—*Standard Refrigeration Co. photo*

Fig. 7-12. Cross section of shell and coil condenser.

But the large number of small water cooled systems that have depended on public water supply has introduced a serious problem in many cities. A condenser requires at least one gallon of water per minute per horsepower while the unit is running. For efficient cooling, two or three time this amount should be used. The city spends large sums of money to obtain and treat water. Users run it through a coil, raise its temperature a few degrees, then dump it into a sewer. The aggregate of many thousands of customers doing this in some cities has overloaded both the water supply system and the sewage system. It has become such a serious problem that many cities have put in restrictive legislation against such use. A cooling tower is required on any but the smallest system.

Besides the above legal restrictions, the cost of water puts an economical restriction on the use of purchased water for large commercial or industrial systems. If available, this may be from wells, rivers, lakes or the ocean. The water is used, then thrown away after it has served its purpose of picking up heat. But such water supplies often are not available when required. In such cases the same water is used over and over again, with a cooling tower to get rid of the heat.

[1] See Chapter 9.

The latent heat of evaporation of water at 86 F is 1045 Btu, but 1000 Btu is usually taken for round numbers. The evaporation of 1 lb of water will then cool 100 lb of water 10 F. Thus the evaporation of 1 lb per 100 lb or 1 percent of water will cool the water 10 F. There may be another 1 to 5 percent water loss due to windage or drift loss, that is, the water blown out of the tower. But this still keeps the water bill within reason where water must be purchased. Water may be cooled to within 5 F to 10 F above the wet bulb[2] temperature of the air. This is always less than the dry bulb temperature read on an ordinary thermometer, and the dryer the air the lower the water temperature. Thus, quite often, water temperature lower than the dry bulb temperature of the air is possible.

Cooling towers may be natural draft, induced draft or forced draft. Natural draft towers in turn may be divided into spray towers or deck towers, either of which must be put out where wind will pass through them.

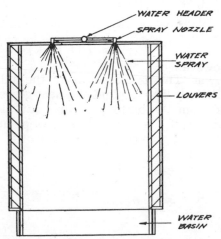

Fig. 7-13. Spray type cooling tower.

Fig. 7-13 shows a typical spray tower. Water is sprayed from the top of the tower through nozzles. As it falls, air passing through the tower evaporates some of the surface of each drop. This evaporation cools the water. It drops into a pan or tank at the bottom of the tower from which it is piped to the condenser. From the condenser, it is pumped back up to the spray nozzles. The louvres on the side of the tower are to prevent the wind from blowing the drops away from the tower as they fall.

[2]See Chapter 19 for a complete discussion of wet bulb.

Fig. 7-14 shows a deck type tower. Here the water is distributed over the top in a trough system. It runs in tiny streams from these troughs and drips to the first deck. It splashes on this, forming drops which fall to the deck below, and splashes again. The added surface of the wet deck, and the interruption of the fall as it splashes, increases the cooling. Also, since there is no nozzle pressure to pump against, the pumping load is not as great as with a spray tower.

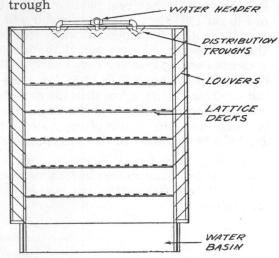

Fig. 7-14. Deck type cooling tower.

Fig. 7-15 shows an induced draft tower. This is closed in on the sides with louvered openings at the bottom. The fan and the heat gives a chimney effect to sweep the air from the bottom up and out the top. Eliminator plates are so placed as to catch the drops swept up. This must still be put outside, but will give cooling on days of little or no wind.

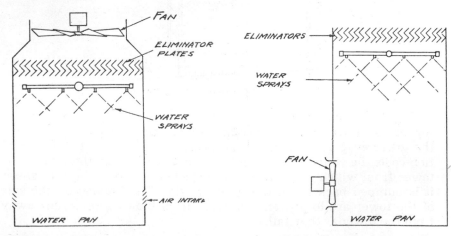

Fig. 7-15. Induced draft cooling tower.

Fig. 7-16. Forced draft cooling tower.

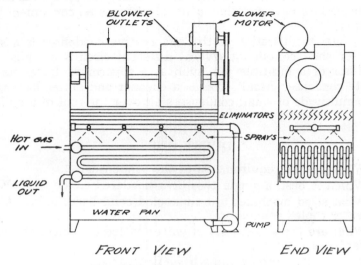

Fig. 7-17. Evaporative condenser.

Fig. 7-16 shows a forced draft tower. This is somewhat similar to the induced draft tower, but the air is forced in at the bottom instead of being sucked out at the top. This may be placed out in the open, or if more convenient, placed inside and the outlet carried outside through ducts.

Evaporative Condensers.—In recent years a condenser which is a combination of an air cooled condenser, a water cooled condenser, and a cooling tower, all in one has been developed. Wherever a cooling tower is used, air is the final cooling medium although a water cooled condenser is used.

The evaporative condenser combines the condenser and cooling tower in one piece of equipment. The water provides evaporative cooling, wets the surface to give good heat transfer and helps increase the surface in the water drops of the spray. Fig. 7-17 shows a typical evaporative condenser. The water is taken from the sump at the bottom by the self contained pump and sprayed in at the top. It sprays over the bank of coils and down to the sump again. The fans pull the air in from the bottom openings and out of the top. Eliminator plates prevent the water being blown out. The coils of the condenser must be well headered to increase to a maximum the separation of liquid and vapor. Such a condenser can be placed outside, or inside with ducts going out, whichever is convenient.

An evaporative condenser is usually cheaper than the combination of a shell and tube condenser and a cooling tower. So it is usually first choice in a new installation unless there is no convenient place to locate it.

A special modification of the evaporative condenser is a single condenser shell containing several different circuits or coils. Each compressor of a multiple job, such as a supermarket, has its own separate condenser circuit. This is a cheaper and better looking job than a multitude of small condensers all over the roof of a building.

QUESTIONS

7-1. What are the requirements of the condenser?

7-2. Which is best, a single pass or a headered condenser? Why?

7-3. What sized machines use air cooled condensers only? Air or water cooled condensers?

7-4. What are the advantages of water cooled condensers? Disadvantages?

7-5. What is counterflow and why is it used?

7-6. List the common types of water cooled condensers.

7-7. What are the advantages of the shell and tube condenser?

7-8. What is the purpose of the cooling tower?

7-9. List the different types of cooling towers?

7-10. Describe the evaporative condenser.

CHAPTER 8

FLOW EQUIPMENT

Liquid Receiver.—The liquid receiver is a tank to hold unused refrigerant after it is condensed but before it is needed in the evaporator. It is a storage chamber for any excess refrigerant in the system. It is also used to store the refrigerant if it is necessary to pump it out of the evaporator for service operations. The receiver should be large enough to hold all the refrigerant required by the largest evaporator.

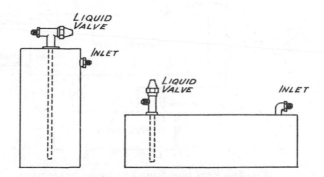

Fig. 8-1. Vertical and horizontal low pressure liquid receivers.

Fig. 8-1 shows two typical liquid receivers. The outlet and liquid line valve (king valve) is usually on top with a pipe inside to draw the refrigerant off near the bottom. The pipe is far enough from the bottom that dirt and sediment which settles will not be picked up and carried into the liquid line. Enough liquid should always be kept in the receiver to give a liquid seal at this pipe. The inlet to the receiver is usually at a point some distance from the outlet so as not to stir up dirt and sediment in the liquid leaving.

Receivers on commercial units with an air cooled or a double pipe water cooled condenser are of either type shown in Fig. 8-1. Where a shell and tube or shell and coil condenser is used, the lower part of the condenser acts as a receiver, Fig. 7-9.

Fig. 8-2 and 7-10 are typical industrial receivers. The larger size makes a horizontal shape necessary. Industrial receivers will have a gage glass to indicate the refrigerant level. Commercial receivers usually lack this. The industrial receiver should also have a drain

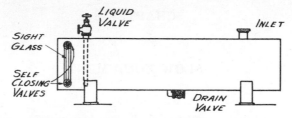

Fig. 8-2. Horizontal ammonia liquid receiver.

valve in the bottom which may be used to drain off oil, water or sediment. The receiver may be directly under the condensers if convenient, or may be considerable distance from them.

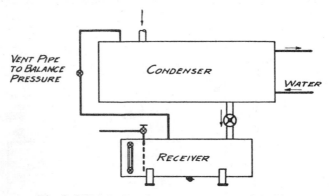

Fig. 8-3. Vent pipe from condenser to receiver.

Most industrial systems have a vent pipe or equalizing line from the top of the receiver to the top of the condenser to balance the pressure, Fig. 8-3. This is to keep an unobstructed flow of refrigerant from the condenser to the receiver. It acts about the same as the second hole in a can of condensed milk. Fig. 8-4 shows what could and sometimes does happen without a vent. Some engineers feel that if the drain from the condenser to the receiver is of adequate size and is not trapped, the vent line is superfluous.

Pipes and Piping.—Copper tubing is used almost entirely with fluorocarbon refrigerants. For domestic and small commercial, soft drawn tubing which is dead soft is usually used. Table A-7 in the appendix gives data and sizes available. Notice the size specified is the outside diameter or OD of the tubing. Although $\frac{3}{16}$ in, $\frac{5}{16}$ in and $\frac{7}{16}$ in sizes are available, they are not common, and fittings are not as easily available. Therefore, the use of such sizes is not recommended. Soft drawn tubing is easily bent to the required shape, and is easily flared. For refrigeration use, this tubing is furnished in rolls. It has been thoroughly cleaned, dehydrated, filled with dry air, then the ends sealed. Care should be taken to keep it in this same clean, dry condition until used.

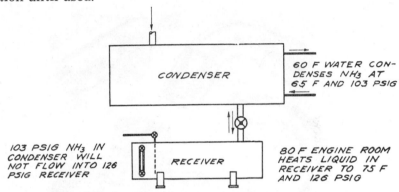

Fig. 8-4. Why a vent pipe is needed.

Except with hermetically sealed units, flare connections are usually used to make up joints on soft drawn copper tubing. Fig. 8-5 shows the type of flare used in refrigeration work. Notice the flare forms a copper gasket between the two fittings. These flares are easily made on the tubing with the proper tool. Fig. 8-6 shows a line of flare fittings available in sizes to fit soft drawn tubing. Flare connections are not used on copper tubing larger than ¾ inch. It is too hard to tighten sufficiently to make a gas tight joint in the larger sizes.

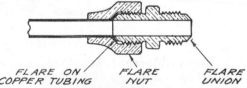

Fig. 8-5. Cross section of a flare connection.

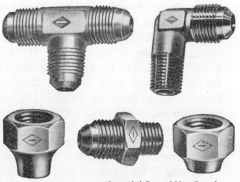

—*Imperial Brass Mfg. Co. photo*

Fig. 8-6. A line of flare fittings.

Larger commercial equipment usually uses hard drawn tubing, also given in Table A-7. This is also occasionally used with smaller equipment. It is much more difficult to bend or form, so special solder or "sweat" fittings often abbreviated ODS fittings, are used, Fig. 8-7. Such fittings are occasionally used with soft drawn tubing. They are almost always used with hermetically sealed domestic equipment.

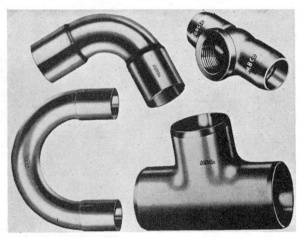

—*Mueller Brass Co. photo*

Fig. 8-7 A line of sweat or solder fittings

Many different types of solder have been used to put these fittings together. Ordinary 50-50 lead-tin solder has had a limited use, but a 95-5 solder (95 percent tin, 5 percent antimony, about 450 F melting point) is considered more satisfactory. Even this has been known to crack or develop leaks where there is vibration. The strongest solder is one of the silver brazing alloys. These are of such composition that their melting point is from 1100 F to 1300 F. Most of them contain some silver, hence their name. A properly made silver brazed joint will be as strong or stronger than the tubing itself. One feature to watch is the fact that many silver brazing alloys do not bond well to iron or steel. If such joints must be made, be sure a suitable alloy is used. Some domestic manufacturers have used silver solder for the joints on their hermetic machines. Most silver solders make dependable joints on iron or steel. They are, however, considered too expensive for general work.

Joints of 95-5 solder can be made with a "Prest-O-Lite torch," Fig. 8-8. An oxy-acetylene torch can be used, but even with a small tip, great care must be taken not to overheat the joint. A soldering iron will not get copper tubing hot enough to do a satisfactory job.

Hard solder, as the silver brazing alloys are sometimes called, is best worked with the oxyacetylene torch. "Prest-O-Lite" torches can be used on small sized tubing. But they are slow in heating and cannot get large fittings or valves hot enough to do a satisfactory job. They do not deliver heat enough for large sized tubing.

Iron pipe has occasionally been used with fluorocarbon refrigerants, particularly in evaporator construction. It has also been used for the refrigerant lines in locations where it is subject to more abuse than copper tubing would stand. But iron pipe causes more trouble from corrosion

—*Linde Air Products Co. photo*

Fig. 8-8. A Prestolite torch.

and pipe scale, so is usually avoided where possible. Where iron pipe is used, welded joints are recommended. If this is not done, a good thread cement such as litharge and glycerine must be used on all threaded joints or a leak will result. Dry pipe threads will not hold a refrigerant either in liquid or vapor form.

Since ammonia cannot be used with copper, and carbon dioxide is too high a pressure for copper, iron or steel pipe is necessary with these refrigerants. If butt welded pipe is used, X-heavy pipe is necessary on the high pressure side for ammonia. Double X-heavy is required for carbon dioxide. Seamless wrought iron or steel pipe has been used to an increasing extent in recent years. Table A-8 gives iron pipe dimensions, working pressures, etc.

Joints may be flanged or welded. Where flanged, the flange fittings must be screwed onto the pipe. Again these screw threads must be soldered or doped with litharge and glycerine to make them refrigerant tight. Welding has been the preferred method used in almost all ammonia plants installed in recent years. A complete line of weld fittings have been developed for this, Fig. 8-9.

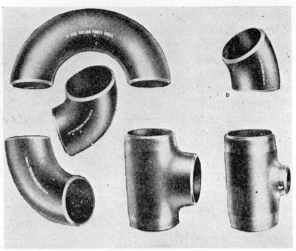

—*Taylor Forge and Pipe Works photo*
Fig 8-9 A line of weld fittings

Hand Valves.—Fig. 8-10 shows a typical hand valve of the packed type available for fluorocarbon refrigerants. The valve body is of forged brass, and the stem and plug of steel, often of a corrosion resistant type. The stem comes out through a packing. To take care of any possible leakage past the packing, a cap is supplied which will go over the stem and fits the valve body against a copper gasket. In the larges sizes this valve cap is so made that it can be used as a wrench to open or close the valve.

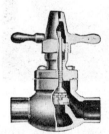

-*Henry Valve Co. photo*
Fig. 8-10. A packed low pressure valve.

Figs. 8-11a and 8-11b show a packless valve. Such valves are used a great deal with fluorocarbon refrigerants for sizes under one inch. They are available in larger sizes, but are quite costly compared to the packed valve. Here, the pressure of the screw stem is applied to a flexible diaphragm. A second stem and plug is on the other side of this diaphragm. Thus, turning the hand wheel in presses the valve closed through the diaphragm. When the hand wheel is turned out, a spring opens the valve. One precaution to always take with this valve is to see that it is so installed that the flow through the valve is from under the plug. If installed the other way, the refrigerant pressure may hold the valve closed when the screw stem is backed out,[1] Fig. 8-12.

---

[1]Some valves are so designed that they may be safely installed either way. See manufacturer's instructions.

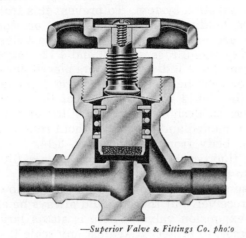

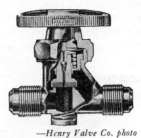

—Henry Valve Co. photo

Fig. 8-11a. (left)
Packless valve.

Fig. 8-11b. (above)
Packless valve.

—Superior Valve & Fittings Co. photo

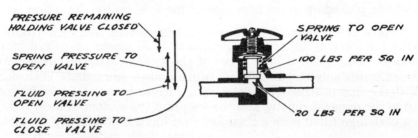

Fig. 8-12. How a pressure can hold a packless valve closed.

Fig. 8-13 shows a typical ammonia valve. It is made of forged steel. The plug may be a ground metal joint, or may have a disk with a babbitt metal face. Notice the back seat on these valves. That is, if the valve is opened wide, the stem is sealed from the open valve body so there can be no leakage out the stem. This makes it possible to repack the valve when it is open regardless of the pressure in the line. In case of a needle type valve such as Fig. 4-2, the back seat also makes it impossible to back the stem out of the threads so the ammonia pressure in the line would blow the valve stem out of the valve and release the ammonia. All ammonia valves should have this feature.

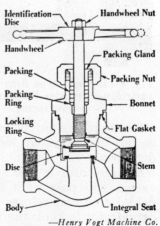

—Henry Vogt Machine Co.

Fig. 8-13. An ammonia globe valve.

Filters and Strainers.—There is always the possibility of some sludge, dirt or scale in a refrigeration system. To prevent this from plugging small valve orifices, holding valve needles open, or scoring compressor parts, filters are used. All small expansion valves have a built in screen ahead of them, Figs. 4-8, 4-9 and 4-12. Larger

—*Henry Valve Co.* photo
Fig. 8-14. "Y" type filter.

valves may have individual filters placed ahead of each one, or there may be one large filter following the liquid receiver. Most of the larger filters are so designed that the filter element may be removed and cleaned without removing the filter body from the line, Fig. 8-14.

Most fluorocarbon compressors have a filter built into the suction of the compressor.

Ammonia systems do not use a filter following the receiver, but there should always be an adequate filter before each expansion valve. There is also a large filter just before the compressor, to protect it against any scale that might be picked up in the iron pipe of the evaporator or suction line.

Driers or Dehydrators.—Moisture has caused so much trouble with refrigerants other than ammonia that driers or dehydrators have been designed to take it out of the system. As previously mentioned, with sulphur dioxide moisture causes immediate corrosion. With the fluorocarbons, beside causing corrosion, the moisture freezes out at the expansion valve and the ice plugs the system. A dehydrator is a cartridge filled with a chemical that has a high affinity for mois-

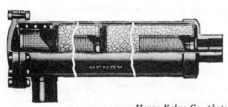

—*Henry Valve Co.* photo
Fig. 8-15. Angle type dehydrator with cartridge, dispersion tube and compression spring.

ture. Such dehydrators may be sealed, or they may be made so they can be opened, Fig. 8-15 and a new cartridge of drier material installed in place of the one that has taken up all the moisture it can hold. These dehydrators may be put in the line at the time the system is installed or when it is opened up for servicing, then removed

after absorbing any moisture that might have entered. Or they may be left in the system indefinitely. It should be remembered that a dehydrator can hold only a given amount of moisture. If there is more moisture in the system than the dehydrator can hold, the excess will pass right through. Also, excessive heat against the dehydrator will release the moisture in it. In fact, the colder the dehydrator is kept, the drier it will leave the refrigerant, and the more moisture it can hold.

A drier works equally well in either the liquid or suction line if kept at the same temperature. In the past, it has been most commonly placed in the liquid line. Here it catches the moisture before it gets to the expansion valve and causes a freeze-up. In this location it also does not cause any suction line restriction.

Calcium chloride was the first moisture absorbent used. But it dissolves in the moisture absorbed, and the resultant brine will flow through the system with the refrigerant. This brine is highly corrosive and will do more damage than the moisture alone. Nonsoluable drying agents such as silica gel, activated alumina, or calcium sulphate are now available. They do a better job than calcium chloride, and they are much safer.

Ammonia holds the water in solution so it does not ice up at the expansion valve and is also much more difficult to remove moisture. Therefore driers are not used in ammonia systems.

Oil Traps.—Lubricating oil is necessary on the cylinder walls of the compressor to prevent wear. It is necessary between valves and valve seats to give a vapor tight valve. But to keep enough oil in the compressor to get this lubrication, and oil seal on the valves, there is enough oil that some of it will be swept into the discharge line with the discharge vapor. On low pressure systems it is customary to allow this oil to travel through the system with the refrigerant, and make provision for its return from the evaporator by the suction vapor. But the oil can contaminate the inside surface of both the condenser and the evaporator. This contamination reduces heat transfer. In larger systems it has been found best to install an oil trap to catch as much of the oil as possible, and return it directly to the crankcase. Even when an oil trap is used, some oil will be circulated, and provision for its return to the compressor must be made.

Fig. 8-16 shows one of these oil traps. For fluorocarbon refrigerants it is necessary to reduce the velocity of the refrigerant, change its direction and run it through a screen or similar device to catch the oil. The cooler the refrigerant the easier it is to trap this oil fog. But with fluorocarbons the cooler the temperature the more refrigerant the oil dissolves. Therefore it has proved to be best practice to place the oil trap as near the compressor as possible. A further help particularly during the off cycle is to insulate the oil trap. Some manufacturers put an electric heater in the oil trap. Anything that helps keep it warm helps prevent refrigerant from condensing in the trap and its being returned to the compressor crankcase. The valve in the bottom of the oil trap acts exactly as a high side float valve. Some oil must be left in the bottom of the trap. But as the oil level rises enough to lift the float, the valve is opened and the oil forced back to the crankcase by the head pressure on it.

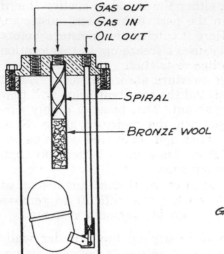

Fig. 8-16. Low pressure oil separator.

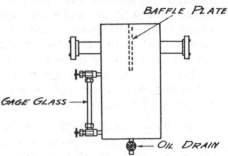

Fig. 8-17. Ammonia oil separator.

Oil traps have always been used as standard practice on ammonia systems. Fig. 8-17 shows a typical ammonia oil trap. Here, the gas velocity must be reduced and the direction changed, but no screening device is necessary. Since ammonia will not mix well with oil, results are best if the trap is placed as far from the compressor and as near the condenser as possible. The cooler the oil refrigerant mixture, the greater the percentage of oil that will separate out.

In the past, a water cooled oil trap or partial desuperheater was sometimes used to cool the discharge vapor and remove oil, Fig. 8-18.

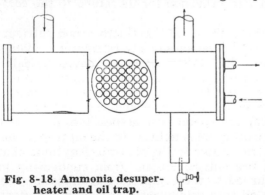

Fig. 8-18. Ammonia desuperheater and oil trap.

This type of ammonia system oil trap is favored by many engineers and operators although water flow must be regulated so that ammonia does not condense in it when the load is light. Some evaporative condensers now have a desuperheater coil in the outlet air stream from the condenser. The oil trap then follows this desuperheater coil. A further advantage of this type of coil in an evaporative condenser is that there will be less scale formation on the coils in contact with water.

Oil in a low temperature ammonia evaporator can be very troublesome. Plants should be arranged to keep oil in these evaporators at a minimum.

Instead of a float return, an ammonia oil trap·usually has a drain valve. Sometimes the oil is drained directly to a bucket or container. But this oil has a small amount of ammonia absorbed in it. That makes this method of draining very smelly and unpleasant as well as wasteful. A method of eliminating

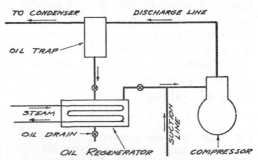

Fig. 8-19. An oil regenerator.

this trouble is to connect the oil drain to an oil purifier or regenerator, Fig. 8-19. The oil is drained to the regenerator tank, then the oil line closed and a valve to the suction line opened. The suction pressure will remove most of the ammonia from the oil. To make the ammonia removal even more complete, a steam coil is sometimes put in the regenerator. The heat reduces the ammonia in the oil to a negligible amount. After the ammonia is removed from the oil, the oil may be drained from the regenerator. Both the oil trap and the regenerator usually have sight glasses so the operator can tell when draining is required.

Automatic Purgers.—There is usually some non-condensable gas collecting at all times in an ammonia system. Non-condensable gas is any gas other than the refrigerant that might collect in the system. Since the compressor drives all the gas it handles over to the high side, and since only liquid drains out of the liquid receiver, any gas that does not condense collects on the high side of the system. This gas adds its pressure to the normal condensing pressure, which increases the high side pressure, and therefore the power costs. Such non-condensable gas can be purged off by hand, but this is wasteful because some ammonia is lost with it.[1]

Automatic purgers have been developed which separate the ammonia from the non-condensable gas, and bleed the latter out to the atmosphere. Fig. 8-20 shows how this is done. Connections from the condenser, or the receiver, or from both are taken to a refrigerated chamber. At the existing pressure and temperature in this chamber, any ammonia gas is condensed. The non-condensable gas gradually collects and builds up the pressure to where it bleeds out through the pressure relief valve. The condensed ammonia is led to a low pressure coil and re-evaporated to produce the chilling

---

[1] See Chapter 14 for a detailed description of hand purging.

necessary to make the process continuous. A separate liquid line with an expansion valve must be connected to the coil to give sufficient liquid to start operation, and occasionally to augment the condensing liquid. With a proper pressure-temperature balance, complete separation of ammonia and non-condensable gas is possible. Automatic purgers are made up in many designs, though they all work on the same principle: chilling and condensing the refrigerant, and bleeding off what will not condense. One such design uses the suction vapor from the evaporators to the compressor to do the required chilling.

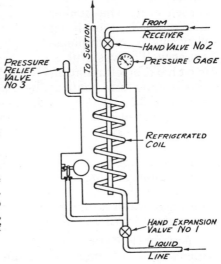

Fig. 8-20. Automatic purger. (1) To start, open hand expansion valve No. 1. This can usually be closed when sufficient high pressure gas has been condensed to maintain operation through the float valve. (2) Hand valve No. 2 must be restricted so the pressure in the purger tank is 20 or 30 psi below the pressure in the condenser. (3) Pressure relief valve No. 3 must be set for a pressure slightly below the condensing pressure. (4) Ammonia gas in contact with the refrigerated coil is condensed to liquid and returned to the suction line through the float valve. Air or other non-condensable gases do not condense, so will gradually collect, build up the pressure, and bleed off through the pressure relief valve.

Since centrifugal compressors operate at a vacuum, sometimes even in the condenser, their purgers include a small reciprocating purge compressor. This draws refrigerant from the condenser and discharges it to a purge device similar to Fig. 8-20.

A water separator is also usually included in a centrifugal purger. Any water condensed floats on top the liquid refrigerant. This shows in a gage glass, and may be drained manually when it appears.

There is not so much need for an automatic purger with fluorocarbon refrigerants in a reciprocating compressor. Their discharge temperatures are low enough that there is no oil or refrigerant breakdown. However, such a device has been developed for low pressure refrigerants with the idea that it can be left on a system for a few days after installation or servicing. After it has had time to remove any air that has been left in the system, it may be removed and is ready to be used on another job.

Sight Glasses.—Small fluorocarbon refrigeration systems are very poorly equipped with means of telling the liquid levels in the different parts. On large fluorocarbon compressors, bulls eyes have been put in the crankcase to show the oil level. Some installation men put a liquid indicator, Fig. 8-21 in the liquid line, either following the receiver or just before the evaporator. This will show if the refrigerant is low, (bubbles or a milkiness caused by many fine bubbles shows in the glass) but still will not show how much refrigerant is in the system.

—*Kerotest Manufacturing Co. photo*

Fig. 8-21. Liquid indicator.

Ammonia systems are better equipped. Sight glasses are common on compressor crankcases, liquid receivers, oil traps, purgers, etc. Fig. 8-22 shows the details of one of these. There is an automatic check valve in each line to the glass. This is supposed to close in case the glass gets broken. The hand wheels will close the valve in case there is need to change glasses, to change the packing, or do any other service operation. These glasses should be well protected by bars, screens, boxes or other devices to protect them from being broken.

Heat Exchangers.—On large commercial and industrial installations, suction lines are insulated and suction vapors are carried back to the compressor with as little heat pick-up as possible. This is because any heat added to the suction vapor expands its volume. The greater this volume be-

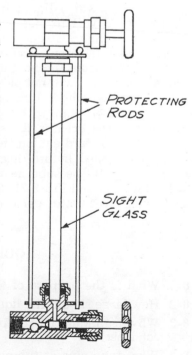

Fig. 8-22. Liquid sight glass.

comes, the larger compressor is necessary to pump it. But on smaller systems, the savings involved is not worth the expense of insulating these lines. On small diameter lines carrying a comparatively small amount of vapor, the heat leakage through an insulated line will heat the vapor somewhat in spite of the insulation. Therefore such suction lines are seldom insulated on this small equipment, and the suction vapor is usually superheated to a point approaching room temperature as it enters the compressor.

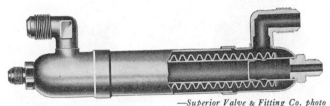

—*Superior Valve & Fitting Co. photo*
Fig. 8-23. Heat exchanger.

Part of this superheating can be made use of by using a heat exchanger, Fig. 8-23. This chills the liquid entering the expansion valve as this warm liquid in turn heats the suction vapor. The chilled liquid will form much less flash gas, leaving more liquid for useful cooling. This does the same amount of refrigeration with a little less refrigerant circulated. On the other hand, the warmer suction vapor from the heat exchanger will be a little nearer room temperature, so it will not pick up as much heat through the suction line. Thus, its temperature entering the compressor will be little, if any, warmer than without the heat exchanger. The colder the evaporator, the greater the savings will be. Heat exchangers are practically standard equipment on ice cream or frozen food cabinets.

As mentioned before, heat exchangers are also used in some cases to supply the superheat to operate a thermostatic expansion valve Fig. 4-17 and Fig. 5-21. They will give a more flooded evaporator which gives better performance in this way.

QUESTIONS

8-1. What is the purpose of the liquid receiver?

8-2. How large should the liquid receiver be?

8-3. Why are industrial receivers vented to the top of the condenser?

8-4. What type pipe or tubing is most commonly used with low pressure refrigerants?

8–5. What type pipe or tubing is most commonly used with ammonia?

8–6. What two methods are used to make gas-tight joints in copper tubing?

8–7. Name two methods used to make gas-tight joints in iron pipe?

8–8. What prevents leakage through the packing of a low pressure packed valve?

8–9. What prevents leakage past the stem of a packless valve?

8–10. What is the purpose of a drier?

8–11. What is the purpose of an oil trap?

8–12. How does a fluorocarbon oil trap differ from an ammonia oil trap?

8–13. What is the purpose of an automatic purger?

8–14. On what principle does the automatic purger work?

8–15. What is the purpose of a sight glass?

8–16. What is the purpose of the heat exchanger?

CHAPTER 9

ELECTRIC CONTROLS AND CONTROL VALVES

General.—Both controls and valves are used to control temperature. However, they are entirely different devices, and should not be confused. A control or electric control is a device for turning off or on an electric circuit. A valve or control valve controls the flow of a liquid or a vapor in a pipe. Either may be actuated by pressure or by temperature, or sometimes by other means. Electric controls turn off the entire system, or a part of the system by electric means. They may stop the compressor, or close a valve on part of the system. Control valves control the liquid flow in some part of the system. The greatest development and use of automatic electric controls and valves has been in automatic small refrigeration. But as these controls and valves have been perfected, they have been rapidly adopted in ammonia work.

Expansion valves, covered in Chapter 4, are one type of control valve. Their purpose is to keep the proper amount of liquid refrigerant in the evaporator. They have nothing directly to do with temperature control. The valves to be considered in this chapter are for the direct purpose of controlling pressure which means temperature, or for controlling temperature directly. For fully automatic operation, both an expansion valve and some form of temperature control is necessary.

Back Pressure Control.—The back pressure control is the commonest form of electric control used, Fig. 9-1. A flexible bellows is connected by tubing to the low pressure side of the system, usually directly at the compressor. The pressure in the system tends to expand the bellows. This expansion is opposed by an adjustable spring. The motion of the bellows is transmitted to an electric switch which controls the driving motor. An increase in temperature of the evaporator increases the low side pressure, which expands the bellows against the spring. This closes the contacts on the circuit to the compressor driving motor. The operation of the compressor reduces the pressure in the low side and in the bellows. When the pressure (and temperature) is sufficiently reduced, the spring pressure collapses the bellows, which opens the switch.

To operate satisfactorily there must be a difference in pressure between the cut-in point (pressure at which it starts) and the cut-out point(pressure at which it stops). This is called the differential. The average temperature or pressure at which the control operates is the range setting. In Fig. 9-2, the difference A—B, 20 psi is the differential. The range is set to average 25 psig.

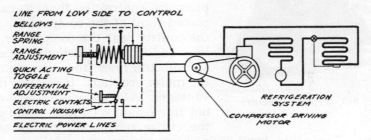

Fig. 9-1. Schematic pressure control.

The range setting may be changed by changing the pressure of the adjustable spring. The adjustment on this spring may be a screw only available to the service man, or it may be a knob placed where the refrigerator owner may change it to suit. Any change in the range does not change the differential.

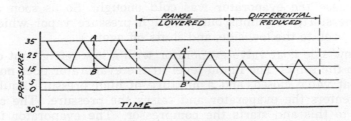

Fig. 9-2. Effect of changing adjustments on control operation.

The differential may be changed by an adjustment which changes the gap between the contacts, or which limits the movement of the arm operating these contacts. Changing the differential moves either the upper or lower limit, depending on the type or construction of the control. Such a change will obviously change the average of the range setting somewhat. This adjustment is nearly always inside the control. Therefore the control must be opened by the

—*Ranco Inc. photo*

Fig. 9-3. Typical pressure control.

service man to reach it. Fig. 9-3 shows a typical back pressure control with the adjustments. The control contacts may be used directly up to ¾ or 1 hp.

A magnetic controller should be used on anything larger than this, and is also used on all sizes of 3 phase power.

The principal advantage of the back pressure control is that it can be placed right at the compressor. With the control near the compressor, pipe lines to the control bellows are short, and electric lines from the control to the motor are short. It has two disadvantages. A crack in the bellows, if not immediately noticed, could drain the entire refrigerant charge of the system. The other trouble is short cycling at certain irregular operating conditions. Short cycling means turning on, then off every few seconds. This is very hard on electric motors.

Leaking compressor valves with a back pressure control will cause this. The head pressure leaks back through the valves during the off cycle, and raises the back pressure. This expands the bellows and immediately starts the machine. But the machine was first shut off because the evaporator was cold enough. So as soon as the machine starts, it pumps out the high pressure vapor which has leaked back to the low side, and shuts off again.

A low side float valve evaporator with a low refrigerant charge will do the same. The liquid level in the evaporator does not hold the float valve closed, and a mixture of high pressure liquid and vapor enters the evaporator and raises the pressure. The control reacts to this and starts the compressor. The evaporator is cold enough, so as soon as the high pressure vapor which leaked into it is evacuated, the control shuts off the compressor. In such cases, the extra pumping on the evaporator sometimes causes too cold a temperature under light load conditions.

Temperature Control.—Fig. 9-4 shows a schematic diagram of a temperature control. This is identical with the pressure control except for the method of applying the pressure to the bellows. A bulb with a refrigerant charge is clamped to the evaporator, or hung in the room to be controlled. The change in temperature of the refrigerant in the bulb changes the pressure of the bellows. Many companies supply temperature controls and pressure controls that are identical except for the type of bellows. Naturally, adjustments would be the same. In the case of a control to be clamped to the evaporator coil, a differential of 10 F to 25 F is used. If the thermostat must operate from room temperature, a much closer differential is needed, 2 F to 4 F.

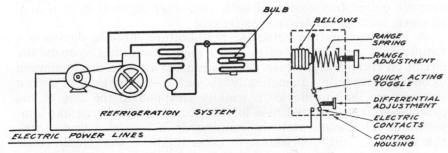

Fig. 9-4. Schematic temperature control.

Temperature controls are the type used on domestic machines. This not only includes the temperature element, but a hand switch, and on some controls, a defrost attachment, Fig. 9-5. This is usually a cam which applies extra pressure to the control spring to raise the cut-in temperature several degrees above freezing. It will maintain some refrigeration in the cabinet, while allowing the ice on the evaporator to melt.

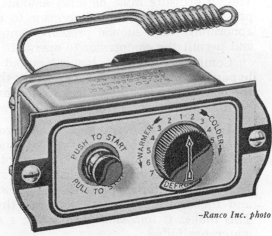

–Ranco Inc. photo

Fig. 9-5. Domestic refrigerator control.

High Pressure; High Temperature Cutouts.—A high pressure cutout or pressure limiting device is the same as a back pressure control, except that it goes on the high pressure side of the system, and shuts off as the pressure rises. It is used to shut off the compressor in case the head pressure rises abnormally. Back pressure or temperature controls can be had either with or without a high pressure cutout built in. A high pressure cutout is recommended on all water cooled condensing units, and on air cooled condensing units containing over 20 pounds of refrigerant. A separate high pressure cutout (not combined with any other control) is, in nearly all cases, used on ammonia installations.

A high temperature cutout or temperature limiting device is a temperature control adapted to safety applications. It also opens the circuit on rising temperature. Some ammonia systems are beginning to be operated fully automatically. In such cases the bulb of such a temperature limiting device is usually strapped to the side of the cylinder wall, or inserted in a location to check discharge gas temperatures. This would stop the compressor in case of a broken discharge valve, faulty lubrication, or other condition that would cause excessive overheating.

Low Oil Cutout.—Another safety device is a low oil cutout. This is a form of pressure control put into the oil line of a force feed lubrication system. In case of no oil, the circuit opens and stops the compressor.

For many compressors, this must be a differential control. That is, it is made with two bellows; and the difference between the pressures in the two bellows operates the contacts. One bellows is connected to the suction pressure and the other to the oil pressure. The oil pressure must be a set amount above the crankcase vapor pressure to permit the compressor to operate. With this setup an abnormally high suction pressure cannot offset a low oil pressure and permit the compressor to operate.

Compressors with a low oil cutout must have some means of bypassing it while starting. Obviously there is no oil pressure before the compressor is started. This would make it impossible to start the compressor if this control was not bypassed.

Low Water Cutout.—Most large sized systems, particularly ammonia systems, using a water cooled condenser have a low water cutout as a safety feature. This is a control very similar to a back pressure control[1]. The pressure element is connected to the water system. In case the water supply fails, the pressure in the water lines drops, and the control opens the contacts, thus stopping the compressor. This makes it impossible to operate a system where the condenser water has failed.

---

[1]Back pressure controls have been used as low water controls.

Float Switch.—As mentioned in Chapter 4, a float valve is a common device used to control the liquid level in evaporators or other liquid headers. Another method, which often makes more flexibility in piping possible is the use of a float switch. A float mechanism opens and closes a set of contacts. These can operate a magnetic valve placed at the most convenient point in the refrigerant circuit, not necessarily near the float switch.

Float switches may be used to start liquor pumps to pump out liquor traps when they fill. Or they may be used to stop compressors in case the refrigerant level in evaporators or accumulators reach a dangerously high level. This prevents floodbacks, which could damage the compressor.

Control Applications.—Normally, either a pressure control or a temperature control can be used on any type of fixture or evaporator coil with two exceptions. A temperature control and not a pressure control must be used with an automatic expansion valve or a capillary tube. It takes a changing pressure to operate the pressure control. But the automatic expansion valve is a constant pressure device.

Even a temperature control would be nearly as bad if the bulb was clamped to the evaporator near the valve. In practice, the bulb is clamped to the last coil of the evaporator. In Chapter 4 it was pointed out that the automatic expansion valve will gradually refrigerate further and further through the evaporator until finally, if nothing stops it, it will refrigerate on back the suction line to the compressor. With the control bulb on the last coil of the evaporator, when this last coil becomes refrigerated, the control shuts off the motor.

The temperature control must not be set too cold for the expansion valve. For instance, if the expansion valve was set for 15 psig with Refrigerant 12, this gives a 10 F evaporator coil. If a colder box was wanted, and the control cut-out point set to 5 F, the coil would never get cold enough to shut off the control, and the machine would run continuously. Thus, the automatic expansion valve is an exception to the rule that the expansion valve is not used to control temperature. It must always have a setting which gives a colder coil than the control setting.

Notice the similarity between the automatic expansion valve plus a temperature control and the thermostatic expansion valve. The thermostatic expansion valve has a bulb which clamps on the last coil. This bulb controls the flow of refrigerant to the coil. In this case, the bulb from the thermostatic control is better set anywhere on the evaporator except near the end. The control will then be effected by the refrigerant temperature in the evaporator, and not by any varying superheat at a point where there is no liquid refrigerant. The automatic expansion valve depends on a temperature control with the bulb clamped to the last coil. It takes considerable time before the last coil becomes actively refrigerated. This chills the control bulb and turns off all refrigeration.

The pressure control is also unsuitable for a system using a capillary tube. Since the pressure balances in this system during the off cycle, the rising low pressure would immediately start the compressor again. Thus, it would run nearly all the time.

The thermostatic expansion valve or either of the float valves will operate equally well on a temperature or a pressure control.

A temperature control operated by the evaporator temperature is used with domestic equipment. Commercial equipment may use a temperature or a pressure control. In case of more than one evaporator or fixture, a pressure control is a simple method of operating the compressor for the best average condition. If a more accurate control of cabinet temperatures is desired, a temperature control operated by the cabinet air temperature is preferred.

Solenoid Valves.—Fig. 9-6 illustrates a magnetic or solenoid valve. These are made in all sizes, suitable for liquid lines, suction lines, water lines, or for any other fluid required. In refrigeration,

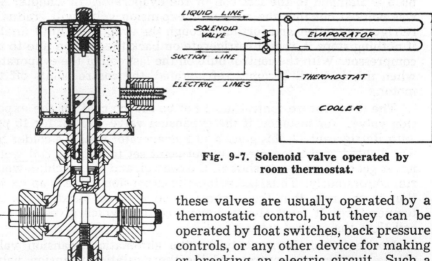

Fig. 9-7. Solenoid valve operated by room thermostat.

—*Alco Valve Co. drawing*

Fig. 9-6. Solenoid valve.

these valves are usually operated by a thermostatic control, but they can be operated by float switches, back pressure controls, or any other device for making or breaking an electric circuit. Such a valve is sometimes used in a single evaporator system, but is more commonly used where more than one evaporator is operated by the same compressor. Any number of boxes could be paralleled to one compressor (if big enough), and each box individually controlled as in Fig. 9-7. They could all be operated at the same temperature, or at different temperatures, depending on the setting of each thermostatic control. A back pressure control can be used to shut off the compressor when all the solenoids are closed, and the suction pressure drops.

For a warm and a cold box operating from the same compressor, the warm box may be controlled by a solenoid valve placed as in Fig. 9-8. The back pressure control on the compressor will be set to give whatever conditions are required in the cold evaporator, in this case, a cut-in of 20 psig and a cut-out of 10 psig. If the solenoid is open, the warm evaporator maintains a high enough pressure to keep the control contacts closed and the compressor in operation. When the solenoid closes, all the refrigerant is pumped from the warm coil so it no longer refrigerates, and the compressor pumps only on the cold coil. When the cold coil pulls down to its cut-out point, the back pressure control opens and the compressor stops.

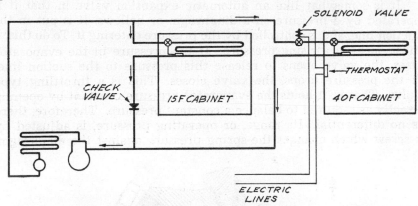

Fig. 9-8. Solenoid valve in liquid line of two temperature system.

In Fig. 9-7 the solenoid is shown in the suction line. It is often placed in the liquid line. A smaller, which means a cheaper valve may be used. Also, since the evaporator is pumped dry after the solenoid closes, there is no danger of flooding the compressor at the beginning of the cycle. Its one disadvantage is that it sometimes allows a coil or box to get too cold while pumping down after the solenoid closes.

The solenoid in the suction line gives instant control, as refrigeration starts or stops with the action of the thermostatic control. But when a warm evaporator full of liquid refrigerant is suddenly opened to a low pressure suction line, it will begin to boil so violently it is apt to "boil over", and flood back to the compressor. Also, if the expansion valve leaks at all during the off cycle, the evaporator coil fills to where it will surely flood back at the beginning of the next cycle.

Small solenoid valves are direct acting. That is, the main valve plunger is lifted by the magnetic coil.

In larger systems, it would take too large a magnetic coil to lift a large valve plug, so a pilot-operated valve is used. The magnetic coil lifts a pilot plunger which releases any gas pressure on the back side of the main valve disk. The line pressure then lifts this main valve disk and holds it open. When the circuit is broken on the magnetic coil, the pilot plunger drops and closes. Enough pressure then builds up behind the main valve disk so this pressure plus the weight of the disk closes the valve.

Constant Pressure or Suction Pressure Regulating Valve.—This valve is known by several different names, constant pressure valve, suction pressure regulating valve, or suction pressure limiting valve, Fig. 9-9. Fundamentally it is to prevent the pressure in an evaporator from going below a set value.

It is somewhat like an automatic expansion valve in that it is operated by a pressure on a diaphragm or bellows. It is put in the suction line, and is controlled by the pressure entering it. To do this, it must open on a rising pressure. If the pressure in the evaporator rises, the valve opens to release this pressure to the suction line. If the pressure drops, the valve closes. This is a throttling type valve. That is, it holds the evaporator pressure constant by opening exactly as required to balance a constant pressure. Therefore, there is no differential. Its range, or operating pressure, is adjusted by a screw which changes the spring pressure against the diaphragm.

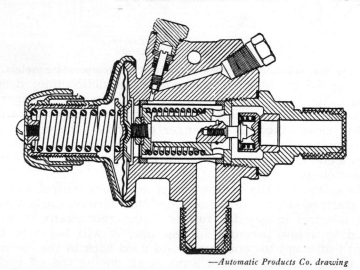

—Automatic Products Co. drawing

Fig. 9-9. Constant pressure valve or suction pressure regulator.

Fig. 9-10 shows how this valve is used to maintain two coil temperatures. Coil 1 opens directly to the suction line. Its operating pressure will be controlled by the back pressure control on the compressor. Coil 2 has a constant pressure valve between it and the suction line. The constant pressure valve will be set for 25 psig to give a 25 F temperature in this coil. The back pressure control will be set for a cut-out pressure of 10 psig. If it was to be set for Coil 1 only, its cut-in point would be about 20 psig. But with the constant pressure valve in the circuit, the cut-in point must be above the valve setting. Otherwise, the pressure bleeding through this valve from refrigerant evaporating in Coil 2 will raise the suction line pressure and short cycle the compressor. So the cut-in point will be set for about 30 psig. This will operate Coil 1 at an average of about 10 F. Thus, a 25 F and a 10 F coil are being operated by the same compressor.

This valve is sometimes used in conjunction with a solenoid valve, Fig. 25-6. If a warm evaporator opened to a low pressure suction line, it would pull the coil down to such a low temperature that goods near the coil might be damaged by freezing before the rest of the box got cold enough. This double valve arrangement is commonly used on the warm boxes where a single large compressor operates on several boxes of different temperatures.

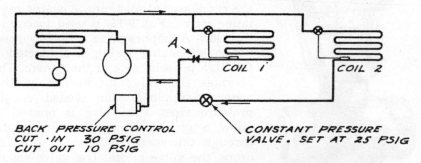

Fig. 9-10. Application of constant pressure valve.

It also is sometimes used on a single coil to limit its temperature. Such an application is common on water coolers. The constant pressure valve will be set for a pressure which gives a temperature above the freezing point of water. Then, regardless of the type of control on the compressor, or regardless of compressor running time, it is impossible to freeze and damage the cooling coil.

Check Valve.—A check valve should always be used on the cold coil in a two temperature system. In Fig. 9-10, during the off cycle, Coil 1 will be somewhere between 10 lbs. per sq. in. and 20 lbs. per sq. in. If Coil 2 gets warm enough to ·open the constant pressure valve, the vapor at 25 lbs. per sq. in. in this coil will flow back to Coil 1, since the latter is at a lower pressure. This vapor will come in contact with the colder liquid in Coil 1 and re-condense. This will continue to produce refrigeration on Coil 2, but will not allow the pressure in the suction line to rise to where it would close the back pressure control. This will warm up Coil 1 to nearly the temperature of Coil 2 before the compressor does start. But worse, Coil 1 is filled with refrigerant from Coil 2 which will flood back to the compressor at the beginning of the on cycle. A check valve placed at A will prevent this. Any refrigerant from Coil 1 cannot get to Coil 2, so will continue to build up the back pressure until the control starts the compressor. A system with solenoids would act similarly.

Figs. 25-2, and 25-4 also show typical applications of all the above mentioned valves.

—*Marsh Instrument Co. photo*

Fig. 9-11. Water regulating valve.

Water Regulating Valves.—Chapter 7 mentioned that city water was sometimes used for condenser cooling. Where the water is not recirculated over a cooling tower, it would not be economical or satisfactory to allow water to flow through the condenser at all times. A water regulating valve, Fig. 9-11, is used to control this flow. A diaphragm or bellows opposed by an adjustable spring is connected to the high pressure side of the system. This operates the valve mechanism so that water is supplied when needed. As the pressure rises, the valve is opened to allow a greater flow of cooling water through the condenser. As the pressure drops, the valve closes. The valve should be so adjusted that it shuts the water off completely during the off cycle. If there is much variation in water pressure, a pressure reducing valve should be put in the water supply line. This should be set for a pressure a little lower than the lowest point reached by the varying water pressure. This keeps a steady flow of water through the condenser for a given valve setting regardless of the water pressure.

Pressure Relief Devices.—In case of a fire in a building with refrigerating equipment, the heat of the fire will raise the refrigerant pressure just like steam pressure in a steam boiler without an outlet. Such could cause a severe explosion if nothing was done to prevent it. Also, excessive pressures can be built up in parts of the system by closing the wrong valves, by excessive air in the high side, by water failure on the condenser, or occasionally by a part of the system trapping liquid refrigerant or oil which warms and expands. Several different types of devices have been designed to release the refrigerant from the system in such cases before an explosion occurs.

One of the simplest of these devices is the fusible plug. This is commonly used on the liquid receivers of most commercial equipment. They are also used on all refrigerant drums except the smallest sizes used for service operations. The heat of a fire will melt the fusible plug and release the refrigerant before excessive pressures are developed. Naturally, this gives no protection against excessive pressures developed by other means than heat.

A device to protect against pressures from any cause, used on medium sized equipment is the rupture disk or rupture member, Fig. 9-12. This is a thin sheet of metal clamped across an opening. The thin metal will break or tear out if excessive pressure is applied to it. They may be used on liquid receivers, flooded brine coolers, compressor discharge lines, etc.

—*Black, Sivalls and Bryson Inc. photo*

Fig. 9-12. Rupture disk.

Larger sized systems, particularly ammonia equipment, usually use pressure relief valves, Fig. 9-13. These are spring loaded valves which open at a predetermined pressure, but will also close when the pressure returns to normal. On refrigerant containing vessels such as receivers and brine coolers, they discharge to the air, or to a line to the roof. On compressors they are so connected that the discharge pressure is discharged back to the low pressure side of the system, Fig. 6-27. Therefore, if this valve opens, the refrigerant is not wasted.

—Henry Valve Co. photo

Fig. 9-13. Pressure relief valves. Two way valve assembly shows the only type of stop valve permitted ahead of a relief valve.

Above — Snap action, diaphragm relief valve.

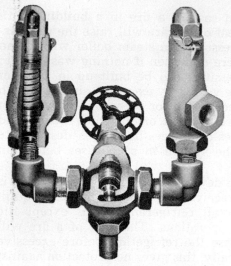

—Rex Engineering & Sales photo

QUESTIONS

9–1. What is the difference between a control and a control valve?

9–2. Is an expansion valve a control or a control valve?

9–3. Why are both an expansion valve and another control device necessary on the simplest automatic system?

9–4. What is the difference between a temperature control and a pressure control?

9–5. Is an increase of pressure in the bellows of a control caused by an increase or a decrease of temperature?

9–6. What is the difference between range and differential?

9–7. What is a high pressure cutout, and what is its purpose?

9–8. With what expansion valves can a pressure control be used?

9–9. What is a constant pressure valve, and what is it for?

9–10. Why is a check valve sometimes needed?

9–11. What is the purpose of a water regulating valve?

9–12. What is the purpose of a low water cutout?

9–13. List the safety devices used on refrigeration equipment.

9–14. Is a solenoid valve more like a constant pressure valve or a snap action valve?

9–15. List the safety devices used on refrigeration equipment.

CHAPTER 10

LUBRICATION

Requirements.—As with any moving piece of machinery, lubrication is an important problem in refrigeration. Crankshafts, connecting rods, and pistons must be lubricated. This requires oil in the compressor. Compressor valves and all automatic valves in the system operate best with some lubrication. This means some oil should be circulated in the system.

Therefore, the problem is to lubricate all compressor parts, and circulate enough oil through the system to supply an oil film on all working valve parts. This circulated oil must be taken care of in some way. With ammonia, most of the excess discharged by the compressor is caught in an oil trap and periodically drained, Fig. 8-17. That which goes on to the evaporator settles to the bottom, and must be periodically drained. Sometimes traps are used with fluorocarbon refrigerants; sometimes not. The oil carried to the evaporator is expected to be swept back through the suction line to the compressor. Here it is separated from the suction vapor by a drain, and allowed to flow back to the crankcase.

Regardless of the refrigerant used, oil in the evaporator introduces certain problems. It tends to thicken and coat the inside evaporator walls, reducing heat transfer. The colder the evaporator, the worse this condition becomes. At very cold temperatures wax may separate out of the oil. Oil mixes in varying amounts with the refrigerant and varies the boiling temperature. This means that for a given evaporator temperature, a lower evaporator pressure is necessary as more oil is dissolved in the refrigerant. This penalizes the compressor. Thus, the oil circulated should be kept at a minimum. That is why oil separators are to be recommended on most fluorocarbon systems, although for reasons of first cost and incomplete oil separation they are often omitted.

Splash lubricating systems are used in many commercial jobs. The amount of oil circulated can be fairly well controlled by the oil level in the crankcase. The higher the oil level, the more oil is splashed up to the cylinders and pistons. This allows more to be carried through the compressor valves, and the refrigerant vapor carries it into the system. The removal of the cylinder head gives an indication of whether the oil is at the proper level in the crankcase. If the discharge valves are perfectly dry, the oil level is too low. If they are just moist with oil, the oil level is proper. If there is considerable oil standing on top of the pistons, the oil level is too high. Such a test should not be made after a quick pull down. When the pressure in the crankcase is reduced rapidly, the oil foams up, and more of it is pumped up to the high side.

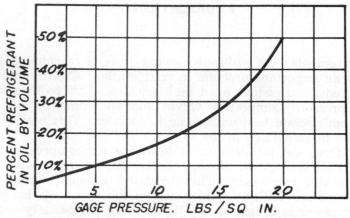

Fig. 10-1. Solubility of a typical fluorocarbon refrigerant in oil.

Force feed lubrication gives a more accurate control of oil distribution. There is less oil foaming on the starting cycle. The amount of oil delivered to the high side is designed for, and is not subject to the variations possible in splash systems.

Oil Foaming.—Oil foaming has been previously mentioned several times. A reference to Fig. 10-1 should help show what causes this to happen. This is the solubility curve of Refrigerant 12 in a particular oil. Values will vary for different refrigerants in different oils, but these conditions are typical. In this case, if Refrigerant 12 is at 20 psig pressure on this oil, about 50 percent by volume of refrigerant vapor will be dissolved in the oil. If the pressure is reduced to 10 psig, only 16 percent of the refrigerant is soluble. The other 34 percent tries to escape immediately. It separates from the oil as bubbles of vapor. Thousands of tiny bubbles, or foam, form through the entire mass of oil. Naturally this foam takes more volume than the solid oil, so it rises, Fig. 6-17. It is exactly the same action that takes place in beer when it is released from the pressure of the keg or bottle.

Since a great deal more oil is soluble in the fluorocarbons than in ammonia, the former will foam much worse than the latter. With the fluorocarbons, there will be a certain amount of foaming on the beginning of each on cycle, as the crankcase pressure is reduced. If all the gas is pumped out of the crankcase to do some work on the compressor, there will be foaming. Modern design has pretty effectively separated the suction gas from this oil foam by the use of check valves, baffles, or screen separators. This prevents the foam from reaching the cylinders and slugging the compressor.

Oil Selection.—The selection of the proper oil for a refrigeration system is a great problem. It is one that has not been wholly solved by all oil companies supplying oil to the refrigeration industry. It is not like the automobile lubrication problem because the oil is not periodically changed. A proper oil does not have to be changed. Many thousands of hermetically sealed machines have been running for as long as 15 years on the same oil, and are good for many more years. So a proper oil can be supplied.

Some of the most important terms used to describe the properties of oil should be introduced. The viscosity of the oil is a measure of how thick or heavy it is. This is measured by the length of time it takes a measured quantity of the oil at a given temperature to flow through a standard orifice. A viscosity of 120 Saybolt seconds at 100 F temperature means it takes 120 seconds for a given sample of the oil at 100 F to flow through the orifice. A viscosity of 200 Saybolt seconds would be a heavier oil since it takes longer for the measured sample to go through the orifice.

The pour point of the oil is the temperature at which a given amount of oil in a standardized vessel thickens to the point where it will sag, but not pour out when the vessel is turned on its side.

The flash point is the temperature at which an inflammable vapor is distilled from the oil. A flash point of 225 F means an inflammable vapor is distilled off at 225 F. It does not mean the oil will ignite at this temperature unless a blaze is provided to light it. Although this does not necessarily form a hazard in the system, it is an indication that the oil will start to break down at this temperature.

The cloud point is the temperature at which wax will begin to separate from the oil. This wax separates as separate crystals which thicken the oil. As these crystals form, their opaque white color gives the oil a cloudy appearance.

A properly refined oil for refrigeration is almost clear, usually with a yellowish tinge. Its viscosity is determined by the refrigerant used, and by the evaporator temperature. All fluorocarbon refrigerants thin the oil considerably, so a heavier oil is used with them to give the required weight after it has been thinned, see Fig. 10-2. Usually viscosities and pour points are closely related. So as evaporator temperatures go down, the viscosity must be decreased to get the required pour point. The thinning of the oil by the fluorocarbon refrigerants will also reduce the pour point and the cloud point. Therefore it is possible in some cases to accept an oil with a pour point or cloud point nearer to the evaporator temperature than normally would be considered safe. Ammonia does not have this thinning action on oil.

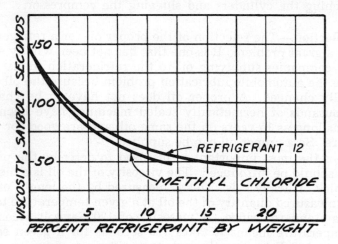

Fig. 10-2. Viscosity of oil refrigerant mixtures.

The flash point of the oil should always be above the compression temperature. Any breakdown of the oil has several harmful effects. Non-condensable gases are formed which, if not purged out, will raise the head pressure. The remaining oil will be left with a higher viscosity, and sometimes a higher pour point. Some oils will begin to sludge in the presence of ammonia after the lighter constitutents have been separated by heat. This sludge may or may not show in the compressor. If it does, it is apt to form on the cylinder walls and piston rings as a "varnish". If sludge is formed some of it will carry over to the low side. Here, as soon as it hits the cold coil surface it thickens to a coal tar consistency. This will insulate the coils from the cold refrigerant. It has been known to stop up coils.

There is one very contradictory set of conditions when choosing the proper oil. The colder the evaporator, the lower the pour point of the oil should be. But a low pour point usually means a low viscosity, and a low viscosity is hard to get without getting a low flash point or breakdown point. The lower the evaporator temperature, the greater is the compression ratio between the low side and the high side. But the higher the compression ratio, the higher will be the discharge temperatures, Fig. 14-9 and Fig. 14-11. Thus unless two stage compression is used, cold temperatures require an oil with a low viscosity and a high flash point, which is very difficult to get in the same oil.

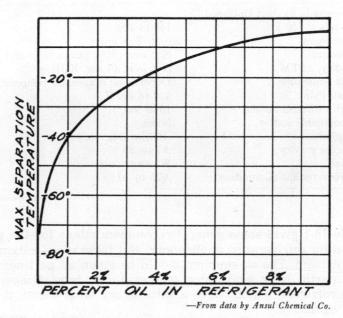

—From data by Ansul Chemical Co.

Fig. 10-3. Effect of different mixtures of one sample of oil with refrigerant 12 on wax separation temperatures.

Most refrigeration oils are sufficiently dewaxed for normal evaporator temperatures, but some of them give trouble on sub-zero temperatures. Fig. 10-3 shows how a typical oil reacts with regard to dewaxing at low temperatures. Notice again, the less the oil in proportion to the refrigerant, the lower the permissable temperatures. This is still another argument for an oil trap on the high side to keep the oil circulation down as much as possible.

Any oil for refrigeration purposes must contain no water. Every effort is made to keep water out of the refrigeration system. An oil with moisture present would undo all other precautions. The moisture in the oil is related to the dielectric strength, which is much easier to measure. A moist oil will break down in a high voltage test sooner than a dry oil. Not only must the oil be purchased dry, but it must be kept dry. It will absorb moisture from the air if left in open containers.

TABLE 10-1—OIL SPECIFICATIONS

Property	
Viscosity in Saybolt Universal seconds at 100 F	150 to 320
Pour Point	—10 F or lower
Moisture	Not over .01% passes 25 to 30 KV test.
Acidity, ASTM	Not over .01 mg. KOH/g.
Wax Separation	Depends on evaporator temperature
Flash Point	320 to 400 F
Sligh oxidation number	10 or less
Saponifiable matter	None
Sulphur	.15% or less
Specific gravity	.87 to .89
Color	White or pale
Carbon residue (Conradson)	.005 to .01%

—From Ansul Chemical Co. Data

Table 10-1 gives some general recommendations for the properties of oil for refrigeration applications. But these specifications alone are not enough. The oil supplier should be given all pertinent information, particularly evaporator temperatures, head temperatures, and the refrigerant used. Once a satisfactory oil is found, it should be used exclusively.

QUESTIONS

10–1. Is it desirable to keep all oil out of all parts of the refrigeration system except the compressor?

10–2. What are the objections to oil in the evaporator?

10–3. Compare splash feed with force feed compressor lubrication.

10–4. What causes oil foaming?

10–5. What is the meaning of pour point, and how is it measured?

10–6. What is the meaning of viscosity, and how is it measured?

10–7. What is the meaning of flash point, and how is it measured?

10–8. What is the importance of the cloud point?

10–9. How does the compressor discharge temperature affect lubrication?

10–10. Why should a refrigerator oil be perfectly dry?

CHAPTER 11

DEFROSTING METHODS

General.—An evaporator surface operating below 32 F will, unless prevented by special means, collect frost. Where frost is formed, some provision must be made to get rid of it. If this is not done, the frost builds up in thickness, and acts as an insulator on the evaporator surface. Where frost is present a colder refrigerant temperature must be carried to maintain the room at the required temperature. This colder refrigerant temperature requires a lower back pressure which penalizes the compressor.

The exact amount of the insulating effect of frost is difficult to calculate. Pure ice is about 20 percent as effective as cork to reduce heat flow. But frost on a coil will contain varying amounts of air which increases the insulating value. Frost having an insulating value up to 50 percent of that of cork has been known. That is, one inch of such frost would hold back the heat flow to the evaporator as much as one half inch of cork would. Frost found at only a few degrees below freezing (32 F) will be nearly solid ice. It forms more slowly at this temperature, but it is so solid that it is slower and more difficult to melt off. At colder temperatures, the frost becomes more snowy. At low sub-zero temperatures, the frost becomes very light and fluffy. It forms much faster, but will melt off faster because it is not so solid. Means of solving the frost problem can be divided into two methods: prevention, and defrosting or periodic removal. In all, defrosting is a necessary evil; a messy job, but one that must be done. To neglect it is to reduce the refrigeration available.

Defrost Cycle.—For rooms operating above freezing, coils operating on a defrost cycle are common. Except for relatively higher room temperatures, a blower coil, Fig. 5-18, is necessary for this. During the running cycle, the coil pulls down below freezing and collects frost. The fan blows the room air through the coil and cools it. During the off cycle, the room air which is above 32 F is blown through the coil. This melts the frost. Some of it is re-evaporated into the room air, and it helps maintain a high humidity. The rest of the melted frost flows out a drain to the sewer. This method of defrosting is very commonly used in commercial applications. This type of evaporator will fail to do any room cooling if allowed to fill with frost. Air circulation is necessary to get the necessary cooling. But there is no air circulation if it fills with frost.

Periodic Removal.—The most obvious method of removing frost is to shut the compressor off until the frost is all melted. With domestic and small commercial systems, this was once common. The defrost setting on the control described in Chapter 9 was a method tried and still used somewhat, to simplify the problem.

Another method was to add a time clock whcih turned the unit off once every 24 hours, usually during night hours. By defrosting daily, less frost collected to be melted off. However, an off cycle of several hours was required. If frozen foods were present this was unsatisfactory.

The time clock plus additional heat, either electric or hot gas, is now used by many domestic manufacturers. Defrost periods can be made in less than an hour, and it is supposed to be done so quickly that frozen foods do not have time to melt.

Some drain the melted frost to a pan which must be dumped manually. Others have tried draining it into a pan on the condenser. Condenser heat is supposed to evaporate the water.

Many two temperature domestic cabinets (separate cooler and freezer sections) defrost the cooler evaporator by one of the above methods or by a defrost cycle, but do not defrost the freezer section.

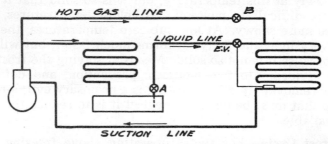

Fig. 11-1. Simple hot gas defrost system—one evaporator.

Hot Gas Defrosting.—A common defrosting method used with commercial and industrial systems is a hot gas defrosting system. Here the hot gas directly off the compressor is fed to the evaporator. Fig. 11-1 shows the elements of this system. By closing valve A and opening valve B, the hot discharge gas from the compressor is fed directly to the evaporator.

This hot gas not only carries sensible heat to the evaporator, but as it strikes the cold evaporator surface, will condense and give up its latent heat. It pushes the cold liquid on ahead of it toward the compressor. This system has been used, but valves must be opened very slowly, carefully, and not too far. Otherwise the liquid pushed from the evaporator will slug the compressor badly.

If a tank such as shown in Fig. 11-2 is put in the suction line to trap the liquid, slugging can be eliminated. During defrosting,

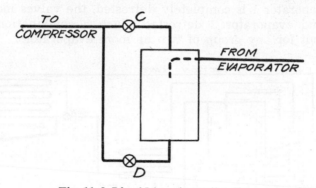

Fig. 11-2. Liquid trap in suction line.

valve C is opened and valve D closed. The tank will trap the liquid, but return it to the compressor as it evaporates. After defrosting, valve C must be closed and valve D opened. Otherwise the trap will catch oil which should be returned to the compressor.

One coil manufacturer has put a combination liquid trap and heat exchanger on the outlet of his evaporator. The coil can be rapidly drained of cold refrigerant without danger of slugging the compressor. Heat is applied to evaporate this liquid.

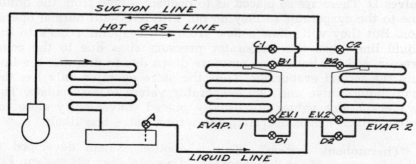

Fig. 11-3. Hot gas system with two evaporators so arranged that liquid from one is forced into the other on defrosting.

If more than one evaporator is in the system, Fig. 11-3 shows a common hook-up. Normally the liquid valve "A" and the suction hand valves "C" are open; and the hot gas valves "B" and the expansion valve bypasses "D" are closed. To defrost evaporator No. 1, the liquid valve "A" and the suction hand valve "C-1" are closed, and "B-1" and "D-1" are opened. The hot, high pressure gas flows into the evaporator through valve "B-1," and pushes the liquid out backwards through valve "D-1" into the liquid line. Thus the liquid required for evaporator 2 is supplied from evaporator 1 instead of from the receiver. Evaporator 1 acts as the condenser to supply this liquid. When evaporator 1 is completely defrosted, the valves may be reversed and evaporator 2 defrosted. Such a combination can be worked out for any group of two or more evaporators.

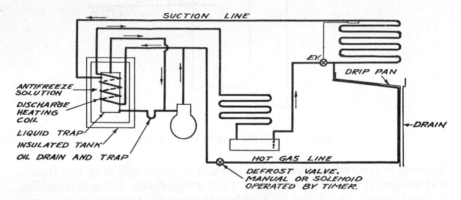

Fig. 11-4. The Thermobank system.

This system is very common on large systems which are in charge of an operating engineer. It has been slightly simplified for commercial installations by putting check valves in place of valves D. These are so placed as to prevent a flow from the liquid line to the evaporator so they do not interfere with normal operation. But they will allow a flow from the evaporator back to the liquid line when the evaporator pressure rises due to the compressor, and the liquid line pressure drops due to draining the line into the second evaporator. Thus the store operator only has the main liquid valve and two evaporator valves to manipulate. The two evaporator valves are usually placed conveniently close together which makes operating the wrong valve less likely.

"Thermobank System".—This is another system developed to overcome some of the disadvantages of a simple hot gas system, Fig. 11-4. It consists of a double chamber heat exchanger. Hot, high pressure vapor directly from the compressor goes through the heat exchanger coil, then to the condenser. It keeps the solution in the outer chamber warm. This is a special anti-freeze solution so there is no danger of damage due to freeze ups. Its purpose is to store heat from the discharge vapor. The suction line from the evaporator goes through the inner chamber of the heat exchanger. This acts as a liquid trap to prevent any liquid refrigerant from returning to the compressor. A small drain line from the bottom of this chamber is provided to drain any oil trapped, back to the compressor crankcase. The hot gas line to the evaporator is soldered to the evaporator drain line, then makes a loop in the drain pan. This prevents any freeze ups in the drain.

The only valve to be manipulated is the one valve in the hot gas line. It could be either a hand valve or a magnetic valve controlled by a time clock. The latter is recommended. To defrost the evaporator, this valve is opened. The hot high pressure vapor flowing into the evaporator pushes the liquid out of the evaporator, back the suction line to the heat exchanging liquid trap. Here the liquid previously warmed by the high pressure vapor supplies heat enough to evaporate the liquid refrigerant. Such a system could be installed so as to work on several evaporators multiplexed to one compressor. The defrost valve is placed in the branch line to the evaporator to be defrosted. Only one evaporator is defrosted at a time, but each evaporator can be defrosted in turn.

With this system the liquid trap will prevent slugging the compressor, whether one or several evaporators are in the lines. When properly installed and operated according to manufacturer's instructions, this system gives very good results.

Water Spray Defrost.— Fig. 11-5 shows a typical water spray defrost system. A spray header fed by a special three way valve is built over the coil. The compressor is stopped and this three way water valve turned on. The water sprays

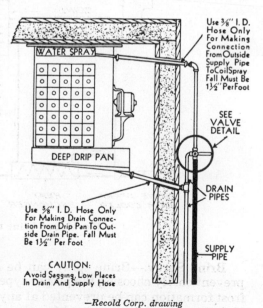

Use ⅜" I.D. Hose Only For Making Connection From Outside Supply Pipe To Coil Spray Fall Must Be 1½" Per Foot

SEE VALVE DETAIL

WATER SPRAY

DEEP DRIP PAN

Use ⅜" I.D. Hose Only For Making Drain Connection From Drip Pan To Outside Drain Pipe. Fall Must Be 1½" Per Foot

CAUTION: Avoid Sagging, Low Places In Drain And Supply Hose

DRAIN PIPES

SUPPLY PIPE

—*Recold Corp. drawing*

Fig. 11-5. A water defrost system.

over the frosted coils. As long as the water velocity is kept high, even cold water will not freeze, and it washes or melts the frost off the coils to the pan below. It must be sufficiently melted that no chunks of frost or ice remain in the drain to plug it up. The valve is then turned to the drain position so that all the water drains out of the spray line and header so this will not freeze later. If properly installed and intelligently operated, this system is very satisfactory, even on freezer work.

Heater Defrost.—Some manufacturers of coil equipment supply evaporators with electric heater defrost. Some have even housed the coil in an insulated box with doors or louvers which are normally kept open to allow a fan to deliver air through them. To defrost, the doors or louvers are closed, the fan turned off, and the heaters turned on. The heat inside the insulated box soon melts the frost. The insulation prevents this heat from raising the cabinet temperature.

Other companies have embedded electric strip heaters, either inside the tubes of the coil or alternating with the coil tubes. Obviously the electric power necessary to operate these heaters must be considered when installing such a system.

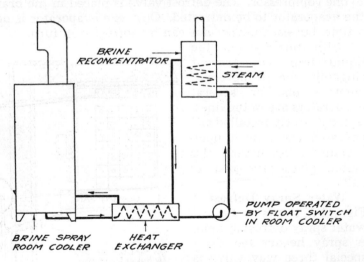

Fig. 11-6. A brine reconcentrator.

Brine Spray.—Brine spray can be classed as a method of frost prevention. By choosing the proper type and concentration of solution, frost formation can be prevented at any required temperature. Table 23-4 gives concentrations and freezing points of sodium chloride (ordinary salt) brine, and Table 23-5 of calcium chloride.

As the moisture which would ordinarily frost is collected, it dilutes the brine used. If nothing is done to correct this, it would become diluted to the point where the solution itself would freeze on the coils. Two methods are used to prevent this. The first is to continually add salt to the solution to maintain its strength, and allow the excess solution which collects to drain to the sewer. This method constantly wastes salt.

The second method of maintaining the solution at the proper strength is to keep boiling off part of the solution, Fig. 11-6. The solution is boiled down, or reconcentrated in a separate chamber that can be heated with steam, gas, electricity, or any other convenient heat source. A heat exchanger is used to help heat the cold liquid from the cooler, and to help cool the hot liquid from the concentrator. This method saves the salt, but requires more equipment, requires a heat source, and requires more refrigeration to recool the liquid back to refrigerating temperatures. It is seldom used with salt or calcium brine, but has been used with special brines which are more expensive and must be recovered.

QUESTIONS

11-1. Why must frost be removed from evaporator coils?

11-2. How does a defrost cycle work?

11-3. Can a defrost cycle be used in a freezer box?

11-4. Briefly describe hot gas defrosting.

11-5. What are some of the possible troubles introduced with hot gas defrosting?

11-6. How does the "Thermobank" system work?

11-7. Briefly describe the water defrost.

11-8. Can a cold water defrost be used on a freezer box?

11-9. Briefly describe the brine spray defrost.

11-10. Give two methods of maintaining the brine strength in a brine spray.

CHAPTER 12

COMPRESSOR DRIVES

Requirements.—The motor drive to supply power to the compressor equipment should be chosen with all requirements in mind. The primary requirement in a refrigerating plant is reliability. Where refrigeration is depended upon to keep food in storage, a single breakdown or power failure at an inopportune time could cause the spoilage of food worth several times the cost of the equipment. This is true whether figuring a large cold storage warehouse, or a small commercial cabinet. Therefore it is of utmost importance that everything else be subordinated to completely *dependable* operation.

The second requirement is *economy*. This is of great importance in the installation of any equipment. Refrigeration equipment is bought as a business proposition. If its cost is greater than the financial return from it, it will not be used for long. The less the cost, the more service can be rendered for a given price, or the more profit it can return. It is important to remember total cost has many factors beside first cost.

First cost is an important part of total cost, but operating costs, and maintenance and repair costs are also a part of total cost. These latter can be more important than first cost where they become excessive, because first cost must be paid only once but operating and maintenance costs go on for the life of the installation. It is very poor economy to jeopardize operating and maintenance costs to save a little on first cost. Another part of economy is space economy. The more space required for the driving equipment, the larger the required engine room, and naturally, the greater the cost. If the available space is limited, a larger engine room reduces the usable or pay space.

The third requirement for driving equipment is *simplicity*. The drive should be simple to understand, simple to operate, simple to maintain, and simple to repair. The easier and simpler it is to properly take care of equipment, the better the care that is usually taken of it.

A refrigeration compressor usually requires a high starting torque drive. Torque is the actual twisting power of a motor whether it is stationary or turning. A compressor which is not unloaded on the off cycle must start under load. That is, it starts to compress and build up a resistance to turning as soon as it starts to revolve. This requires a motor which has lots of twisting power, or torque, before it gets up to speed. Some types of drive have good starting torque. Others have almost none, and must be gotten up to speed before a load is applied or they will stall. Motors of this latter type may be used where the compressor is unloaded and can be brought up to speed before it starts pumping.

Electric Drives.—Electric motors have proven to be the most satisfactory drive for average conditions. An electric motor can only be as dependable as the electric power lines supplying it. But power systems have been so interconnected that power failures are so infrequent they are almost non-existent, except in isolated localities.

An electric motor will run longer with less care than any other type of drive. Therefore they are one of the most dependable types of drive available. They are very simple. Their principal need is to be kept clean and dry, with sufficient oil in the bearings. Power cost can be greater than with other types of equipment, but this is usually offset by lower maintenance and repair costs. Space requirements are smaller than with any other drive. High torque motors are available where required. These all point to the electric motor as being dependable, economical, and simple. Its application to almost all domestic except the absorbtion type, to practically all the commercial, and well over half of all industrial drives prove it to be so.

Fractional horsepower (less than one horsepower) are nearly all single phase motors, that is, they will work from the common two wire system used for lights or small power. The commonest type of single phase motor used at the present time is some form of induction motor. An induction motor has a set of field coils and a rotating armature, Fig. 12-1. The armature may be made up of copper or aluminum bars, sometimes called a squirrel cage, shorted so that each bar makes a coil or electric circuit with the next one. Or they may be wound coils that are shorted on each other. In either case they are set in a laminated iron armature to give a path for the magnetic flux or forces. The bars or windings in the armature act as the secondary of a transformer, while the stator or field coils act as a primary. Current is induced in the armature, and no brushes needed; hence the name induction motor.

A single phase induction motor with one set of windings can

be compared to a single cylinder gasoline or steam engine which always stops on dead center. Therefore, it will not start by itself. (A resistance split phase induction motor) is one of the commonest methods used to obtain starting. Such a motor has two sets of field coils, a running winding and a starting winding. The running winding has a high inductance or choke coil effect and a low resist-

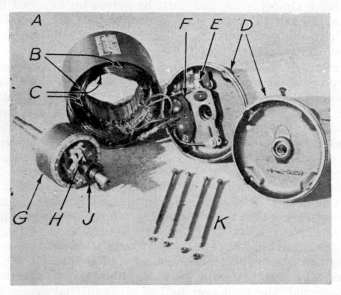

Fig. 12-1. Dismantled single phase (split phase) induction motor. A. Stator containing field windings; B. Low resistance running winding; C. High resistance starting winding; D. End bells; E. Starting switch in series with starting winding, operated by collar J; F. Back of connection block; G. Rotor with squirrel cage winding; H. Centrifugal weights; J. Collar moved by centrifugal weights; K. Through bolts.

ance. The starting winding has a low inductance and a high resistance. The greater choke coil effect in one set of windings than in the other holds back, or causes the current to lag sufficiently that the alternating current impulses do not act at exactly the same time. This gives an effect that could be compared to a two cylinder gasoline engine, Fig. 12-2. The angle between the cylinders is not much, but is sufficient to get the motor started. When the motor is started both coils are in the circuit. When it gets up to speed, the starting winding is cut out of the circuit, usually by a centrifugal switch. The motor then runs on the running winding only.

The common, general purpose fractional horse-power motors are of this type. But due to the small difference in electrical effect possible between the high inductance and low inductance coils (like the small angle between the cylinders of Fig. 12-2) their starting torque is poor. For this reason a general purpose induc-

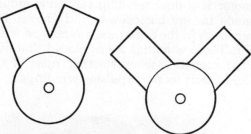

Fig. 12-2. Gas engine analogy of split phase induction motor.

Fig. 12-3. Gas engine analogy of capacitor motor.

tion motor is not satisfactory for refrigeration unless the compressor is unloaded.

A capacitor split phase motor is the most common single phase motor used for those refrigeration systems that must start under load. It works very similar to the resistance split phase motor, except that the capacitor acts just the opposite to the inductance ór choke coil effect. This gives a condition similar to the gasoline engine of Fig. 12-3. There is sufficient difference in the angle betwen the electrical effects of the two coils to give excellent starting torque. As with the resistance split phase motor, the starting winding and the capacitor are cut out of the circut when the motor gets up to speed. This is an excellent motor for refrigeration use where there is no unloading.

A repulsion start induction run motor is another motor with a good starting torque, Fig. 12-4. It is so wired that while start-ing, individual coils are brought out to the brushes, and connected to form a complete coil circuit. A current is induced in the rotor as with the induction motor. But the rotor coil arrangement is such that the coils in the rotor repel those in the stator. This gives good starting torque, but not good running characteristics. Therefore when the motor gets up to speed, a centrifugal device lifts the brushes which operate it as a repulsion motor, and short circuit the commutator bars to each other so as to make a wound rotor induc-tion motor.

This motor has excellent starting and running characteristics but the commutator, short circuiting device, and centrifugal oper-ating levers complicate its construction, and give more mechanical parts to be potential sources of trouble. Before the development of the capacitor split phase motor, it was the only high starting torque fractional horse power motor available. Therefore it has had a great deal of use. It is still popular with some manufacturers.

A motor somewhat similar to the repulsion start induction run motor is a dual winding repulsion-induction motor. This is usually made in one horsepower and above. This motor has two separate windings in the armature, a repulsion winding and an induction winding. These windings are so placed that due to electrical and magnetic characteristics, when starting, most of the magnetic force from the field reacts on the repulsion windings.

—*Wagner Electric Corp. photo*

Fig. 12-4. Repulsion start induction run motor (cross section).

When the motor is revolving at rated speed most of the magnetic force reacts with the induction winding. Thus approximately the same results are obtained with this motor as with the repulsion start induction run, but with fewer mechanical parts. Also the transfer from repulsion drive to induction drive is gradual as the motor comes up to speed, rather than with a jerk at one point.

Single phase motors are available in either 110 or 220 volts. Many single phase motors have the winding made in two sets of 110 volts each, Fig. 12-5. These can be hooked up in parallel for 110

volt operation, or in series for 220
volts. For ¾ horsepower or smaller,
either 110 volts or 220 volts may be
used, depending on the power available in the building. Smaller wire can
carry the required power to a 220 volt
motor without excessive line losses
or voltage drops. Therefore 220 volts
is preferred if it does not require an
additional electric service.

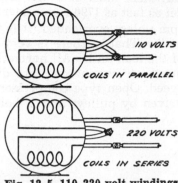

For one horsepower or larger, 110
volts should not be used. Line voltage
drops particularly in starting, are excessive. For either 110 or 220 volts it
is best to run separate lines from the
switch box to the refrigeration unit.

Fig. 12-5. 110-220 volt windings
with proper hook-ups for both
voltages.

There is always a surge of heavy starting current when a motor
starts and comes up to speed. This causes a voltage drop in the feed
lines which will affect anything else on the same circuit.

Small hermetically sealed motors are usually the resistance split
phase type. They are unloaded by the capillary tube as it balances
pressures during the off cycle. If it is to be used with an automatic
or thermostatic expansion valve, a capacitor split phase motor is
needed.

Centrifugal devices, as used in open motors, cannot be used
for starting. The arcing of the switch will burn the oil and break
down the refrigerant sealed in with the compressor and motor.
Therefore a starting relay which is operated by the starting surge
is used, Fig. 12-6.

On starting, the surge of current is sufficient to pull the magnetic contactor closed, which connects the starting winding in the
circuit. As the motor comes up to speed, the current drops to a
value too low to hold the contactor closed, so it opens the starting
winding circuit. This relay is mounted outside the compressor case,
and the starting, common, and running leads brought from the
case through insulated, pressure tight bushings.

As mentioned above, a single phase motor could be compared to
a one cylinder gasoline engine. Like a one cylinder engine, the
power is in pulsations which gives rise to considerable vibration.
Therefore single phase motors are nearly always rubber or spring
mounted so this vibration is cushioned from the foundations.

Single phase induction motors usually have a speed of 1725 to 1740
revolutions per minute. The magnetic pull rotates at 1800 rpm.

But there must be some "slip" to create any power. Some of them get as fast as 1790 rpm under no load. Few of them drop below 1725 rpm unless overloaded. It is therefore, practically a constant speed motor. That is, there is very little variation in its speed regardless of the load on it. All hermetically sealed compressors, whether domestic or commercial, are direct connected so they run at motor speed. Open type compressors may be direct connected, or may be driven by pulleys and V belts at something less than motor speed.

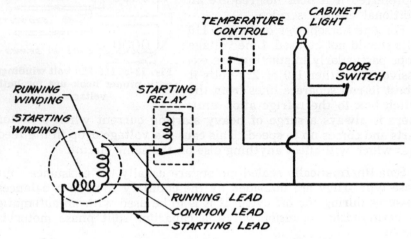

Fig. 12-6. Domestic system showing starting relay.

Wherever possible, motors over one horsepower should be three phase. Above 3 horsepower, they are the only type of A-C motor commonly used. Three phase motors are available in fractional horse power sizes if so required. Naturally, a three phase electric circuit is necessary to run any three phase motor. The three phase motor in a given power rating is smaller and usually cheaper than a single phase motor.

Up to about 50 horsepower, the three phase induction motor is the type commonly used. This is similar to the single phase induction motor except there are three sets of windings in the stator. Since electric impulses in each of the three phases come at a different time, no special starting devices or centrifugal switches are needed. The three phases are in the circuit at all times, which makes a simpler motor which is self starting and smoother running. Vibration is negligible. Its power pulsations could be compared to a three cylinder gasoline engine.

As sizes go up speeds usually go down. Some drives are belted, using either V-belts or flat belts. As motor speeds go down, direct connected motors become more common. Motors are available for

220 volts, 440 volts or 550 volts. As sizes go up, manual operation with manual unloading on the start becomes more common. This makes standard rather than high starting torque motors applicable. Where no unloading is done, high starting torque motors are still required.

Above 50 horsepower either synchronous or induction motors can be used. The synchronous motor is usually more expensive than an induction motor. It also requires direct current for the field coils, which is usually supplied by a motor generator set. But it gives better efficiency and a better power factor than an induction motor. In fact, where other induction motors are on the line (induction motors have a notoriously poor power factor) the synchronous motor can be so operated as to improve the line power factor.

A synchronous motor is something like a single phase induction motor in that special starting means are necessary. The synchronous motor is usually started as a three phase induction motor with special built in windings for this purpose. When it gets up to as near synchronous speed as it can on the induction windings, switches throw it into synchronous operation. It then pulls into step at synchronous speed. But with such a system as this the starting torque is very poor. This makes unloading during starting essential. Thus as sizes (and power bills) go up, the greater first cost of a synchronous motor, and more manual operation becomes justified to offset the power savings possible.

TABLE 12-1—STANDARD MOTOR SPEEDS

MOTOR SPEEDS ON 60 CYCLE POWER

Synchronous Motors	3600	1800	1200	900	600
Induction Motors	3450	1740	1160	875	

Synchronous motors run exactly at synchronous speed with no variation due to changing loads. They can be selected to run at any speed shown in Table 12-1.[1] As sizes go up, slower speeds are possible without exorbitant increases in cost. Therefore the proper speed for direct connection to the compressor is usually selected. Where electric motors are used to drive centrifugal compressors the required speeds can only be obtained through step up gears.

Voltages available for synchronous motors are the same as with three phase induction motors. Higher voltages are sometimes used,

---

[1]The speed is obtained by dividing 3600 (60 cycles per second for one minute) by the number of pairs of poles in the motor.

but as a rule are not recommended because of the hazard involved.

Where direct current is the power supplied, direct current motors must be used. These are more costly than alternating current motors. Brushes and commutators increase the maintenance required. A shunt wound or compound wound motor is usually used to get nearly a constant speed. The operating speed of these motors can easily be changed, so they do give a simple method of capacity control. Direct current is standard on most shipboard work.

Some thought should be given to the different power rates available when considering electric drive. Not only must the actual cost per kilowatt be considered, but such factors as demand rate, power factor, etc. Demand is the greatest amount of power used in a given time compared to the total power consumed. Large amounts of power used for only short periods of time can be more costly than more total power used at a steadier rate. Thus, although one large motor may be more efficient than two small ones, the power cost of one large motor cycled may be greater than that for two smaller motors, one cycled and the other running steadily.

Most power companies charge penalties for low power factor loads or allow bonuses for high power factor loads. Therefore the use of synchronous motors to raise the power factor may more than pay for the extra cost of this type of motor. Or in sizes where a synchronous motor is hardly justified, an investment in static condensers may be worth while. These are all factors that vary with different power rate schedules, but they should not be overlooked when selecting a motor. Static condensers have been applied to the compressors used on window air conditioners to reduce the total current. This makes it possible to get larger capacity units on ordinary house circuits.

Steam Drive.—Before electric drives were so well developed or power lines so dependable, steam was the time honored power drive for refrigeration as well as other requirements. In some cases it is used today; even installed in new plants. With proper equipment and proper care it can be as dependable as electricity. Fuel costs are usually cheaper than electric power costs. But the greater amount of equipment necessary: boilers, steam engines and auxiliaries make first cost and space requirements much greater than with electric drives. The greater amount of equipment, machinery, etc., increases the maintenance costs and problems.

Where fuel is cheap and electric rates high, steam power may be justified. One place steam power is particularly well suited is where steam heat is used for processing. Boilers must be installed to generate the process steam needed. The extra cost of generating steam at a higher pressure for power is small. The steam is first used in the steam engine, then the exhaust steam is used to do the required heating. Dairies, breweries, and such are excellent examples of where such an installation works out well. One other advantage of a steam drive is the ease with which the refrigeration capacity can be controlled by controlling the speed of the engine.

Many older steam systems using Corliss engines are still in use. Where new steam driven refrigeration installations are made, either a poppet valve engine or a uniflow engine is usually selected.

Direct connected steam turbines are a natural drive for centrifugal compressors because they are both high speed machines. Turbine driven electric generators which in turn drive electric motors on the compressors have been installed in some plants. But such installations are very costly, and other considerations usually dictate the choice of equipment in such cases.

Diesel, Gas Engines.—Many plants have found Diesel engines, or in natural gas areas, gas engines very economical. Somewhat like steam plants, they are as dependable as the care taken of them. Their first cost, operating cost and repair costs are usually much more than with electric power. But fuel costs may be low enough to offset these. This is particularly true where oil or gas is cheap and electric power expensive. Such engines may be direct connected, but more often drive through a belt. The latter makes it possible to operate the engines at higher and more economical speeds.

QUESTIONS

12-1. What is the greatest requirement of a refrigeration power drive?

12-2. Give two other important requirements of a refrigeration power drive.

12-3. Why are electric drives so common in refrigeration?

12-4. What is the most common type of fractional horsepower motor used for refrigeration at the present time?

12-5. What is the principal disadvantage of the repulsion start induction run motor?

12-6. How are hermetically sealed motors started?

12-7. What is the operating speed of most single phase refrigeration motors?

12-8. How do three phase induction motors compare with three phase synchronous motors?

12-9. What is the purpose of static condensers?

12-10. Where, in modern plants, have steam drives proved very suitable and economical?

CHAPTER 13

FOOD PRESERVATION

General.—A refrigeration man sometimes becomes so engrossed in the technical aspects of his business that he forgets refrigeration is only a means to an end. In most cases, that end is the preservation of foods. It is important that someone responsible for the operation of the refrigeration system understand what the refrigeration is for, and how to control it to get best results.

Where short time storage is required (average domestic and commercial applications) conditions are not critical, and some variation from best conditions is allowable. But for industrial storage, an understanding of food technology is necessary. Some products cannot be kept over a week, even under refrigeration. Others can be kept for months, or with proper freezing, for years. Some varieties of certain fruits and vegetables will keep in storage better than others. Sometimes the same variety grown under two different climatic conditions shows marked differences in keeping properties. There is a great variation in the temperatures and humidities at which different foods keep best. Sometimes other factors than temperature play an important part in proper storage. Wrapping with treated papers, an atmosphere with an excess of carbon dioxide, and ultra violet radiation are common aids to storage.

A book of this size cannot include such data in detail. It would fill at least a whole volume in itself. But a few guiding principles should be understood by anyone using refrigeration to aid in the storage of food products. The most important fact of all; one that is too often overlooked, is that no food is improved by refrigeration. It never comes out of storage better than it goes in, except for the one exception of the aging of meat. And here the aging is only controlled, and not produced by the refrigeration. Too often in early years the best food products have been sold fresh, and that which could not sell in competition with the highest quality was put in storage.

Such food brought from storage and offered to the public gave something of a "black eye" to all cold storage products. Yet cold storage has made fresh food products available in all communities all year around. Our present economy with millions of people grouped in cities, some of which are long distances from food growing regions would be impossible without our present cold storage system. Any good food products, properly stored, will leave the storage plant in good condition. Often they are in much better condition than so-called fresh foods that have taken a week or two to get from the farm, through commission houses to retail stores, and finally to the consumer without refrigeration.

Natural Ripening—Enzymic Action.—There are several processes going on in any growing thing which tend to cause spoilage. First is the natural ripening process. Any food picked green will gradually ripen. Anything picked ripe will become overripe. Fruits will get so soft they are easily bruised or mashed. Vegetables become hard, woody or pithy. This effect is speeded up by warm temperatures and slowed down by cold temperatures. Meats are not effected in this way.

One effect of this ripening process that is sometimes overlooked is that it generates a certain amount of heat, vital heat it is called. This varies considerably with different products. Also, since ripening is faster at warm temperatures, more heat is evolved at warmer temperatures than cold. This is usually not enough to materially increase the load on the refrigeration plant. But it does explain why the center of a closely packed stack of food in a cooler will remain at very nearly the same temperature for weeks, instead of pulling down to room temperature. The vital heat evolved by the food offsets the heat that is able to escape from the center of the closely stacked pile.

All plant and animal products have within themselves chemicals which cause their deterioration or breakdown. These chemicals are called enzymes. During life, their actions are controlled by growth and life processes. After harvesting or slaughtering, growth and life cease, but the enzymic action continues. This will turn green vegetables yellow, and give them off flavors. It is slow enough that it is not an important factor in short term storage. But in frozen foods which may be kept up to a year or sometimes more, it is of great importance.

This action can be controlled by heat which destroys the enzymes. The enzymes present in fruits, in most cases, cause no trouble in the frozen product. In meats, the enzymic action tends to break down or dissolve the meat tissue. It is a much more rapid action than with vegetables. A certain amount of this action is desirable, and is used to "tenderize" the meat by holding it long enough for this action to take place. Enzymic activity, like all chemical processes, is slowed down by a reduction in temperature.

Bacteria and Molds.—Bacteria causes "rotting". Molds cause spoilage as they form over the surface. The food must be contaminated. Bacterial spoilage takes place inside the food under the surface. Molds attack the surface, and may taint the food a short distance below the surface.

The activity or growth of both molds and bacteria can be slowed down by lowering the temperature. At temperatures sufficiently low, usually considerably below freezing, their growth is entirely stopped. The temperature at which this happens varies, both for different food products, and for different varieties of bacteria or molds. Although the growth of the mold or bacteria has stopped, they are not killed. They are still there and will immediately become active when the food is brought up to warm temperatures again.

Other Changes.—If food is allowed to dry out or dehydrate, other undesirable changes take place. Fruits and vegetables will wilt, causing them to look and taste unappetizing. Meats lose their juicy, fresh, red look on drying. Both meat and vegetable products lose weight, which penalizes the commercial seller. If he has to buy 100 pounds and it dries to 90 pounds, he has 10 pounds less to sell. This drying or shrinkage will depend on whether the food is stored in a dry or humid storage room.

Certan foods require an atmosphere that is not too humid. Dried foods of all kinds, nuts, onions and cheese are some of these. High humidities decrease keeping qualities and increase surface molds.

The vitamin content of many foods deteriorates rapidly after picking. Temperature has a very material effect on this change. Storage at cold storage temperatures will retain from 40 to 70 percent of this. Some foods such as corn and peas lose much of their sugar content if kept at ordinary temperatures. This means a loss of sweetness or flavor. Cold temperatures reduce this loss.

Cold Storage.—Since so many undesirable changes take place at ordinary temperatures, storage at reduced temperatures is desirable for any perishable food product. Experience has shown that ripening and bacterial spoilage is cut approximately in half for each 18 degree F reduction in temperature. This means that for each 18 degree reduction in temperature, the possible storage period could be doubled. Thus, the colder the temperatures used, the better the results, unless the foods involved have a low temperature tolerance. Certain foods, particularly tropical foods such as citrus fruits, bananas, tomatoes, avocados, melons and pineapple have such temperature tolerances which cause other undesirable changes if temperatures are brought too low. Table A-2 outlines generally accepted storage conditions.

Mold growths are reduced by a reduction in temperature. But they are also much less active in a dry atmosphere than in a moist one. But a dry atmosphere causes more dehydration. So a dry atmosphere is desirable to hold down molds, but undesirable because of dehydration. The compromise which must be effected depends on the type of food stored, and its exact requirements. Sometimes, where high humidities are required and molds give trouble, ultraviolet light will eliminate nearly all molds. Therefore high humidities are possible without molds by combining other food preservation methods with refrigeration.

To make cold storage most effective, food products should be chilled as soon as possible after picking, and not allowed to warm up again until ready for use. In some warm climates, this fact is beginning to be accepted for all perishable produce. It could be applied with worthwhile results to practically all perishable products for all markets in warm and even in temperate climates.

Freezing.—Many changes take place in food products when they are frozen. Some of these changes are beneficial some are not. The biggest change is the formation of ice crystals, and the solidification of all other parts of the product. These do not happen simultaneously. The ice crystals begin to form around 30 F to 28 F. The freezing points of the other parts of the food are lower, but vary. The colder the temperature, the more is frozen solidly. Some food constituents are not completely frozen at temperatures below 0 F.

This progressive freezing, first water, then other products tends to separate the moisture from the other parts of the food. Also, the slower the rate of freezing, the more the water combines to form a few large crystals of ice. At rapid freezing rates, the water forms a myriad of microscopic ice crystals. The large crystals have two undesirable effects on the food. They puncture or damage the individual cell walls, and they cause a more complete separation of moisture from the other food constituents. Then, when the product thaws, the moisture with soluble flavors run out of the punctured cells as juice. Fruits and vegetables become bruised, wilted and usually discolored. The juices run out of meat products leaving them dry and tasteless. These results only differ in degree with storage products accidently frozen, or with sharp frozen or quick frozen produce poorly or improperly frozen.

When the freezing is done very rapidly, the crystals are so small they break through comparatively few cell walls. On thawing, there is very little leakage. Also, since the ice crystals are so small, each one thaws to such a tiny bit of water that it can be easily reabsorbed by the surrounding food matter. This leaves the product in a condition similar to when it was frozen.

Freezing has various effects on enzymic action. With meats, it is practically stopped. Therefore, meats must be aged or tenderized before freezing. They will not age while frozen. With most frozen fruits, if enzymic action is present, it has no outward effect on the food properties. This effect may, therefore, be neglected. With frozen vegetables, the enzymes present will in time destroy the chlorophyll (green coloring matter). This turns the product yellow, and gives it a hay-like flavor. The enzymes producing this effect can be destroyed by heat. Vegetables are, therefore, blanched (heated) with scalding water or steam before freezing.

The lower the temperature, the slower is the evaporation rate. Therefore, the evaporation or sublimation from frozen products will be slower than from products above freezing. The freezing is only incidental as far as the evaporation is concerned, and has no direct effect. It is the reduced temperature that makes the difference. Although drying is slow, frozen goods are usually held for long term storage. A great deal of dehydration will take place over this extended period of time if some means of prevention is not used.

The method most commonly used at the present is to keep the food in a moisture proof container, either tin or a vapor proof wrapping. The latter may be a parchment paper, wax paper, or metal foil. A method commonly used on sharp frozen fish is glazing. After freezing, the fish is dipped in water. The frozen fish is cold enough to freeze a shell of ice around it. Any evaporation then takes place from the outside ice instead of from the product. Drying can also take place during the freezing process. Such drying causes a characteristic effect known as "freezer burn".

The great increase in production, popularity, and use of quick frozen foods in recent years has been well justified in the quality of the product produced. But freezing is only one link in a chain. This chain consists of the selection of proper food varieties for freezing, picking at the proper stage of ripeness, proper grading, proper processing, proper freezing within a few hours of picking time, and finally proper storage.

Although "quick frozen" has caught the public fancy, some of the above mentioned points are of more importance than the speed of freezing. But for best quality results, no link of the chain can be overlooked.

To repeat a statement made at the beginning of the chapter, food taken from storage (frozen or otherwise) will be no better than the food put in. Only if first quality food is frozen will first quality be available. But if properly done, the freezing process plus the other above mentioned quality points make it possible to market a food product which is far superior to the average fresh produce reaching our retail markets.

QUESTIONS

13–1. What is vital heat? Why is it important?

13–2. How do enzymes affect meat?

13–3. How do enzymes affect vegetables?

13–4. What is bacterial spoilage?

13–5. What is mold spoilage?

13–6. How do humidities affect foods?

13–7. Will humidities affect frozen foods?

13–8. How does the reduction in temperature affect the keeping properties of foods?

13–9. Will the process of freezing a food make it keep indefinitely?

13–10. Is quick freezing alone sufficient to give high quality food?

CHAPTER 14

OPERATING

General.—There are four principle requirements to operating: (1) to *maintain the required temperature,* (2) to *get the required results economically,* (3) to *get the required results safely,* and (4) to *maintain the plant* so that it will remain in shape to continue to give these results year after year.

Maintain Temperatures.—The operation of the refrigeration plant must be such that required temperatures are maintained. With domestic and commercial systems, after the equipment is started and controls are adjusted, this is done more or less automatically. Occasionally some attention is required by the owner to readjust temperatures slightly, to defrost coils, sometimes to start and stop units when required. The balancing of the load to the system is taken care of by controls which cycle the unit as required.

With a few large commercial systems, and most all industrial systems more or less manual operation is necessary. The proper number of compressors must be kept running to balance the load. Constant back pressure must be maintained to maintain required temperatures. As loads increase and the back pressure begins to rise, another compressor must be started to hold the pressure and the temperature constant. If back pressures go down, one or more compressors must be shut off. Where only one compressor is available, it can be cycled. If clearance pockets are available, they can be manipulated to balance the load.

Where heavy loads strike the plant suddenly, such as when milk starts over a milk cooler, a carload of warm produce is loaded in, or any similar cooling, refrigeration equipment to handle this load should be "on the line" (running and ready) when the load hits. Otherwise temperatures may get too high while the equipment is getting started. It is much harder to get high temperatures down than to prevent temperatures from rising above a point already established.

One thing that helps the operator in all load fluctuations is a condition which can be termed a self regulating characteristic of

190

refrigeration equipment. This self regulation is apparent at two points, in the evaporator and in the compressor.

The heat transfer to the evaporator is proportional to the temperature difference between the cooler temperature and the refrigerant temperature.[1] Thus, if the refrigerant is maintained at 20 F in a 30 F room, this is 10 F temperature difference. Warm produce loaded into the room would raise the air temperature. Assume it rises to 40 F. The temperature difference is now 20 F. This is twice the 10 F temperature difference, so twice as much heat would be transferred through the coils to the refrigerant. In such a case, twice as many compressors would be needed to maintain the refrigerant at 20 F. Normally, the room temperature would not be allowed to raise this much, but this serves as an illustration. If there is a 10 F temperature difference between the refrigerant and the room, each degree rise in the room temperature will increase the heat flow to the evaporator 1/10 or 10 percent. The opposite is also true. As this temperature difference becomes less, less heat will flow to the coil. If the refrigerant was at the same temperature as the room, no head could flow to the coil. Thus, the room could get no colder. Thus, the more heat on the evaporator, the more heat it absorbs. This is what is meant by the self regulating characteristics of the evaporator.

The above case assumed the evaporator pressure was held constant by using just the right amount of compression equipment to withdraw the vapor at exactly the same rate it was formed. If this pressure is allowed to vary, the compressor has some self regulating characteristics. A given amount of heat in the evaporator will vaporize a given amount of refrigerant. But the volume of the evaporated vapor depends entirely on pressure. If the absolute pressure is doubled, the volume of the vapor is cut in half. If the vapor is only half the volume, a given compressor will be able to pump twice as much by weight. It is the weight of the refrigerant pumped which determines the amount of refrigeration produced.[2] Therefore a given sized compressor can produce twice as much refrigeration if the absolute pressure of the suction vapor is doubled. With only one compressor running, an increased load increases the back pressure, and the compressor pumps a greater amount of refrigerant. Thus, more liquid can evaporate to a vapor in the evaporator. As usually stated, the higher the back pressure, the greater the refrigeration produced. Fig. 14-1 shows this in graphic form.

---

[1]See Chapter 18 for a complete analysis of this.

[2]See Chapter 20 for a complete analysis of this.

This condition will also work in reverse. With a decreased load the pressure will drop, and the volume of the vapor increase. Therefore the compressor will not remove as much refrigerant by weight as previously, and will not produce as much refrigeration. Thus,

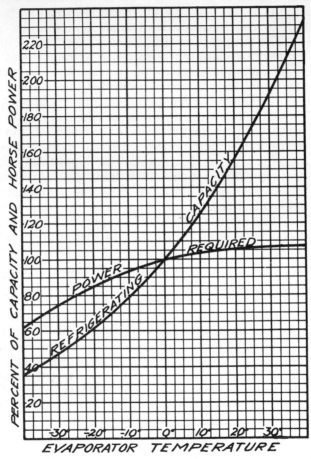

Fig. 14-1. Capacity and power for a given compressor for varying evaporator temperatures. Ammonia system—80 F condenser. 100 percent is based on 0 F evaporator.

instead of getting colder and colder, each degree the evaporator drops requires more work from the compressor, and makes it harder to do the job. Thus, a point will be reached where the extra work required balances the drop in temperature, and the temperature will go no lower.

To depend entirely in these self regulating characteristics would cause too great a temperature variation in the cold rooms. But it helps to smooth out small irregularities in the load without continual attention from the operator. And it helps correct extreme load variations when they do occur.

Economy.—It is only proper that the required conditions be maintained as economically as possible. Part of the cost of operating a plant is dependent on the original installation. But power and maintenance costs can vary considerably with operating conditions. Fig. 14-1 shows the variation in refrigeration capacity and the variation in power for a given sized compressor operating at different suction temperatures. This is figured for ammonia, but the results are similar for any refrigerant.[3]

Notice that although it takes more power to operate a compressor at a higher suction temperature, the power curve does not rise as rapidly as the capacity curve. This means more refrigeration is produced per horsepower used at higher suction temperatures. Fig. 14-2 shows this a little differently. This is the amount of horsepower required to produce the same amount of refrigeration at different suction temperatures. Notice that the higher the suction temperature, the less the power, which means the less the cost to produce it. *The higher the suction temperature can be maintained and still maintain the required temperatures in the rooms, the cheaper will be the operation.* Too often, the operator has no control of the amount of coil surface in the room. The more coil, the higher the suction temperature that can be used to hold the room. But the operator can at least be sure that all the evaporator coil is properly filled with refrigerant and active. A coil with liquid refrigerant in only ⅔ of its length is no more effective than ⅔ as much coil properly filled. The proper adjustment of the expansion valve controls this.

It might seem to be an anachronism that to open the expansion valve which allows the coil temperature and pressure to rise would increase the refrigeration done by the coil on the room. But such is the case. A review of exactly what happens shows why. An open expansion valve allows more refrigerant into the coil, making more of the coil surface effective in evaporating the liquid. This greater amount of evaporated vapor raises the back pressure which allows the compressor to pump more vapor. The expansion valve should be kept as wide open as can be done without running liquid

---

[3]These are theoretical figures neglecting variations in compressor efficiencies. Such variations may cause even larger changes than those shown on the curve. See Chapter 21 for a complete analysis of this.

back the suction line. All these things mentioned have more effect on lowering the room temperature than the slight lowering of the coil temperature caused by pinching down the expansion valve could possibly make.

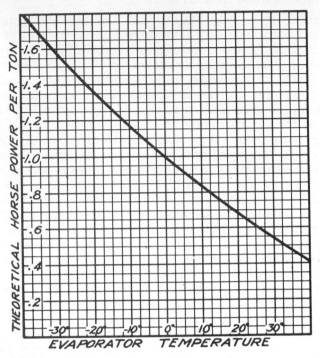

Fig. 14-2. Effect of varying evaporator temperature on the theoretical horsepower per ton. Figured for ammonia with 80 F condenser.

Fig. 14-3 shows the effect of varying condensing temperatures on the capacity and power. As the condensing temperature and head pressure raises, the capacity is slightly decreased but the power is rapidly increased. Thus, *the lower the head pressure, the cheaper refrigeration can be produced.* Under extreme conditions the condensing pressure could be brought so low that it is not sufficient to force the required liquid around the system and through the expansion valves. But such conditions are unusual in a plant with properly balanced equipment. It might happen in a poorly engineered plant, or under winter conditions with excessively cold condensing water. In general, the lower the condensing temperature, the cheaper the operation.

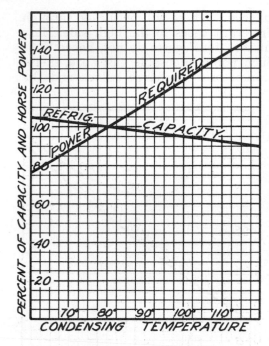

Fig. 14-3. Effect of varying condensing temperature on capacity and power requirements of a given compressor. Figured for ammonia with 0 F evaporator, 100 percent is based on 80 F condenser.

There are cases where condensing water is purchased, or is obtained at the expense of large pumping costs. Beyond a certain point, the cost of excess water is more than the savings in power. Fig. 14-4 shows how this can be worked out for an individual problem. The cost of the compressor operating at different condensing temperatures is plotted. The amount of condensing water to produce these condensing temperatures with existing equipment is then found by test or calculations,[4] and its cost plotted.

A third curve which is the sum of these two curves is then plotted. The compressor power cost decreases with lower head pressure, but the cost of water is increased. The curve showing the sum of these two costs has a low spot which gives the proper operating condition for cheapest operation. Notice that this low point is rather shallow, so anywhere from 82 F to 95 F condensing in this case could be taken as the proper operating condition. The steep rise below the 80 F condensing temperature is caused by the fact that for any given sized condenser with a given condensing water temperature there is a point where additional water will pick up very little additional heat. Such a curve would have to be worked out for each individual case, using the individual costs involved.

One of the commonest causes of too high a condensing pressure is non-condensable gas. Air may get into the system, either through leaks in a suction side operating at a vacuum, or allowed to enter while part of the system was open for repairs. Or the breakdown of oil or refrigerant by compression heat, or acids from oil, or mois-

[4] See Chapter 18.

ture reactions may cause "foul gases." These will be sucked through the compressor with the refrigerant gases to the high side. Here the refrigerant condenses, but the "foul" gases do not, hence their name of non-condensables. Such non-condensable gases are, therefore, trapped between the compressor discharge valves and the liquid in the receiver.

In Chapter 1 it was pointed out that each gas acts independently of the other, but creates a pressure equal to the sum of their individual pressures. Thus, if a system which normally condensed at 150 psig (164.7 psia) had air introduced which alone would amount to atmospheric pressure (14.7 psi), the total pressure would be 179.4 psia or 164.7 psig. The compressor would then have to pump this mixture up to 164.7 psig to get the conditions that normally took place at 150 psig. The ammonia vapor will not condense until it reaches a vapor pressure of 150 psig itself, regardless of what other gases at what other pressures are present. Such excess pressures due to non-condensables often get much higher than the above example.

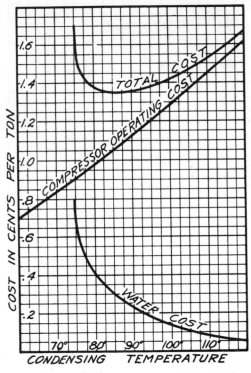

Fig. 14-4. Operating costs for varying amounts of condensing water. Figured at ¾ cents per kilowatt and for 65 F water at 20 cents per 1000 cubic feet.

Two methods may be used to remove this air. The most economical is with an automatic purger, Fig 8-20. The time-honored method used before purgers were developed, and still used with fluorocarbon and many ammonia plants, is to purge or let out this mixture of air and refrigerant by hand. To do this most effectively, the machine should be run long enough to know that all the air or non-condensable gas is pumped to the high side. Then the compressor is stopped. To continue to run it keeps adding fresh refrigerant to the mixed gases. Water is allowed to run over the condenser until it is as cool as it will get. This condenses all the refrigerant possible. Then a valve or joint at the highest point of the system is opened slightly, cracked as it is called. This allows the mixture of refrigerant and non-condensable gas to escape. Fresh refrigerant re-evaporated in the receiver pushes this impure mixture toward the opening, Fig 14-5. The purging should be slow enough that the refrigerant from the receiver does not churn up the impure mixture it pushes out.

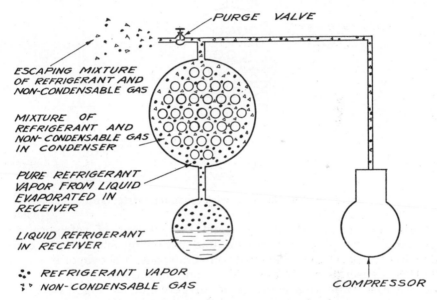

Fig. 14-5. What happens when purging.

At the beginning of the purging, the high pressure gage will show a steadily decreasing pressure. This decrease becomes continually slower as the impure mixture escapes and the proportion of pure refrigerant increases. As soon as the pressure stops dropping, the valve should be closed. Do not purge so rapidly that the evaporation of the liquid in the receiver cools it sufficient to bring the pressure of the pure refrigerant down. To do so and to wait for the pressure to stop dropping would eventually bring the pressure down to atmospheric. If a lot of air or non-condensable gas is in the system, it may have to be purged several times to get rid of all of it. The compressor should be operated between each purging long enough to warm the condenser to a normal condensing temperature, then stopped and the water allowed to cool it off.

Another thing which may cause too high a head pressure is too large a refrigerant charge, Fig. 14-6. If the liquid covers part of the condensing surface, this does not leave sufficient surface exposed to the vapor to extract the heat from it. It acts exactly like too small a condenser for the compressor. The only effective cure for this is to remove some of the refrigerant from the system.

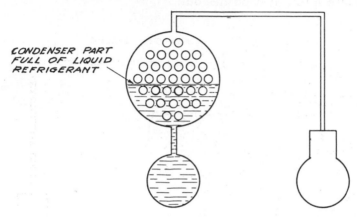

CONDENSER PART
FULL OF LIQUID
REFRIGERANT

Fig. 14-6. What happens with too much refrigerant.

Fig. 14-7 combines in one chart the amount of refrigeration produced by a given compressor under varying suction and condensing temperatures. Standard ton conditions, 5 F evaporator and 86 F condenser, are taken as 100 percent capacity, and the increase or decrease from this point given in percentages. Fig. 14-8 gives the variation in horsepower of a given sized compressor operating under different conditions. Again, 100 percent is taken at standard ton conditions, and variations figured from there.

Safety.—All the above required conditions must be maintained safely. This means it must be done in such a manner that it is not a hazard to the men working in the plant, to the equipment, to the plant, or to any surrounding inhabitants. The first thing necessary is to be sure of all valves. Always check to be sure of all results of opening a closed valve or closing an open valve. Particularly, never close a discharge valve on an operating compressor, or start a compressor with this valve closed, unless a bypass is open. With water cooled jobs, always see that water is circulating in the condenser before starting.

Small machines may be easily started with all valves open. With intermediate sized machines (5 to 25 horsepower) if the motor seems to labor on starting, closing the suction service valve makes

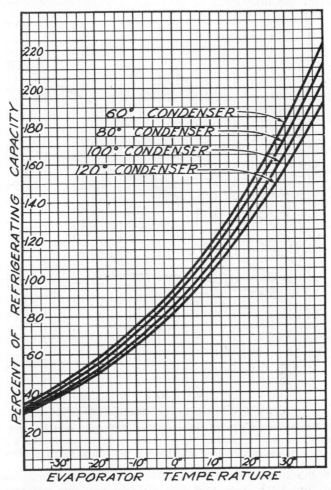

Fig. 14-7. Refrigerating capacities at different suction and discharge temperatures. Ammonia system. 100 percent is based on standard ton conditions.

starting easier. This is often necessary when starting a system for the first time with a warm evaporator. If the compressor cannot pump any vapor it will start much easier. When it gets up to speed, the suction service valve can be cracked, then gradually opened.

Be careful that the back pressure does not drop fast enough to start oil slugging. If such begins to happen, open the suction valve faster to let pressure enough into the compressor to increase the pressure on the oil.

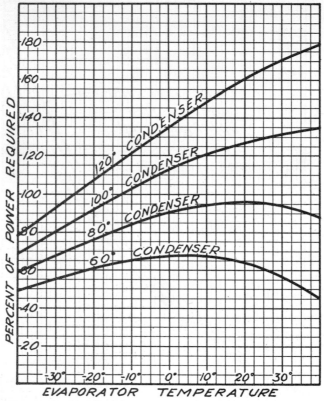

Fig. 14-8. Variation in power required for different suction and discharge temperatures. Ammonia system. 100 percent is based on standard ton conditions (approximately one horsepower per ton of refrigeration).

Large machines are started with the bypass open. Care must be taken that both high and low side valves are not open at the same time. This would allow all the high pressure gas in the system to blow directly to the low side. The machine is usually started with the discharge bypass valve and the suction valve open, and the suction bypass and the discharge valve closed, Figs. 6-26 or 6-27. When up to speed, the discharge bypass valve is closed. Just as this begins to seat, the discharge valve must begin to open. Otherwise, the compressor would be pumping against a closed valve.

As previously mentioned in Chapter 6, the clearance on a compressor head is so small that it will not safely handle any liquid. Therefore liquid refrigerant or excess oil must not be allowed to enter the suction. Proper manipulation or adjustment of the expansion valve is the first line of defense against liquid refrigerant returning. Surges or "boil overs" at sudden loads are best caught by liquid traps in the suction line. If these are not provided, the only safe procedure is to keep expansion valves pinched down.

As previously described, this is not efficient operation. But if the plant is so designed that it will "slop over," efficiency must be sacrificed to safety. In an emergency, to stop slugging already started, the only out for the operator is to throttle (partially close)the suction service valve. Unless absolutely essential, this valve should not be completely closed. To do so allows the suction line to fill completely with liquid. Then unless another compressor is available to pump it out, it is particularly difficult to get rid of, because to open the valve later feeds raw liquid directly to the compressor.

Two very important indications can tell the operator the condition of the returning vapor, whether it is wet, saturated, or superheated. The first is the frost line. On small low pressure machines, the suction line usually is not insulated. It will not frost out of the cabinet except on freezer jobs unless the vapor is wet. On larger machines, whether low pressure or ammonia, particularly with insulated suction lines, usually sufficient vapor at a temperature below freezing is present to cause frost. This frost should end at the compressor, and should not spread over a large part of the compressor castings. The latter condition indicates liquid with the suction vapor.

A more exacting check of the condition of the compressor suction is the compressor discharge temperature. This is varied by three separate factors. First, different refrigerants will have different discharge temperatures for the same operating conditions. Table 3-1 lists the discharge temperatures of the common refrigerants at standard ton conditions. Note that ammonia has the highest and Refrigerant 12 the lowest. Secondly, the discharge temperature varies for the same refrigerant operating at different pressures. The more the vapor entering the compressor has to be compressed, the more work must be done on it, and the more heat is added to it.

Fig. 14-9 is worked out for ammonia at different evaporator temperatures, but at a constant 80 F condensing temperature. It is figured for dry saturated vapor entering the compressor. That is, there is no unevaporated liquid present, but the evaporated vapor has picked up no superheat. The third factor: the wet, saturated, or superheated condition of the suction vapor varies the above conditions. Fig. 14-10 is figured for ammonia at a constant 0 F evapo-

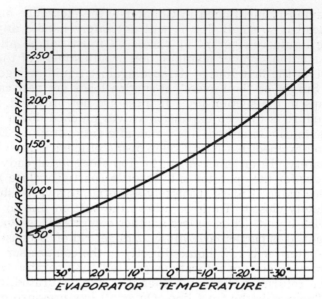

Fig. 14-9. Effect of varying evaporator temperature on discharge superheat temperature. Figured for dry saturated suction and 80 F condenser.

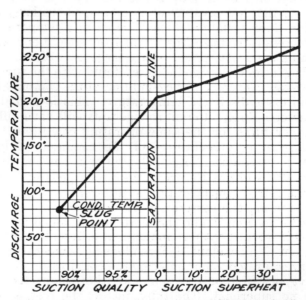

Fig. 14-10. Discharge temperatures for various superheats in the suction vapor. Figured for ammonia at 15.7 psig suction and 80 F condenser.

rator and a constant 80 F condensing temperature, but for different suction vapor conditions. The saturation point shows that the temperature of the discharge gas is 205 F when the suction vapor is dry saturated. This could also be taken from Fig. 14-9.

If the discharge temperature is any less than this, unevaporated liquid is entering the compressor. This liquid evaporates as the vapor carrying it is heated by compression. The evaporation of this cools the vapor so it will be at a lower temperature. If enough liquid is present, its evaporation brings the temperature of the discharge

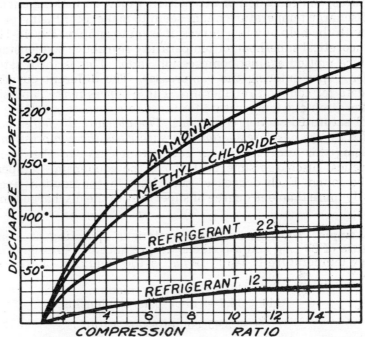

Fig. 14-11. Discharge temperature use at different compression ratios for various refrigerants.

gas down to 80 F. In this case, an 89 percent quality vapor, which means 89 percent vapor and 11 percent liquid would do this. If more than 11 percent liquid is present, the additional would be unevaporated, and would slug. From the operator's point of view, whether he knows the percent of liquid or not is unimportant. But when the discharge temperature drops, and begins to approach the condensing temperature, he knows the danger point is approaching.

The other side of the saturation point, Fig. 14-10, is a measure of the superheat in the suction line. The warmer the vapor entering the evaporator at a given suction pressure, the hotter will be the discharge temperature. For every 10 F the discharge temperature is above 206 F, the suction vapor has nearly 10 F of superheat. Any plant will usually have a small amount of superheat in the suction vapor. But this superheat should be kept to a minimum. Its rise increases the unit volume of the suction vapor, which decreases the capacity of the compressor and the refrigeration plant. Also, the added superheat, when added to the discharge vapor, increases temperatures to the point where lubrication can begin to give trouble.

The three above mentioned factors, refrigerant, operating temperatures, and condition of the suction vapor, all making changes in the discharge temperature might seem to make a confusing problem. But with the help of a few curves, it is quite simple. Fig. 14-11 gives the theoretical superheat, or temperature rise above condensing temperature plotted against compression ratio. This is for a saturated suction vapor entering the compressor. The different curves give this data for common refrigerants. These curves make it possible to find the discharge temperature for these refrigerants operating at different saturated suction conditions. *The absolute discharge pressure divided by the absolute suction pressure gives the compression ratio.* By using this with the proper refrigerant curve of Fig. 14-11, the theoretical discharge superheat above the condensing temperature can be found. Each degree of superheat in the suction line adds slightly more than one degree of superheat to the discharge temperature.[5]

Example 14-1.—An ammonia system is operating at a suction pressure of 30 psig and a condensing pressure of 140 psig. The discharge temperature is 143 F. What is the condition of the suction vapor?

$$30 + 14.7 = 44.7 \text{ psia suction.}$$
$$140 + 14.7 = 154.7 \text{ psia condensing.}$$
$$\frac{154.7}{44.7} = 3.45 \text{ compression ratio}$$

From the 3.45 compression ratio on the ammonia curve, it is found that the discharge temperature would be 90 deg. above the condensing temperature if the suction vapor was saturated. From the 140 psig pressure the condensing temperature is 81 F. Therefore the theoretical discharge temperature would be

$$90 + 81 = 171 \text{ F.}$$

Since a discharge temperature of 143 F was given, the suction vapor is slightly wet. This small amount of liquid returning is not enough to cause a hazard if the conditions remain constant. But if the dis-

---

[5]There are some errors in finding exact discharge temperatures by this method. But these errors are small enough that they make no appreciable difference in the results obtained.

charge temperature is gradually dropping, it is a sign that there are worse things to come.

Example 14-2.—If the discharge temperature of the machine working at the pressures of Example 14-1 rose to 205 F, what is the condition of the suction vapor?

In this case the discharge temperature is
$$205 - 171 = 34 \text{ F above the theoretical temperature.}$$
Therefore the suction vapor must have nearly 34 F of superheat. This is higher than it should be, and indicates a starved expansion valve, uninsulated suction lines or a faulty compressor.

Example 14-3.—If a Refrigerant-12 system was operating at the same suction and condensing temperatures as Example 14-1, and had a discharge temperature of 112 F, what is the condition of the suction vapor?

The 30 psig suction pressure of ammonia gave a 17 F evaporator temperature. The 140 psig condenser gave 81 F. A Freon-12 system would have to work at 19 psig and 85 psig for these temperatures.

$$19 + 14.7 = 33.7 \text{ psia}$$
$$85 + 14.7 = 99.7 \text{ psia}$$
$$\frac{99.7}{33.7} = 2.96 \text{ compression ratio.}$$

This compression ratio and the Refrigerant-12 curve shows a theoretical discharge superheat of 11 degrees. The theoretical discharge temperature is then:
$$81 + 11 = 92 \text{ F}$$
The discharge temperature given is 112 F.
$$112 - 92 = 20 \text{ degrees}$$
Therefore the suction gas must have about 20 degrees of superheat. This is about normal for a Refrigerant-12 system if the suction lines have a least some insulation on them.

A properly designed and operated system will not slug oil. But some old low pressure compressors may slug when starting, due to the reduction of crankcase pressure. If this is a problem, lower crankcase oil levels will help. If this will not remember the situation, stop the compressor as soon as it starts to slug. Give the oil a few minutes to subside, then restart. It may slug again but not so quickly or so violently. Stop for a few minutes more, then restart. Each start after a short rest period will remove more refrigerant from the oil, and soon make normal operation possible. Compressors that are particularly bad about slugging oil on automatic starting cycles have been helped by keeping them warm. Manufacturers have inserted heaters in the crankcase to keep the oil warm. A small electric lamp burning directly under the crankcase has been known to help. The warm oil will not absorb as much refrigerant.

Part of the operator's duty with respect to plant safety is to keep an eye on the lubrication system. Low oil, plugged oil lines, broken oil lines, etc. all have happened. If caught in time, the compressor can be stopped and the condition remedied. But to allow a compressor to operate for long without oil will damage it, sometimes beyond repair.

Another duty of the operator is to see that coils are defrosted. Sometimes this must be done in cooperation with the plant manager to clear rooms or otherwise prevent damage to stored produce. Economy dictates that coils should be defrosted before the frost forms too great an insulation on the coils. But another reason is that if allowed to go indefinitely, the frost can build up to where its weight may pull down the coils. A simple method of defrosting is to allow the frost to melt loose from the coils by hot gas or other methods. Then if the frost is stuck with a mallet or similar tool, it will crack and fall off. But the striking cannot be done too roughly or with too heavy a tool. Welded joints and corroded pipe have been known to break.

One more very important safety precaution. Never apply heat to a coil with refrigerant in it when it is closed off so the refrigerant cannot escape. Some disastrous accidents have happened by closing both the inlet and outlet of coils like milk coolers, then turning a steam hose on them to sterilize them.

Automatic Refrigeration—The trend has been toward more and larger automatic plants. Automatic controls and valves were first applied to domestic and small commercial systems. As the reliability of automatic devices was proved on this equipment, they were applied to ever larger systems. Systems of over 100 tons capacity, both with fluorocarbon refrigerant and with ammonia are successfully operating automatically today.

This does not mean such large systems will run automatically with no more attention than is given domestic refrigerators. They must be checked regularly to forestall any condition that might cause trouble. If trouble does develop, automatic controls shut down the compressor and indicate trouble on a pilot light. Often, when this happens, a trouble signal is sent to a central office, and a maintenance man is dispatched to the faulty installation to make necessary repairs.

The operators or maintenance men who are hired to maintain such plants must be better qualified men than the operators of days gone by. The old time operator maintained the mechanical equipment to the best of his ability. When trouble did occur, knocking or odors usually would indicate the trouble, and often indicate the source of the trouble. Today, with automatic and semi-automatic operation, it is of utmost importance to find conditions that might cause trouble, and eliminate them before the trouble develops. If a plant is down, the operator must be able to trace and check the automatic equipment to find why it is down; this without too much lost time.

This calls for a better knowledge of the principles of refrigeration operation, and particularly of the automatic controls and valves. These automatic devices both keep the system balanced to its load, and shut it down in case of trouble.

General Maintenance.—A refrigeration plant must be properly maintained so it can continue to produce the required conditions economically and safely over a period of years.

Hermetically sealed domestic units need nothing more than to be kept clean, to defrost them, and if the condenser has a fan, to keep the dirt and lint out of the condenser. Small commercial machines with open type compressors should, in addition to the above, have the motor oiled and belt checked once a year.

Larger automatic systems should have periodic checks. At least every six months the following should be checked.

1. Condition of the compressor valves.
2. Crankcase oil level.
3. If oil level is low, is evaporator full of oil?
4. All expansion valve settings.
5. Clean the condenser.
6. Check the flow of condenser air or water.
7. If water cooled, check condition of water drain.
8. Thoroughly check the entire system for leaks.
9. Clean the motor.
10. If there are motor brushes, check their length.
12. Check that motor lead insulation is not cracked or oil soaked.
13. Check motor bearing oil.
14. Clean control contacts.
15. Check control settings.
16. Check that insulation on control wires is not cracked or oil soaked.
17. Check motor and belt alignment.
18. Check belt tension.
19. Check for frayed, worn or cracked belts.
20. If there are any fans, check air circulation, fan oil, fan leads.
21. If there are any pumps, check water flow, lubrication, motor leads, packing glands.

Beside the above thorough six months check, a quicker check should be made monthly. This need not cover all the above items, but it should include a check of all points of lubrication and a thorough leak check. On a system of any size, if one leak is caught before it becomes bad, it will save more than the cost of several years of monthly checking. This monthly check should include a check of all cabinet or fixture temperatures. Only when something is not right with these, are more checks than this usually made.

Automatic equipment, if given such maintenance, should not need a complete overhauling for many years. Systems have run for ten or 15 years with nothing more than replaced valve plates and shaft seals where proper care is taken of them, and they are properly checked so that any trouble that develops can be "nipped in the bud."

In large plants, these checks may be made by qualified operators. Small plants or commercial systems where there is not enough work to justify a permanent, adequately trained employee may use a contract service. Such service is supplied by many reputable refrigeration service organizations. For a monthly fee the service organization contracts to check the system periodically and make necessary minor repairs and adjustments. The owner is notified of the need of any major repairs. Or service contracts are available which include any and all work necessary at no additional cost to the owner; for a larger fee of course. Such contracts can give any owner of refrigeration equipment the benefit of proper inspection and maintenance by trained personnel.

Large industrial machines which are operated 24 hours a day for months at a time are usually torn down and all wearing parts gaged or accurately measured once each year. A record of the wear on these parts is kept so that it will be possible to estimate whether they will go through another season when they do begin to show wear. In this way, these machines can be depended upon to go through a busy season with 24 hour operation without fear of a breakdown.

Beside the equipment itself, the condition of the refrigerated space must be watched and kept in good repair. Insulation of both rooms and lines must be kept in good condition. Any damaged places should be properly patched before frost can get under the insulation and cause serious damage. In the occasional cases where sawdust or shavings are used for insulation, it must be kept dry. Doors must fit properly, and any wear in the hinges or latches must be corrected. Door gaskets must be kept in good condition or replaced.

QUESTIONS

14-1. Why is an operating engineer used on most industrial refrigeration jobs, but not on commercial jobs?

14-2. Why should back pressures be maintained as high as possible?

14-3. Does closing down on the expansion valve with the same compressor capacity raise or lower the back pressure?

14-4. Does closing down on the expansion valve with the same compressor capacity raise or lower the room temperature?

14-5. Will the cost of condensing water have any effect on the economics of operation?

14-6. What keeps the temperature from continually getting colder and colder when the room load diminishes, but the compressor capacity is not reduced?

14-7. Why should condensing temperatures be kept as low as possible?

14-8. Why should non-condensable gas be eliminated?

14-9. How can non-condensable gas be eliminated?

14-10. What would happen if the discharge service valve of an operating compressor was closed?

14-11. What would happen if a water cooled job was started up with no water flowing through the condenser?

14-12. How can bypasses be used to aid in starting?

14-13. Why should liquid slugging be guarded against?

14-14. An ammonia plant is operating at 0 psig suction and 155 psig discharge pressure. The discharge temperature is 290 F. What is the condition of the suction vapor?

14-15. If the discharge temperature of question 14 dropped to 140 F, what is the condition of the suction vapor?

14-16. If a Refrigerant-12 plant is working at a 30 F suction temperature and a 90 psig discharge pressure, and the discharge temperature is 84 F, what is the condition of the suction vapor?

14-17. If the discharge temperature of question 16 rose to 140 F, what would it indicate?

14-18. Briefly describe a desirable commercial maintenance service.

14-19. When is minor maintenance done on industrial machines?

14-20. When are industrial machines usually completely overhauled?

CHAPTER 15

SERVICING

General.—Most industrial refrigeration plants are kept in proper repair by the operating crew or maintenance men kept on duty in the plant. Domestic and commercial equipment will work automatically if nothing is wrong. But when there is faulty operation, a refrigeration service man must be called in to find and correct the difficulty. There are two parts to the service man's problem: first, to find the trouble, second, to correct it. To find the troub'e requires a complete knowledge of the exact requirements of each part of the refrigeration plant. Then it is possible to search out and find the missing requirement. Once the trouble is found, its correction should be evident to one who knows the equipment. He must decide whether the faulty part needs adjusting, repairing, or replacing. Service manua's printed by the company who made the equipment are invaluable in listing adjustments, replacement parts, assembly procedures, etc.

Variations From Refrigeration Requirements.—Fig. 2-13 gave pressure and temperature conditions for an entire ammonia refrigeration system. The service man must know how such conditions vary for different refrigerants, and for different operating conditions. Then he must trace out the system to find where conditions are not as they should be.

Table 15-1 is given to show how conditions vary for different faults. First, for reference, the approximate normal operating conditions are given. Of course there will be some variations in these conditions for light or heavy loads and any other operating variables. Where variations are given, they are in cases where they vary sufficiently to make noticeably greater changes than normal operating variables. Many of the conditions given will give some refrigeration, but with more or less excessive operating costs. But these are not readily apparent to the service man who only sees it for a short time, so are not listed.

If controls are out of adjustment, back pressures and temperatures are the only thing greatly effected. If everything including the cycling time appears normal except the required temperatures, control adjustments should be checked first.

An expansion valve open too wide will flood liquid refrigerant back the suction line to the compressor. This actively refrigerates the suction line and the crankcase. As explained in Chapter 14 this gives a low discharge temperature. If enough refrigerant floods back, the evaporation in the suction line and crankcase uses up the compressor capacity, and the back pressure rises. This brings the evaporator temperature up. If this happens, the running time will increase. The unit may even run continuously.

A starved expansion valve does not let enough refrigerant through to actively refrigerate the entire evaporator. Therefore the latter part of the evaporator will be warmer than it should. This causes a higher than normal suction line temperature and discharge temperature. Sometimes enough refrigerant is not evaporated to supply the full compressor capacity, and the back pressure and temperature drop. As explained in Chapter 14, this does not mean better refrigeration. A trouble that starved evaporators are apt to give which is not apparent from without, is oil trapping in the evaporator. Enough refrigerant is not flushed through the coil to carry the oil on through to the suction line. This allows the oil that should be returned to the compressor crankcase to collect in the evaporator. An evaporator too warm for its suction pressure will indicate this.

A plug or stoppage in the system is usually found in the liquid line or on the low side of the system. Strainers or driers may fill and plug up. Expansion valves may stick closed, or stop up with dirt. If water is present in a fluorocarbon refrigerant, it will freeze at the expansion valve and plug it. This stops refrigeration which usually allows the ice to melt. Intermittent refrigeration; proper freezing, then defrosting is the usual result. Occasionally, the ice only partially plugs the expansion valve, which allows enough refrigerant to pass to prevent it from melting. Such will not give the intermittent operation characteristic of an iced expansion valve.

With a plugged system, the back pressure will be low. If there is a temperature control, the system will run continuously and produce a high vacuum. If there is a pressure control, the system will pull down to the cutout point and cut off. If the stoppage is complete, the unit will remain off. More often there is enough leakage through the stoppage to allow the pressure to build up, and the machine short cycles. Naturally the evaporator will be warm. Since

TABLE 15-1—FAULTS AND CONDITIONS INDICATING THEM

| | PRESSURES | | TEMPERATURES | |
	Low	High	Evaporator	Suction Line
Normal Conditions	From Evaporator Temperature	From Condensing Temp.	As Required	Cool or Cold
CONTROL SETTING				
Too High	High	Normal	High	Normal
Too Low	Low	Normal	Low	Normal
EXPANSION VALVE SETTING				
Open Too Wide	Normal or High	Normal or High	Normal	Low
Closed Too Much	Normal or Low	Normal or Low	Normal Latter part high	High
Plugged Up System	Low	Low	High	High
Air In System	Normal	High	Normal	Normal
Dirty Condenser	Normal	High	Normal	Normal
Cabinet Overloaded	High	High	High	Normal or High
Faulty Compressor Valves	High	Low	High	Normal or High
TOO MUCH REFRIGERANT				
High Side Float or Capillary Tube	Normal or High	Normal or High	Normal or High	Low, Frosted
Other Systems	Normal	High	Normal	Normal
NOT ENOUGH REFRIGERANT				
High Side Float or Capillary Tube	Normal or Low	Normal or Low	Top high, Bottom normal	Normal or High
Low Side Float	Normal	Normal	Normal or High	High
Dry Expansion Evaporator	Normal	Normal or Low	Normal or High	High

TABLE 15-1—FAULTS AND CONDITIONS INDICATING THEM—Continued

TEMPERATURES				CYCLE TIME	
Crankcase	Discharge Line	Condenser	Receiver	Temperature Control	Pressure Control
Room Temp. or Warm	Hot	20F to 30F Above Cool. Medium	Condensing Temperature or Warmer	Run ⅔ Time	Run ⅔ Time
Normal	Normal	Normal	Normal	Normal	Normal
Normal	Normal	Normal	Normal	Normal	Normal
Low	Low	Normal	Normal	Normal or excessive running	Normal or excessive running
Normal	High	Normal or Low	Normal	Normal	Normal
Normal	Low	Low	Normal or Low	Runs continuously	Short cycle or remains off
Normal	Normal or High	Normal	Normal	Normal	Normal
Normal	High	High	Normal or High	Normal	Normal
Normal or High	High	High	Normal or High	Runs excessively	Runs excessively
Normal or High	Normal or Low	Normal or Low	Normal	Runs excessively	Runs excessively or short cycle
Low	Low	Normal	Normal	Normal or runs excessively	Normal or runs excessively
Normal	High	High	Normal or Low	Normal or runs excessively	Normal or runs excessively
Normal	Normal	Normal or Low	Normal	Normal	Normal
Normal	Normal or High	Normal	Normal or High	Normal or runs excessively	Short cycles
Normal	Normal or High	Normal or Low	Normal or High	Normal or runs excessively	Normal or short cycles

no refrigerant is being pumped, even when the unit is running, the head pressure, head temperature, and discharge temperature are low. The receiver temperature may be low because the receiver is filled with liquid pumped from the evaporator. The receiver usually feels a little cooler to the hand where liquid is present.

If air is in the system it raises the head pressure, sometimes excessively. This usually increases the discharge temperature because the compressor must work harder against the greater pressure. If the head pressure becomes excessive, high pressure cutouts or motor overloads may stop the unit. The biggest change from normal will be in power consumption. But the refrigeration service man cannot check this without a record of normal power consumption for comparison.

A dirty condenser will show high head pressure, high condensing temperature, and a high discharge temperature. The condensed liquid will usually be so warm the receiver is quite warm. This also increases power costs.

An overloaded cabinet will show high evaporator temperature and pressure, high condensing temperature and pressure, and a high discharge temperature. The unit runs continuously or nearly so. The entire compressor including the crankcase overheats.

Faulty compressor valves cause high back pressure because they do not remove vapor from the evaporator rapidly enough. Because less vapor is pumped, head pressures and temperatures are usually low. High back pressure and low head pressure give low discharge temperatures. If there is a temperature control on the system, the system runs continuously or nearly so. A pressure control may run continuously or may short cycle. The latter happens when the back pressure gets low enough to shut the control off, then the head pressure leaks back through the faulty valves to raise the low pressure and start the machine again. Where the unit runs continuously, the crankcase often overheats. A broken discharge valve will cause the cylinder and compressor head to overheat.

Too much refrigerant, that is, an overcharge reacts differently with different refrigerant controls. If there is a high side float valve or capillary tube, most of the refrigerant charge is stored in the evaporator. Therefore, too much refrigerant will fill the evaporator to overflowing, and flood back the suction line. This gives the same effects as an expansion valve that is open too wide. The suction line temperature, crankcase temperature, and discharge temperatures are low, with perhaps, higher than normal evaporator temperatures.

If there is too much refrigerant with a low side float valve, automatic expansion valve or thermostatic expansion valve, the valves do not let any more liquid through to the evaporator than is required. So

any excess backs up into the receiver. If there is so much refrigerant that the receiver is filled, and liquid backs into the condenser
as shown in Fig. 14-6, insufficient condenser surface is exposed to
the vapor to give adequate condensation. This results in high head
pressure and temperature.

Insufficient refrigerant in a high side float valve or capillary
tube system starves the evaporator, with about the same results as
starving it with an expansion valve closed too much. The lower
part of the flooded evaporator will be down to temperature, but
the top will be warm. The suction line temperature and the discharge temperature will be high.

With a low side float valve, if there is insufficient refrigerant,
it will not raise the float enough to close the needle. This allows
high pressure gas to leak to the evaporator. High suction line and
high discharge temperatures result. Running time will be greater
with a temperature control, although not always enough to be readily apparent. If there is a back pressure control, the high pressure
gas leaking to the low side causes short cycling. Also, when the refrigerant is low, a distinct hiss is heard at the valve needle as gas
instead of liquid rushes through.

Too little refrigerant with an automatic expansion valve or thermostatic expansion valve is not always readily apparent, unless the
shortage is bad. It acts similar to a starved expansion valve, with
high suction line temperatures and high discharge temperatures. But
with a shortage, the expansion valve will hiss just as mentioned
with the low side float valve.

Table 15-1 is given to help familiarize the reader with the different results of common faulty operating conditions. It does not
list all possible faults, or all possible checks. To be able to find trouble
without loss of time, a systematic method of checking the entire
system should be followed. Table 15-2 gives a suggested procedure.
Checks do not have to be made in this exact order, but it is important to establish a routine system of checks which goes down the
complete list of possible faults and eliminates them one by one.
Some checks can be made at a glance. Others take a little more time.

First, a glance will tell whether the compressor runs or not. If
it does not, a check should be made as to whether the compressor
is stalled, or whether the motor does not run. If the motor does not
run, the electric power supply should be checked. Check that
switches are not off. Then check fuses. Fuses fail more often than
anything else in the electric system. If these are O.K. the control
shou'd be checked. Of course, if the control setting is higher than
the box temperature, whether due to improper control setting or too

TABLE 15-2—OPERATING TROUBLES AND THEIR CAUSES

Trouble	Preliminary Check	Caused by
Compressor does not run.	Motor runs if belts removed.	Stalled compressor

	Motor will not run.	Switch off
		Fuse burned out
		Control off due to:
		    Cabinet cold enough
		    Improper control setting
		    Faulty control
		Faulty or broken wiring
		Faulty motor

	Motor runs, compressor does not	Broken or slipping belts Sheared key on flywheel Loose flywheel
Compressor runs but faulty refrigeration	Low suction pressure and low discharge pressure	Low side valves closed Refrigerant lines plugged up Strainers plugged up Expansion valve plugged with dirt, ice or wax Expansion valve stuck closed High side float valve air bound
	High suction pressure and low discharge pressure	Faulty compressor valves No refrigerant
	Normal or high suction pressure and high discharge pressure.	Overloaded system Low refrigerant Too little water or air over condenser Too warm water or air over condenser Dirty condenser Dirty or plugged discharge line Valves in discharge line closed Air in the system Too much refrigerant
	Compressor short cycles	Leaky compressor valves. Low refrigerant, particularly with low side float valve Expansion valve starving coil Partially plugged expansion valve Improper multiplexing High pressure cutout cycling
	Erratic refrigeration; too cold, then too warm	Sticky control Oil logged float valve or evaporator
	Frost backs	Improperly set expansion valve Thermostatic expansion valve bulb loose Thermostatic expansion valve bulb in warm draft or other heat source Expansion valve stuck open Dirt in valve seat

TABLE 15-2—OPERATING TROUBLES AND THEIR CAUSES—Continued

Trouble	Preliminary Check	Caused by
	Leaks	All joints
		All gaskets
		Service valves, gage port plugs
		Expansion valve bellows or diaphragms
		Control bellows or diaphrgams
		Oil plugs
		Compressor cap screws
Noises	In compressor	Worn parts
		Squeaking shaft seal
		Slugging oil or refrigerant
		Loose flywheel
	Elsewhere	Poor foundation
		Chattering water valve
		Loose parts
		Rattling refrigerant lines
		Squeaking belts
		Shipping bolts

FOOD STORAGE TROUBLES

Trouble	Preliminary Check	Caused by
Food freezes	Cabinet too cold	Improper control setting
		Faulty control; stuck closed
		Unbalanced multiplex system
		Leaky expansion valve
		Low refrigerant charge
		Oil logged evaporator
Food does not keep satisfactorily	Cabinet too warm	Any of the points given under faulty refrigeration
		Improper control setting
		Faulty control; bellows lost charge
		Poor air circulation in cabinet
		Overloaded cabinet; too much warm food or too high surrounding temperatures
		Faulty insulation
		Faulty door hardware
		Coils need defrosting
Foods dry out	Too low humidity	Poor air circulation
		Too small cooling coil
		Starved cooling coil
		If blower coil, not operating on defrost cycle
Foods slime	Too high humidity	Excessively large cooling coil
		Light cabinet loads
		Excessive warm damp food
Odors, tastes		Too high temperature
		Too high humidity
		Improper location of foods
		Dirty cabinets
		Wrong motor oil in blower motor
		Improper insulation
		Improperly sealed cabinet getting musty
		Clogged drain pipes

cold a box, the control switch will remain open. A temperature control which has lost its charge (no pressure in the bellows) acts exactly like a control which is cold enough to reduce the bellows pressure. Or sometimes control points burn or become so worn that they do not come together. If there is electric power at all these points, check for power at the motor. If there is, and the motor still fails to run, it must be faulty.

Very loose or broken belts allow the motor to run without driving the compressor. Flywheel keys have been sheared. Some small compressors use a taper fit between the flywheel and shaft without a key. These may come loose. In such cases, the compressor appears to be running because the flywheel is turning, but the shaft is stationary. The locknut on the end of the shaft is the easiest thing to see to check this.

If the compressor runs but produces little or no refrigeration, pressures should be checked. Large machines usually have gages permanently installed. If there are no gages, service gages must be connected. Table 15-2 lists the troubles to be found if pressures are not normal. Table 15-1 pretty well covers the reasons for abnormal conditions.

A quick, sure check for faulty compressor valves is to front seat the suction service valve to pump the compressor down. It should be able to pull a 25 inch vacuum or better. Be careful that it does not slug oil during the pull-down. If it does, stop it long enough for the oil to subside, then restart it. After all the refrigerant is pumped from the oil, shut off the compressor. The vacuum on the low side should hold, or if it rises, do so very slowly. If the compressor can pull a vacuum and hold it, there is nothing wrong with it, and one must look elsewhere for faulty operation.

Occasionally a refrigeration system will work very erratically. It will be too warm for a while, then suddenly get too cold. This may be caused by a faulty control, or an oil logged evaporator. A sticky control that requires considerable force to turn it on or off will allow the pressure, and therefore the temperature to vary excessively. An oil logged evaporator can reduce the boiling by coating the liquid refrigerant with a layer of oil which reduces its boiling action. Under this condition the cold control is set colder to get proper refrigeration. Then a larger heat load will at some time start a violent boiling which will force the oil back to the compressor. Then the colder control setting with the normally boiling refrigerant causes too cold an evaporator.

Any time a service man finds insufficient refrigerant, he should check the entire system for leaks. The refrigerant in the system does not wear out, and if not lost it is good indefinitely. Therefore low refrigerant indicates a leak. And finding one leak does not prove that was the only one in the system. All joints should be checked, as well as all mechanical parts containing refrigerant, such as the compressor, all valves, controls, etc. Oil seepage around any joint indicates a leak which otherwise may be difficult to find.

Noisy equipment is usually caused by worn parts. If they are so badly worn they are noisy, they need replacing. In such cases the entire compressor must be torn down for a complete check. The most common knocking noise not caused by worn parts is the slugging of liquid refrigerant or oil. This can seriously damage the compressor so should be corrected. One knocking noise sometimes hard to trace is a loose flywheel. It may become loose enough that it knocks against the key on each compressor stroke, without being loose enough to be easily found. Squeaks or squeals may come from a shaft seal or from belts. A squealing seal may need polishing, may need more oil than it is getting, or may need replacing. For a squeaking belt, clean it with a wire brush, then apply a little soap.

Practically all domestic and many small commercial machines are mounted on rubber or spring cushions to deaden vibration and noise. To prevent damage during shipment, these units are fastened solidly with shipping bolts. These bolts are to be removed to allow the unit to float on its cushion mounting before putting it into service. Occasionally someone fails to do this. If a new unit is objectionably noisy, this is one of the first things to check.

Food Storage Troubles.—As mentioned in Chapter 13 one should not lose sight of the fact that the prime purpose of refrigeration is to improve food preservation. The condition of the food kept under refrigeration is the best indication as to whether the system is operating properly, and is properly adjusted. It is possible that the refrigeration system can be operating perfectly as a mechanical device, and still food preservation is unsatisfactory. So food storage problems must be considered as well as mechanical problems.

If there is any trouble with the freezing of produce, the cabinet is too cold, or the food may be too close to coils or cold air blasts. The service man must determine whether a rearrangement of the product or a resetting of the control is necessary. A faulty control could also cause this. Sometimes it is caused by faulty multiplexing. Consider two cabinets operating from the same compressor without auxiliary valves. If there is a heavy load in one cabinet and a light load in the other, that with the heavy load will keep the compressor running. But the continuously running compressor will continue to cool the other cabinet, and its temperature may go too low. In apartment house systems, where all the cabinets were operated from one compressor, if one door was left open, the machine would freeze up all the other cabinets in trying to cool the one with the open door.

Too cold a cabinet has in some cases been caused by a slight short-age of refrigerant in a system with a back pressure control. Enough refrigerant is supplied to refrigerate the coil, but with just enough high pressure vapor to keep the control on continuously.

If food does not keep satisfactorily it points to too warm a tem-perature. Faulty or poor refrigeration will cause this. A faulty con-trol can do the same. A leaky and collapsed bellows in a temperature control will have the same effect as a sufficiently cold evaporator which would keep the control bellows collapsed.

Sometimes the coil is cold enough, but there is poor or insufficient air circulation. This will not carry the heat from the different parts of the cabinet to the coil. Forced draft fans must not have the air flow blocked with stored products or any other material. Cabinets with convection coils must not be too crowded.

An overloaded cabinet, whether the overload is due to too much warm products in the cabinet, too high an outside temperature, or leakage due to faulty insulation will naturally be warmer than it should be. Yet the compressor may be doing all that is possible, so the only cure is to remove the cause of the overload; or sell the customer a larger system.

Frost on the coils will partially insulate them, and prevent their proper absorbtion of heat. Cabinet temperatures will often drop as much as 5 F with the same coil temperature or control setting after coils are defrosted.

If foods dry out excessively, the cabinet air is too dry. The cabi-net humidity is closely tied in with the design of the system (see Chapter 19). But in general, anything that reduces the temperature difference between the coil and the cabinet air increases the hu-midity. The easiest way to do this is to raise the cabinet tempera-ture. This reduces the load on it. If this cannot be done, a larger coil is about the only answer.

A forced draft system designed to cycle must do so to keep the humidity up. It is during the off cycle that moisture removed from the air in the form of frost is melted off the coils and blown back into the room.

If there is trouble with foods sliming, it is due to too high a humidity. Less coil or a colder coil will reduce the humidity. Some jobs properly engineered for summer conditions are oversize for winter conditions. Oversize equipment is one cause of high humidi-ties. In such a case, starving the expansion valve sometimes helps.

A slower speed fan, or a two speed fan which operates at slow speed during the off cycle is sometimes used. This problem can be very troublesome in cases where there is a large variation between summer and winter load.

Sometimes there are complaints of odors or off flavors in the food. Foods with strong odors are apt to flavor other foods. If strong odored foods must be placed in the same cabinet with other foods, they should be covered. Onions or garlic, or foods containing them, cheese and cantaloupes are some of the foods which may be troublesome. Dairy products, particularly butter and cream, will absorb other odors. They are best kept in cabinets by themselves. If this is impossible they should be covered. It helps to place them directly under the coils where air from the frosted coil flows over them.

QUESTIONS

15-1. On what class or size of equipment does the refrigeration service man usually work?

15-2. What are the two principal parts to any service problem?

15-3. How many parts of a system will a control set too warm affect?

15-4. How many parts of a system will an expansion valve open too wide affect?

15-5. How will a liquid line strainer filled with dirt affect the system?

15-6. How does an expansion valve plugged with ice affect the system?

15-7. What is apt to be the difference between the effects of question 5 and question 6?

15-8. Give two entirely different difficulties that can be caused by a leak in the low side of a system operating on a vacuum.

15-9. What are the results of a dirty condenser?

15-10. What are the results of an overloaded cabinet?

15-11. What are the symptoms of insufficient refrigerant?

15-12. On what types of systems is too much refrigerant apt to give the most trouble? What is this trouble?

15-13. If a compressor will not run, what should be looked for?

15-14. If there is no refrigeration, high back pressure, and low head pressure, what troubles should be looked for?

15-15. How would you check to see if compressor pumps properly?

15-16. If there is no refrigeration, low back pressure, and low head pressure, what troubles should be looked for?

15-17. What are some of the causes of short cycling?

15-18. What are some of the causes of high head pressure?

CHAPTER 16

REFRIGERATED ENCLOSURES

Requirements.—Any refrigerated enclosure such as a cabinet or a room has several requirements. It must be well insulated against heat. It must provide a vapor barrier against the infiltration of moisture. It must have doors to bring food in and out, but these doors must close tight and form a continuation of the insulated wall. And it must be protected against excess heat such as stoves, boilers, and where possible, direct sunshine.

Insulation.—A good insulator should have the following requirements.
1. It must provide a maximum resistance to heat flow.
2. It should not rot or otherwise decompose.
3. It should be non-inflammable.
4. It should not settle.
5. It should not absorb moisture.
6. It should be non-odorous.
7. It shou'd be rodent and vermin proof.
8. It should be self supporting.
9. It should be reasonable in price.
10. It should not be difficult to handle or install.
11. It should be light in weight.

1. A good insulator must provide a maximum resistance to heat flow. The first purpose of an insulator is to hold out the heat. Its insulation value is measured by the number of Btu or heat units that will leak through one square foot of the substance one inch thick. (See Chapter 18) This figure is called the k factor. For the time being, it is sufficient to remember the smaller the k factor, the less the heat flow that will get through the surface. Therefore, for maximum effectiveness, the k factor should be as small as possible. Most good insulators will have a k factor of not over 0.3.

2. A good insulator should not rot or otherwise decompose. Naturally, if this would happen, in time the insulation would no longer be effective, and would have to be replaced.

3. A good insulator should be non-inflammable. If so, it not only reduces the fire hazard, but in case of a fire would act as a fire stop.

4. A good insulator should not settle after being put in place. To do so would leave uninsulated spaces around the tops of the walls.

5. A good insulator should not absorb moisture. Water is a very poor insulator. If the insulation becomes water soaked, the heat will travel through the water very rapidly. A hot iron rod can be held with a dry rag, but with a wet rag it will soon become too hot to hold.

6. A good insulator should be free of odors. If not it will taint the food stored with these odors.

7. A good insulator should be rodent and vermin proof. An insulator that makes good rat nests, or which ants or other such insects tunnel through or make nests in, becomes a definite sanitary hazard.

8. A good insulator should be self supporting. It is then not necessary to build walls to support it.

9. A good insulator should be reasonable in price. Naturally, the cheaper in price, the more desirable from the customer's point of view. If it is too expensive, it might be cheaper to buy a larger machine or operate the machine longer than to pay for a well insulated wall.

10. A good insulator should not be difficult to handle or use. Anything that adds to the difficulty of installation adds to the installation cost. Just as the material cost cannot be excessive, neither can the installation cost.

11. A good insulator should be light in weight. When installed in cabinets excessive weight adds to the difficulty of moving or cost of shipping. If installed in buildings its weight affects the cost of foundations and other supporting members.

As in most other cases where a list is made of desirable properties, nothing available meets all these requirements. So the requirements of the individual job must be studied, and an insulation chosen that makes the best compromise.

As mentioned in Chapter 1, heat may be transferred by conduction, convection or radiation. Conduction is by physical contact. It can be reduced by using a minimum mass of material to conduct the heat, and by using a material which is a poor conductor. Nonmetals are poorer conductors than metals.

Convection is the movement of air or other medium, which carries heat with it. The reduction of the amount of air which flows, or the distance it flows will reduce convection heat losses.

Radiation is a heat effect which shines or is radiated. Light colored or shiny surfaces are the poorest radiators of heat and the poorest absorbers of radiant heat. Polished metal, glass, or certain plastics keep radiant heat transfer at a minimum.

All these methods of heat transfer contribute to heat leakage in most insulations. But the importance of each transfer method will vary with different forms of insulation.

The perfect insulator would be a vacuum. If there is nothing to conduct or convect heat through a space, and if radiation is guarded against, no heat will flow. But outside such a small device as a thermos bottle, the cost and technical difficulties of maintaining an air tight wall space necessary to hold a vacuum make it prohibitive.

The next best single insulation is air, if it could be held still. It has a k factor of 0.16, about half that of the common insulating materials used. But air in an open wall will not remain still. It will carry or convect heat from the warm side to the cool side, Fig. 16-1. The only way air can be held still is to divide it up into so many small spaces that the movement of any part of it is negligible, Fig. 16-2. That is all many insulations do, is to trap or hold the air so it cannot circulate around. Some heat will be conducted through the solid parts of the insulating material, but not as much as would be carried by the air if it was left free to circulate.

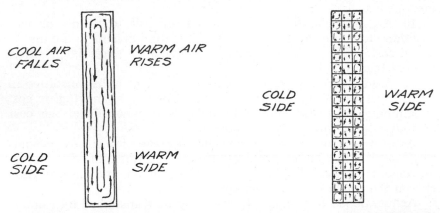

Fig. 16-1 Air circulation in   Fig. 16-2. How air circulation is
a "dead air space."   reduced by reducing size of space.

Two different methods are used to trap and hold this air. One is to enclose it in microscopic bubbles. The bubbles are small enough that the convection within each bubble is negligible. And the walls are thin enough that there is a minimum mass to conduct heat across the material. Cork is a natural form of insulation of this type, Fig. 16-3. Glass foam and plastic foams are synthetic materials of this type.

Some radiation takes place across the individual walls of such materials. The addition of aluminum flakes to some of the plastic foams has been found to reduce radiation more than it increases conduction.

The second method of trapping and holding air is with felted fibers. The tangle of fibers causes restriction enough that air flow is negligible. The denser the felted mass, the less convection, but the more the conduction. Much study has been given to determining the proper size fiber, and the proper packing density to give a minimum overall heat flow. Natural fibers such as shredded wood or bark, or synthetic fibers such as glass or mineral wool are of this type.

Another method of classifying insulations is in board, bat, or loose fill form. Any insulator can be mixed with a binder and pressed together into a board. In some, like cork, use can be made of a natural resin in the material. Under heat and pressure, this natural resin will cement the particles together. Sugar cane fiber has been matted together by what is essentially a paper making process to form a material of the required size and thickness to make insulating board[1]. Foamed plastics are usually made in board form.

In bat form, felted materials are put in the proper size and shape to fill the required space. Some cling together like cotton batting, and can be shipped, handled, and placed in position with no further protection. Others are glued between sheets of paper as a protection and an aid in holding their size and shape. Some bats can be compressed for shipping; many cannot.

Loose fill insulation may be supplied in bales or sacks. Some can be poured or blown directly into the space to be insulated. Others must be stuffed in by hand to get the proper packing.

In many cases a single insulating material can be supplied in any of the above three forms. Any of the fibers can be cemented together into board form, although all suppliers of insulating fibers do not do this. The board form is usually best from a self-supporting, or ease of handling point of view. But where a binding material must be used, it adds to the density of the insulating material which increases its conductivity. It is, therefore, usually cheaper to handle or install, but gives less insulating value. Bats or loose fill require support, and more labor to install, but the k factor is usually better.

Cork.—In early refrigeration cork was the best known quality insulation. But the entire supply must be imported from Spain, Portugal or North Africa. Shipping costs plus processing costs make it expensive compared to most other insulations. So as synthetic insulations have been improved in quality, they have taken over a larger and larger percent of the insulation market.

[1]"Celotex"

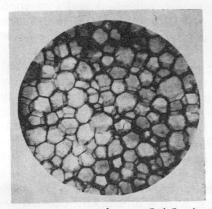

Fig. 16-3. Microscopic view of cork.

Cork is made up of a myriad of tiny bubbles of wood fiber, each trapping a small amount of air, Fig. 16-3. The raw cork is granulated, and in this form has been used as a loose fill insulation. But most of it was made into board form by compressing and baking this granulated cork.

The insulation factor of the corkboard is good, with a k factor of 0.27 to 0.33 depending on the weight (the heavier has the higher k factor). It is permanent, does not settle, rot or deteriorate. It is odorless. The board is strong enough, not only to be self supporting, but can be used in floors where some other forms of insulation would be crushed.

Vegetable Fiber.—A great many insulations now on the market are made of some kind of vegetable fiber processed to put it in the desired form. These are made into a shredded or wool form. Shredded bark, exploded or shredded wood fiber, kapok, and other similar materials are used. They are available in loose wool form, in blanket form, and in pressed board form. The different products are too numerous to give detailed data for each. Any desired information can be obtained from manufacturers or suppliers of this type of insulation.

In general, the loose or blanket forms have the best k factors, some as low as 0.24. But they require mechanical support, and require labor to handle and place. Many which are not naturally repellent or resistant to vermin or rodents are treated to make them so. Some are treated to make them fire resistant. Most of them are less moisture repellent than cork. Some need the utmost care taken to keep them dry. This is sometimes done by sealing the bats or blankets in moisture proof packages or wrappings. Most of them cost less than other types of insulation.

Mineral, Glass Insulations.—Molten limestone or molten glass can be formed into threads which when cool resemble wool. This wool can be made into bats, blankets, or boards just as can the vegetable fibers. Its insulation value is good, but also varies according to the form used. Different sized fibers and different packing densities give k factors from over 0.3 down to about 0.24. It is fireproof, non-odorous and rodent proof. It is moisture proof in that it will not absorb moisture, but it should not be overlooked that it is possible for the air spaces in a bat of this material to fill with water. Its weight is also low except in the board form.

A glass foam has also been developed, and is available in board form. Its structural form is similar to cork, being made of a multitude of air or gas bubbles. But the walls of these bubbles are completely inert; fireproof, waterproof, odor proof, rodent proof, etc. Its biggest disadvantage is that it is brittle, so should not be used in any application where there is vibration.

Because of the inertness of glass and mineral wool products, because of their very good insulating values, and because they are available in a variety of forms to fit almost any insulation need, they have become quite popular.

Plastic Insulations.—Plastics have also been foamed similar to glass foam. Their properties vary considerably according to the plastics used, and the exact form of the insulation. Some plastics used are inflammable; some are not. All can be softened and the foam collapsed by heat. Therefore welding fabrication should not be used around them.

Plastics can be foamed into board form and handled similar to any other board insulation. However, the manufacturer's instructions should be followed regarding adhesives and sealers. Hot asphalts, used with many board insulations will damage most plastics.

Plastics are available which can be foamed in place. The raw materials are shipped separately in cans or barrels. To use, the ingredients are combined in the proper proportion, mixed thoroughly, and measured amounts poured into prepared spaces. One of the ingredients is a foaming agent which causes the material to foam up and fill the space. It hardens in this shape. This is an excellent method of insulating spaces otherwise hard to reach.

Foamed-in-place plastics can also be used to insulate awkwardly shaped objects such as pumps, valves, etc. A temporary mold is built around the object, and the prepared plastic poured in.

Plastics are available that can be sprayed on a surface. It foams up and solidifies as it strikes the surface. Any desired thickness can be built up by repeated sprayings.

Reflective Insulations.—Crushed metal foil, curtains of cloth or paper painted with aluminum or coated with aluminum foil, and layers of polished aluminum or steel plates have all been used as insulations. The theory is to reduce radiant heat transfer to almost nothing, and do it in such a way that conduction and convection is at a minimum. Such insulations have the advantage of being light. But they have not had much acceptance for refrigeration work.

Other Insulations.—Many other materials have had occasional use as insulators, or may be used in certain areas because of local availability or other special reasons. Foamed rubber has been used for some applications. It has been made into what might be called a flexible board form for domestic and commercial sized cabinets. But its principal use is to insulate pipe, mostly in the copper tubing sizes.

Hair felt is commonly used in certain industries, both as an insulation and as a sound deadener. But it has not had much acceptance in the refrigeration industry. It is expensive, it is not fire proof, vermin proof, or moisture proof.

Sawdust, wood shavings, rice hulls, and vermiculite have all been used as insulations. If space is not at a premium so twelve inches of insulated space can be used instead of six inches; and if this type of insulating material can be obtained for little or no cost at all, it may be the economical choice. Such are more often the choice on coolers or small cold storage plants built on the farm, than in any type of plant in the city. And even on the farm, better, more permanent insulations are more apt to be used at the present time than in the past.

The question is sometimes asked why asbestos or other common heat insulators are not used in refrigeration. Or what is the difference between insulating for heat and insulating for cold? Theoretically, there is no difference. In either case we must retard the flow of heat. But there are two very important practical considerations. A heat insulator must be more than fire resistant. It must be fire proof. Therefore such substances as cork will not serve for insulating a boiler. It so happens most of the best heat retarders can be burned or easily melted. Therefore their use would be very limited on a boiler, and they would be useless on a firebox. And asbestos is not used for refrigeration because there are many insulations available having at least twice the insulating value of asbestos.

A second practical consideration is that a cold insulator must be moisture proof. There is no worry about this with heat insulators because the heat keeps them dry.

Moisture Proofing.—When a glass of ice water is allowed to stand in a room at normal temperature, moisture or dew collects on the outside surface. Similarly, if a refrigerator cabinet was so built that air could reach the inside surface, moisture would collect at this point, Fig. 16-4. The least this moisture would do would be to soak up the insulation. As previously stated, a wet insulation is a very poor heat retarder. Even with those fiber insulators which

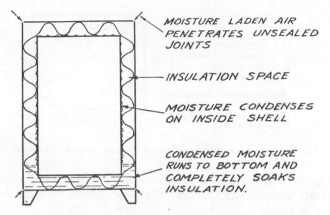

Fig. 16-4—Moisture in cabinet insulation.

will not absorb moisture, such as glass wool, if the spaces between the fibers are filled with water, there are no trapped air spaces left to form the required insulation. With such insulations, water has been known to fill the space in the bottom of the cabinet, and up the walls several inches, Fig. 16-4. If the insulation absorbs moisture, it will soak up this water like a blotter. This keeps all the insulation wet.

At below freezing temperatures, such moisture would freeze. Freezing water expands. This will crush and destroy the insulation. If allowed to continue long enough it may even damage the cabinet walls. For these reasons moisture must be kept out of the insulation. Three general methods are used to do this. The first is to make both the inside and the outside walls moisture proof and practically

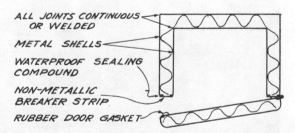

Fig. 16-5. Refrigerator section with inside and outside walls made airtight.

air tight, Fig. 16-5. If no moisture or moist air can enter the insulated space, it cannot cause trouble. This sealing is done by using metal walls, or wooden walls with a moisture seal of waterproof paper, special non-odorous asphalt, or both. Domestic and small commercial cabinets usually use the metal walls. Larger commercial cabinets or locally built cabinets may be of wood construction.

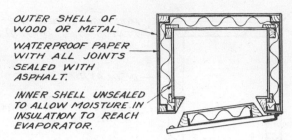

OUTER SHELL OF WOOD OR METAL

WATERPROOF PAPER WITH ALL JOINTS SEALED WITH ASPHALT.

INNER SHELL UNSEALED TO ALLOW MOISTURE IN INSULATION TO REACH EVAPORATOR.

Fig. 16-6. Section with inside wall porous, outside wall sealed.

The second method is to seal only the outside wall, and leave the inside wall unsealed or porous, Fig. 16-6. With this method all the moisture possible is kept out of the insulation. The porous inside wall allows any moisture that might get through to go on through the inside wall. It eventually reaches the coils where it collects as frost. Here it can cause no damage to the insulation. This method is used for larger commercial cabinets, and rooms or buildings of cheaper construction.

The third method of sealing out the moisture is to build up the wall with insulation blocks, sealed in asphalt or other sealer. First the inside of the wall is made true and flat with cement plaster. Then the entire wall is given a heavy moisture resistant coating. Fig. 16-7. This

—*Armstrong Cork Co. photo*

Fig. 16-7. a. Dipping corkboard in hot asphalt.

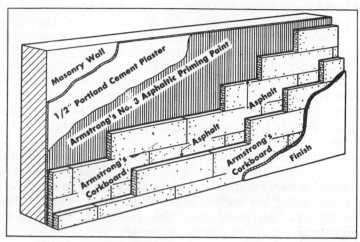

—*Armstrong Cork Co. drawing*

Fig. 16-7. b. Method of laying up a cork wall.

is accepted as the surest way of making a wall and its insulation vapor proof. But a block insulation is usually more expensive than other forms, and this method of sealing is also more expensive. Therefore it is used mainly in cold storage construction where the insulated walls are expected to last indefinitely.

Openings, Doors.—The doors into a cabinet or cooler introduce many problems. To be effective the door must be as well insulated as the cabinet walls. The thicker the insulation, the heavier this makes the door. These heavy doors must be strongly built and hung from a strongly built frame. The door must have a gasket which fits tight when the door is closed. The hardware must be heavy enough to hold the door, yet adjustable so that it pulls the gasket up tight.

Where glass windows, glass doors or glass front show cases are used they introduce special problems. Glass itself is a poor insulator. To improve its insulating effect several thicknesses of glass are used with air spaces between them. Even this makes a poor insulation compared to a standard insulated wall. The spaces between the glass must be dehydrated and filled with dry air. Otherwise dew forms on the glass as a fog that interferes with vision. Then the glass must be so sealed in its frame that no air or moisture can leak in. Some manufacturers place a chemical drier in each air space to absorb any moisture that might leak in during the life of the case. This all makes glass expensive to install as well as expensive to refrigerate. It is, therefore, only used when the display through the glass has a definite sales value.

Cabinet Construction.—Domestic and small commercial cabinets were at one time made up around a wooden frame. Large cabinets are still made in this way. Most small cabinets now are nearly all steel with plastic breaker strips and sometimes a plastic door liner. Outer and inner shells are formed and welded into the required shape. The inner shell is given an inside finish of porcelain enamel. The sides of these shells next to the insulation may be painted, or may have a special anti-corrosion treatment. The outside finish is usually a synthetic enamel paint, but on a few higher priced models it may be porcelain enamel.

Practically all types of insulation have been tried and are being used by the various manufacturers. Cork has had some use in the development of early domestic models, but most manufacturers have adopted something less costly. Wood fiber, mineral wool, glass wool and plastics have all been used. The present trend is away from wood fiber and toward synthetic materials.

Design is usually such that the inner shell will go in through the door opening of the outer shell. The door jamb or breaker strip between the inner and the outer shell is made of plastic. This dresses off the finish, and breaks the metal connections so there is no metal to metal conductivity from the outer to the inner shell. These breaker strips are usually put in against gaskets or sealing compound to prevent the penetration of air and moisture through the joint into the insulation. In many, only the outer edge is sealed. Any leakage at the inner edge would be from the insulation to the inside where it could reach the evaporator.

The inner door wall may be porcelain on steel with plastic breaker strips, or the entire inner face may be of one piece molded plastic. Extra steel reinforcements are added to the shells at the necessary points to hold the screws from the hardware.

Factory built commercial cabinets are built in fewer numbers, and are required in many different sizes and shapes. Therefore, the mass production methods used to build steel cabinets are not justified. Many commercial cabinets are also so much larger and heavier that some framing is necessary. Therefore most commercial cabinets are constructed around frames, usually of wood. Both inside and outside shells may be a single welded shell similar to the all steel construction, or they may be made up with joints at the corners. Again, great care must be taken that all joints are waterproofed. The interior finish can be either porcelain enamel or a special non-odorous paint.

Doors are similar to those made for domestic cabinets. But more often, part of the wood frame is used as the breaker strip. Where glass is required in a door, there is usually no insulation. The multiglass panes are set in a wood or plastic frame that form the breaker strips.

Many commercial cabinets are made locally by store fixture manufacturers. The larger the cabinet, the more this is apt to be the case. Such cabinets may have metal shells similar to those just described, or may be made up of waterproof plywood.

Several types of construction are used on large industrial boxes or entire cold storage buildings, depending on the type of insulation used and the type of building construction. Fig. 16-7b shows the recommended assembly method for a board type insulation. The material may be corkboard, mineral or glass wool board, fiber board, or one of the newer synthetic plastic boards. It may be laid up against a concrete, brick or wood wall. In case of an insulated partition, it is sometimes built up without any other support.

Fig. 16-6 shows a construction suitable for a loose fill or bat type insulation. Some framing is necessary regardless of the type of wall it is laid against.

If the room is to operate below 20 F, it is desirable to have it above the first floor, or have an air space between it and the ground. If it must be placed directly on the ground, two things are necessary. The first is adequate drainage. A sand or gravel fill must be placed directly under the room to allow any water to drain away from the floor. The second requirement is to determine for sure that ground water levels do not rise to a level near the floor. The floor of a freezer room laid directly on the ground will, over a period of years, cool the ground to below freezing. Tests have shown freezing temperatures many feet below the floor of a 0 F room. If water is encountered it is frozen and pulls more moisture in to freeze. The pressure exerted by the expansion will buckle or lift the floor. Floors have been ruined in this way, so it is an expensive mistake to make. Frequently ventilating ducts or pipes for heating are run under freezer sub-floors when they are built on the ground.

Cold storage doors are usually purchased from builders who specialize in their construction. The prefabricated door mounted in its door frame with all hardware properly set is shipped complete.

Tank and Pipe Insulations.—Beside walls, most cold surfaces in plants of any size should be insulated. Not only does this prevent losses of refrigeration, but also prevents sweating and dripping of cold surfaces.

Tanks can be insulated with bats, with boards molded to fit the proper curvature, or in some cases, with flexible boards bent to fit the required shape.

Pipes are usually insulated with a molded form made in halves. The halves are put together over the pipe, and cemented, wired or taped in place. Small pipe may be covered with a molded foam rubbr tube of the proper dimensions. This rubber insulation can be slipped over the pipe before it is assembled. Or a split insulation is available that can be slipped over the pipe.

Excessive Heat.—As far as protecting a cold storage cabinet against excessive heat, it is only common sense not to place it too near a range or boiler. If it must be placed in the sun it is sometimes desirable to build a shading roof over the building with an air space between it and the main roof. If this cannot be done, white or aluminum paint helps to reflect the heat away.

QUESTIONS

16–1. What are the requirements of a refrigerated room?

16–2. What are the requirements of a good insulator?

16–3. What are some of the difficulties caused by moisture penetration into insulation?

16-4. What methods are used to protect insulation against moisture?

16–5. Why is a vacuum not used commercialy as an insulator?

16–6. How do most insulators hold back the flow of heat?

16–7. What material is the best known insulation? Why?

16–8. How have metals been used as insulators?

16–9. What are the objections to windows in refrigerators?

16–10. Why is it best not to build freezer rooms directly on the ground?

CHAPTER 17

INSTRUMENTS AND METERS

General.—Nearly everything that goes on in a refrigeration system is enclosed in pipes and is, therefore, invisible. What conditions are detectable from the outside such as the temperature of the pipe surfaces can only be guessed at without accurate means of measurement. Therefore, to intelligently know what is going on in a refrigeration system, means of measuring temperatures and pressures are essential. Liquid indicators to show liquid levels are desirable. If any check is to be made of electric driving equipment, electric meters and instruments are the only way of knowing the power consumed. Therefore, the refrigeration man should know something of these indicating and recording devices which show temperatures, pressures, liquid levels, and electric quantities.

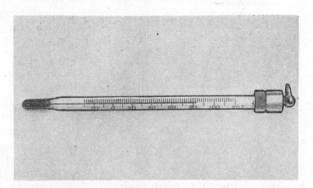

Fig. 17-1. Stem thermometer, engraving on stem.

Stem Thermometers.—Since the control of temperature is the primary purpose of a refrigeration system, means of accurately measuring this temperature must be had. This is done with a thermometer. The commonest form is the stem thermometer with mercury or spirit in a glass tube, Fig. 17-1. The bulb is filled with a liquid that expands as it is heated and contracts as it is cooled. The change in volume of the liquid causes it to rise or fall in the tube or stem. The volume of the bulb is large compared to the stem. Therefore, the temperature of the stem makes very little difference in the volume compared to the temperature of the bulb. In laboratory work corrections are sometimes made for the small error introduced by this. In practical work the error is not enough to be recognized.

The temperature readings may be engraved directly on the glass stem of the thermometer, Fig. 17-1, or may be on the background or support of the thermometer, Fig. 17-2. The latter is easier to read but is not considered quite as accurate. There are two reasons for a better accuracy of the scale on the stem. There is always a chance of the stem shifting or slipping slightly in its clamps. This would introduce an error in the entire reading if the figures were on the background. Also, if the reading is not taken at right angles to the thermometer, the sighting error (parallax) is greater with the engraving on the background, Fig. 17-2.

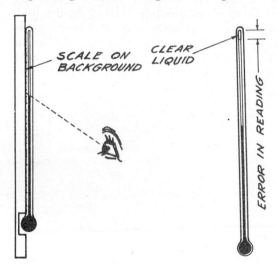

Fig. 17-2. Parallax in reading.

Fig. 17-3. Spirit thermometer with vapor condensed at tip.

The fluid in the thermometer may be mercury or a spirit such as alcohol or turpentine with a colored dye to make it visible. The mercury filled thermometer is considered more accurate above —38 F. Since mercury freezes at this temperature, it will not work below —38 F. Its purity is easily controlled so it will remain the same for all thermometers made. It does not change in any way with age. Its expansion is directly proportional to temperature. When the proper scale is found for the size bore of the tube used, this is standard for all thermometers using the same bulb size. Readings at the top of the scale will have the same spacing as readings at the bottom of the scale.

The big disadvantage of a mercury thermometer is that it is difficult to read. The mercury is approximately the same color as a reflection on the glass, so if the light is not right, the height of the mercury column may not be visible.

A spirit which has been dyed a red, blue or green is much more easily seen. For this reason it is preferred by some, although its accuracy is not considered as dependable. It may change slightly with age. Its expansion is not proportional, so the scale is not evenly divided. Under some conditions part of the fluid will vaporize and recondense at the top of the stem, Fig. 17-3. Since this is a distilling process, the color is left behind, and that condensed is colorless. It can be seen if looked for, but when one is looking at a colored column, the clear fluid at the top of the stem may be easily overlooked. Naturally an error due to the length of the distilled fluid will be introduced into the thermometer reading. Spirit thermometers are also slower in reacting to a change of temperature than are mercury thermometers.

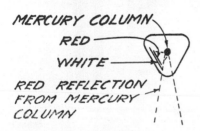

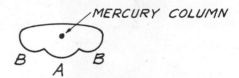

Fig. 17-4. (left) Reflecting type mercury thermometer.

Fig. 17-5. (above) Binoc thermometer.

Special designs of mercury thermometers have been introduced to get the accuracy of mercury with improved visibility. Fig. 17-4 shows the cross section of one so designed that a red ribbon is invisible from the front of the thermometer, but reflects on the mercury column like on a mirror. This red reflection is seen up the height of the mercury column, but there is no reflection above it. Therefore, it looks exactly like a red spirit thermometer from the front. It has one disadvantage. It must be viewed from the exact front. If the eye of the observer is a little to one side, the diffraction of the glass makes both the mercury column and the reflection invisible.

Fig. 17-5 shows another method of improving the visibility of the mercury thermometer. The center round section, A, magnifies the mercury column similar to the way a round stem does. But the two side bulges, B, B, collect and concentrate light on the mercury column. This makes the mercury show up much better. It cannot if viewed from as extreme an angle as is possible with a round stem, but it can be seen through a much greater angle than the

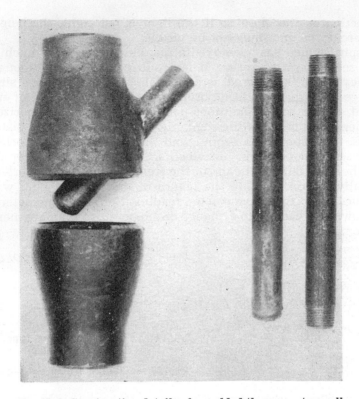

Fig. 17-6. Construction details of a welded thermometer well.

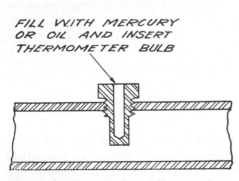

FILL WITH MERCURY
OR OIL AND INSERT
THERMOMETER BULB

Fig. 17-7. Thermometer well, screw type.

reflecting type mentioned above.

Thermometer wells, either stubs of small pipe welded in, Fig. 17-6, or threaded wells Fig. 17-7, should be installed where temperature measurements may be required. Or an insertion type thermometer should be used. The thermometer well should be filled with oil or mercury to give good conductivity from the well to the thermometer bulb. Insertion type thermometers are available in a variety of shapes to fit different requirements. Fig. 17-8 shows the points in a system where thermometers or thermometer wells are needed to get a complete record of the operation of the equipment. This is, of course, beside thermometers in the rooms or products being cooled.

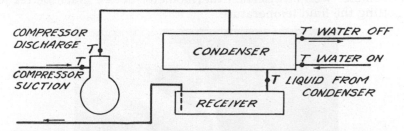

Fig. 17-8. Points in refrigeration system requiring thermometers.

Temporary wells which clamp onto the outside of the pipe are available. One type is a set of brass blocks made in sizes to fit onto the commoner sizes of copper tubing. A hole drilled in this block holds the thermometer bulb. Another type is a ribbon of silver (one of the best known conductors) which is wrapped around the pipe and held with a spring and chain arrangement. One end of the silver is curled up to hold the thermometer bulb. Temporary

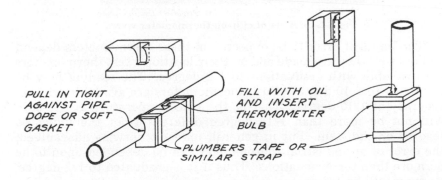

Fig. 17-9. Temporary thermometer wells cut from wood.

wells can also be fashioned from wooden blocks, Fig. 17-9, or from a piece of sheet metal cut and bent to fit, and soldered to the pipe. For a quick check, a wad of putty or similar material has been used. Grease sometimes works well on cold lines where the low temperature thickens it. Fig. 17-10 illustrates a set of temporary thermometer wells.

But it should be remembered that any check on the outside of the pipe measures the pipe temperature, and not the temperature of the fluid in the pipe. These may or may not be the same. The thermometer well or insertion thermometer does a much better job of getting the fluid temperature.

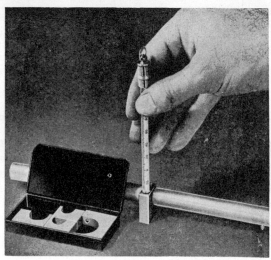

—Frigidaire Division photo
Fig. 17-10. A set of clip-on thermometer wells.

The limits of error to be expected in these thermometers depend on how well they are made and on their location. Test thermometers are available with graduations to 1/2 degree. The reading may be estimated to 1/10 degree. Such thermometers are available with an accuracy of 1/10 degree. That is, the true temperature at the bulb will not be more than 1/10 degree different from the indicated reading on the stem. But in general, unless otherwise guaranteed, the error of an industrial thermometer can be depended upon to be no more than the graduations. Thus if it is graduated to 1/2 degree, its error will be 1/2 degree or less.

The second error in a thermometer can be an error of location. The readings of a thermometer on the wall does not always mean the products in the room are at that temperature. Temperatures may be several degrees different in different parts of a cabinet. Goods have frozen in one part of a cabinet when temperatures at another point in the same cabinet are unsatisfactorily high. Naturally, the thermometer will only record the temperature at the bulb location. But it is too often overlooked that the bulb location is not always where it will give a good average of the temperature required.

The accuracy of a thermometer can easily be checked by placing it in a mixture of ice and water. Ice and pure water will be 32 F, and the thermometer should show this. If the thermometer reads as high as 212 F, this end of the scale can be checked with boiling water. But most refrigeration thermometers do not go this high. As for a check of the location of the thermometer in a room, this is not so easy. Probably the best procedure would be to locate several in different parts of the room. But this is expensive, and many of them might be hid by produce. If there are inside posts, these make good locations. Thermometers are often put on walls near doors for convenient reading, but checks show this is often a poor place for them.

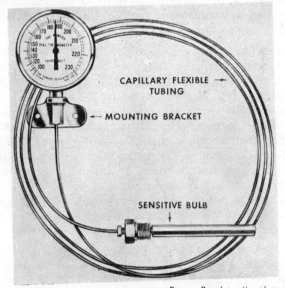

—*Powers Regulator Co. photo*

Fig. 17-11. Dial thermometer.

Dial Thermometers.—Another type of thermometer available is the dial thermometer, Fig. 17-11. This has the advantage that it can be easily seen and read from a distance. Their accuracy is not as great as that of a stem thermometer, but they are easily recalibrated if a check shows them to be off. Dial thermometers may be either self contained or remote type. The self contained type is usually activated by a bimetallic coil. This is made up of two different metals having different rates of expansion. This makes the coil wind up or unwind with a change of temperature. This movement turns a needle which travels over a suitable scale.

The remote dial thermometer may use an expanding liquid to operate it. Or it may operate from the vapor pressure of a liquid. In either case the liquid is in a bulb which is connected to the thermometer mechanism by a capillary tube. The operating part is fundamentally a pressure gage, a closed, circular tube. An increase in the pressure in the tube forces it to straighten. This motion is suitably transferred to a needle. The quantity of liquid in the bulb is so great compared to the rest of the instrument that, unless the connecting tube is too long, the temperature of the liquid any place but in the bulb has a negligible effect on the needle. The bulb may be placed in an air stream, in a pipe, tank, or any other place a temperature reading is required. If excessively long tubes are necessary to connect the bulb to the instrument, special means have been devised to correct for the error introduced by the temperature of the liquid in the tube.

Recording Thermometer.—A recording thermometer is a dial thermometer with a pen on the end of the needle. A clockwork turns a calibrated paper chart under this pen point to give a graph or picture of the temperature conditions, Fig. 17-12. Some such instruments are self contained. These must be placed in the box or other location where a temperature record is required. They are valuable for a service man to check conditions over a 24 hour period. The remote type is commonly used in large plants, permanently mounted on an instrument board to give a continuous record or log of temperatures at required points.

It should also be noted that a thermostat is nothing more than a thermometer with electric contacts instead of a needle or recording pen. It may be self contained or of the remote type.

Pressure Gages.—A pressure gage is a device to measure the gas or liquid pressure in a closed system. Fig. 17-13 shows the essentials of a common pressure gage. It employs a circular tube of flattened section. Such a tube will tend to straighten out as the pressure is increased inside of the tube. The action is the same as in a coil of hose that tends to straighten out when the water is turned on. This is because an increased internal pressure makes the tube more nearly round. Such a tube is called a Bourdon tube after the name of its inventor. The movement of the end of the tube is linked to a rack and gear which moves a needle. A suitable dial is placed under the needle, Fig. 17-14. A pipe connection with a standard pipe thread is supplied to make connections to the system where a pressure measurement is required.

Any reduction in pressure inside the tube causes the opposite action. The atmospheric pressure outside the tube flattens it further, and it bends into a smaller circle. This moves the needle in the opposite direction. Such a gage can be used to measure vacuums. Gages are made with bronze or steel Bourdon tubes, depending on whether the pressure of ammonia or other substances are to be measured. They are available in different sizes. The larger

—*Bachrach Industrial Instrument Photo*

Fig. 17-12. Recording thermometer.

—*Marsh Instrument Co. photo*

Fig. 17-13. Interior of a pressure gage.

Fig. 17-14. Pressure gage 0 psi to 300 psi.

Fig. 17-15. Compound gage scale.

the size, the larger the scale, and the greater the accuracy. They are also available in different pressure ranges. A 0 to 300 psi gage will measure any pressure between 0 psig and 300 psig pressure. Notice the difference between 40 psi and 45 psi would be difficult to read on such a scale, Fig. 17-14. A 0 to 60 psi scale would have more spread, so such a reading could be determined with more accuracy. But if much over 60 psi were applied to this gage, it would damage it.

Such gages are called pressure gages. A gage showing 0 to 30 inches of vacuum is called a vacuum gage. Gages are available showing vacuums on one side of the scale and pressures on the other. These are known as compound gages, Fig. 17-15.

Most gages used in refrigeration are calibrated in pounds per square inch for pressures, and inches of vacuum for vacuums. Since pressures are so high with carbon dioxide, gages used with this refrigerant are often calibrated in atmospheres. Atmospheres are converted to pounds per square inch by multiplying by 14.7. Thus a pressure of 20 atmospheres is $20 \times 14.7 = 294$ psig.

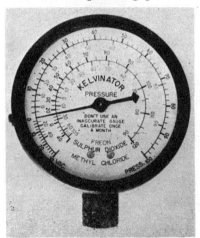

Fig. 17-16. Temperature scales on a gage.

Since evaporating pressures and condensing pressures are often used to determine evaporating and condensing temperatures, some gages have a temperature scale as well as a pressure scale printed in them. If the gage is permanently mounted on a system, the temperature scale is for the refrigerant in the system. Some service men's gages have all the common scales printed on them, Fig. 17-16. Although this is valuable in giving a temperature scale in convenient form, the figures are so small they are not easily seen. Even the pressure figures must be reduced in size to make room for the additional scales. For this reason, most service men do not like these temperature scale gages.

It should always be remembered a gage only measures a gage pressure. That is, it measures the difference between the pressure imposed on the inside of the Bourdon tube and the atmospheric pressure on the outside of the tube. If the gage is being used to check the safety of the system, the difference between these two pressures is what is wanted. But if the pressure is being checked to be a guide to evaporator or condensing temperatures, a correction must be made if the gage 0 is not at an atmospheric pressure of 14.7 psi.[1]

To maintain the accuracy of a gage, it should be checked. A gage on a board should be checked at least once a year. A gage used by a service man which gets banged around in a tool box, and is subjected to all kinds of pressures, pressure fluctuations, temperatures, etc., should be checked once a month. A rough check can be made by opening the gage to atmospheric pressure and seeing whether it registers zero or not. Some gages have a screw to adjust the needle and bring it back to zero if it is found to be off. To know the gage is accurate over the entire scale it should be checked against a gage known to be accurate. Or better, have it checked on a dead weight gage tester, and adjusted if it is off. Instrument companies are available in any large city who can do this job.

It is further recommended that to keep a gage accurate, it should be protected from vibration, either internal or external, as much as possible. By internal vibration is meant a pressure which fluctuates so much the needle continually vibrates. A valve or restriction in the gage line is the proper remedy for this.

Recording gages are also available. These are similar to a standard gage, but have the pen, clockwork and chart similar to a recording thermometer.

To measure pressures at or near atmospheric and to measure vacuums with greatest accuracy, a mercury column is sometimes used, Fig. 17-17. This is approximately the same as a barometer. The difference in height between the mercury in the two legs is the pressure or vacuum in inches of mercury. If the open end is higher than the connected leg the pressure is greater than atmospheric. If the connected leg is higher there is a vacuum in the system being checked. Mercury tubes are more common in testing than for measuring conditions in operating systems. They are valuable in operating systems to show certain conditions. One is where it

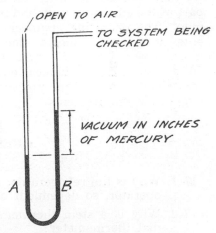

Fig. 17-17. Mercury column.

---

[1]See Chapter 27 for a complete discussion of this.

is desired to carry as low a pressure as possible without going into a vacuum. The other is to accurately determine temperatures from pressures. If a check is made of the refrigerant tables, it will be found that the higher the vacuum, the greater the error in temperature if the pressure reading is missed by one inch.

Electric Instruments.—Since so many refrigeration systems are electric driven, it is sometimes necessary to measure electric quantities. Electric measuring instruments are best divided into portable and switchboard mounted types. The portable instruments are sometimes necessary to find trouble in commercial or industrial systems having no switchboard instruments of their own. Voltmeters are necessary to check improper voltages or widely fluctuating voltages. Wattmeters are the surest check as to whether systems are overloaded or not. Ammeters are of use to determine reasons for thermal overloads going out.

For domestic or commercial units, self starting electric clocks are sometimes paralleled with the motor to check running time. Such instruments are standard electric test equipment, and are available to electricians. Often an electrician is called in to make required electric checks. Some refrigeration service companies will have these instruments for their own checks.

Large industrial plants usually have voltmeters, ammeters and watthour meters mounted on an instrument panel. This again is part of the electric circuit, and is installed with the electrical equipment. The operating engineer must take readings from these to enter into the log sheets. Such data keep an accurate record of power costs. They will sometimes show the gradual decrease of efficiency of the mechanical equipment, or a sudden occurance of something wrong, if the power supplied is correlated with the refrigeration requirements.

QUESTIONS

17–1. Why is the refrigeration man whether he be service man or operator, so dependent on instruments and meters?

17–2. Why is a stem thermometer more commonly used than a dial thermometer?

17–3. What is the advantage of a dial thermometer?

17–4. Why is a mercury thermometer more commonly used in the refrigeration industry than a spirit thermometer?

17–5. What is the advantage of a spirit thermometer?

17-6. What is the purpose of a thermometer well?

17-7. How can a thermometer be checked on the job?

17-8. What is the difference between a thermostat and a thermometer?

17-9. How does a pressure gage work?

17-10. What is the difference between a compound gage and a pressure gage?

17-11. How can a gage be checked?

17-12. What pressures are mercury tubes used to check?

17-13. What instrument should be used when an electric overload release continues to kick out?

17-14. What would be used to check power consumed by a motor?

CHAPTER 18

HEAT CALCULATIONS

General.—The first 17 chapters have been devoted to a description of the mechanical or practical aspects of a refrigeration system. The following chapters will show how calculations are made to choose or check the proper size of equipment to do a given refrigeration job. Basic, fundamental methods are stressed. Short cut factors, or short cut tables are often used to choose commercial equipment. In smaller sizes, guesses based on past experience are often depended on. But it is of great value to know something of the data from which such short cuts are made. And if the different factors which vary the results are known and understood, even guesses, can be better modified to fit existing conditions. And finally a beginner with a knowledge of a few fundamentals can do a better job of selecting equipment than some experienced men who depend only on guesses.

Design Temperature.—One of the first factors to be well understood is design temperatures. *The design temperature is the basic temperature from which to calculate heat loads.* It is sometimes called the ambient temperature, meaning the temperature surrounding the equipment. There is sometimes some variation in the methods used to choose the design temperature, which sometimes gives a few degrees difference in the results obtained. That is, all tables do not show exactly the same design temperatures for the same place. But in general, the design temperature is supposed to be the average of the hottest conditions the unit has to work under.

Or sometimes it is considered as a temperature which is not exceeded for more than a certain percent of the time. For instance, the highest temperature ever recorded in a certain city is 104 F. But a temperature of 100 F is only reached on an average of every other year. A temperature of 90 F is reached or exceeded on an average, for three days per month for the three summer months. A temperature of 87 F is reached or exceeded on an average of five days per month. Temperatures of more than 87 F are never experienced for over five hours per day, and usually for not over three hours. The average of the hottest temperature reached each day for July (the hottest month of the year) is 80 F. Different tables show design temperatures from 87 F to 90 F for this city. But in general, this difference will make less variation in the final results of a problem than other variables encountered.

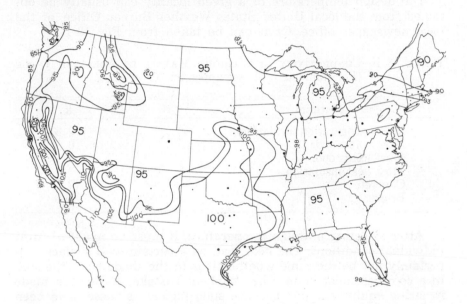

Fig. 18-1. Map of outside design dry bulb temperatures for summer cooling estimates.

The question might be asked, why not choose a machine that will operate at average conditions? The reason is that on the hottest days when refrigeration would be most needed, the equipment chosen on the basis of average temperatures would be too small. That might bring up the question, why not choose a system based on the maximum temperature, instead of on some theoretical temperature less than this? Any insulated box or building will have considerable cold holding capacity. If the outside temperature goes above the design temperature, it will take some time for this higher temperature to leak through the walls.

Before the extra temperature becomes effective in increasing the load on the equipment, the outside temperature drops again. This, plus the fact that the equipment should be chosen with a factor of safety makes it possible to figure from a temperature less than the worst condition to be encountered. It works out best to choose a unit that will be approximately fully loaded at average operating conditions, rather than one that is too big most of the time. These are the reasons for working from a design temperature which has been worked out to give an economical choice of equipment.

The design temperature of a given locality can usually be obtained from the local United States Weather Bureau Office, or the local newspaper office. Or it can be taken from Fig. 18-1.

TABLE 18-1—CONDUCTIVITY OF VARIOUS MATERIALS ABRIDGED TABLE
(For complete table see appendix, Table A-9)

Material	k
Most refrigeration insulations	0.3
Most soft woods	0.8
Most hardwoods	1.4
Most heat insulation	0.5
Concrete	12.0
Brick	5.0

After selecting a design temperature, it must be modified to fit individual conditions. The heat load on a certain wall surface will certainly not be the same whether it is in the shade or in the sun, in a cool basement or in a hot kitchen. Mistakes have been made in sizing equipment just because such factors as these have been overlooked.

k Factors.—Chapter 16 told something of how heat leaks, or is conducted through insulated walls. Test data has been collected on practically all substances used for wall construction or insulations. This data is given in the form of k factors, Table 18-1, or more completely in Table A-9 in the appendix. Fig. 18-2 shows the condition this k factor is to represent. *The k factor is the number of Btu's that will leak through one square foot of surface one inch thick in one hour's time for one degree temperature difference between the two sides of the surface.*

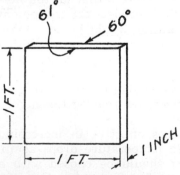

Fig. 18-2. Diagram of k factor conditions.

The k factor is used in the following formula.

$$Q_1 = \frac{Ak(t_2 - t_1)}{x} \quad \text{where}$$

Q_1 = total heat in Btu per hr leaking through the surface
A = total area in sq ft
k = leakage factor from Table 18-1 or A-9
t_2 = temperature on the warm side
t_1 = temperature on the cold side
x = thickness of the surface in in.

Example 18-1: How much heat will leak into an ice box 5 ft high, 3 ft wide, 2 ft 6 in deep with 3 in of corkboard insulation if the inside temperature is 40 F and the outside temperature is 75 F, Fig. 18-3?

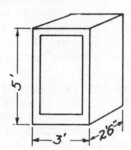

INSULATION
3" CORKBOARD

AMBIENT TEMPERATURE
75°

BOX TEMPERATURE
40°

Fig. 18-3. Reach in refrigerator. (Example 18-1)

The wall areas are as follows:
Front and back.............. $2 \times 5 \times 3$ = 30 sq ft
Both sides .... $2 \times 5 \times 2.5$ = 25 sq ft
Top and bottom.............. $2 \times 3 \times 2.5$ = 15 sq ft
Total Area...................... 70 sq ft

The formula is $Q_1 = \dfrac{Ak(t_2 - t_1)}{x}$

Substituting: $Q_1 = \dfrac{70 \times 0.28(75 - 40)}{3} = \dfrac{70 \times 0.28 \times .35}{3}$

= 229 Btu per hour heat leakage.[1]

Example 18-2: How much ice would be required to maintain the refrigeration of Example 18-1?

In Chapter 1 we found the latent heat of ice is 144 Btu per pound. Therefore it would require
$$\frac{229}{144} = 1.59 \text{ lb of ice per hour.}$$

[1]All figuring is to slide rule accuracy.

If a check is made of the insulating value of materials usually used for refrigeration insulation, it will be found that their k factors vary from 0.24 to 0.30 Btu per sq ft, with an average value nearer the latter figure. Therefore, for general figuring 0.30 can be used for the k factor of most insulations. The little error involved gives a small factor of safety which could help offset the fact that the insulation used might not be exactly like the test sample, or it may not be installed under the same conditions as the test sample. However, do not use 0.30 as the k factor of sawdust, shavings, or to any insulation that has been allowed to become wet.

If an insulated wall is made up of two or more types of material, the insulation usually has such a large insulating value compared to the other materials in the wall that everything but the insulation can be neglected for all practical purposes. If it is desired to make a check of the value of other than the insulating material, the insulation equivalent, or cork equivalent can be figured.[2] To do this, the k factor of the cork, 0.28, is divided by the k factor of the material considered.

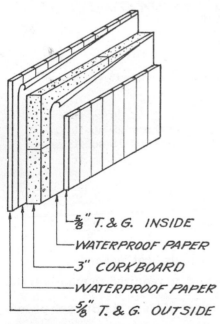

—⅝″ T.& G. INSIDE

—WATERPROOF PAPER

—3″ CORKBOARD

—WATERPROOF PAPER

—⅝″ T.& G. OUTSIDE

Fig. 18-4. Wall construction, cork and tongue and groove. (Example 18-3)

Example 18-3: A wall is made up of 3 in of corkboard with a layer of ⅝ in Oregon pine tongue and groove on each side. A layer of building paper is between each side of the cork and the tongue and groove, Fig. 18-4. What is the cork equivalent to the total wall?

The building paper is so thin that it can be neglected entirely as far as insulation is concerned (although it is essential for water proofing). The k factor of cork is 0.28 Btu per sq ft and that of the Oregon pine 0.80. The cork equivalent of the pine is

$$\frac{0.28}{0.80} = 0.35 \text{ inches}$$

This means one inch of this pine has the same insulation value as 0.35 inches of cork. This wall has two layers of ⅝ inch pine which makes a total of 1¼ inches. This 1¼ inches of pine is equivalent to 1.25 × 0.35 = 0.437 in. of cork.

[2]See Appendix page 489 for the mathematical method of doing this.

The decimals can be shortened to 0.44 inches for this type of calculation. Thus, the entire wall of Fig. 18-4 has the same insulating effect as a cork wall with no wood of the following thickness.

$$3 + 0.44 = 3.44 \text{ in of cork.}$$

Example 18-4: A 4 inch cork wall is set against a 12 inch brick wall, Fig. 18-5. What is the cork equivalent of the entire wall?

The k factor for brick is 5.0.

$$\frac{0.28}{5.0} = 0.056 \text{ in cork equivalent to 1 in of brick.}$$

$12 \times 0.056 = 0.66$ in cork equivalent to 12 in brick.

$4 + 0.66 = 4.66$ in of cork total equivalent wall thickness.

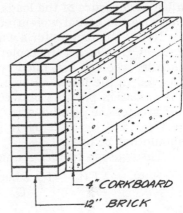

Thus, a 12 inch brick wall makes so little difference it is hardly worth figuring, and is usually neglected.

Fig. 18-5. Wall construction, cork and brick. (Example 18-4)

Usage Factors.—Examples 18-1 and 18-2 included only leakage loads, with no provision for cooling the food or other products going into the cabinets, the air that fills the cabinet at each door opening, etc. For small sized cabinets, the easiest way to figure the usage, as the food loads are ca'led, is on a volumetric basis. This is done with the help of volumetric factors, Table A-11 in the Appendix. The factors given are averages that have been worked out from experience. They give the Btu load per cubic foot per degree per hour. They are given for low, medium and heavy usage. That is, there is considerable variation in the use different establishments will give a certain sized cabinet. In general, heavier loads are applied to busy down town markets or to chain stores. The lightest loads are for small community stores.

Two factors which determine the size of the load are the temperature of the goods as they are loaded into the cabinet, and the frequency of loading or the amount loaded at a time. The warmer the product loaded, naturally, the heavier is the load. If everything loaded is already precooled, there will be little load on the system. The more product loaded at a time, or the more loaded per hour, the heavier is the load. By more product is meant more weight. Bulky foods such as leafy vegetables will not create as great a load per crate as solid products. More weight of meat is often handled in a given sized cabinet than most other products. Some judgment is required to properly survey a job and extract from the owner sufficient information to make an intelligent guess as to the usage factor to use. But these usage factor guides have been found to give a better measure of the loads in average cabinets than to attempt to measure the actual weight of food to be loaded in and refrigerated.

Notice the factors for a walk in cooler are less than for a reach in cabinet. The larger the cooler, the less in proportion can it be loaded. Smaller coolers are filled with shelves, and the shelves may be "loaded to the limit." However, the larger the cabinet, the greater the variation possible between a light load and a heavy load. And the greater the possible error if one is made. Above about 1500 cubic feet (a 15 ft by 10 ft by 10 ft cabinet), this method of calculation should not be used.

These usage factors are used with the following formula.

$$Q_u = VF(t_2 - t_1) \text{ where}$$

Q_u = heat load due to usage, Btu per hour.
V = net volume in cubic feet.
F = usage factor from Table A-11.

Example 18-5: What would be the total heat load for Example 18-1 using average usage?

The net inside dimensions of the cabinet will be the outside dimensions minus the thickness of two insulated walls. In this case the inside dimensions become

4½ by 2½ by 2 ft

The net volume is $4.5 \times 2.5 \times 2 = 22.5$ cu ft

The formula is $Q_u = VF(t_2 - t_1)$
Substituting: $Q_u = 22.5 \times 0.22(75 - 40)$
             $= 173$ Btu per hr

In Example 18-1, we found the leakage load to be 229 Btu per hr.

Therefore the total load will be

$229 + 173 = 402$ Btu per hr.

Condensing Unit Size.—Commercial size condensing units should not be chosen to operate continuously. They should have rest periods to cool off if they are to give a maximum of trouble-free service. Most condensing units are chosen on a 16 hour running time per 24 hours. That is, if all the time per day the unit was running was added up, it would amount to not over 16 hours. To choose a condensing unit under this condition use the following formula:

$$Q_c = Q_t \times \frac{24}{16} = 1.5 \, Q_t \text{ where}$$

Q_c = Btu per hr capacity of the required condensing unit.
Q_t = Total Btu capacity of load.

In some cases, conditions may justify units chosen for other than 16 hours per day running time. However, 16 hours is considered good practice.

K Factors. — The heat leakage through some surfaces is better given for the average thickness such surfaces are made, rather than for one inch. Glass is one of these. This is given per square foot per degree per hour, but not per inch thick. It is given for the average thickness or average construction used. Data for this is also given in Table A-9. Notice capital K is used. The capital K means no thickness is involved. The only difference in its use is that the thickness factor x is eliminated from the heat leakage formula. Where different walls of a box are made up of different construction, each must be figured separately.

Example 18-6.—What is the Btu capacity of the required condensing unit for the cabinet in Fig. 18-6? A 40 F cabinet is required in Sacramento, California. The usage is estimated to be average. The cabinet has 3 in of a standard insulation. The doors are triple glass.

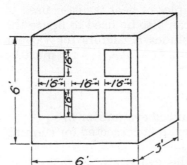

INSULATION: 3"

DOORS: TRIPLE GLASS

AMBIENT TEMPERATURE: 105°

BOX TEMPERATURE: 40°

Fig. 18-6. Reach in box with glass doors. (Example 18-6)

Since this will go in a retail store, the ambient temperature around the cabinet will probably be no higher than the design temperature. This is given as 105 F for Sacramento.

The gross area of the cabinet is as follows:

Front and back	2 x 6 x 6 =	72 sq ft
Side	2 x 3 x 6 =	36 sq ft
Top and Bottom	2 x 3 x 6 =	36 sq ft
Total gross area	=	144 sq ft

There are five glass doors, each 1.5 feet square.
Therefore the area of the glass is:

$$5 \times 1.5 \times 1.5 = 11.25 \text{ sq ft}$$

Net insulated wall area = **133** sq ft
to the nearest even figure.

Heat leakage through insulated walls:

$$Q_l = \frac{Ak\ (t_2 - t_1)}{x}$$

$$= \frac{133 \times 0.3(105 - 40)}{3} = 864 \text{ Btu per hr}$$

Heat leakage through glass doors:

$$Q_{lg} = AK(t_2 - t_1)$$

$$= 11.25 \times 0.29(105 - 40) = 212 \text{ Btu per hr}$$

The net volume will be:

$$5.5 \times 5.5 \times 2.5 = 75.6 \text{ cu ft}$$

The usage load will be:

$$Q_u = VF(t_2 - t_1)$$

$$= 75.6 \times 0.22 \times (105 - 40) = \underline{1081} \text{ Btu per hr}$$

The total heat load will be $\qquad$ 2157 Btu per hr

The required size condensing unit corrected for running time will be:

$$Q_c = 1.5\ Q_t = 1.5 \times 2157 = 3236 \text{ Btu per hr.}$$

Evaporator Sizing.—The same principles of heat transfer used to calculate the heat flow through a wall can also be used to figure the size evaporator needed. Table A-12 includes K factors for various types of evaporator surfaces. The formula $Q = AK(t_2 - t_1)$ must be rearranged to solve for A.

$$A = \frac{Q}{K(t_2 - t_1)}$$ In this case

> A = surface area of required evaporator in sq ft
> Q = Total Btu load on cabinet corrected for running time
> K = Heat transfer of the evaporator under conditions of operation.
> t_2 = Temperature of the air in the cabinet.
> t_1 = Temperature of the refrigerant in the evaporator.

Example 18-7.—How much $\frac{5}{8}$ in bare copper tubing would be needed to make an evaporator for the cabinet in Example 18-6? Assume 20 F temperature difference between the cabinet and the refrigerant, and a dry expansion evaporator. K factor for the copper tube can be assumed as 2.5 Btu per sq ft per deg. temperature difference.

$$A = \frac{Q}{K(t_2 - t_1)}$$

$$= \frac{3236}{2.5 \times 20} = 64.7 \text{ sq ft}$$

From Table A-7 we find that it takes 6.1 lineal feet of ⅝ inch tubing to make one square foot. Therefore this evaporator requires:

6.1 × 64.7 = 395 lineal feet of ⅝ in copper tubing.

Most evaporators for low pressure refrigerants are made of finned tubing. The fins give extra heat transfer surface which makes it possible to get the same results with less tubing and a smaller sized evaporator. However, the size of the fins with relation to the size of the tubing, the number of fins per inch, and the type of contact between the fins and the tubing all effect the heat transfer. For this reason it is almost impossible to accurately figure the heat transfer from a finned coil.

Manufacturer's tables, which are based on test data, should be depended on to tell what their equipment will do. These tables are set up in different ways by different manufacturers. But any variation in these coils follows the formula just given for evaporator areas. A given coil can give a variety of capacities, depending on the temperature difference between the refrigerant and the cabinet air. Table 18-2 shows how one manufacturer sets up his rating table. Notice how a correction is made for different temperature differences:

Example 18-8.—What forced draft coil from Table 18-2 would be suitable for the cabinet in Example 18-6 if 20 F temperature difference was permissible?

A C3C195 coil has a capacity of 3900 Btu per hour. The next size smaller does not have the required capacity of 3236 Btu at 20 F temperature difference, so the C3C195 coil must be chosen.

Some tables only give the coil ratings for one temperature difference, usually 15 F or 20 F. Sometimes it is necessary to find the capacity of these coils at some different temperature difference to fit a particular job. Even when ratings are given for several temperature differences as in Table 18-2, it is sometimes desirable to figure them at some temperature difference not given. The easiest way to do this is to find the Btu capacity per degree from the conditions given, then figure it for the required condition.

Example 18-9.—What is the Btu capacity of the C3C195 coil in Table 18-2 at 12 F temperature difference?

If its Btu capacity at a temperature difference of 10 F is 1950 Btu, its capacity per degree is:

$$\frac{1950}{10} = 195 \text{ Btu per degree.}$$

Its capacity for 12 F would then be:

$$12 \times 195 = 2340 \text{ Btu.}$$

Example 18-10.—If the coil C3B130 of Table 18-2 was chosen for

Example 18-6, what temperature difference between the cabinet air temperature and the refrigerant temperature would be necessary?
The capacity per degree would be:
$$\frac{1300}{10} = 130 \text{ Btu.}$$
The require load is 3236 Btu. Therefore a temperature difference of the following is required:
$$\frac{3236}{130} = 24.9 \text{ F or 25 F as near as it is practical to read it.}$$
Since the required cabinet temperature is 40 F, the required evaporator temperature for the job would be:
$$40 - 25 = 15 \text{ F.}$$

Example 18-11.—A walk in cooler, Fig. 18-7 is to be maintained at 38 F. It is in Denver, Colorado. The walls are 3½ in of glass wool. The floor is 4 in of corkboard. The floor is on a concrete slab which is laid directly on the ground. The cooler is to be used for meat in a busy market. What is the Btu rating of the required condensing unit and coil, if a blower coil with a 10 F temperature difference is to be used?

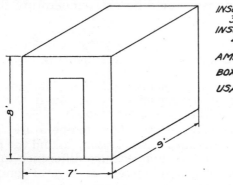

INSULATION: WALLS AND CEILING
3½ GLASS WOOL
INSULATION: FLOOR
4" CORKBOARD

AMBIENT TEMPERATURE: 90°
BOX TEMPERATURE: 38°
USAGE: HEAVY

Fig. 18-7. Walk in cooler. (Example 18-11)

Cabinet wall and ceiling areas.

Front and back	2 x 8 x 7	= 112 sq ft
Sides	2 x 8 x 9	= 144 sq ft
Ceiling	7 x 9	= 63 sq ft
Total area of glass wool		= 319 sq ft
Floor area	7 x 9	= 63 sq ft

Heat leakage figures:

$$(\text{Walls}) \; Q_1 = \frac{Ak(t_2 - t_1)}{x}$$
$$= \frac{319 \times 0.29 \times (90 - 38)}{3.5} = 1380 \text{ Btu per hr.}$$

TABLE 18-2—TYPICAL RATINGS AND DATA ON UNIT COOLERS

| Unit Model No. | BTU Per Hr. at Specified TD Between Ent. Air and Refrig.* | | | CFM | Outlet Air Vel. FPM | Motor | | Fan Dia. | Pounds Freon—12 Charge (30% Vol.) | *** Pounds Methyl Chloride Charge (30% Vol.) | **** Pounds Sulphur Dioxide Charge (30% Vol.) |
	20° TD	15° TD	10° TD			RPM	HP				
C3A90	1,800	1,350	900	285	528	1500	1/30	8 in.	0.85	0.59	0.88
C3B130	2,600	1,950	1,300	451	543	1500	1/30	10 in.	1.23	0.85	1.27
C3C195	3,900	2,925	1,950	738	590	1500	1/30	12 in.	1.46	1.01	1.50
C3D304	6,080	4,560	3,040	1040	518	1140	1/20	14 in.	2.12	1.46	2.18
C3E428	8,560	6,420	4,280	1300	518	1140	1/20	16 in.	3.02	2.08	3.11
**C3E600	12,000	9,000	6,000	1437	573	1140	1/12	18 in.	4.03	2.78	4.15
**C3F780	15,600	11,700	7,800	1880	595	1140	1/8	20 in.	5.30	3.66	5.46
**C3G900	18,000	13,500	9,000	2065	570	1140	1/9	20 in.	6.15	4.24	6.33

* Capacity based on continuous running of compressor and unit at test conditions of 40° Ent. DB and 85% RH. To select unit it will be necessary to take into consideration the off period of the condensing unit.
** Capacities based on units equipped by the user with valves having an external equalizer.
*** If units are used with Methyl-Chloride, the Btu Ratings will be as listed. Suitable compressor operation is assumed.
**** If units are used with Sulphur-Dioxide, the Btu Ratings will be as listed. Suitable compressor operation is assumed.
NOTE: On some applications it may be disirable to operate at 25° TD. In such cases multiply the 20° TD Btu Ratings by 1.25.

GENERAL UNIT COOLER RECOMMENDATIONS

As a general practice we do not recommend these Unit Coolers for temperatures less than 38 degrees F., Average (36 to 40 degrees F.)

An attempt to operate these Unit Coolers to maintain lower than 38 F. temperatures may create a tendency to build up an excessive amount of frost on the unit cooler core. We recommend fans on all Unit Coolers to operate continuously. An intermittent control switch may be used provided no difficulty is experienced in obtaining the proper setting in synchronization with Condensing Unit. Motors furnished with these Unit Coolers are satisfactory for continuous operation and only require attention for oil occasionally.—Courtesy Fedders Manufacturing Co.

Due to the poor insulating value of the concrete, it will be neglected. Where a floor is laid directly on the ground, it is not necessary to figure the heat transfer from the design temperature. Probable the best method is to assume the ground is at the mean (day and night) summer temperature. Such mean temperatures are also available from weather bureau data. If this mean temperature is not available for the job being figured, an average between the design temperature and the required temperature can be used. If this average is below 50 F, (this only happens on freezer jobs) 50 F should be used instead of the average. In this case the average temperature is:

$$\frac{90 + 38}{2} = 64\,F$$

$$(\text{Floor Leakage})\ Q_l = \frac{Ak(t_2 - t_1)}{x}$$

$$\frac{63 \times 0.28 \times (64 - 38)}{4} = 115\ \text{Btu per hr.}$$

The net volume will be:
6'5" x 7'4½" x 8'5" =
6.42 x 7.38 x 8.42 = 400 cu ft
A meat load in a busy market will certainly be heavy usage.
The usage load will be:

$$Q_u = VF(t_2 - t_1)$$
$$= 400 \times 0.12 \times (90 - 38) = 2500\ \text{Btu per hr}$$

The total heat load will be:
1380 + 115 + 2500 = 3995 Btu per hr
The Btu rating of the required condensing unit and coil is:

$$Q_c = 1.5\,Q_t = 1.5 \times 3995 = 5993\ \text{Btu per hr.}$$

The coil will be chosen at a 10 F temperature difference, and the condensing unit will be chosen for a 28 F suction temperature.

Boxes Over 1500 Cubic Feet.—As previously mentioned, usage factors are apt to give misleading results if used on boxes or cabinets over 1500 cubic feet. In such cases, the amount of product loaded into the cabinet, its temperature, and the time allowed to cool it should be accurately determined. Its heat load is then figured by the method given in Chapter 1. Also, all cases where a liquid or foods are frozen should be figured. A large freezer load can be put in a small space, and average volumetric factors are not large enough to cover them.

Example 18-12.—A cooler, 20 ft × 20 ft × 8 ft ceiling is to be built. It will set out in the sun in a location where the design temperature is 90 F. The walls are insulated with 12 inches of sawdust. It should have capacity to cool 15 tons of peaches per 24 hours from a field heat of 90 F to a temperature of 35 F. What is the refrigeration load?

Since the building sets out in the sun, a correction on the design temperature must be made for sun effect. Corrections for sun effect are given in Table A-10. Here we find even the color of the wall makes a difference. Dark colors absorb more heat than light colors. Aluminum paint or polished metal surfaces absorb the least. In this case, a recheck shows the building will be painted a light color. This does not reflect as much heat as aluminum paint, so average figures are used. This gives 30 F to be added to the temperature of the roof, 20 F to the east or west wall, and 10 F to the south wall. Since the sun cannot shine on the east and west wall at the same time, either can be chosen on which to make the correction, but not both.

Roof area $\qquad$ $20 \times 20 = 400$ sq ft
Area of one wall $\quad 20 \times 8 = 160$ sq ft
Heat transmission (roof)

$$Q_1 = \frac{Ak(t_2 - t_1)}{x}$$

$$= \frac{400 \times 0.57 \times (90 + 30 - 35)}{12} = 1620 \text{ Btu per hr}$$

Heat transmission (north and east wall)

$$Q_1 = \frac{(160 + 160) \times 0.57 \,(90 - 35)}{12} = 835 \text{ Btu per hr}$$

Heat transmission (south wall)

$$Q_1 = \frac{160 \times 0.57 \times (90 + 10 - 35)}{12} = 493 \text{ Btu per hr}$$

Heat transmission (west wall)

$$Q_1 = \frac{160 \times 0.57 \times (90 + 20 - 35)}{12} = 570 \text{ Btu per hr}$$

Heat transmission (floor)

$$Q_1 = \frac{400 \times 0.57 \times \left(\dfrac{90 + 35}{2} - 35\right)}{12} = 523 \text{ Btu per hr}$$

Total heat leakage $\qquad\qquad\qquad$ 4041 Btu per hr

Beside the actual leakage through the walls, there will be some loss every time the door is opened. This loss is not only caused by the warm air that enters and must be cooled, but by the latent heat of the moisture in the air as it condenses and freezes on the coils. The usage factors given in the previous method of calculation include this. But here a separate allowance must be made for these losses. A common allowance is 15 percent of the leakage load. So in this case;

Door leakage $= 0.15 \times 4041 = 606$ Btu per hr
Usage load: to cool 15 tons of peaches:
$Q_u = WS(t_2 - t_1)$
$\quad = 15 \times 2000 \times 0.92 \times (90 - 35) = 1{,}520{,}000$ Btu per day

Since this can be done in 24 hours, this will be:

$$\frac{1{,}520{,}000}{24} = 63{,}200 \text{ Btu per hr}$$

The total heat load will be:

Leakage	4,041 Btu per hr
Door losses	606 Btu per hr
Usage	63,200 Btu per hr
Total	67,847 Btu per hr

If a machine using a low pressure refrigerant was to be chosen for this, we still have to correct for running time.

$Q_c = 1.5 \ Q_t = 1.5 \times 67,847 = 101,770$ Btu per hr

Ammonia equipment is usually made to stand continuous operation. Therefore if an ammonia machine was to be chosen for this job, it should be picked on a different basis. However, it would not be safe to choose a machine with a capacity of 67,847 Btu per hour, because this gives no factor of safety. An increase of 25 to 50 percent should be made to cover variables such as higher temperatures, extra loads, etc. Therefore a machine as small as:

$1.25 \times 67,847 = 84,809$ Btu per hr might be chosen.

Where it might be necessary to cool a product load such as this without affecting other goods already in storage, it is not uncommon to double estimated loads. Also, ammonia machines are usually rated in tons of refrigeration instead of in Btu per hour. In this case the actual load would be:

$$\frac{67,847}{12,000} = 5.65 \text{ tons of refrigeration.}$$

To cover the above mentioned factor of safety, equipment capable of producing 7.06 to 11.3 tons of refrigeration should be chosen. Whether it should be the lower figure or the higher depends on the dependability and accuracy of the data submitted, on the possible results of an overload, and on permissible costs.

Example 18-13.—An ice maker is to be put in a restaurant kitchen in Chicago, Illinois. The cabinet is identical to the cabinet in Fig. 18-3. It must be able to produce 25 lb of ice every four hours. Assume the water must be cooled from 70 F. What is the Btu load?

A small ice maker usually operates at a 0 F refrigerant temperature. It will be assumed the cabinet air chills to 15 F. The design temperature in Chicago is 95 F, but a check shows the kitchen rises 15 F above outside temperatures.

The heat transfer is:

$$Q_1 = \frac{Ak(t_2 - t_1)}{x}$$

$$= \frac{70 \times 0.28 \times (95 + 15 - 15)}{3} \qquad = 621 \text{ Btu per hr}$$

The door losses are: 0.15×621 $\qquad\qquad = \ \ 93$ Btu per hr

The product load per pound of water is as follows:

To cool water to 32 F	(70 — 32)	= 38 Btu
To freeze water (latent heat)		= 144 Btu
To cool ice, 32 F to 4 F, 0.5 (32 — 0)		= 16 Btu
Total load per lb of water		= 198 Btu

Therefore the load to freeze 25 lb of water in 4 hours is:

$$\frac{198 \times 25}{4} = 1240 \text{ Btu per hr.}$$

The total load will be:

Leakage	=	621 Btu per hr
Door Losses	=	93 Btu per hr
Usage	=	1240 Btu per hr
Total		1954 Btu per hr

Correction for running time:

$Q_c = 1.5 \, Q_t = 1.5 \times 1954 = 2931$ Btu per hr.

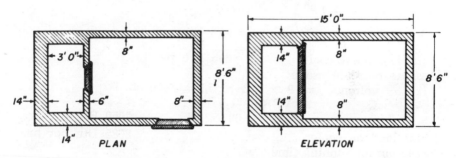

Fig. 18-8. Cooler-Freezer. (Example 18-14).

Example 18-14.—A combination cooler-freezer, Figure 18-8, is to hold a temperature of 35 F in the cooler and −10 F in the freezer. The insulation is shredded redwood bark. The design temperature is 90 F. There is a fan in the freezer compartment drawing 50 watts. It is specified that the freezer must be able to freeze up to 25 pounds of miscellaneous food products per hour. What is the Btu capacity of the required compressor?

Areas 90 F to 35 F (1)

Sides	2 × 8.5 × 10	=	170	sq. ft.
End	8.5 × 8.5	=	78.2	sq. ft.
Ceiling	8.5 × 10	=	85	sq. ft.
	Total	=	327.2	sq. ft.

Area of cooler floor (2)

	8.5 × 10	=	85	sq. ft.

Areas 90 F to −10 F (3)

Sides	2 × 4.5 × 8.5	=	76.5	sq. ft.
End	8.5 × 8.5	=	72.2	sq. ft.
Ceiling	8.5 × 4.5	=	38.2	sq. ft.
	Total	=	186.9	sq. ft.

Area of freezer floor (4)
$$4.5 \times 8.5 = 38.2 \text{ sq. ft.}$$

Area 90 F to 35 F (5)
$$8.5 \times 8.5 = 72.2 \text{ sq. ft.}$$

Heat transfer, Area (1)

$$Q_1 = \frac{Ak\,(t_2 - t_1)}{x}$$

$$= \frac{327.2 \times 0.25\,(90 - 35)}{8} = 562 \text{ Btu per hr.}$$

Heat transfer, Area (2)

$$Q_1 = \frac{85 \times 0.25\left(\dfrac{55}{2}\right)}{8} = 73 \text{ Btu per hr.}$$

Total leakage to cooler   635 Btu per hr.

Assume medium usage

$$\text{volume} = 9 \times 7.2 \times 7.2 = 466 \text{ cu. ft.}$$
$$Q_u = VF\,(t_2 - t_1)$$
$$= 466 \times .08 \times 55 = 2050 \text{ Btu per hr.}$$

Total load on cooler................   2685 Btu per hr.

Correction for running time

$$Q_c = 1.5\,Q_t = 1.5 \times 2682 = 4027 \text{ Btu per hr.}$$

Heat transfer, Area (3)

$$Q_1 = \frac{186.9 \times 0.25\,[90 - (-10)]}{14} = 334 \text{ Btu per hr.}$$

Heat transfer, Area (4)

$$Q_1 = \frac{38.2 \times 0.25\left(\dfrac{100}{2}\right)}{14} = 34 \text{ Btu per hr.}$$

Heat transfer, Area (5)

$$Q_1 = \frac{72.2 \times 0.25\,[35 - (-10)]}{6} = 136 \text{ Btu per hr.}$$

Total leakage to freezer   504 Btu per hr.

The freezer load is to be made up of a variety of products. A check of the tables will show that the following figures will give a fair average.

Specific heat before freezing   0.8 Btu per lb
Specific heat after freezing   0.4 Btu per lb
Freezing point   28 F
Latent heat of freezing   110 Btu per lb

The load per pound of food will be:

To cool to 28 F   0.8 × (90 — 28)   = 49.6 Btu per lb
To freeze   = 110 Btu per lb
To cool to —20 F 0.4 × [28 — (—20)] = 19.2 Btu per lb

Total .... 178.8 Btu per lb

The load for 25 lb per hr is:

$$25 × 178.8 = 4470 \text{ Btu per hr}$$

The heat from the fan is:

50 × 3.41   = 170 Btu per hr.

Total load on freezer _____

Leakage   = 504 Btu per hr.
Product   = 5101 Btu per hr.
Fan   = 170 Btu per hr.
Total   5775 Btu per hr.

Correction for running time

$$Q_c = 1.5 \, Qt = 1.5 × 5775 \qquad = 8662 \text{ Btu per hr.}$$

The total load could be handled by two condensing units. The one to the cooler would require a capacity of 4027 Btu per hr at 15 F suction temperature. The second to the freezer would require a capacity of 8662 Btu per hr —20 F suction. Or the load could be handled by one condensing unit of 4027 + 8662 = 12,689 Btu capacity at —20 F. More will be given on methods of two-temperature multiple hook ups in Chapter 25.

Thickness of Insulation.—The cost of refrigeration is made up of two parts, the cost of cooling the product and the cost of holding the temperature. The cost of cooling the product cannot be changed, other than the savings made by economical operation. The cost of holding the temperature is directly proportional to the heat transmission. This is proportional to the thickness of insulation. Economical thicknesses of insulation have been pretty well worked out for different temperature differences, Table 18-3.

TABLE 18-3—RECOMMENDED THICKNESS OF INSULATION

Cooler temperature	Thickness in inches
Over 45	2
35 to 45	3
20 to 35	4
5 to 20	5
— 5 to 5	6
—20 to — 5	8
—35 to —20	10
—50 to —35	12

The thicker the insulation, the more it costs, but the less operating costs will be. The thicknesses of Table 18-3 have been established by practice for all types of insulation having a good k factor, although they were first worked out for corkboard. With sawdust, shavings, or an insulation of similar k factor a greater thickness is used to make up for the poorer insulating value. However, some designers feel that in many cases where overall economy is important, it is good practice to use a greater thickness of one of the cheaper insulations, as long as it had a good k factor. If 8 inches of one type of insulation can be installed for the same price as 4 inches of another having the same k factor per inch, the annual savings in refrigeration can be considerable.

Domestic and commercial freezer boxes are an exception to the above rules. An additional factor is that a domestic box must be able to go through a 2 ft 8 in door, and a commercial box through a 3 ft door. If not, they cannot be moved into the buildings where they are to be used. To install the conventional thickness of insulation in such cabinets with these limiting exterior dimensions would make the usable space too small. Therefore compromises must be made between space limitations and desirable insulation standards. This makes a wonderful application for some of the synthetic, low k factor insulations.

Condensers.—The heat transfer in a water cooled condenser has several variables. One of the first of these is the fact that as the water absorbs heat, its temperature rises. Therefore the temperature difference is not constant. Fig. 7-5 shows graphically the temperature changes actually taking place. Since there is a much higher temperature difference at the beginning with the highly superheated discharge gas, it would seem the heat transfer would be greatest at this point. However, a wet surface is a better heat conductor than a dry surface. Therefore the k factor of the metal is less until sufficient condensation starts to wet the condensing surface. So these two items more or less cancel each other.

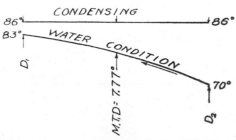

Fig. 18-9. **Mean temperature difference conditions.**

In practice, the superheating and sub-cooling are usually neglected for calculations. Conditions for a typical problem are assumed as in Fig. 18-9. Even here, notice there is a variation in temperature differences. The temperature difference that must be used in the heat transfer formula is a logarithmic mean temperature difference. This can be calculated from the following formula.

$$MTD = \frac{D_2 - D_1}{2.3 \log \frac{D_2}{D_1}} \quad \text{where}$$

MTD = log mean temperature difference.
D_2 = greater temperature difference.
D_1 = least temperature difference.

Example 18-15.—What is the log mean temperature difference of Fig. 18-9?

$$MTD = \frac{D_2 - D_1}{2.3 \log \frac{D_2}{D_1}}$$

$$= \frac{16 - 3}{2.3 \log \frac{16}{3}} = 7.77 \text{ F}$$

To save time and the need of logarithmic tables to solve this formula, tables of answers have been made up, Table A-14. From this table the answer to the above or any other similar problem can be read directly.

This formula or table will work whether the temperature of one or both sides of the heat transfer surfaces vary. For instance, if one fluid was used to cool another fluid, the temperature of both will vary. But this formula or tables can still be used with accurate results.

A second variable in the performance of a condenser is the total quantity of water circulated. The less the water used, the higher will be its temperature rise to carry away the required heat. But the higher the temperature rise, the higher will be the condensing temperature. And the higher the condensing temperature, the more heat of compression is generated by the compressor, which means more heat to be absorbed by the water. Fig. 18-10 shows the total heat per ton per minute to be removed by the condenser for different operating conditions. This is figured for ammonia, but the results are very close to the same for any common refrigerant.

A third variable which ties in very closely with the quantity of water is the effect of the velocity of the water. The faster the flow, the higher the heat transfer or k factor of the surface. Naturally, the more water through a given sized condenser, the faster it must flow. Its effect is shown in Fig. 18-11 or Table A-12.

Still another variable in condenser operation is the condition of the heat transfer surface. This is also shown for a particular condenser and a particular water condition in Fig. 18-11. Its exact condition for any condenser will depend on the water hardness, water treatment, and the length of time between cleanings. The designer must take this into account if the condenser is to be adequate under

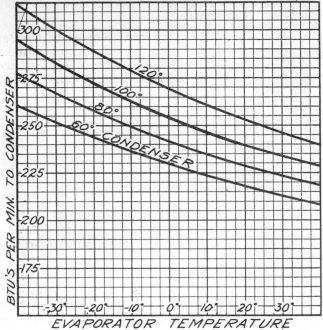

Fig. 18-10. Btu per minute to condenser per ton refrigeration.

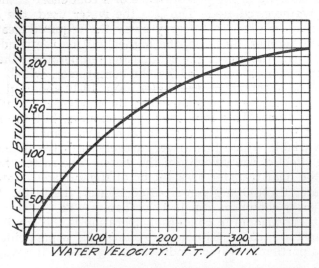

Fig. 18-11. Heat transfer in horizontal shell and tube condenser.

average cleaning schedules. The operating engineer must recognize the significance of this, and maintain proper cleaning schedules.

To combine all these factors, complete data on the condenser to be used must be had. Different manufacturers set their rating tables up differently. But they should include all the above variables. It is usually possible with these manufacturer's tables to choose two or three sizes of condensers to fit a particular job. But it is important to recognize the fact that to save a little money on the first cost of a condenser usually results in higher operating costs for the life of the equipment. It should also be remembered that the only disadvantage of an adequate size condenser is the first cost. But it will keep condensing pressures at a minimum which means reduced power costs. An oversize condenser is cheaper than an oversize compressor. Yet the oversize condenser will aid the compressor in handling an overload by keeping the head pressure down. But an overload on even an oversize compressor will overload everything in the system if the condenser is inadequate.

Example 18-16.—A horizontal shell and tube condenser is to be chosen for an ammonia plant rated at 50 tons at a 5 F evaporator and an 86 F condenser. If 70 F water is available, what size condenser would be suitable?

From Fig. 18-10, the heat to the condenser would be 242 Btu per minute per ton at these conditions.

$$50 \times 242 = 12{,}100 \text{ Btu per min total load.}$$

High water velocities are desirable for best heat transfer values, but undesirable because they increase pumping costs. If a velocity of 250 ft per min is chosen, from Fig. 18-11 we find a k factor of 190 Btu per hr per degree temperature difference.

If the same water is recirculated over a cooling tower, a 5 F rise is permissible. To absorb 12,100 Btu with a 5 F rise requires:

$$\frac{12{,}100}{5} = 2420 \text{ lb of water per min.}$$

There are 8.34 pounds of water per gallon, so this is:

$$\frac{2420}{8.34} = 290 \text{ gal of water per min.}$$

The heat transfer formula uses heat in terms of Btu per hour. Therefore the load of 12,100 Btu per min is:

$$12{,}100 \times 60 = 726{,}000 \text{ Btu per hr.}$$

If a mean temperature difference of 7 F is assumed, the required heat transfer area would be:

$$A = \frac{H}{K\,td} \qquad \text{where } td = (t_2 - t_1), \text{ which in this case is the mean temperature difference.}$$

$$= \frac{726{,}000}{190 \times 7} = 546 \text{ sq ft of pipe surface.}$$

If 2 inch pipe is used, from Table A-8 we find it takes 1.61 lineal feet of pipe to make one square foot of surface. Therefore the condenser must have a total of:

546 × 1.61 = 880 lineal ft of 2 in pipe.

If a condenser 10 feet long is chosen, this would be:

$$\frac{880}{10} = 88 \text{ tubes.}$$

The volume flowing through a pipe is found by multiplying the pipe area by the velocity of flow. From Table A-8 the internal area of a 2 inch pipe is 0.0233 sq ft. Then the volume flowing through one pipe is:

250 × 0.0233 = 5.82 cu ft per min.

There are 7.48 gallons per cubic foot. Therefore:

5.82 × 7.48 = 43.6 gal per min per pipe.

Therefore, to carry 290 gal per min of water the condenser would have to be built so the following number of pipes were paralleled.

$$\frac{290}{43.6} = 6.65 \text{ or } 7 \text{ tubes.}$$

To parallel 7 tubes with a total of 88 tubes would require the following.

$$\frac{88}{7} = 12.6 \text{ passes.}$$

The total number tubes, the number of tubes per pass, and the total number of passes must all be rearranged to make them come out whole numbers. Usually the inlet and outlet water headers are on the same end of the condenser for convenience in piping. This requires an even number of passes in the condenser. In this case, 12 passes of 7 tubes per pass would not give the required surface. Therefore 12 passes of 8 tubes each would be required.

Since a 70 F water temperature was included in the data given, and we assumed a 5 F rise in water temperature and a 7 F mean temperature difference, the condensing temperature will be less than 86 F. However, the figures given follow more nearly the conditions found in practice where plenty of water is available. As mentioned before, 5 F evaporator and 86 F condenser is a standard at which refrigeration equipment is rated. Actual operating conditions are usually at different temperatures.

Example 18-17.—What would be the condensing temperature for the condenser chosen under the conditions of Example 18-16?

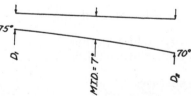

Fig. 18-12. Mean temperature difference conditions. (Example 18-17)

The data given tells us there is a mean temperature difference of 7 F, entering water is at 70 F, and leaving water at 75 F. Fig. 18-12 shows graphically what is known of the problem. The beginning and final temperature differences are 5 F apart. So by trial and error from Table A-14, temperatures 5 F apart are checked until a mean temperature of 7 F is found. A start can be made with temperature differences of 4 F and 9 F. This gives a mean temperature of 6.17 F which is too small. Temperatures of 5 F and 10 F give a mean of 7.21. This is slightly over the 7 degrees required, but is the nearest even temperature. This will give a condensing temperature of:

70 + 10 = 80 F or
75 + 5 = 80 F

Example 18-18.—What would be the condensing temperature if the water over the condenser of Example 18-16 was reduced to 4 gallons per minute per ton?

The total water over the condenser will then be:

4 × 50 = 200 gal per min.
200 × 8.34 = 1668 lb of water per min.

To absorb 12,100 Btu with 1668 pounds of water would cause the following temperature rise.

$$\frac{12,100}{1668} = 7.25 \text{ F}$$

The velocity of the water is the volume divided by the area of pipe through which it flows. The area will be the area of eight 2 inch pipes. The volume of water in cubic feet is:

$$\frac{200}{7.48} = 26.8 \text{ cu ft}$$

The velocity will then be:

$$\text{Velocity} = \frac{26.8}{8 \times 0.0233} = 143.5 \text{ ft per min.}$$

From this velocity and Fig. 18-11, we find the K factor is 140 Btu per square foot per degree per hour. To find the required temperature difference, the heat transfer formula must be rearranged.

$$H = A K \, td$$

$$td = \frac{H}{AK}$$

$$= \frac{12,100 \times 60}{546 \times 140} = 9.5 \text{ F}$$

Fig. 18-13 shows graphically what is now known about the problem. Now by trial and error we must find a D_2 and D_1 7 F apart (7.25 F if we could) which give a mean temperature difference of 9.5 F. Temperatures of 6 F and

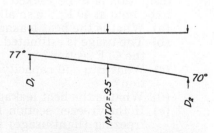

Fig. 18-13. Mean temperature difference conditions. (Example 18-18)

13 F give a mean of 9.08; 7 F and 14 F give a mean of 10.1. The 6 F and 13 F figures give the closest to the required answer, and if the 13 F was increased to 13.25 F which is the accurate figure, this would raise the 9.08 F to a point even closer to the required 9.5 F. To use the 13.25 F figure the condensing temperature would be:

70 + 13.25 = 83.25 F

QUESTIONS

18–1. A reach in cabinet is 7 feet high, 8 feet long, and 3 feet deep. The insulation is 3 inches of corkboard. It is to be maintained at 40 F in New Orleans. (Design Temp 94 F).
(a) What is the heat leakage load?
(b) If average usage is expected, what is the usage load?
(c) What is the Btu rating of the required evaporator coil and condensing unit?

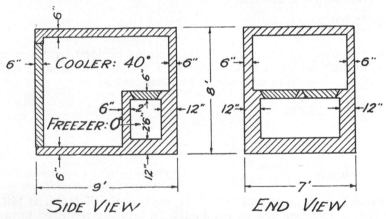

Fig. 18-14. Combination cooler and freezer box. (Question 18-2)

18–2. A combined cooler and freezer, Fig. 18-14, is to be built for farm use in New York near Buffalo (Design Temp 83 F). The insulation is to be packed mineral wool. The walk in space is to be held at 40 F; the small compartment at 0 F.
(a) What is the heat leakage on the 40 F section?
(b) The usage is estimated as light. What is the usage load on the 40 F section?
(c) What Btu coil capacity should be chosen for the 40 F section?
(d) What is the heat leakage on the freezer section?
(e) If the freezer section is to be used only for storage, no freezing (light usage) what would be the usage load?
(f) If the freezer had to be able to freeze 300 pounds of mixed food products per 24 hours, and cool them to 0 F, what would be the usage load?

(g) What Btu capacity condensing unit would be chosen for the entire job if the freezer was used only for storage?

(h) What Btu capacity condensing unit would be chosen for the entire job if the freezer was used as in (f).

18–3. A small steak box the size of Fig. 18-3 is to go beside the stove in a restaurant in Atlanta, Georgia (Design temp 91 F). It has 3 inches of average insulation. It is estimated the kitchen will be 20 F warmer than the design temperature. One of the 5 ft × 2½ ft sides face the stove. It is estimated this side will get 20 F warmer than the kitchen.

(a) What is the heat leakage load?

(b) What is the usage load? (Use heavy usage).

(c) What is the required Btu capacity of the condensing unit?

18–4. The following data is known about a water cooled condenser.

Temperature of the water on: 66 F

Temperature of the water off: 72 F

Quantity of water circulated: 412 gal per min

Condensing temperature: 78 F

Total surface in the condenser: 960 sq ft

(a) How much heat is the condenser absorbing?

(b) What is the mean temperature difference?

(c) At what K is the condenser surface operating.

(Rearrange the formula to $K = \dfrac{H}{A\ td}$)

(d) If the quantity of water was reduced to 280 gallons per minute, what will be the temperature of the water off. Neglect the effect of a rising condensing temperature on the total heat to be absorbed.

(e) If the change of K due to reduced velocity in (d) was neglected, the mean temperature difference will not change. In this case what would be the new condensing temperature?

CHAPTER 19

HUMIDITY IN REFRIGERATION

Relative and Absolute Humidity.—Humidity is the amount of moisture in the air. This moisture is in the form of water vapor, or low pressure steam. *Absolute humidity is the actual weight of water vapor in a given amount of air,* usually in grains[1] of moisture per pound or grains per cubic foot. *Relative humidity is the amount of moisture in the air compared to what it could hold without any change of temperature.* That is, a relative humidity of 60 percent means the air has absorbed, or is holding 60 percent as much moisture as it is capable of holding with no change in temperature. Air at 100 percent humidity can absorb no more moisture. It is called saturated air.

Although absolute humidities are a measure of the actual moisture in the air, relative humidities are a better measure of how the air will affect other things. An air with 100 percent relative humidity can hold no more moisture, so it will not cause any drying. Air at anything less than saturated will absorb moisture from any wet product. The lower the relative humidity, the faster is this moisture absorption or drying action. Air at 50 percent relative humidity is very drying to food products. As mentioned in Chapter 13, high humidities will prevent drying, but will also increase molds and sliming. Therefore the best humidity at which to keep food products is something of a compromise. Table A-2 gives the recommended humidities for different products for long term storage. Table 19-1 gives this data in a simpler form. This latter is usually used as a guide for commercial applications.

The thing that complicates the problem of relative humidity is the fact that air can hold different amounts of moisture at different temperatures. For every 20 F rise in temperature, air can hold approximately twice as much moisture. Air at 60 F can hold 5.8 grains per cubic foot. If it has this much moisture, it is saturated and can pick up no more moisture. If this same air was heated to 80 F it

---

[1]A grain is 1/7000 of a pound.

TABLE 19-1—EFFECT OF COIL TEMPERATURE DIFFERENCES AND HUMIDITIES ON
FOOD PRODUCTS

Temp. Dif.		6 F	10 F	16 F	20 F Up
	Forced Air	6 F	10 F	16 F	20 F Up
	Gravity Coil	15 F	20 F	25 F	30 F Up
Relative Humidity		Over 90%	80 to 90%	70 to 80%	55 to 70%
Effect on Food Products		No drying or Shrinkage. Surfaces usually moist. Molds and slimes hard to control	Shrinkage noticeable on long term storage. Molds and slimes easier to control, but not eliminated.	Drying, shrinkage, wilting are noticeable; very objectionable on long term storage.	Drying and "case hardening" excessive
Foods Suitable For		Fish and shellfish. Long term storage of frozen foods.	Meats and poultry. Average fruits and vegetables.	Nuts. Bulbs. Dried food products.	Packaged goods only.

could hold 11.5 grains per cubic foot. Since it only contains 5.8 grains, it has a relative humidity of

$$\frac{5.8}{11.5} = .50 \text{ or } 50\%$$

Air at 50 percent humidity is very drying. If the temperature of the saturated 60 F air was dropped to 40 F, it could only hold 2.9 grains per cubic foot. It would spill out or condense the extra 2.9 grains and still be saturated. The moisture condensed would form as dew on the cooling coils or whatever else was used to cool this air.

Fig. 19-1 shows the moisture solubility in air for different temperatures. Actually this is nothing more than the lower end of Fig. 2-2 drawn to a larger scale. The light lines in Fig. 19-1 show various relative humidity points. That is, the 50 percent relative humidity line is half way up from the line corresponding to no moisture, to the saturated line.

Humidity Measurement.—Throughout our refrigertation work we have constantly stressed the fact that evaporation absorbs heat. The evaporation of water is no exception; and the more water evaporated, the more heat is absorbed. Without the application of additional heat, this heat absorption causes cooling. This fact is made use of to measure the relative humidity of air. Two thermometers are used with a wet wick around the bulb of one, Fig. 19-2. The evaporation of water on the wet wick cools the bulb of this thermometer below the temperature of the other. The drier the air, the greater is the evaporation and cooling. The thermometer with the wet wick is called the wet-bulb thermometer. The plain thermometer without a wick is called the dry-bulb thermometer. The complete device is called a sling psychrometer.

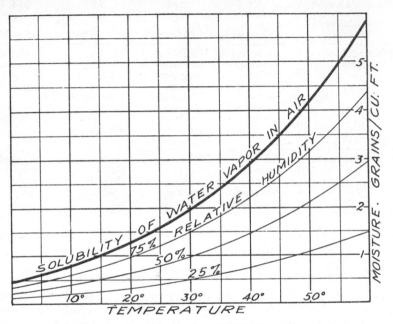

Fig. 19-1. Moisture solubility in air.

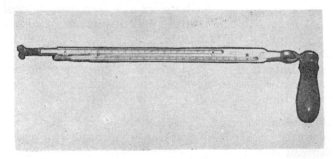

Fig. 19-2. A sling psychrometer.

From the readings taken from the dry bulb and wet bulb thermometers, tables or charts give the relative humidity of the air. Fig. 19-3 shows such a chart. Notice it is nothing more than the

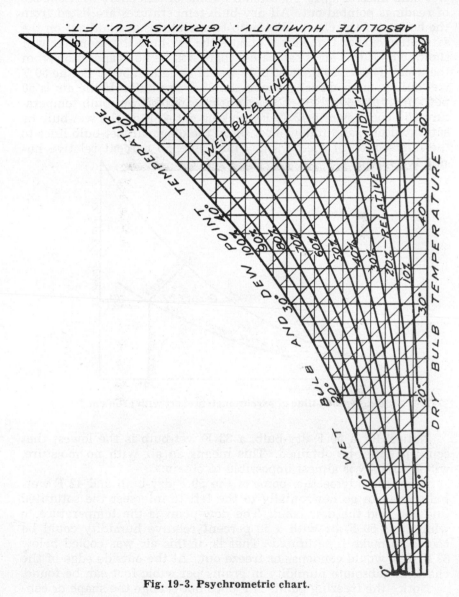

Fig. 19-3. Psychrometric chart.

moisture vapor solubility chart of Fig. 19-1 with the addition of the wet-bulb lines. Fig. 19-4 shows an outline of this chart with one set of readings pointed out. All dry-bulb temperatures are listed from the bottom of the chart. Wet-bulb temperatures are laid out on the saturation curve. If the air is at 50 F the dry-bulb thermometer will show 50 F. If this air is saturated, there will be no evaporation from the wick. Therefore the wet-bulb would remain at 50 F. So the 50 F wet-bulb point is directly above the 50 F dry-bulb. If the air is 50 percent saturated, there is evaporation, and the wet-bulb temperature will cool down to 42 F. By picking out 42 F on the wet-bulb or saturated line, and following it in on the diagonal wet-bulb lines to the intersection of the 50 F dry bulb line, 50 percent relative humidity is found.

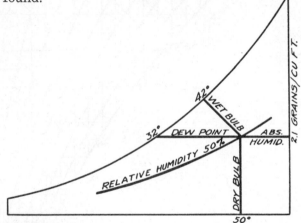

Fig. 19-4. Outline of psychrometric chart with problem.

Notice, for a 50 F dry-bulb, a 33 F wet-bulb is the lowest that could possibly be obtained. This means an air with no moisture, which actually is almost impossible to obtain.

From the intersection point of the 50 F dry-bulb and 42 F wet-bulb, one can go horizontally to the left to intersect the saturated line and find the *dew-point*. The dew-point is the temperature to which this 50 F air with a 50 percent relative humidity could be cooled to make it saturated. That is, if this air was cooled below 32 F, dew would condense or freeze out. At the outside edge of the chart, the absolute humidity in grains per cubic foot can be found.

Notice the freezing point, 32 F does not change the shape or continuity of the chart. The lower the temperature, the less moisture air is able to hold. But it still contains some moisture as it goes below 32 F. Vapor will be present in air even though any moisture condensed will form a solid (ice) instead of a liquid. The fact that water freezes somewhere along this curve 'has no direct effect on the moisture vapor still held by the air.

Example 19-1.—Psychrometric readings give a dry-bulb of 46 F and a wet-bulb of 39 F. What is the relative humidity, dew-point, and absolute humidity?

From the psychrometric chart the following is found.

Relative Humidity = 52%
Dew-Point   = 29 F
Absolute Humidity = 1.9 grains per cu ft

Example 19-2.—Air at 60 F and 60% relative humidity is cooled to 40 F. Exactly what happens?

The air contains 3.5 grains of moisture per cubic foot. As it cools, it will first come to its dew-point of 45.5 F. At this point the absolute humidity has not changed, but the relative humidity has increased to 100 percent. As the air cools further it remains saturated, dew condenses out, and the absolute humidity decreases. At 40 F the air is still saturated, and now contains 2.9 grains of moisture. Notice that when saturated, the dry-bulb, wet-bulb, and dew-point are all equal. In this case the air has lost:

3.5 - 2.9 = 0.6 grains per cu ft.

Example 19-3.—Air at 60 F dry bulb and 40 percent relative humidity enters a refrigerator. It first passes over a coil where it is chilled to 23 F. Then in passing through the cabinet it is heated to 38 F by cabinet walls, food, etc. What is its final condition?

Fig. 19-5 illustrates on a skeleton psychrometric chart exactly what happens. First the air is cooled to its dew point, 34.5 F. Then moisture condenses as it cools on down to 23 F. As it reheats from 23 F to 38 F, it changes from a saturated condition at 23 F to a relative humidity of 53% at 38 F.

Effect of Evaporator Temperature.—As with many other things, the desired temperature difference between an evaporator and the cabinet air is something of a compromise. If a large temperature difference is chosen, a small evaporator will be sufficient. But this requires a lower back pressure which penalizes the condensing unit. It may, in extreme cases, require a larger compressor and a larger motor. It also results in a very dry air in the cabinet. The smaller the temperature difference, the larger the coil required. Back pressures can be brought up to approach a pressure corresponding to the box temperature, but can never reach it. Also, the lower the temperature difference, the less moisture will be taken out of the air as it passes over the coil. This gives a higher cabinet humidity.

Table 19-1 gives temperature differences that have been worked out from practice for average commercial applications. These figures

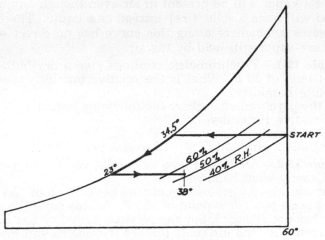

Fig. 19-5. Outline of example 3.

assume approximately 16 hours running time out of the 24. Much variation from this running time will give different results. What

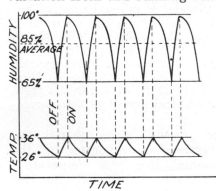

Fig. 19-6. Chart from recording humidistat.

actually happens on a typical job with a blower coil is shown by Fig. 19-6. During the running cycle, the air flowing over the coils is cooled down to very nearly coil temperature. This brings its dew point down to the temperature to which it is cooled, 26 F at the end of the running cycle. As this air rises to cabinet temperature of 38 F, its relative humidity is reduced to about 65 percent. During the off cycle the air is not actively refrigerated, and it soons begins to warm the coil. Thus the dew point of the air leaving the coil rises, and with it the cabinet humidity. Toward the end of the cycle, the cabinet humidity approaches 100 percent. Thus, the 80 to 90 percent given in Table 19-1 is an average over a period of time.

A colder coil would lower the dew point and relative humidity on the running cycle, thus lowering the average relative humidity. A longer running cycle would increase the length of time at low humidity and decrease the time at high humidity. Therefore this lowers the average relative humidity. Thus, where a certain job is chosen to control humidity as well as temperature, it must be accurately figured. If temperatures only are involved, an adjustment of the temperature difference will correct any variations from design conditions. But every change of the temperature difference also changes humidities. So where humidities are involved, one item cannot be changed without affecting the other.

One difficulty encountered with this is in the seasonal variations of refrigeration loads. When equipment is properly sized to give 16 hours running time in the summer time, this running time will decrease in the winter. This decrease may be enough that the humidity rises to the point where cabinet walls sweat and food begins to slime. Such conditions have been reduced in many ways, although a simple, economical solution has not yet been found for this problem.

Starving the coil by closing down on the expansion valve is probably the simplest solution. This makes less of the coil surface active, so requires a greater temperature difference. This in turn lowers the back pressure which increases the running time. Special types of controls have been used. Some are started by coil temperature and stopped by back pressure. Some are started by coil temperature and stopped by cabinet temperature. They all attempt to do a better job by balancing coil temperatures to cabinet temperatures than can be done by either a common pressure control or temperature control. Two speed fans have been used, which cut down to a slow speed on the off cycle. This returns less moisture to the cabinet on the off cycle.

QUESTIONS

19– 1. What is the difference between relative humidity and absolute humidity?

19– 2. Why is relative humidity important in conjunction with food storage?

19– 3. How is the relative humidity of a space found?

19– 4. If the dry-bulb is 52 F and the wet-bulb 41 F, what is the relative humidity, the dew-point and the moisture content?

19– 5. If the dry-bulb is 50 F and the relative humidity is 40%, what is the wet-bulb, dew-point, and moisture content?

19– 6. If the dry-bulb is 54 F and the dew-point 40 F, what is the wet-bulb, relative humidity, and moisture content?

19- 7. Show exactly what happens when 60 F air at 80% relative humidity enters a refrigeration box where it is first cooled to 25 F as it passes over the coil, then heats to 35 F in the box.

19- 8. Show why, in Question 19-7, if the air was cooled to 15 F instead of 25 F by the coil then reheated to 35 F, the cabinet humidity would be lower.

19- 9. What temperature difference should be chosen for a blower coil to get an 85% cabinet humidity?

19-10. How would an increase in the percent of running time decrease the relative humidity?

CHAPTER 20

COMPRESSOR CALCULATIONS

General.—It has previously been shown how liquid is evaporated to vapor in the evaporator. To absorb a given amount of heat in the evaporator, it is necessary to evaporate a certain amount of liquid. Depending on the pressure, the vapor from this liquid will have a certain size or volume. This volume of vapor must be removed, or pumped out of the evaporator by the compressor. This in turn determines the size of compressor needed.

Refrigerant Tables.—The weight of liquid to be evaporated to absorb a given amount of heat varies with the refrigerant, and with the temperature of that refrigerant. The size of each pound varies with the refrigerant and with the pressure. All these variables must be found from tables. These tables are a tabulation of the required properties of each refrigerant which have been determined by laboratory tests.

PROPERTIES OF SATURATED VAPOR

Temp.	Pressure		Volume		Density		Heat content from − 40°			Entropy from − 40°		Temp.
°F	Abs. lb./in.²	Gage lb./in.²	Liquid ft.³/lb.	Vapor ft.³/lb.	Liquid lb./ft.³	Vapor lb./ft.³	Liquid Btu./lb.	Latent Btu./lb.	Vapor Btu./lb.	Liquid Btu./lb.°F	Vapor Btu./lb.°F	°F
t	p	p_d	v_f	v_g	$1/v_f$	$1/v_g$	h_f	h	h_g	s_f	s_g	t
5†	26.51	11.81	.0111	1.485	90.00	.6735	9.32	69.47	78.79	.02097	.17052	5†

* Inches of mercury below one atmosphere.
† Standard ton temperatures.

Fig. 20-1. Line from Refrigerant 12 table (5 F).

Fig. 20-1 illustrates one line from the Refrigerant 12 Saturated Table. The first column gives the temperature for which these conditions will be true. The second and third columns give the absolute and gage pressures at which Refrigerant 12 will evaporate at 5 F. This is the same information as is given in graphic form in Fig. 3-1. The next two columns give the volume of the liquid and vapor. This is the size in cubic feet of one pound at the pressure given. Following this is the density of the liquid and vapor. The density is the weight of

283

one cubic foot of the substance at these conditions. It could be calculated by dividing the volume into one, but here it is calculated for us. Actually, the volume is more often used in calculations than density.

The next three columns give heats, sometimes called enthalpies. The first of these is the heat of the liquid. This is the heat necessary to heat the liquid from some point established as zero (−40 F for common refrigerant tables) up to the point under consideration. The second heat column is latent heat. As previously mentioned, latent heat is the heat necessary to evaporate one pound of fluid without a change of temperature. The third heat of the column is the total heat of the vapor, which is the sum of the heat of liquid and the latent heat.

The last columns are entropies. Entropy is a useful relationship between heat and temperature. The entropy of the liquid and the entropy of the vapor are given. For most work, the entropy of the vapor is the only one needed. The complete table gives this information for all temperatures required from low evaporator temperatures to high condensing temperatures. Complete tables for ammonia, Refrigerant 12 and Refrigerant 22 are given in the appendix.

Following the saturated tables of each of these is a table of superheated vapor. For each saturation temperature, if the vapor is superheated after leaving the liquid, its volume, heat and entropy are increased. It would take a whole book to list all the possible combinations of superheats and pressures. So this data is given for each 10 F change of superheat for various pressures.

Some tables give a little different order than that described. But if the column heading is always checked, there should be no reason for making an error.

Compressor Size.—Fig. 20-2 represents a schematic compression system operating at standard ton conditions of 5 F evaporator and 86 F condenser. The refrigerant is Refrigerant 12. A liquid at 86 F enters the expansion valve and evaporator. Leaving the evaporator is a 5 F vapor. From the Refrigerant 12 tables, the heat of liquid at 86 F is 27.72 Btu per lb, and heat of the vapor at 5 F is 78.79 Btu per lb. Thus with 27.72 Btu per lb brought into the evaporator, and 78.79 Btu per lb taken out, the difference or

$$78.79 - 27.72 = 51.07 \text{ Btu}$$

is absorbed in the evaporator for every pound of liquid circulated. This is called the refrigerating effect. As pointed out in Chapter 1, one ton of refrigeration is 200 Btu per minute. Therefore if one pound of refrigerant gives 51.07 Btu, to get one ton of refrigeration requires the circulation of

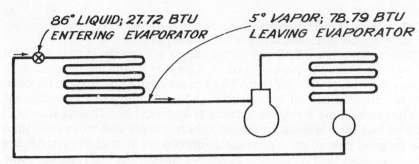

Fig. 20-2. Schematic refrigeration system with conditions entering and leaving the evaporator.

$$\frac{200}{51.07} = 3.92 \text{ lb per min of refrigerant.}$$

From the tables, the size of one pound of vapor at 5 F is 1.48 cu ft per lb. Therefore, to get one ton of refrigeration would require

$$3.92 \times 1.48 = 5.81 \text{ cu ft per min}$$

of vapor to be withdrawn from the evaporator. This must be pumped out by the compressor, so a compressor with a theoretical displacement of 5.81 cu ft per min per ton of refrigeration must be chosen. This must be further corrected for losses in the compressor. If the compressor is 70 percent efficient, the actual displacement required is

$$\frac{5.81}{.70} = 8.31 \text{ cu ft per min per ton.}$$

To help as a guide through the above figuring, formulas can be set up.

$$RE = h_g - h_f$$

$$w = \frac{200}{RE} = \frac{\cdot\ 200}{h_g - h_f}$$

$$D_t = wV$$

$$D_a = \frac{D_t}{E_v}.$$

where

RE = refrigerating effect in Btu per lb

h_g = heat of vapor at evaporator temperature in Btu per lb (from tables)

h_f = heat of liquid at condensing temperature in Btu per lb (from tables)

w = weight of refrigerant circulated in lb per min per ton

V = Volume of vapor

D_t = theoretical displacement in cu ft per min per ton

D_a = actual displacement in cu ft per min per ton
E_v = volumetric efficiency of the compressor

The volumetric efficiency factor, E_v, is a variable that is difficult to pick exactly. As pointed out in Chapter 6, the volumetric efficiency will vary with different head pressures, back pressures, compressor clearances and valve actions. It will also vary for different refrigerants, being lower for a dense refrigerant like fluorocarbons. It will be less for a worn compressor where valves and rings leak than one in good condition. For some compressors it will vary with the

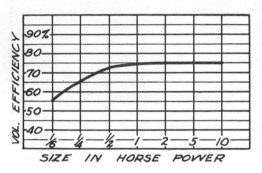

speed. At high speeds, some valve actions are not as fast as they should be. With other types that depend on inertia to open and close the suction valves, efficiency goes very low below certain speeds. Usually the smaller the size machine, the lower the efficiency. Fig. 20-3 shows variations in efficiencies for different sized compressors made by one manufacturer.

Fig. 20-3. Efficiency vs horsepower.

The effects of head pressure and back pressure can best be combined under compression ratio, although even here at low pressures, vapors may be so light as to affect valve action. Fig. 20-4 gives the range of efficiences for ammonia, and Fig. 20-5 for Refrigerant 12 and Refrigerant 22. (Compression Ratio is the absolute discharge pressure divided by the absolute suction pressure). Some manufacturers claim higher efficiencies for their equipment than is shown. But worn compressors may show lower values than the lowest shown. Therefore, to be safe, the average value given is nearer the lower limit than the upper. If it is suspected that a compressor is better or worse than average, the efficiency can be varied within the limits shown.

Example 20-1.—What is the theoretical and actual displacement for an ammonia compressor at 5 F evaporator and 86 F condenser?
It saves time to pick as much data as possible from the tables before starting calculations. Then one is not interrupted repeatedly by having to go back to the tables for more information. From the ammonia tables the following is found.

The heat of liquid at 86 F = 138.9 Btu per lb
The heat of vapor at 5 F = 613.3 Btu per lb
The volume of vapor at 5 F = 8.15 cu ft per lb
The absolute pressure at 86 F = 169.2 psia
The absolute pressure at 5 F = 34.27 psia

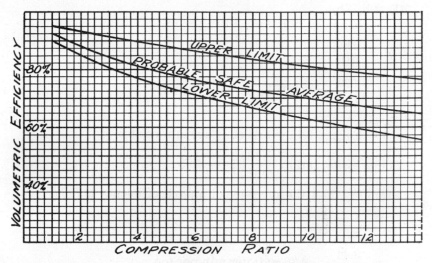

Fig. 20-4. Volumetric efficiency of ammonia compressors.

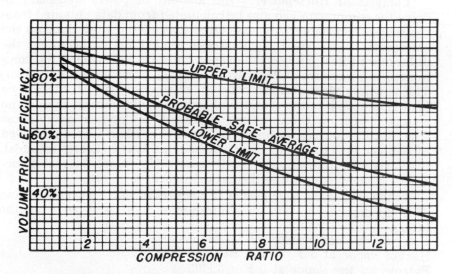

Fig. 20-5. Volumetric efficiency of Refrigerant 12 and 22 compressors.

From this data the following is calculated.

$$RE = h_g - h_f$$
$$= 613.3 - 138.9 = 474.4 \text{ Btu per lb}$$

$$w = \frac{200}{RE}$$

$$= \frac{200}{474.4} = 0.422 \text{ lbs per min per ton}$$

$$D_t = wV$$
$$= 0.422 \times 8.15 = 3.44 \text{ cu ft per min per ton}$$

$$\text{Compression ratio} = \frac{169.2}{34.27} = 4.93$$

From Fig. 20-4, the average volumetric efficiency is 79%.

$$D_a = \frac{D_t}{E_v}$$

$$= \frac{3.44}{0.79} = 4.36 \text{ cu ft per min per ton}$$

Compressor Horsepower.—The amount of power necessary to drive the compressor can also be calculated from data obtained from the tables. In Chapter 2 it was stated that all the work done on the refrigerant vapor by the compressor ended up as heat. So the difference in heat between the vapor entering and leaving the compressor is a measure of the power necessary to compress that vapor. This is where the useful relationship, entropy, is used. If there is no heat gain or loss to the compressor from outside sources, there is no change in entropy through the compressor. By no heat gain or loss from outside sources means if the vapor is neither heated or cooled by contact with the compressor. Although this is a theoretical ideal, the variations from this are usually small. Therefore the real horsepower is very close to the theoretical figure.

In the case of the Refrigerant 12 compressor at 5 F evaporator and 86 F condenser, the following information can be taken from the tables.
Entering the compressor:
Heat of vapor at 5 F = 78.79 Btu per lb
Entropy of the vapor at 5 F = 0.1705

Leaving the compressor:
Entropy of the vapor = 0.1705 (Same as entering)
Absolute condensing pressure = 107.9 psia

To find the remaining conditions leaving the compressor, turn to the Refrigerant 12 superheat tables. First find the section headed as near 107.9 psia as possible. On page 475 are found the pressures 100 psia and 110 psia. The latter is the closest. The last of the three columns under this heading labeled S is entropy. Go down this entropy column until you find a figure as near 0.1705 as possible. The nearest is 0.1700. From this we find a heat of 89.51 Btu. On the left column of the page we find a temperature of 100 F. This 100 F temperature is the discharge temperature, and is of interest to check probable head temperatures.

If the heat of vapor leaving the compressor is 89.51 Btu per lb and that entering is 78.79 Btu per lb the difference is

$$89.51 - 78.79 = 10.72 \text{ Btu per lb}$$

That is, for every pound of Refrigerant 12 circulated, mechanical energy enough to create 10.72 Btu of heat must be used. In this case, 3.92 lbs per min per ton is circulated. Therefore this uses

$$3.92 \times 10.71 = 42 \text{ Btu per minute.}$$

From Table A-4, we find 42.42 Btu per min is equivalent to one horse power. Therefore this will require

$$\frac{42}{42.42} = 0.99 \text{ hp per ton.}$$

Since this is only the power necessary to compress the vapor, sufficient additional power must be used to supply the mechanical losses in the compressor. The relation between the theoretical power and the actual power is the mechanical efficiency. This will also vary according to compressor design, speed, size, etc. About 85 percent is a fair estimate for large equipment, and 75 percent for small or fractional horse power equipment. Where this data is being used to choose a motor for a small compressor, the motor size is usually taken as 50 percent larger than the theoretical horsepower. This gives some factor of safety. If a mechanical efficiency of 85 percent is assumed here, the actual driving power will be

$$\frac{0.99}{.85} = 1.16 \text{ horsepower}$$

The formulas for these horsepower calculations are:

$$\text{theoretical horsepower} = thp = \frac{w(H_s - h_g)}{42.42}$$

$$\text{actual horsepower} = ahp = \frac{thp}{E_m} = \frac{w(H_s - h_g)}{42.42 \, E_m}$$

where
   thp = theoretical horsepower
   ahp = actual horsepower

H_s = heat of superheated vapor leaving compressor
h_g = heat of vapor leaving evaporator (entering compressor)
E_m = mechanical efficiency

Actually there is some error involved in the above problem by taking the nearest figure instead of interpolating to get an exact figure. But a four way interpolation is usually required, which is somewhat tedious. An easier method, taking these figures from a chart, will be given later.

Example 20-2.—What is the horsepower per ton in the case of Example 20-1?

The required data worked out in Example 20-1 is as follows:

    w = 0.422 lbs per min per ton
    h_g = 613.3 Btu per lb

From the saturated ammonia tables we can find the following:

    Entropy of the vapor at 5 F = 1.3253
    Condensing pressure at 86 F = 169.2 psia

Then in the superheat ammonia tables, the nearest to 169.2 psia to be found is 170 psia. The entropy nearest 1.3253 found under this pressure is 1.3249. From this the heat of superheat leaving the compressor H_s is 713.0 Btu per lb, and the discharge temperature is 210 F. The 210 F discharge temperature explains why water jacketed cylinders are used with ammonia to reduce lubrication troubles on the cylinder walls.

$$thp = \frac{w(H_s - h_g)}{42.42}$$

$$= \frac{0.422(713.0 - 613.3)}{42.42} = 0.99 \text{ hp, theoretical}$$

$$ahp = \frac{0.99}{0.85} = 1.16 \text{ hp, actual}$$

Complete Analysis of Expansion Valve and Evaporator.—The above method of considering only the heat entering and leaving the evaporator gives the quickest method of finding the conditions required. But a more exact analysis brings out some interesting points. For the Refrigerant 12 example, the heat of liquid at 86 F entering the expansion valve was found to be 27.72 Btu per lb. As this liquid passes through this expansion valve, at the reduced pressure it cools to 5 F. From the table we find the additional data:

    Heat of liquid at 5 F = 9.32 Btu per lb
    Latent heat at 5 F = 69.47 Btu per lb

In passing through the expansion valve, the heat of liquid must be reduced from 27.72 Btu to 9.32 Btu per lb.

    27.72 — 9.32 = 18.40 Btu per lb

This 18.4 Btu is removed from this liquid by evaporation of part of the liquid. To get 18.40 Btu of cooling requires the evaporation of

$$\frac{18.40}{69.47} = 0.265 \text{ lbs.}$$

This 0.265 lbs evaporated per lb of liquid circulated is 26½ percent. So at a 5 F evaporator and 86 F condenser, 26½ percent of the Refrigerant 12 liquid must be evaporated to cool the rest of it. The remaining 73½ percent of the liquid enters the evaporator where it can do useful cooling. Since the latent heat was 69.47 Btu and 18.4 Btu were used up in getting to 5 F.

69.47 — 18.40 = 51.07 Btu per lb remaining.

This is the same refrigerating effect as was found on page 300 by the shorter method.

Example 20-3.—What percent of ammonia is evaporated in the expansion valve of Example 20-1?

Heat of liquid at 86 F = 138.9 Btu per lb
Heat of liquid at 5 F = 48.3 Btu per lb
Heat reduction   90.6 Btu per lb
Latent heat at 5 F = 565 Btu per lb

$\dfrac{90.6}{565} = 0.16$ or 16% of liquid evaporated in the expansion valve

565 — 90.6 = 474.4 Btu per lb refrigerating effect

The Mollier or Pressure-Heat Diagram.—The Mollier diagram or pressure-heat diagram gives the same information as is given in the tables. The properties of saturated vapor can be more accurately read from the tables. But as previously mentioned, superheat conditions leaving the compressor are more easily found from this diagram. Also, problems involving wet or superheated suction vapor entering the compressor, as well as special problems such as two staging, dual effect, etc. are much more easily worked out with the help of the chart.

Fig. 20-6 shows an outline of this Mollier diagram. Heats in Btu per pound are given along the bottom and top, and absolute pressures on the side. Line A-B gives the heat of saturated liquid for different pressures. The area between A-B and the left hand border corresponds to a subcooled liquid, that is, a liquid cooled below its boiling temperature. The dotted lines give temperatures. Any point on line A-B represents a saturated liquid, that is, a liquid at its boiling temperature for the pressure indicated. Line C-D gives the heat of the saturated vapor. The distance between A-B and C-D represents the latent heat of vaporization. Any point between A-B and C-D represents some liquid and some vapor. The partial distance from A-B to C-D is the percent of liquid that has evaporated to vapor. That is, one tenth of the distance from A-B to C-D represents an evaporation

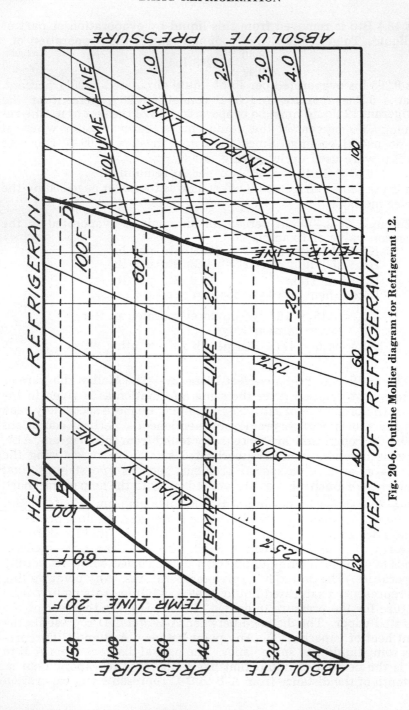

Fig. 20-6. Outline Mollier diagram for Refrigerant 12.

of 10 percent of the liquid to vapor leaving 90 percent liquid still unevaporated. This is called 10 percent quality. Notice the temperature lines are horizontal in this area. This is because the addition of heat to an evaporating liquid does not change its temperature.

The space to the right of C-D is superheated vapor, that is, vapor heated above its corresponding condensing temperature. Here the temperature lines turn down again, but are not straight because the specific heat of the vapor changes at different temperatures and pressures. Here also are constant entropy lines. The vapor, when compressed, will rise in pressure parallel to these lines. Also in this region are plotted the volume lines, giving the volume of the vapor.

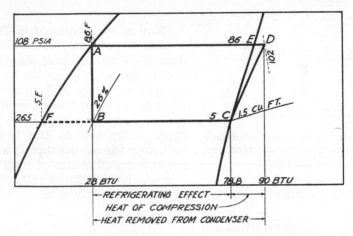

Fig. 20-7. The compression cycle on the Mollier diagram.

Fig. 20-7 shows the Refrigerant 12 Mollier diagram with the 5 F evaporator and 86 F condenser cycle drawn in on it. The point A represents 86 F saturated liquid entering the expansion valve. It has a pressure of 108 psia, and a heat of 28 Btu (as near as can be read from the scale on the chart). In passing through the expansion valve the pressure drops, but there is no change in total heat. This is shown by the line A-B. The line F-B-C is drawn at constant pressure from the 5 F point on the saturated liquid line. It is at 26.5 psia pressure. The point B represents the condition of the refrigerant as it leaves the expansion valve and enters the evaporator. Its heat is still 28 Btu but its quality is 26 percent.

The line B-C represents the change in the evaporator. The refrigerant evaporates at constant pressure and constant temperature, increasing in heat content as it does so. At C it leaves the evaporator to enter the compressor with 78.8 Btu of heat. The difference,

78.8 — 28 = 50.8 Btu per lb refrigerating effect.

The length of the line B-C represents this refrigerating effect. The line C-D represents the vapor through the compressor. This rises from C at 26.5 psia to D at 108 psia pressure. It follows the entropy lines up to the condensing pressure. At D the heat, 90 Btu, and the temperature, 102 F, can be read directly. The difference,

$$90 - 78.8 = 11.2 \text{ Btu}$$

is the heat of compression of the compressor, so is the amount of energy in heat units necessary to compress the vapor.

The line D-A represents the condition in the condenser. From D to E, the superheat is removed from the vapor. From E to A the vapor is being condensed back to a liquid. The total heat removed in the condenser is

$$90 - 28 = 62 \text{ Btu per lb.}$$

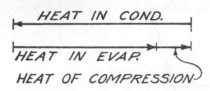

Fig. 20-8. Heat from condenser equals heat to evaporator plus heat of compression.

Notice, as mentioned in Chapter 2, this heat removed in the condenser equals the heat absorbed in the evaporator plus the heat of compression, Fig. 20-8. Also notice the heat of compression which is a measure of the power involved, is small compared to the heat absorbed in the evaporator. If we considered the efficiency of such a system where 50.8 Btu of refrigeration are produced with 62 Btu handled, the efficiency would be

$$\frac{50.8}{62.0} = 0.82 \text{ or } 82\%.$$

However, this is of less interest than the relationship between the refrigeration produced and the power required. In this case this would be

$$\frac{50.8}{11.2} = 4.52$$

Since this is more than 1.00 or 100 percent it cannot be considered an efficiency. It is called the Coefficient of Performance. In this case there is 4.52 times as much refrigeration produced as power consumed. This is not a form of perpetual motion, since the heat is merely transfered from the evaporator to the condensing water. The compressor is acting in the form of a heat pump to move the heat to the condenser.

Sizing Compressors.—When data is worked out to give the displacement needed per ton, where the required tonnage is known, a machine with the required displacement can be chosen. Actually, most of this is worked out in tables or charts to save having to repeatedly calculate it. Fig. 20-9 and Fig. 20-10 give the required theoretical displacement per ton for ammonia, Refrigerant 12, and Refrigerant 22 for various operating conditions. These figures must still be corrected for actual displacement by using the volumetric efficiency data of Fig. 20-4 or Fig. 20-5. Fig. 20-11 gives the theoretical horse power per ton. This is calculated for ammonia. But the variation in power between most refrigerants is so small that this curve is suitable for these three.

Example 20-4.—An ammonia compressor is required to give 25 tons of refrigeration at a 20 F evaporator and an 80 F condenser. What size compressor and what size driving motor is required?

From Fig. 20-9 we find 2.4 cubic feet per min. is required theoretically. From the tables, the 20 F evaporator is at 48.21 psia, and the 80 F condenser is at 153.0 psia. The compression ratio is

$$\frac{153.0}{48.21} = 3.17.$$

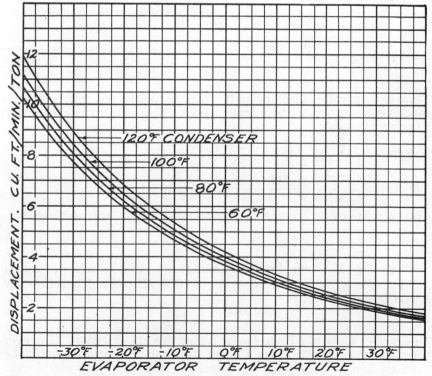

Fig. 20-9. Displacement per ton, ammonia.

From Fig. 20-4, a 3.17 compression ratio gives a volumetric efficiency of 84 percent. Therefore the actual required displacement per ton is

$$\frac{2.4}{0.84} = 2.86 \text{ cu ft per min.}$$

For a 25 ton compressor, the total displacement must be
$$25 \times 2.86 = 71.5 \text{ cu ft per min.}$$

The actual displacement of a compressor can be calculated by multiplying the volume of each cylinder by the number of cylinders and by the speed. In formula form this is

$$D = \frac{0.7854 \, B^2 \, L \, N \, rpm}{1728}$$

where
D = displacement in ft per min
B = diameter of bore in inches.
L = Length of stroke in in
N = number of cylinders
rpm = revolutions per minute
1728 = cu in per cu ft
Let us first try a 2 cylinder 6 in. x 6 in. compressor turning 400 rpm.

$$D = \frac{0.7854 \times 6^2 \times 6 \times 2 \times 400}{1728.}$$

$$= 78.5 \text{ cu ft per min}$$

This is a greater displacement than is necessary, but this size machine could be used at a lower speed. The formula is rearranged to solve for speed.

$$rpm = \frac{1728 \, D}{0.7854 \, B^2 \, L \, N}$$

$$= \frac{1728 \times 71.5}{0.7854 \times 6^2 \times 6 \times 2} = 364 \text{ rpm.}$$

Thus a 6 in. x 6 in. compressor running 364 rpm will suffice.

From Fig. 20-11 we find the theoretical horse power per ton is 0.67 hp. We will assume the motor is 85% efficient. Therefore the actual power needed is

$$\frac{25 \times 0.67}{0.85} = 19.7 \text{ hp}$$

This is very close to a 20 hp motor which is a standard size. However before choosing a 20 hp motor for this job, conditions should be checked that neither head pressures or back pressures could ever get above design conditions. If they should, a 25 hp motor should be chosen so it will not be overloaded at any abnormal condition.

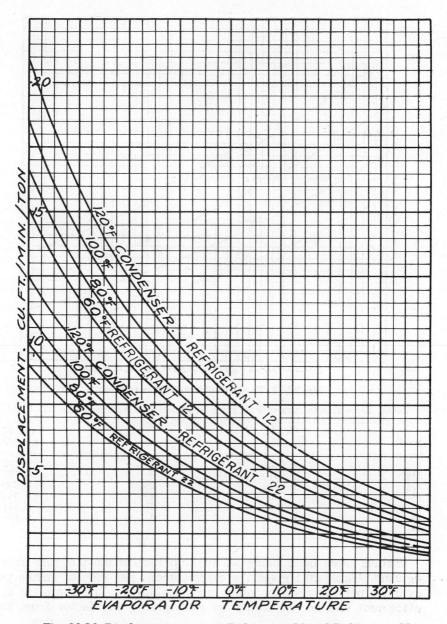

Fig. 20-10. Displacement per ton, Refrigerant-12 and Refrigerant-22.

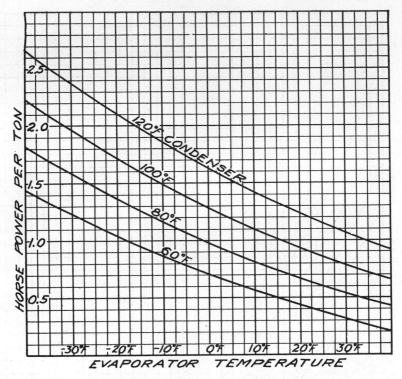

Fig. 20-11. Theoretical horsepower per ton.

TABLE 20-1—DISPLACEMENT PER INCH STROKE PER CYLINDER PER 100 RPM.

Bore	Cu. Ft. per Min.	Bore	Cu. Ft. per Min.
1	0.0454	1⅞	0.160
1⅛	0.0575	2	0.182
1¼	0.0710	2¼	0.230
1⅜	0.0857	2½	0.2841
1½	0.1022	2¾	0.344
1⅝	0.1196	3	0.409
1¾	0.1390		

Tables have been made up to help reduce most of the above figuring. Table 20-1 gives the displacement per inch of stroke per cylinder per 100 rpm for small sized machines. The complete displacement can be calculated by multiplying the factor from the table by the length of stroke, number of cylinders, and $\frac{rpm}{100}$, or

$$D = F\,L\,N\,\frac{rpm}{100}.$$

where F = volume factor from the table.

Example 20-5.—What is the displacement of a two cylinder compressor with a 1⅝ in bore x 1¾ in stroke turning 575 rpm?

From Table 20-1, a 1⅝ in bore compressor pumps 0.1196 cu ft per in of stroke per 100 rpm. The displacement is

$$D = 0.1196 \times 1.75 \times 2 \times \frac{575}{100}$$

$$= 2.41 \text{ cu ft per min}$$

Larger sized compressors, particularly ammonia compressors are usually made in a two cylinder square design. Square design means the bore equals the stroke. Table 20-2 gives the displacement in cu ft per min of such a compressor per 100 rpm in column 3. Therefore the only figuring needed is to multiply the factor from the table by $\frac{\text{rpm}}{100}$, or

$$D = F \, \frac{\text{rpm}}{100}$$

The displacements at various speeds are also given directly.

Example 20-6.—Check the results of Example 20-4 with Table 20-4.

From table 20-2 a two cylinder 6 in. x 6 in. compressor has a displacement of 19.64 cu ft per min per 100 rpm. Therefore to get a displacement of 71.5 cu ft per min, the speed must be

$$\frac{71.5}{19.64} \times 100 = 364 \text{ rpm}$$

Most manufacturers furnish tables which give actual capacities of their equipment under different operating conditions. Table 20-3 is such a table for Refrigerant 12 equipment. This is for air cooled condensing units, and is rated at a condensing temperature assumed to be average. At the bottom of the table is a correction factor to be applied for any other condensing temperature. Evaporator temperatures are listed across the top. All one has to do is to pick out the required evaporator temperature, then go down that column until the required rating is found. It is sometimes of interest, however, to check these tables, as some manufacturers claim very high volumetric efficiencies. In such cases, the machines may be able to deliver the stated capacity when new and in good condition, but there is often a question as to how it will deliver when it begins to wear. It is seldom possible to choose a machine that has exactly the required rating. But where tables are based on such high volumetric efficiencies as to be doubtful, this should be taken into account when a machine size does happen to come very close to the required rating.

Example 20-7.—What size machine would be required for Example 18-6 if a 20 F temperature difference is used for the evaporator?

TABLE 20-2. DISPLACEMENT OF 2 CYLINDER SINGLE-ACTING COMPRESSORS

Bore x stroke in inches	cu. in. per rev.	cfm per 100 rpm	Displacement in cubic feet per minute at various revolutions per minute										
			200	220	240	260	280	300	330	360	400	450	500
4 x 4	100.5	5.818	11.64	12.80	13.96	15.13	16.29	17.45	19.20	20.94	23.27	26.18	29.09
4½x 4½	143.1	8.283	16.57	18.22	19.88	21.54	23.19	24.85	27.34	29.82	33.13	37.28	
5 x 5	196.4	11.36	22.73	25.00	27.27	29.54	31.82	34.09	37.50	40.91	45.45	51.13	
5½x 5½	261.3	15.12	30.25	33.27	36.30	39.32	42.35	45.37	49.91	54.44	60.50	68.06	
6 x 6	339.3	19.64	39.27	43.20	47.12	51.05	54.98	58.90	64.79	70.68	78.54	88.36	
6¼x 6¼	383.5	22.19	44.39	48.82	53.26	57.70	62.14	66.58	73.24	79.90	88.77	99.87	
6½x 6½	431.4	24.96	49.93	54.92	59.91	64.91	69.90	74.89	82.38	89.87	99.86	112.3	
7 x 7	538.8	31.18	62.36	68.60	74.83	81.07	87.31	93.54	102.9	112.2	124.7	140.3	
7¼x 7¼	598.6	34.64	69.28	76.21	83.14	90.07	97.00	103.9	114.3	124.7	138.6		
7½x 7½	662.7	38.35	76.70	84.37	92.04	99.71	107.4	115.0	126.6	138.1	153.4		
8 x 8	804.2	46.54	93.08	102.4	111.7	121.0	130.3	139.6	153.6	167.6	186.2		
8¼x 8¼	882.0	51.04	102.1	112.3	122.5	132.7	142.9	153.1	168.4	183.8	204.2		
8½x 8½	964.7	55.83	111.7	122.8	134.0	145.1	156.3	167.5	184.2	201.0	223.3		
9 x 9	1145	66.27	132.5	145.8	159.0	172.3	185.6	198.8	218.7	238.6			
9¼x 9¼	1243	71.94	143.9	158.3	172.7	187.1	201.4	215.8	237.4	259.0			
9½x 9½	1347	77.94	155.9	171.5	187.0	202.6	218.2	233.8	257.2	280.6			
10 x10	1571	90.90	181.8	200.0	218.2	236.3	254.5	272.7	300.0	327.2			
10½x10½	1818	105.2	210.5	231.5	252.6	273.6	294.7	315.7	347.3	378.8			
11 x10	1900	110.0	220.0	242.0	264.0	286.0	316.0	330.0	363.0	392.0			
12 x12	2714	157.0	314.0	345.5	376.8	408.4	439.8	471.2					

—From A.C.R.M.A. Equipment Standards

The total required capacity is 3236 Btu per hr at an ambient temperature of 105 F. The evaporator temperature would be

$$40 - 20 = 20 \, F$$

From Table 20-3, in the 20 F column, a ½ hp machine turning 300 rpm delivers 3220 Btu per hr; and turning 355 rpm delivers 3780 Btu. Since a correction must be made for a higher condensing temperature, the 3220 Btu figure would be too small. The ambient temperature of 105 F is 15 F above the rated condensing temperature. Since there is a 6 percent correction for each 10 F, this requires a 9 percent correction, or the machine will be good for 91 percent of 3780 Btu.

$$0.91 \times 3780 = 3440 \, Btu$$

This is more than the 3236 Btu required so this unit, ½ hp turning 355 rpm would be satisfactory.

Example 20-8.—The A-5 unit chosen in Example 20-7 is a 2 cylinder, 1¾ in. x 2 in. compressor. What is the volumetric efficiency of this unit at the conditions of Example 20-7? Is this volumetric efficiency reasonable?

From Table 20-1, the displacement per inch of stroke per cylinder per 100 rpm is 0.139 cu ft per min. For a 2 cylinder compressor with a 2 in. stroke turning 355 rpm this would be

$$D = 0.139 \times 2 \times \frac{355}{100} = 1.97 \text{ cu ft per min.}$$

For an air cooled condenser, a condensing temperature 20 F warmer than the condensing air is assumed. For a 90 F room this would be a 110 F condensing temperature. From Fig. 20-10, for a 20 F evaporator and a 110 F condenser, the required displacement per ton is 4.79 cu ft per min. Thus, a theoretical displacement of 4.79 cu ft per min would give one ton or 12,000 Btu per hr of refrigeration. A displacement of 1.97 cu ft per min would give

$$\frac{1.97}{4.79} \times 12,000 = 4930 \text{ Btu per hr.}$$

This manufacturer gives this machine a rating of 3780 Btu per hr. Therefore the volumetric efficiency at this condition is

$$\frac{3780}{4930} = 0.766 \text{ or } 76.6 \text{ percent}$$

The evaporator temperature of 20 F gives a suction pressure of 35.75 psia. The condensing temperature of 110 F gives a condensing pressure of 150.7 psia. Therefore the compression ratio is

$$\frac{150.7}{35.75} = 4.2$$

Fig. 20-5 shows an average volumetric efficiency of 71 per cent with a possible maximum of 85 per cent for a compression ratio of 4.2. Therefore this compressor has a rating above average worn machines, but conservatively below top maximums.

TABLE 20-3—CAPACITIES—AIR COOLED REFRIGERANT 12 CONDENSING UNITS (BTU PER HOUR 90F ROOM TEMPERATURE)

Model No.	H.P.	R.P.M.	Suction Temperature, Degrees F.												
			−20	−15	−10	−5	0	5	10	15	20	25	30	35	40
			Suction Pressure, Lbs. Per Square Inch												
			.6	2.5	4.5	6.7	9.2	11.8	14.6	17.7	21.0	24.6	28.5	32.6	37.0
A-2-L / A-2-S / A-2-H	1/4	300 / 285 / 275	675	790	890	1080	1310 / 1230	1440	1750	2060	2450 / 2200	2450	2540	2630	2700
A-3-L / A-3-S / A-3-H	1/3	360 / 345 / 335	840	1100	1240	1540	1790 / 1680	1890	2220	2530	2940 / 2800	2960	3100	3240	3380
A-5-L / A-5-S / A-5-H	1/2	410 / 355 / 290	1450	1600	1880	2240	2520 / 2180	2450	2860	3260	3780 / 3220	3480	3880	4100	4430
A-7-L / A-7-S / A-7-H	3/4	300 / 290 / 255	2430	2750	3200	3750	4050 / 3570	4100	4700	5300	6070 / 5170	5520	5900	6360	6650
A-10-L / A-10-S / A-10-H	1	390 / 340 / 290	3870	4380	5100	5950	6500 / 5500	6200	7150	8500	8650 / 7350	7850	8400	8960	9600
A-15-L / A-15-S / A-15-H	1½	295 / 255 / 220	6280	7100	8200	10200	10700 / 8800	9600	10200	11700	13000 / 11000	11900	13000	14100	15300
A-20-L / A-20-S / A-20-H	2	390 / 340 / 290	8200	9200	10600	13200	13750 / 11900	12800	14300	15600	17300 / 14600	16000	17600	19200	21000

For Each 10° Increase in Room Temperature Decrease Capacity 6%
For Each 10° Decrease in Room Temperature Increase Capacity 6%

Where tables are given for ammonia machines, they are often made up in even more detail. Table 20-4 gives the displacement and brake horsepower per ton at various suction and discharge pressures. It is based on a 6x6 compressor and the machine factors given in this table should be applied to other sizes.

Compressor Indicator Diagrams.—In Chapter 6, reference was made to the compressor indicator diagram. A complete analysis of the compression line A-B of Fig 6-4 requires some figures and charts. A discussion of it was, therefore, put off to this point. Fig. 20-12 is a similar indicator diagram with the addition of two other lines. The first line, labeled isothermal, would be obtained if the compression was such that the vapor in the cylinder remained at exactly the same temperature throughout the compression stroke.

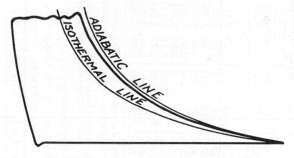

Fig. 20-12. Ammonia indicator diagram.

That is, the compression would have to be slow enough, and the water cooling around the cylinder thorough enough, that the heat developed by normal compression would be absorbed by the cooling water. This would leave the temperature at the end of compression at exactly the same point as at the beginning of compression. That

SELECTION OF MODEL (See Table 20-3, opposite page)

All Highsides are available with three optional compressor speeds, designated by the affix L. S. and H. We recommend the application of units only within the temperature ranges on which capacity figures appear.

L—Models bearing the affix L are designed for use on Freezer Cases—Ice Cream Cabinets—Hardening Cabinets—Ice Makers, and other low temperature work where coil temperatures from −20 to +5 degrees F are desired.

S—Models bearing the affix S are designed for use on Display Cases—Walk-In Coolers —Grocery and Florist Cases—Milk Coolers—Beverage Coolers—Water Coolers, Multiple Apartment Installations, and other applications, where coil temperatures from +5 to +25 degrees F are required.

H—Models bearing the affix H are designed for use in air conditioning, comfort cooling and other high temperature coil applications.

TABLE 20-4—AMMONIA COMPRESSOR PERFORMANCE* AT VARIOUS OPERATING CONDITIONS FOR VERTICAL SINGLE-ACTING AMMONIA COMPRESSORS AND SINGLE-STAGE COMPRESSION

Pressure and corresponding saturated temperature of suction gas		Discharge pressure, lb./sq. in. ga.														
		135		145		155		165		175		185		195		205	
		78.7		82.5		86.2		89.7		93.0		96.2		99.3		102.3	
		Corresponding saturated temperature, °F														
Pressure lb./sq. in. ga.	Temperature °F	CFM/TON	BHP/TON	CFM/TON	BHP/TON	CFM/TON	BHP/TON	CFM/TON	BHP/TON	CFM/TON	BHP/TON	CFM/TON	BHP/TON	CFM/TON	BHP/TON	CFM/TON	BHP/TON
0	−28.0	12.34	2.51														
5	−17.2	8.42	2.02	8.64	2.12	8.89	2.22	9.16	2.32	9.40	2.41	9.66	2.50				
10	−8.4	6.36	1.694	6.53	1.782	6.70	1.869	6.84	1.955	7.01	2.04	7.16	2.12	7.35	2.20	7.53	2.28
15	−1.0	5.09	1.449	5.21	1.531	5.34	1.611	5.45	1.690	5.56	1.765	5.67	1.839	5.79	1.911	5.93	1.980
20	5.5	4.28	1.270	4.39	1.341	4.46	1.412	4.55	1.482	4.64	1.552	4.72	1.621	4.80	1.688	4.90	1.755
25	11.3	3.69	1.127	3.75	1.259	3.84	1.259	3.91	1.324	3.98	1.387	4.06	1.449	4.12	1.509	4.20	1.568
30	16.6	3.24	1.011	3.31	1.073	3.38	1.133	3.44	1.193	3.50	1.251	3.56	1.307	3.63	1.363	3.69	1.419
35	21.4	2.92	0.910	2.96	0.971	3.00	1.029	3.06	1.085	3.11	1.140	3.16	1.193	3.22	1.244	3.27	1.293
40	25.8	2.62	0.825	2.66	0.883	2.71	0.938	2.75	0.992	2.81	1.044	2.85	1.094	2.90	1.144	2.94	1.193
45	30.0	2.39	0.755	2.43	0.807	2.47	0.859	2.50	0.910	2.54	0.961	2.58	1.009	2.62	1.057	2.65	1.103
50	33.8	2.18	0.689	2.21	0.739	2.25	0.789	2.28	0.838	2.33	0.886	2.36	0.934	2.39	0.980	2.42	1.026

*Based on two-cylinder compressors with 6 in. bore and 6 n. stroke. For other compressor sizes, multiply by machine factors of Table 2. Values above heavy line are for ratios of compression above 8.0, and for these conditions it is recommended that multi-stage compression be considered.

CFM/TON = average values of swept volume, in cubic feet per minute, required per ton refrigeration based on a suction superheat of 10°F and on liquid ammonia entering the refrigerant control valve at the saturated temperature corresponding to the discharge pressure.

BHP/TON = Average values of actual compressor brake horsepower per ton refrigeration.

MACHINE FACTORS FOR VARIOUS COMPRESSOR SIZES

COMPRESSOR BORE AND STROKE, INCHES

	4	4½	5	5½	6	6½	7	7½	8	8½	9	9½	10	10½	12
CFM/TON	1.022	1.017	1.012	1.006	1.000	.993	.986	0.979	0.972	0.966	0.960	0.954	0.948	0.943	0.94
BHP/TON	1.063	1.044	1.027	1.013	1.000	0.988	0.977	0.968	0.960	0.952	0.944	0.937	0.930	0.924	0.917

—From A.C.R.M.A. Equipment Standards

is the meaning of the term isothermal, at the same temperature. This line is such that

$$PV = C$$

where

P = absolute pressure in psi

V = volume

C = a constant

The volume of the cylinder being checked could be used for V. But it is simpler to let the volume of the cylinder at the beginning of the stroke equal 1.00 or 100 percent. Then a percentage of this is taken for all other points. In this case, the pressure at the beginning of the stroke is 35 psia. Therefore with $V = 1$:

TABLE 20-5—COMPRESSOR CALCULATIONS—I

% of Volume or Stroke	Isothermal Compression	R-12 n=1.14	NH₃ n=1.32	R-22 n=1.20	CO₂ n=1.30
100%	1.00	1.00	1.00	1.00	1.00
90%	1.11	1.13	1.15	1.13	1.15
80%	1.25	1.29	1.34	1.31	1.34
70%	1.43	1.47	1.60	1.53	1.59
60%	1.67	1.79	1.96	1.85	1.94
50%	2.00	2.20	2.50	2.30	2.46
40%	2.50	2.84	3.33	2.87	3.29
30%	3.33	3.95	5.10	4.24	4.78
20%	5.00	6.26	8.33	6.90	8.10
15%	6.67	8.90	12.3	9.75	11.8
10%	10.00	13.7	20.9	15.8	20.0

$$PV = C$$
$$35 \times 1 = C$$
$$C = 35$$

This C = 35 is then used to find the other points required. At 80 percent or 0.8 stroke:

$$P = \frac{C}{V} = \frac{35}{0.8} = 43.7 \text{ psia}$$

At 60 percent or 0.6 stroke:

$$P = \frac{C}{V} = \frac{35}{0.6} = 58.3 \text{ psia}$$

Enough such points can be calculated and plotted to raise this isothermal pressure to a point above the condensing pressure. Or to save solving for the constant C, the initial pressure can be multiplied by the proper multiplier taken from Table 20-5.

The second line or curve is labeled the adiabatic curve. This is the curve that would be obtained if there was no cylinder cooling, and the cylinder was insulated. All the heat of compression would go to raise the temperature of the vapor. Adiabatic means without gain or loss of heat to an outside source. This heating would raise the pressure of the vapor above the condition found on the isothermal curve, as it shows on Fig. 20-12. The adiabatic curve is found by the formula

$$PV^n = C$$

where

n is the gas constant that varies with each refrigerant.

Such a formula must be solved logarithmically. To save time and the logarithmic calculations, multipliers for this are taken from the ammonia column of table 20-5.

At 80% stroke, P = 35 × 1.34 = 46.9 psia

At 60% stroke, P = 35 × 1.96 = 68.6 psia

The actual compression curve drawn by an indicator should fall between these two mathematical curves. Theoretically, it would be better to have it as near the isothermal curve as possible. This is because the extra heat raises the pressure in the cylinder. This requires more power to force the piston against this additional pressure. But such operation is practically impossible. Most of the vapor is compressed and heated without coming in contact with the cylinder walls. Even that which does contact these walls is against them for so short a time that very little cooling can be done. Actually the water jacket or cooling fins are only suitable to keep the metal cylinder walls and lubricating oil temperatures down to a point where lubrication does not become too great a problem. Therefore the true compression curve will actually be found close to the adiabatic curve. The calculations at constant entropy used earlier in the chapter assumes the compression is adiabatic.

Fig. 20-13 shows the steps in laying out these curves on an indicator diagram. At (1) is the diagram as taken on the card. The suction pressure and the discharge pressure should be bypassed to the indicator before removing the card to give lines G-H and E-F. At the same time, the pressures should be read on the gages. Occasionally an atmospheric line is also drawn by opening the indicator port to atmospheric pressure. These give pressure reference points on which to lay out scales as at (3).

Also lay out J-K through A, perpendicular to the pressure lines. This represents the end of the suction stroke. Make an estimate of the clearance of the compressor in percent. This clearance should include not only the space between the piston and safety head, but all the valve port space open directly to the cylinder. For accurate

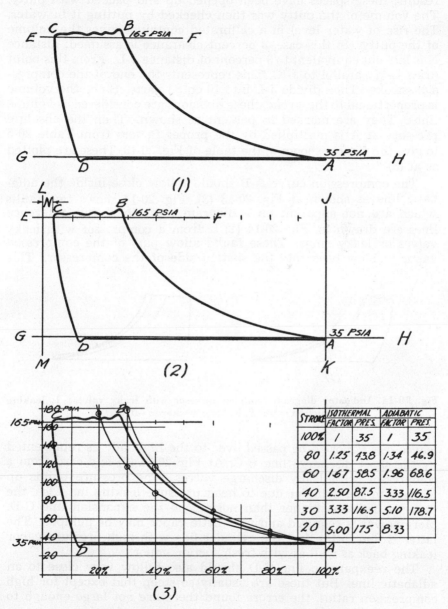

Fig. 20-13. Laying out isothermal and adiabatic curves.

results, these spaces have been opened up and packed with putty. The volume of the putty was then checked by putting it in water. The rise of water level in a calibrated container gives the volume of the putty. In this case, 3 percent clearance is assumed; distance N is laid out equivalent to 3 percent of distance J-L. From this point draw L-M parallel to J-K. This represents the end of the compression stroke. Then divide J-L into 10 equal parts. Since the volume is proportional to the stroke, these divisions are considered as volume lines. They are marked in percent as shown. Then the absolute pressure at A is multiplied by the proper factors from Table 20-5 to give the figures shown in the table of Fig. 20-13. These are plotted as at (3).

The compression curve A-B should follow close inside the adiabatic line as shown at Fig. 20-13 (3). Fig. 20-14 shows two faults which are not apparent on a diagram until these two reference lines are drawn in. Fig. 20-14 (1) is from a compressor with leaky valves or leaky rings. These faults allow part of the compressed vapor to blow back into the suction side of the compressor. This

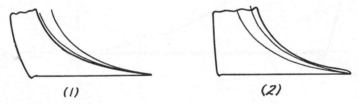

(1)   *(2)*

Fig. 20-14. Indicator diagram from compressor with leaky valves: 1, leaking suction valve; 2, leaking discharge valve.

leaves less vapor to be passed over to the high side as represented by the short discharge line B-C. At Fig. 20-14 (2) is a card from a compressor with leaky discharge valves. The pressure builds up too fast in the cylinder due to head pressure leaking in. Also, the pressure remains higher than normal on the expansion line C-D. More power is required and very little vapor may be pumped. The latter is due to the fact the cylinder fills with high pressure vapor leaking back as well as with fresh suction vapor.

The reexpansion line C-D should also follow very close to an adiabatic line. But these are usually so steep that except for high compression ratios, the errors found there are not large enough to be accurately read.

QUESTIONS

20–1. What is the theoretical and actual displacement per ton for a Refrigerant 22 compressor at a 5 F evaporator and 85 F condenser?

20–2. Check the answer from Question 20-1 on Fig. 20-10.

20–3. What is the required power per ton for Question 20-1?

20–4. Check your answer on Fig. 20-11.

20–5. What is the percent flash gas at the expansion valve in Question 20-1?

20–6. What is the actual displacement of a 2 in. x 2¼ in., 2 cyl compressor turning 425 rpm? Figure from the formula on page 312.

20–7. Check the answer of Question 20-6 from Table 20-1.

20–8. What is the volumetric efficiency of a 6x6 compressor of Table 20-4 operating at 25 psig suction pressure, 185 lbs. psig condensing pressure?

20–9. What is the volumetric efficiency of the A-5 unit of Example 20-8 at a —20 F evaporator?

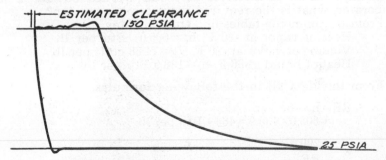

Fig. 20-15. Indicator diagram for Question 20-10.

20–10. The indicator drawing of Fig. 20-15 is from an ammonia compressor. Lay out the adiabatic and isothermal curves on it to determine if the compression line indicates normal compression.

CHAPTER 21

COMPRESSOR CALCULATIONS—II

Capacity Variations.—In the last chapter various tables and charts were introduced to help choose the proper size equipment to do a given refrigeration job. In this chapter, the refrigerant tables and Mollier diagram are used to completely analyze the operation of a refrigeration system under different operating conditions, and to analyze the operation of other than simple refrigeration circuits.

One thing very apparent in Fig. 20-9 to 20-11 and Table 20-3 is the reduction in capacity at lower evaporator temperatures. This is mainly due to the increase in volume of the refrigerant vapor at lower pressures. A problem worked out should illustrate the difference.

Example 21-1.—If Example 20-1 was worked out for a -20 F evaporator, what is the required displacement per ton?

From the ammonia tables find the following.

Heat of vapor at -20 F, $h_g = 605.0$ Btu per lb.
Volume of vapor at -20 F, $V_g = 14.68$ cu ft per lb.
Heat of liquid at 86 F, $h_f = 138.9$ Btu per lb.

From this data fill in the following formulas.

$RE = h_g - h_f$
$\quad = 605.0 - 138.9 = 466.1$ Btu per lb.

$w = \dfrac{200}{RE},$

$\quad = \dfrac{200}{466.1} = 0.429$ lbs per min per ton

Displacement $= D_t = wV$
$\quad = 0.429 \times 14.68 = 6.30$ cut ft per min per ton

Compare the volume of vapor at 5 F with the volume at -20 F. Although the refrigeration effect is a little less at -20 F, the volume is the factor that makes the greatest difference. It must be remembered that the actual displacement will vary more than the figure

310

shown above, because the volumetric efficiency also gets worse at lower temperatures.

The above variations will naturally make a difference in the performance of a given sized compressor. The variation in volume makes the greatest difference, so a rough check on the change of capacity of a machine can be made by taking only this into account. The capacity will be inversely proportional to this volume. But the volume is also inversely proportional to the absolute suction pressure. So this can be further simplified by using a direct proportion with the absolute pressures. In formula form

$$\frac{R_1}{R_2}=\frac{P_1}{P_2}$$

$$R_2=\frac{R_1 P_2}{P_1}$$

where

R_1=refrigeration produced at original condition
R_2=refrigeration produced at final condition
P_1=absolute suction pressure at original condition
P_2=absolute suction pressure at final condition

Example 21-2.—An ammonia machine is chosen to give 10 tons of refrigeration at 5 F evaporator and 86 F condenser. What is its capacity at -15 F evaporator?

The absolute pressures are as follows:

At   5 F=34.27 psia

At -15 F=20.88 psia

$$R_2=\frac{R_1 P_2}{P_1}$$

$$=\frac{10 \times 20.88}{34.27}=6.09 \text{ tons}$$

Effect of Changing Suction Temperature.—Occasionally it is desirable to make up a table or chart showing the effects of variations in operating conditions. At first this might seem to be quite a task. But if the work is properly systematized, it can be reduced to a minimum.

Example 21-3.—A 4 in x 4½ in x 3 cylinder Refrigerant 12 compressor operates at 300 rpm. The condensing pressure is to be held constant at 90 F. How will the capacity and horse power of this machine vary with evaporator temperatures varying from −40 F to +40 F?

The actual displacement is found by formula.

$$D_a = \frac{0.7854 \, B^2 \, L \, N \, rpm}{1728}$$

$$= \frac{0.7854 \times 4^2 \times 4.5 \times 3 \times 300}{1728}$$

$$= 29.4 \text{ cu ft per min}$$

From the tables the following data is found from the condensing temperature.

Absolute condensing pressure $= 114$ psia
Heat of liquid at 90 F $= 28.7$ Btu per lb

For the different evaporator conditions a table such as Table 21-1 is set up. The various evaporator temperatures to be checked are listed in the first row. Then the information needed from the tables follows. Letters are assigned to each item to simplify formulas. At the end of each row is given the formula or method of finding the data required. By setting up the work in this manner, it is routinized so that the arithmetic involved becomes the only real chore to the problem. It is suggested the reader check several of these figures himself.

The relationships of the data worked out above is more apparent if a curve is plotted of the results. Fig. 21-1 shows this curve giving

TABLE 21-1—EFFECT OF VARYING EVAPORATOR TEMPERATURE ON 4 x 4½, 3 CYL. REFRIGERANT 12 COMPRESSOR, 300 RPM

Displacement $= 29.4$ cfm, Condensing Temp. $(t_c) = 90$ F, Condensing Press. (P_c) $= 114$ psia, Heat of liquid at 90 F $(h_c) = 28.7$ Btu per lb.

Evaporator TemperatureF, t	−40	−20	0	20	40	
Evaporator Pressure, psia, P	9.3	15.3	23.9	35.7	51.7	From Tables
Heat of Vapor, Btu, h_g	73.5	76.0	78.2	80.5	82.7	From Tables
Volume per lb, cu ft, V_g	3.9	2.5	1.64	1.12	0.79	From Tables
Heat of Superheated Vapor, Btu, H_s	92.7	91.5	90.5	89.5	89.0	From Mollier Diagram
Refrigerating Effect, Btu, RE	44.8	47.3	49.5	51.8	54.0	$h_g - h_f$
Lb per min per ton, w	4.47	4.23	4.04	3.86	3.70	200/RE
Theoretical Displacement per ton cu ft, D_t	17.1	10.57	6.62	4.32	2.92	wV
Compression Ratio, CR	12.3	7.45	4.77	3.19	2.20	P_c/P_e
Volumetric Efficiency, % E_v	.45	.58	.68	.75	.80	From Fig. 20-5
Actual Displacement, cu ft, D_a	13.2	17.1	20.0	21.1	23.5	$29.4 \times E_v$
Refrigeration in tons, R	0.77	1.62	3.02	4.89	8.05	D/D_t
Heat of Compression, Btu	19.2	15.5	12.3	9.0	6.3	$h_s - h_g$
Theoretical hp per ton	2.02	1.55	1.17	0.82	0.55	$\dfrac{w(h_s - h_g)}{42.42}$
Actual hp	1.83	2.96	4.16	4.71	5.21	$\dfrac{R \times thp}{0.85}$

the capacity and horsepower for different suction temperatures. If some point such as 0 F evaporator on such a curve is taken as 100 percent, variations each way can be figured in percentage and be made to apply to any compressor working under the same conditions. Fig. 14-1 is just such a curve.

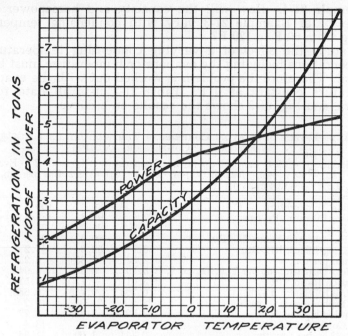

Fig. 21-1. Effect of varying evaporator temperatures. (3 cylinder 4 x 4½ Refrigerant-12 compressor, 300 rpm).

Notice that both the capacity and horsepower decrease at lower temperatures. But the capacity decreases faster than the power. This requires a greater amount of power for a given amount of refrigeration. If the capacity at these lower temperatures is divided by the power, data for a curve similar to Fig. 14-2 is obtained. This also will help explain why equipment properly chosen for a freezer job may be so badly overloaded as to open a motor overload when first started up with a warm evaporator. It also shows why a unit properly chosen for a freezer job will be overloaded on a higher temperature job.

Effect of Changing Condensing Temperature.—Besides suction temperature, there are many other factors which, if varied, can change the compressor capacity and power. Although they do not make as great a change as does suction temperature, their effects should be recognized. In Chapter 14 it was pointed out that for economy, condensing pressure should be as low as possible. It would be of interest to analyze the effect of changing condensing temperatures.

Example 21-4.—How will the capacity and horsepower of the compressor of Example 21-3 vary with condensing temperatures varying from 60 F to 120 F?

To study the effect of a varying condensing temperature, all other conditions including the evaporator temperature must be held constant. Therefore the problem is worked out with the evaporator temperature constant at 0 F. Table 21-2 lists all data for this problem, and Fig. 21-2 shows the results on a curve.

TABLE 21-2—EFFECT OF VARYING CONDENSING TEMPERATURE ON 4 x 4½, 3 CYL., REFRIGERANT 12 COMPRESSOR, 300 RPM

Displacement = 29.4 cfm, Evaporator Temperature (t_e) = 0 F, Evaporating Pressure (P_e) = 23.9 psia, Heat of Vapor at 0 F (h_g) = 78.2 Btu per lb, Volume per lb at 0 F (V_g) = 1.64 cu ft per lb.

	60	80	100	120
Condensing Temperature, t_c, F	60	80	100	120
Condensing Pressure, P_c, psia	72.4	98.8	131.6	171.8
Heat of Liquid, h_f, Btu	21.5	26.2	31.0	36.0
Heat of Superheated Vapor, H_s, Btu	86.7	89.2	91.6	93.9
Refrigerating Effect, RE, Btu	56.7	52.0	47.2	42.2
Lb per min per ton, w	3.53	3.85	4.23	4.73
Theoretical Displacement Per Ton, D_t, cu ft	5.79	6.31	6.94	7.75
Compression Ratio, CR	3.01	4.12	5.52	7.15
Volumetric Efficiency, E_v, %	0.765	0.715	0.655	0.600
Actual Displacement, D, cu ft	22.5	21.0	19.2	17.6
Refrigeration in tons, R	3.89	3.33	2.77	2.27
Heat of Compression, Btu	8.9	11.0	13.4	15.7
Theoretical hp per ton, thp	0.741	1.00	1.34	1.75
Actual horsepower	2.88	3.33	3.71	3.97

Detailed Standard Ton Conditions.—Both the above examples assume no subcooling of the liquid entering the expansion valve, or no superheating of the vapor entering the compressor. Actually this is a highly theoretical condition seldom attained in practice. Small variations from this theoretical ideal usually do not make enough difference to take them into account when figuring the size of equipment. But it is well to know how to figure these differences, and to have an understanding of their effects.

In the previous chapter, all standard ton calculations were based on a 5 F evaporator and 86 F condenser. In Chapter 2 the complete standard ton was described as including 9 F of subcooling in the liquid entering the expansion valve, and 9 F of superheating in the vapor entering the compressor. These conditions are plotted in Fig.

21-3. The heat of liquid at 77 F can be taken either from the chart or the tables. But it must be taken from the temperature rather

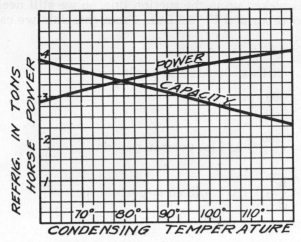

Fig. 21-2. Effect of varying condensing temperature. (3 cylinder 4x4½ Refrigerant 12 compressor, 300 rpm).

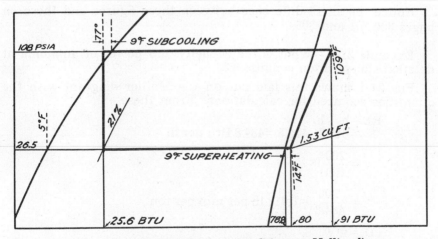

Fig. 21-3. Outline of detailed standard ton conditions on Mollier diagram, Refrigerant-12.

than the pressure, because it is the temperature that determines the heat. The condition entering the compressor with the 9 F of superheat is easiest found on the chart as in Fig. 21-3. Its heat is

80 Btu and its volume 1.53 cu ft per lb. Following the entropy lines up to the discharge pressure of 108 psia gives the condition leaving the compressor. This has a heat of 91 Btu. It is assumed the 9 F of superheat is picked up in the suction line, so we still need the heat of saturated vapor at 5 F, 78.8 Btu. From this data we can find the following.

$$RE = h_g - h_c$$
$$= 78.8 - 25.6 = 53.2 \text{ Btu per lb}$$

$$w = \frac{200}{RE}.$$

$$= \frac{200}{53.2} = 3.76 \text{ lbs per min per ton}$$

$$D_t = wV$$
$$= 3.76 \times 1.53 = 5.75 \text{ cu ft per min per ton}$$

$$\text{Horsepower per Ton} = \frac{w(H_s - h_g)}{42.42}$$

$$= \frac{3.76 (91 - 80)}{42.42} = 0.98 \text{ hp per ton}$$

Notice the small difference between these figures and those on pages 300-301 and 305.

Example 21-5.—What is the capacity and power of ammonia at detailed standard ton conditions?

Fig. 21-4 shows this laid out on the Mollier diagram with the quantities required for calculations. From these

$$RE = h_g - h_c$$
$$= 613.3 - 128.5 = 484.8 \text{ Btu per lb}$$

$$w = \frac{200}{RE}.$$

$$= \frac{200}{484.8} = 0.413 \text{ lb per min per ton}$$

$$D_t = wV$$
$$= 0.413 \times 8.3 = 3.43 \text{ cu ft per min per ton}$$

$$\text{Horsepower per ton}_t = \frac{w(H_s - h_g)}{42.42}$$

$$= \frac{0.413 (721 - 619)}{42.42} = 0.995 \text{ hp per ton}$$

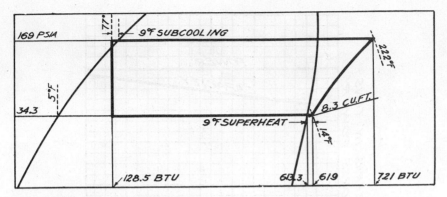

Fig. 21-4. Outline of standard ton conditions on the Mollier diagram, ammonia.

Effect of Subcooling.—Any subcooling of the liquid to the expansion valve decreases the flash gas and increases the refrigeration effect. This increases the refrigeration produced in the evaporator with no increase in power. Table 21-3 shows this worked out, and Fig. 21-5 shows it in graphic form.

TABLE 21-3—EFFECT OF VARYING LIQUID SUBCOOLING WITH CONSTANT CONDENSING PRESSURE ON 4 IN. X 4½ IN., 3 CYL. REFRIGERANT-12 COMPRESSOR, 300 RPM

Condensing Temperature (t_c) = 100 F;   Condensing Pressure (P_c) = 132 psia; Evaporating Temperature (t_e) = 0 F;   Evaporating Pressure (P_e) = 23.9 psia; Compression Ratio (CR) = 5.52;   Displacement = 29.4 cfm; Volumetric Efficiency (E_v) = 0.655;   Actual Displacement (D) = 19.25 cfm;   Heat of Vapor at 0 F (h_g) =78.2 Btu per lb; Heat of Superheat (H_s) =91.6 Btu per lb.

Temperature of Liquid to Expansion Valve, F	100	80	60	40
Heat of Liquid, h_f, Btu	31.0	26.2	21.5	17.0
Refrigerating Effect, RE, Btu	47.2	52.0	56.7	61.2
Lb per min per ton, w	4.23	3.85	3.53	3.27
Theoretical Displacement per ton D_t, cu ft	6.94	6.31	5.79	5.36
Refrigeration in tons, R	2.78	3.05	3.33	3.59
Theoretical hp per ton, thp	1.34	1.22	1.11	1.03
Actual horsepower, ahp	3.72	3.72	3.70	3.70

Effect of Superheated Suction Vapor.—Superheating the suction vapor increases its volume which reduces the capacity of the compressor. This takes place with little or no change in horse power. Also notice the temperature of the discharge vapor can be read directly from the Mollier diagram for any condition entering the compressor. This method of determining the discharge temperature is to be recommended over the method given in Chapter 14. Table 21-4 and Fig. 21-6 show the variations for these varying superheats.

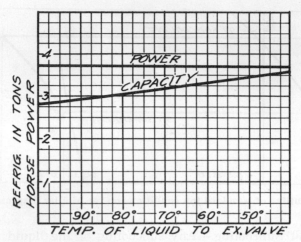

Fig. 21-5. Effect of varying liquid subcooling. (3 cylinder 4x4½ Refrigerant-12 compressor, 300 rpm).

TABLE 21-4—EFFECT OF SUPERHEATED SUCTION VAPOR WITH CONSTANT EVAPORATING AND CONDENSING PRESSURE ON 4 IN. X 4½ IN., 3 CYL. REFRIGERANT 12 COMPRESSOR, 300 RPM

Condensing Temperature (tc) = 90 F; Condensing Pressure (Pc) = 114 psia; Evaporating Temperature (te) = 0 F; Evaporating Pressure (Pe) 23.9 psia; Compression Ratio (CR) = 4.77; Displacement = 29.4 cfm; Volumetric Efficiency (Ev) = 0.68; Actual Displacement (D) = 20.0 cfm; Heat of Vapor at 0 F (hg) = 78.2 Btu per lb; Heat of Liquid at 90 F (hf) = 28.7 Btu per lb; Refrigerating Effect (RE) = 49.5 Btu per lb.

Superheated Suction Temperature, ts, F	0	20	40	60
Volume Per Lb, V, cu ft	1.64	1.73	1 82	1.90
Heat of Vapor, hg, Btu	78.2	81.0	84.0	86.8
Heat of Superheated gas, Hs, Btu	90.5	93.8	97.3	100.8
Theoretical Displacement Per Ton, Dt, cu ft	6.62	7.00	7.35	7.67
Refrigeration in tons, R	3.02	2.86	2.72	2.61
Heat of Compression, Hs − hg, Btu	12.3	12.8	13.3	14.0
Theoretical hp per ton, thp	1.17	1.22	1.27	1.33
Actual horsepower, ahp	3.54	3.49	3.46	3.47

Wet Compression.—Another check that can be made on the Mollier diagram, is the results of wet compression. This is where some liquid comes back the suction line to enter the compressor. Fig. 21-7 shows this plotted on the skeleton diagram. If a small amount of liquid returns, such as at A-B-C, the heat generated by the first part of the compression stroke would evaporate this liquid. But this evaporation would keep the vapor from superheating until all the liquid was evaporated as at B. Then from B to C the vapor would superheat. Naturally, it would be cooler at C than if a dry vapor entered the compressor. The compression line D-E illustrated the maximum quantity of liquid that could be returned without trouble. Here there is just enough cooling effect in the liquid refrigerant present to match the heat of compression that would

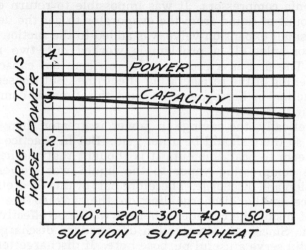

Fig. 21-6. Effect of varying superheat in suction vapor (Refrigerant-12 compressor, 3 cylinder 4 x 4½ at 300 rpm).

cause superheating. Thus a dry but saturated vapor is left in the cylinder at the end of the stroke. But if more than this quantity of liquid was returned as at F-G, this leaves the quantity G-E of liquid left at the end of the stroke. Since a compressor is designed

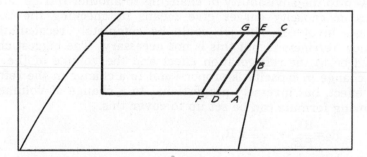

Fig. 21-7. Outline of wet compression on the Mollier diagram.

to pump vapor instead of liquid, this non-compressable, unyielding liquid would be pounded against the valve plate with damaging results. However, since about 5 percent liquid refrigerant can be returned and still be vaporized, it is easy to see why a small amount of refrigerant is not as damaging to a compressor as a small amount of oil.

Wet compression was used to a considerable extent at one time on ammonia compressors. It was impossible to return exactly the right amount of liquid from the evaporator to get the desired cooling, so a small expansion valve was added to the suction line at the compressor inlet. If a problem is worked out, two results are noticed. The first is a reduction in refrigeration capacity due to the shortening of the refrigerating effect line. But the second result is a reduction in horsepower because this type of compression is more nearly isothermal.

Theoretically, the savings in power is greater than the loss in capacity, so there should be a net gain. But in practice the results did not seem to bear this out. It is thought that the heat transfer from the compressing vapor to the liquid was slower than the compression and discharge. Therefore part of this theoretical cooling took place in the discharge line on the way to the condenser, instead of inside the cylinder where it would be effective in power reduction. Since wet compression does reduce discharge temperatures, it did serve a useful purpose here. If discharge temperatures would get much above 250 F with normal compression, wet compression helped reduce or eliminate oil breakdown. However, wet compression is very seldom used at the present time.

Changing Refrigerants.—In Chapter 3 it was mentioned that although a machine always worked better if used with the refrigerant it was designed for, there are times when consideration is given to the advisability of changing to another refrigerant. The tables or capacity curves give means of checking the capacity changes involved. The job could be completely recalculated for the new refrigerant, but this is not necessary. The biggest changes would be in the refrigeration effect and the volume of the vapor. The change in capacity is proportional to a change in the refrigeration effect, but inversely proportional to a change of volume. The following formula can be set up to cover this.

$$R_2 = \frac{RE_2}{RE_1} \times \frac{V_1}{V_2} \times R_1$$

where

R_1 = refrigerating capacity with the first refrigerant
R_2 = refrigerating capacity with the second refrigerant
RE_1 = refrigeration effect with the first refrigerant
RE_2 = refrigeration effect with the second refrigerant
V_1 = Volume of the first refrigerant vapor
V_2 = volume of the second refrigerant vapor

This gives the capacity at the new condition if no other changes were made. If R_1 is not definitely known, 100 percent may be used instead, and the answer obtained in percent of the first capacity. If the compressor speed is divided by this percentage, a driving speed is obtained which will give the same capacity as the compressor working with the original speed and refrigerant.

Example 21-6.—A Refrigerant 12 condensing unit operates at a 15 F evaporator and a 100 F condenser. It rotates at 660 rpm. What would be the proper speed if the refrigerant was changed to Refrigerant 22?

From the tables the following is found.

Heat of R-12 liquid at 100 F   = 31.16
Heat of R-12 vapor at 15 F   = 79.93
Volume of R-12 vapor at 15 F   =   1.230
Heat of R-22 liquid at 100 F   = 40.80
Heat of R-22 vapor at 15 F   = 106.35
Volume of R-22 vapor at 15 F   =   1.0277

$$R_2 = \frac{RE_2}{RE_1} \times \frac{V_1}{V_2} R_1$$

$$= \frac{106.35 - 40.80}{79.93 - 31.16} \times \frac{1.23}{1.0277} \times R_1 = 1.61 R_1$$

There would be 1.61 times as much refrigeration with Refrigerant 22 if nothing more was done. If corrected for speed, the new speed would be

$$\frac{660}{1.61} = 410 \text{ rpm}$$

This example could also be checked from Fig. 20-10. The following conditions are found.

Required displacement per ton = 5.0 cu ft per min.
Required displacement per ton = 3.1 cu ft per min.

The required speed could be worked out from this data and a direct proportion.

$$\frac{rpm_1}{rpm_2} = \frac{D_1}{D_2}$$

$$rpm_2 = \frac{rpm_1 \times D_2}{D_1}$$

$$= \frac{660 \times 3.1}{5.0} = 408 \text{ rpm}$$

The slight difference is due to the fact Fig. 20-10 can be read to only two figures instead of three.

Heat Exchangers.—Heat exchangers, as mentioned in Chapter 8, are commonly used on low temperature compressors with fluoro-carbon refrigerants. They may be used with other refrigerants or on warmer applications. Many tables have been prepared to show savings made with heat exchangers, but these tables often show widely different results. The reason for this is often that widely different conditions are assumed to start with. To fully understand the effects of a heat exchanger, let us first study individual effects separately.

Fig. 21-8 illustrates on the Refrigerant 12 diagram the effect of different compression ratios on the expansion valve and evaporator. A constant 80 F condenser, but different evaporator temperature are

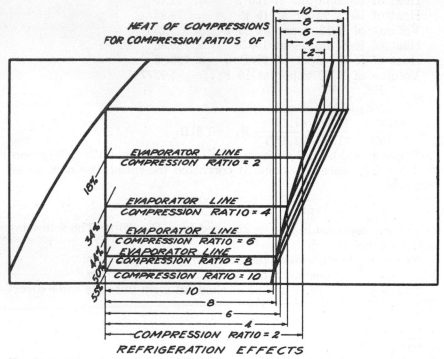

Fig. 21-8. Effect of different compression ratios (on Mollier diagram), Refrigerant 12.

assumed. Notice that a lower evaporator temperature means more flash gas and a shorter refrigerating effect line. This reduces the capacity of a given size expansion valve because it has to pass more liquid to get a given refrigeration effect. It also reduces the capacity of the compressor because of the flash gas the compressor has to pump, beside the vapor formed in the evaporator.

For a given compression ratio, the cooler the liquid entering the expansion valve, the less the flash gas, and the greater the refrigerating effect line, Fig. 21-9. Therefore, it is desirable to cool the liquid entering the expansion valve as much as possible.

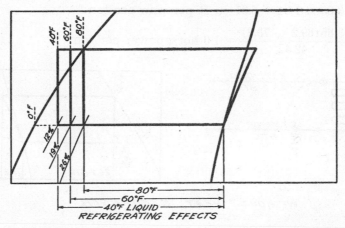

Fig. 21-9. Effect of subcooled liquid, Refrigerant 12 (on Mollier diagram).

At the compressor end, anything that superheats the suction vapor increases its size, so reduces the quantity a given compressor will pump, Fig. 21-6. This reduction in capacity is usually with little or no decrease in power.

A heat exchanger will help where it reduces the liquid temperature, but is a hinderance where it increases the superheat of the suction vapor. In considering a heat exchanger, the gain at one end must be balanced against the loss at the other, and the net result found. Besides the effect on capacities, there are other points to be considered. On sub-zero jobs and on flooded jobs, there is difficulty in obtaining superheat enough to properly operate a thermostatic expansion valve. Uninsulated, cold suction lines may collect frost or dew which drips on the floor and becomes a nuisance.

For the simplest type of problem consider a system such as Fig. 21-10, with and without a heat exchanger. We will figure the size machine necessary to give one ton of refrigeration with Refrigerant 12. A 0 F evaporator and an 80 F condenser are chosen. Where the heat exchanger is used, one which will superheat the vapor to 40 F is assumed. The diagrams with Fig. 21-10 give all the data necessary.

Following are the figures for the system without the heat exchanger.

Heat of saturated vapor at 0 F = 78.2 Btu per lb
Heat of liquid at 80 F   = 26.2 Btu per lb
Refrigerating effect   52.0 Btu per lb

$$\frac{200}{52} = 3.85 \text{ lb per min per ton}$$

$$3.85 \times 1.64 = 6.31 \text{ cu ft per min per ton}$$

$$\frac{3.85(89.2 - 78.2)}{42.42} = 1.0 \text{ horsepower per ton}$$

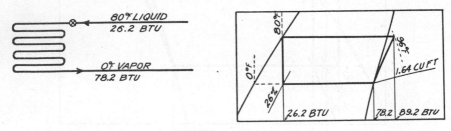

WITHOUT HEAT EXCHANGER

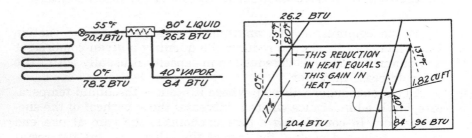

WITH HEAT EXCHANGER

Fig. 21-10. Effect of heat exchanger, Refrigerant 12.

Thus a compressor of 6.31 cu ft per min theoretical displacement will be necessary, and will draw 1.0 hp.

With the heat exchanger, it would be possible to figure the reduction in temperature of the liquid, and the reduction in flash gas as shown in Fig. 21-10. But it is much easier to take the method of page 300, and consider the heat exchanger part of the evaporator. Any gain in total heat above that of the liquid entering this part of the system must come from the evaporator. The figures follow:

Heat of vapor superheated to 40 F = 84.0 Btu per lb
Heat of liquid at 80 F   = 26.2 Btu per lb
Refrigerating effect   57.8 Btu per lb

If we used the same 6.31 cu ft per min compressor, it would pump the following:

$$\frac{6.31}{1.82} = 3.47 \text{ lbs per min}$$

The new refrigeration capacity is

$$3.47 \times 57.8 = 200 \text{ Btu per min}$$

This is exactly one ton of refrigeration, so is the same capacity as without the heat exchanger. The power required would be

$$\frac{3.47(96-84)}{42.42} = 0.98 \text{ horsepower per ton}$$

The superheated suction vapor has larger volume so less is pumped. At this particular condition, the extra cooling obtained by superheating the suction vapor is just enough to offset the loss due to the increased volume of vapor. But since less weight of vapor is pumped, less power is needed to do the same job. The compressor discharge temperature is raised to 137 F. But this is not an excessive figure.

The same job using ammonia as the refrigerant is illustrated in Fig. 21-11. The calculations follow:

Heat of saturated vapor at 0 F = 611.8 Btu per lb
Heat of liquid at 80 F   = 132.0 Btu per lb
Refrigerating effect   479.8 Btu per lb

$$\frac{200}{479.8} = 0.416 \text{ lb per min per ton}$$

$$0.416 \times 9.12 = 3.8 \text{ cu ft per min per ton}$$

$$\frac{0.416(713.0-611.8)}{42.42} = 0.995 \text{ hp per ton}$$

The calculations with the heat exchanger follow.

Heat of vapor superheated to 40 F = 634.5 Btu·per lb
Heat of liquid at 80 F   = 132.0 Btu per lb
Refrigerating effect   502.5 Btu per lb

$$\frac{3.8}{9.9} = 0.384 \text{ lbs per min}$$

$$0.384 \times 502.5 = 193 \text{ Btu per min}$$

$$\frac{193}{200} = 0.965 \text{ tons of refrigeration}$$

$$\frac{0.384(744.0 - 634.5)}{42.42} = 0.993 \text{ hp}$$

$$\frac{0.993}{0.965} = 1.03 \text{ hp per ton}$$

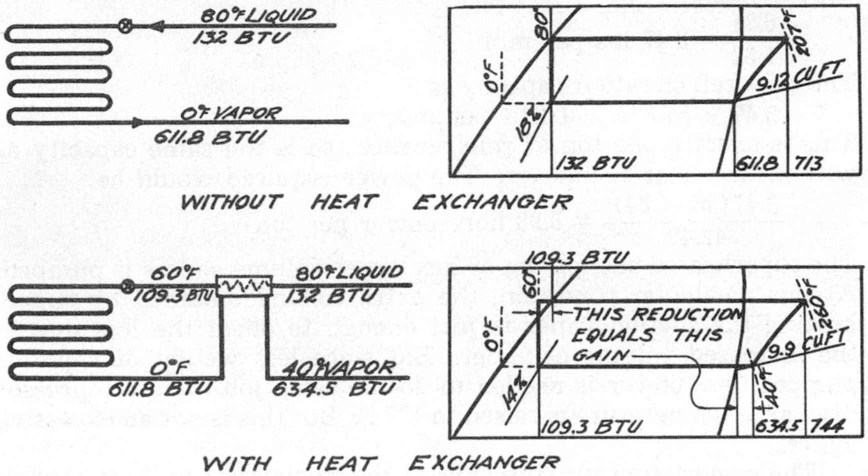

WITHOUT HEAT EXCHANGER

WITH HEAT EXCHANGER

Fig. 21-11. Effect of heat exchanger, ammonia.

Here we find a condition where the losses are more than the gains, but with no savings in power. The compressor discharge temperature with ammonia becomes 260 F, which is too high to be desirable.

The results of these figures are tabulated in Table 21-5. From this we can draw the following conclusions.

1. With a Refrigerant 12 system, a heat exchanger increases the operating efficiency.

2. With an ammonia system operating at or near a saturated suction condition, a heat exchanger reduces the efficiency. It also raises the compressor discharge temperature to an undesirable figure.

Actually such heat exchangers are never used with ammonia. Carbon in the compressor heads and discharge valves, and burned discharge valves would result.

TABLE 21-5—EFFECT OF HEAT EXCHANGERS WITH DIFFERENT REFRIGERANTS

	Without Heat Exchanger		With Heat Exchanger		
Refrigerant	Capacity in Tons	Hp	Capacity in Tons	Hp	Hp Per Ton
Refrigerant 12	1.00	1.00	1.00	0.98	0.98
Ammonia	1.00	0.995	0.965	0.993	1.03

Two Stage Systems; Booster Systems.—Low evaporator temperatures result in high compression ratios. High compression ratios require greater power, and increase discharge temperatures to a point where lubrication problems are aggravated. In the last chapter it was mentioned it would be desirable to have isothermal compression. This would require less power, and would eliminate high temperature lubrication problems. Although the vapor cannot be successfully cooled during compression, this condition can be more nearly approached by two staging. That is, half the compression is done in one cylinder, the vapor then run through a cooler, then the compression finished in another cylinder. These two cylinders may be built in the same machine, or may be two separate machines.

Fig. 21-12 illustrates this system with an outline of the cycle on the Mollier diagram. If the vapor can be cooled to the saturation point A between the two stages, it will be found that the total distance B-C + A-D, which represents the power required in the two stages, is less than the distance B-E, which would be the power

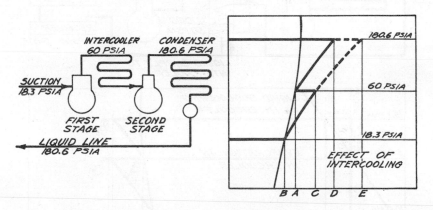

Fig. 21-12. Two stage system, ammonia.

for single stage operation. Fig. 21-13, shows an indicator diagram of the same set of conditions. The top half of such a diagram is corrected for the volume of the second cylinder, which is smaller than the low pressure cylinder. The cross hatched section shows the savings in power over single stage.

There is another place a savings in power can be made in such a system. The liquid to the expansion valve is chilled by passing it through the intermediate cooler. This reduces the flash gas by about one half. The flash gas formed must be compressed from the

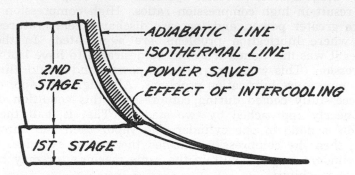

Fig. 21-13. Indicator diagram for two stage system.

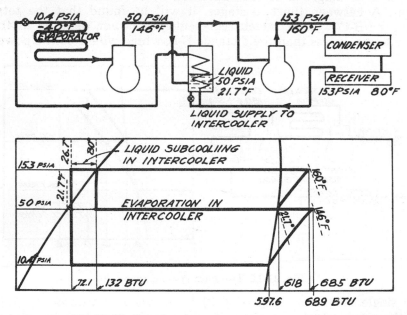

Fig. 21-14. Complete two stage system, ammonia.

low pressure to the high pressure. The chilling done in the intermediate cooler evaporates some liquid, which approximately corresponds to the other half of the flash gas. But this vapor need only be
compressed from the intermediate pressure to the high pressure.
Thus, there is a savings of about half the power used in compressing
about half the flash gas.

Such small savings as these may seem too small to be important. This is so on fractional horsepower equipment. But on large systems they have been found to begin to pay for themselves where compression ratios get greater than 10 to 1.

The intermediate pressure chosen is such that half the power is used in each stage. This pressure can be found by the following formula

$$P_I = \sqrt{P_E P_C}$$

where

P_I = Intermediate absolute pressure.

P_E = Evaporator absolute pressure.

P_C = Condenser absolute pressure.

Because of variations from design conditions, this formula has been found to work better in actual practice if modified as follows:

$$P_I = \sqrt{P_E P_C} + 5$$

Fig. 21-14 shows such a system operating on ammonia, with the cycle outlined on the Mollier diagram. This is worked out per ton of refrigeration. The intermediate pressure will be

$$P_I = \sqrt{P_E P_C} + 5$$
$$= \sqrt{10.4 \times 153} + 5 = 44.9 \text{ psia}$$

This is as near 50 psia as can be read on the chart or on pressure gages on the job. From the tables this gives an intermediate temperature of 21.7 F. It will be assumed the liquid to the expansion valve is cooled to within 5 F of the intermediate temperature. This will be

21.7 + 5 = 26.7 F

Heat of vapor at —40 F = 597.6 Btu per lb

Heat of liquid at 26.7 F = 72.1 Btu per lb

Refrigerating effect   525.5 Btu per lb

$$\frac{200}{525.5} = 0.381 \text{ lb per min per ton}$$

0.381 × 24.9 = 9.5 cu ft per min per ton
         displacement of the low pressure cylinder.

$$\frac{0.381 \,(689.0 - 597.6)}{42.42} = 0.822 \text{ hp per ton on the low pressure cylinder.}$$

Vapor to the high pressure cylinder is supplied by three sources: first, the discharge from the low pressure cylinder; second, the liquid evaporated by the superheat in the low pressure discharge; and third, the liquid evaporated by the cooling of the liquid to the low temperature expansion valve.

The first, the weight discharged from the low pressure cylinder will be the same as that entering the high pressure cylinder, 0.381 lb per min per ton. This vapor is discharged at 146 F, and contains 689 Btu per lb. To cool it to saturation reduces its heat content to 618 Btu per lb.

The liquid supply from the receiver to the intercooler is 80 F. It is 21.7 F at the intermediate pressure. Therefore its refrigerating effect will be

Heat of vapor at 21.7 F = 618.2 Btu per lb
Heat of liquid at 80 F   = 132.0 Btu per lb

Refrigerating effect   486.2 Btu per lb

To remove 71 Btu will require

$$\frac{71}{486.2} = 0.145 \text{ lb evaporated per lb of ammonia circulated.}$$

Since 0.381 lb per min per ton is circulated
0.381 × 0.145 = 0.055 lb per min per ton

This is the second source of vapor mentioned above.

The liquid to the low temperature expansion valve is cooled from 80 F to 26.7 F.

Heat of liquid at 80 F = 132.0 Btu per lb
Heat of liquid at 26.7 F = 72.1 Btu per lb

Heat removed   59.9 Btu per lb

$$\frac{59.9}{486.2} = 0.123 \text{ lb evaporated per lb of ammonia circulated.}$$

Since 0.381 lb per min per ton are circulated
0.381 × 0.108 = 0.041 lb per min per ton.

This is the third source of vapor mentioned.

Vapor from evaporator   = 0.381 lb per min
Vapor from removing superheat = 0.055 lb per min
Vapor from subcooling liquid   = 0.047 lb per min

Total high pressure vapor   0.483 lb per min

Therefore 0.483 lb per min per ton will be handled by the high pressure cylinder.

$$\frac{0.483 (685 - 618)}{42.42} = 0.765 \text{ hp per ton on high pressure cylinder}$$

Low pressure power   = 0.822 hp per ton
High pressure power = 0.765 hp per ton

Total power   1.587 hp per ton

Therefore a total of 1.587 hp per ton is required.

If such a system was operated single stage, the following would be required.

Heat of vapor at -40 F $=$ 597.6 Btu per lb
Heat of liquid at   80 F $=$ 132.0 Btu per lb
Refrigerating effect   465.6 Btu per lb

$$\frac{200}{465.6} = 0.43 \text{ lb per min per ton}$$

$$\frac{0.43 \ (778 - 597.6)}{42.42} = 1.83 \text{ hp per ton}$$

$183 - 1.587 = 2.43$ hp per ton saved

$$\frac{0.243}{1.83} = 0.133 \text{ or } 13.3\% \text{ power savings by using two stage.}$$

If the superheated discharge from the first cylinder could be cooled with a water intercooler down to something near the 80 F condensing temperature, this would further reduce the savings made by two staging. Fig. 21-15 shows how this water cooled intercooler would be connected. The only change in the above problem would be in the second item supplying vapor to the second stage.

Heat of vapor at 80   F $=$ 630.7 Btu per lb
Heat of vapor at 21.7 F $=$ 618   Btu per lb
Heat to be removed   12.7 Btu per lb

$$\frac{12.7}{552} = 0.023 \text{ lb evaporated per lb of ammonia circulated.}$$

$0.381 \times 0.023 = 0.009$ lb per min per ton
Since 0.049 lb per min was required for this item in the previous case, this is a savings of
$0.049 - 0.009 = 0.040$ lb per min.
The total high pressure vapor will be
$0.471 - 0.040 = 0.431$ lb per min per ton.
The power required would then be

$$\frac{0.431 \ (685 - 618)}{42.42} = 0.681 \text{ hp per ton on the high}$$
$$\text{pressure cylinder.}$$

Then the total power would be
$0.822 + 0.681 = 1.503$ hp per ton.

The above problem was worked out for a job where the -40 F evaporator was the only temperature required. Where this is the case, and the second cylinder handles only the vapor from the first cylinder and the intercooler, it is called a two stage system. In a cold storage plant, higher temperatures are also required. Where there is plenty of compressor capacity for this high pressure suction, a compressor is sometimes added to the system which raises the low pressure vapor to the higher evaporator pressure, Fig. 21-16. Such a compressor is called a booster compressor. It is the same problem as that above, except the high pressure compressor handles

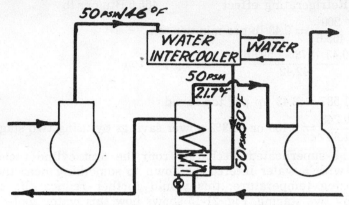

Fig. 21-15. Intercooling with water plus liquid ammonia.

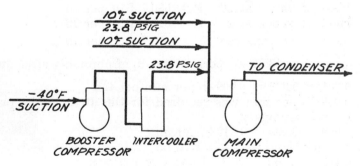

Fig. 21-16. Booster compressor system, ammonia.

suction vapor direct from the warmer evaporators as well as the discharge from the booster.

For the most economical condition, the intercooling done between stages requires consideration. If plenty of cold water is available and intermediate pressures high, it might be cheapest to use only a water cooled intercooler with no liquid ammonia intercooling. Sometimes a combination of watercooling and liquid ammonia cooling as in Fig. 21-18 is used. This is usually the most efficient. However, in some cases, the extra water cooler is not considered worth the savings involved. Each problem must be considered separately with proper consideration given to operating costs, equipment costs, and total operating time per year.

With the above systems, the refrigerant was ammonia. The oil goes to the bottom of the liquid refrigerant in receivers, intercoolers, etc. It can be drained from these points if proper drain valves are supplied.

The oil will not separate from a Refrigerant 12 mixture, so makes an oil rich mixture on top of the liquid refrigerant. With Refrigerant 22, the oil and refrigerant separate at low temperatures, the oil floating on top of the liquid refrigerant. In either case the oil would be trapped in a flooded intercooler. And under many operating conditions flooded evaporators will trap oil.

To prevent such oil trapping in the intercoolers and other points, a system such as Fig. 21-17 is used. Even here if two compressors are used, the oil levels in each must be watched and manually corrected if needed. Often certain operating conditions will flush the oil from one compressor, and it collects in the other.

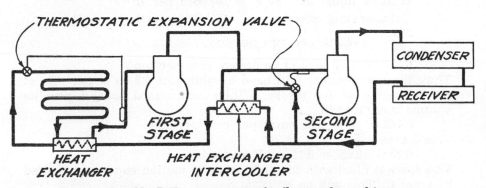

Fig. 21-17. Two stage system for fluorocarbon refrigerants.

Cascade System.—Certain problems inherent in high compression ratio systems are eliminated by a casc.le system, Fig. 21-18. This uses two separate systems, but the evaporator of the higher temperature system furnishes the cooling for the condenser of the low temperature system.

The advantages of such a system over a two stage system are in getting a better separation of the high pressure, high temperature end from the low pressure, low temperature end. Oil suitable for the low temperature evaporator does not have to stand the heats of the high pressure compression, and vice versa. In cases where temperatures of 50 F to 100 F below zero are required, they are more easily obtained with refrigerants such as Refrigerant 13. The evaporator of the second stage, using Refrigerant 12 or 22, keeps the condensing pressure of the high pressure stage within reasonable limits. The disadvantages of such a system are that more equipment is required which means higher first costs, and the double heat transfers through the extra condenser-evaporator make it less efficient.

Dual Effect.—Dual effect compressors were mentioned in Chapter 6 and shown in Fig. 6-30. This is a method of obtaining two different suction pressures from a single compressor. It is also a method of increasing the efficiency of low pressure suctions by using a high pressure suction to do part of the compressing. Fig. 21-19 gives the data for such a job. The low pressure suction comes into the cylinder at A. As the high pressure suction port is uncovered, the higher pressure vapor compresses the low pressure vapor from A to B. At B it has a volume of 7.0 cu ft per lb. The job is figured for one ton of refrigeration at the —20 F evaporator (ammonia).

Heat of vapor at —20 F = 605 Btu per lb
Heat of liquid at   80 F = 132 Btu per lb
Refrigerating effect $\overline{473}$ Btu per lb

$$\frac{200}{473} = 0.422 \text{ lb per min per ton}$$

$0.422 \times 14.7 = 6.20$ cu ft per min per ton

Thus, the low pressure will have a volume of 6.2 cu ft per min at the beginning of the stroke. When compressed to 48.2 psia its volume is reduced to

$0.422 \times 7 = 2.95$ cu ft per min per ton.

This leaves

$6.20 — 2.95 = 3.25$ cu ft per min.

This space is filled with the high pressure suction vapor represented by point C. This will be

$$\frac{3.25}{5.90} = 0.55 \text{ lb per min}$$

Heat of vapor at 20 F = 617.8 Btu per lb
Heat of liquid at 80 F = 132.0 Btu per lb
Refrigerating effect $\overline{485.8}$ Btu per lb

The refrigeration produced at the high pressure suction will then be:

$$\frac{0.55 \times 485.8}{200} = 1.33 \text{ tons}$$

0.55 lb at C contain 0.55 $\times$ 617.8 =   339 Btu
0.422 lb at B contain 0.422 $\times$ 659.5 =   279 Btu
$\overline{0.972}$ lb at D contain $\overline{618}$ Btu

$$\frac{618}{0.972} = 635 \text{ Btu per lb}$$

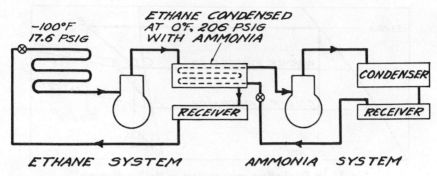

Fig. 21-18. Cascade system.

This gives a figure that makes it possible to accurately establish point D on the chart. This is the starting point of the compression that must be finished by mechanical power. The line D-E is this compression line. The power required will be

$$\frac{0.972\ (709\ -\ 635)}{42.42} = 1.69 \text{ hp}$$

Thus, for one ton of refrigeration at —20 F and 1.32 tons at +20 F, a total of 2.33 tons, 1.69 hp is required.

$$\frac{1.69}{2.33} = 0.725 \text{ hp per ton}$$

This is only a little above the figure given in Fig. 20-11 to produce refrigeration at 20 F. It is way below the power requirements if the +20 F and —20 F powers were figured separately and added up. Thus, the 1.33 tons of +20 F refrigeration is produced with no more cylinder displacement than that already required for the —20 F refrigeration. And the one ton of —20 F refrigeration is obtained at a much better power efficiency than normal.

To give satisfactory capacity in the higher pressure suction, there must be considerable difference in pressure between the two suction pressures. For instance, if they were equal, no vapor would enter the cylinder from the cylinder wall ports. Fig. 21-20 gives the amount of refrigeration produced in the higher pressure evaporator per ton of low pressure refrigeration at different conditions.

One difficulty with such a system is that it must be reasonably well balanced to reasonably steady loads. For the problem worked above, there would have to be 1.33 tons of +20 F refrigeration for every ton of —20 F refrigeration. Variations in the higher pressure would have little or no effect on the low pressure. But any variation in the low pressure suction immediately affects the higher pressure capacity. A rise in the low pressure suction greatly reduces the

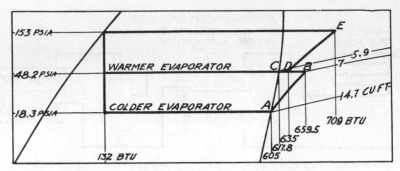

Fig. 21-19. Dual effect compression on Mollier diagram.

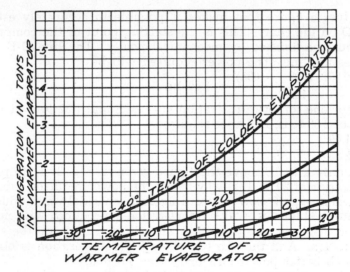

Fig. 21-20. Refrigeration balance with dual effect.

capacity of the higher pressure suction. In the above problem, notice from Fig. 21-20 the effect of a rise of low pressure suction to 0 F. The higher pressure capacity drops from 1.33 tons to 0.488 tons.

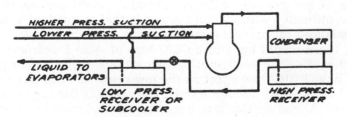

Fig. 21-21. Intermediate subcooler on dual effect.

Where such a job is installed, efficiencies can sometimes be further increased by subcooling the liquid to the colder coil by the higher pressure part of the system, Fig. 21-21. Since the intermediate subcooler of the two stage system is not available, a separate piece of equipment is required. For this reason, it is not used as often as with a two stage system.

QUESTIONS

21- 1. An ammonia machine is chosen to give 10 tons of refrigeration at 5 F evaporator and 86 F condenser. What is its capacity at 40 F evaporator?

21- 2. Make a table similar to Table 21-1 showing the capacity and horsepower of the compressor of Question 21-1 at evaporator temperatures from +40 F to —40 F.

21- 3. A Refrigerant 22 compressor is operating at — 15 F suction and 90 F condensing. Its speed is 825 rpm. If it was changed to Refrigerant 12, but with a 0 F suction and the same condensing temperature, what new speed would maintain the same load on the motor?

21- 4. What is the required displacement per ton and the horse power per ton for a single stage Refrigerant 12 system operating at —40 F evaporator and 100 F condenser without a heat exchanger?

21- 5. In question 21-4, what would be the required displacement per ton and the horsepower per ton if a heat exchanger was added which would heat the suction vapor to +20 F?

21- 6. In question 21-4, what intermediate pressure would you choose if this was to be two staged? Use the formula $P_I = \sqrt{P_E P_C}$ for Refrigerant 12

21- 7. If an intercooler was added to question 21-6 as in Fig. 21-22 how much refrigerant would have to be evaporated from line A to bring the vapor discharged from the low pressure compressor down to saturation, assuming the use of the heat exchanger of Question 21-5?

21- 8. What would be the required displacement and horsepower of the low pressure and high pressure compressor of question 21-7?

21- 9. What additional refrigerant from line A, Fig. 21-22 would be evaporated if line B was passed through the heat exchanger (dotted line), and cooled to within 10 F of the intermediate saturation temperature?

21-10. How much will this increase the required capacity and horse power of the high pressure compressor?

21-11. How much additional refrigeration will be produced at the low pressure evaporator?

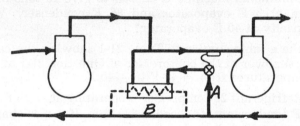

Fig. 21-22. Two stage Refrigerant 12 system, examples, Question 21-7.

CHAPTER 22

REFRIGERANT LINES—PRESSURE DROPS

General.—It has previously been stated that the high side of the system has the same pressure from the compressor to the expansion valve, and the low side has the same pressure from the expansion valve to the compressor. This is only approximately true. There is a slight pressure drop in all lines which have a flow through them. This pressure drop may be only a fraction of a pound per square inch, or can be several pounds. The higher the velocity through the lines, the greater this pressure drop is. It is this change of pressure that forces the fluid to flow in the lines. The lines of any refrigeration system should be of sufficient size that these pressure drops do not interfere with efficient operation.

TABLE 22-1—ALLOWABLE REFRIGERANT VELOCITIES
IN FEET PER MINUTE

Refrigerant	Suction	Discharge	Liquid
Ammonia	3000 to 5000	4000 to 6000	100 to 400
Fluorocarbons	800 to 1800	1800 to 2250	80 to 300

NOTE 1: Liquid velocities should not be over 300 ft. per min. if instant closing valves are in the liquid line.
NOTE 2: If oil must be returned back the suction line, suction velocities must be at least 750 ft. per min. on horizontal runs and 1500 ft. per min. on vertical lifts.

Line sizes are often chosen directly on a velocity basis. Table 22-1 gives ranges of velocities found in operating systems. However, it should be remembered that the actual pressure drop is of more importance than the velocity. On the other hand, where oil circulates with the refrigerant, vapor velocities must be kept high enough that this oil is carried or blown along with the vapor.

Effects of Pressure Drops.—A pressure drop in the suction line reduces the compressor capacity due to conditions brought out in the previous chapter. Any reduction of pressure in the suction line increases the volume of the vapor without the benefit of obtaining a

339

colder evaporator. For a 10 F Refrigerant 12 evaporator, a 29.3 psia pressure is required. If there is a 5 psi pressure drop in the suction line, this gives a pressure of 24.3 psia at the compressor. This would reduce the compressor capacity by about 18 percent. Thus, undersized lines which cause such a pressure drop are very poor economy. Table 22-2 gives pressure drops recommended as permissible values. It certainly does no harm to have pressure drops even lower than these if velocities do not get too low. For oil return, a velocity of 750 ft. per min. on horizontal runs, and 1500 ft. per min. on vertical runs should be a minimum.

TABLE 22-2—ALLOWABLE PRESSURE DROPS

Suction Line				Discharge Line	Liquid Line
—20F	0F	20F	40F		
¼ Psi.	½ Psi.	1 Psi.	2 Psi.	1 Psi.	2 to 4 Psi.

Between the compressor and the condenser, any pressure drop causes a rise in the compressor head pressure. The condensing temperature is fixed by the temperature and amount of cooling water. If the pressure has to fall to reach this point, the compressor has to increase the head pressure by that amount. As shown in Fig. 21-2, this decreases the capacity and increases the power. The head temperature will also be found to run much higher. Again, small line sizes which cause much of a pressure drop here are poor economy.

A pressure drop in the liquid line would have very little effect on operating conditions at light loads, but can cause considerable trouble at heavy loads. There are two reasons for this. The biggest reason is the formation of flash gas in the liquid line. If the liquid pressure is reduced below its condensing pressure, its temperature must come down to match the new pressure. Some of the liquid evaporates (flashes to gas) to produce this temperature reduction, just as if the pressure was reduced in an expansion valve. This produces some cooling or refrigeration in the liquid line where it is wasted. The vapor formed has to pass through the expansion valve where it takes the place of useful liquid. This reduces the capacity of the expansion valve. Also, this warm, high pressure vapor leaking into the evaporator can start surging, or erratic operation as gas bubbles push liquid ahead of them as they try to escape from the evaporator. The second effect of a lower liquid line pressure is a reduction in capacity of a given sized expansion valve. A lower pressure will force less liquid through it. Table 4-1.

Beside losses due to pipe friction, there is a second loss in a liquid line if the evaporator is above the receiver. This is the drop in static head or pressure due to the height of the liquid. Whenever liquid is lifted in a column, as in Fig. 22-1, the pressure at the top is less than the pressure at the bottom by the weight of the liquid column. Table 22-3 gives pressure drops for different refrigerants.

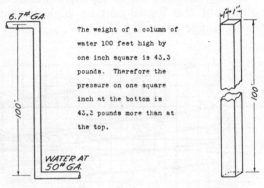

The weight of a column of water 100 feet high by one inch square is 43.3 pounds. Therefore the pressure on one square inch at the bottom is 43.3 pounds more than at the top.

The permissible pressure drop in the liquid line is greater than in the suction or discharge line if the above facts are taken into account, and the proper sized expansion valves are chosen.

Fig. 22-1. Pressure drop in liquid column.

However, for good practice, unless liquid lifts make such impossible, this pressure drop should not be over 4 psi.

The principal effect of a pressure drop in the evaporator will be to give different temperatures in different parts of the evaporator. Actually, this reduces the capacity of the system similar to a pres-

TABLE 22-3—PRESSURE DROPS PER FOOT OF LIFT

Ammonia	0.26 Psi per foot
Methyl Chloride	0.39 Psi per foot
Refrigerant-12	0.56 Psi per foot
Refrigerant-22	0.51 Psi per foot

sure drop in the suction line. This is because the compressor must operate at the lowest pressure, but the average evaporator temperature will be higher than this. Such a pressure drop could be caused by too long a coil of too small a diameter, or by an evaporator built so there is a high static head of liquid on the bottom coils.

Sometimes evaporators fed by thermostatic expansion valves give difficulty if the velocity is too high. The vapor leaving the coil travels so fast it is back to the compressor before the expansion valve bulb can respond to its temperature. Such a condition gives erratic operation, particularly hunting. The maximum velocities indicated by Table 22-1 should not be exceeded.

Figuring Velocities and Pressure Drops.—Velocities can be easily calculated, once the volume to be circulated is known. The velocity is the volume divided by the area of the pipe used. But to save this figuring, the velocity can be picked directly from Fig. 22-4 once the volume is known. The volume of the suction vapor can be obtained from Fig. 20-9, 20-10, or 20-11, depending on the refrigerant. The volume of the liquid can be picked from Fig. 22-2, and the discharge vapor from Fig. 22-3.

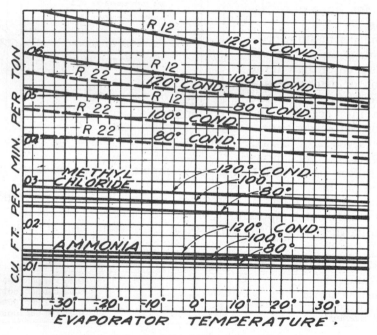

Fig. 22-2. Volume of liquid per ton refrigeration.

Example 22-1.—A ten ton Refrigerant 12 system is to be operated with a 20 F evaporator. Choose suitable line sizes by the velocity method.

From Fig. 20-10 the required displacement per ton (assuming an 80 F condenser) would be 4.2 cu ft per min. From Fig. 22-2 the liquid is 0.046 cu ft per min per ton, and the discharge vapor is 1.63 cu ft per min per ton, Fig. 22-3. This gives the following data for 10 tons.

Suction vapor	42	cu ft per min	
Discharge vapor	16.3	cu ft per min	
Liquid	0.46	cu ft per min	

From Fig. 22-4 a 2⅛ in. suction line would give a velocity of 2100 ft per min, which is above the 1800 ft per min limit of Table 22-1. The 2⅝ in. line drops to 1300 ft per min which would have to be chosen. The discharge line would have to be 1⅝ in., and its velocity 1400 ft per min. A ⅝ in. liquid line would give a liquid velocity of 310 ft per min, near enough to the 300 ft per min limit to be satisfactory.

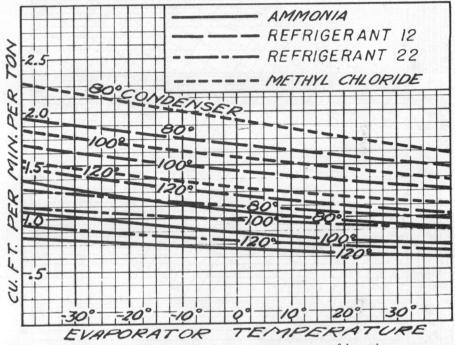

Fig. 22-3. Volume of discharge vapor per ton refrigeration.

The pressure drop is affected by many variables. The roughness of the pipe, the velocity of flow, the viscosity or stickiness of the refrigerant, and the density of the refrigerant all have their effects. Formulas have been worked out which take friction factors from special curves, but the number of variables involved makes them tedious to use. For that reason various tables and charts have been made up to help solve pressure drop problems. Fig. 22-5 to 22-7 give charts to help calculate pressure drops for the common refrigerants. Pick the tons of refrigeration, or Btu per hr, on the upper right hand corner, drop down to the proper line for the information

NOTE: Figures 22-5 to 22-7 are furnished loose for more convenient use. They are in the back cover pocket.

required, then go horizontally to the left of the pipe size, then down to the pressure drop. Or for suction lines of systems at or near 0 F, the chart may be entered directly from the left.

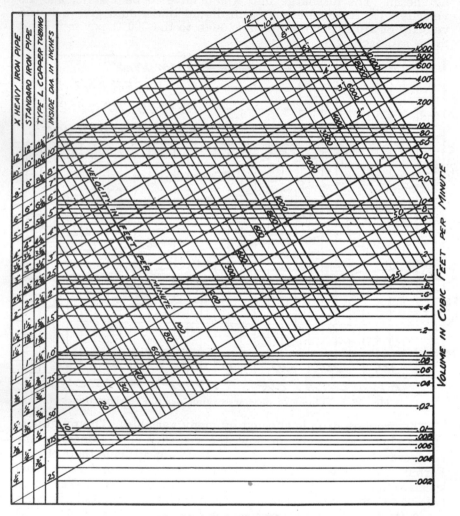

Fig. 22-4. Velocity of flow.

Notice the pressure drops are given per equivalent 100 ft of line. If the equivalent length of the line of the job considered was 40 ft, the pressure drop would be 40 per cent of the figure given by the chart. But often 100 ft is considered as a minimum length to take care of fittings, etc. To find the equivalent length of line, add the actual length of all pipe in the line to the equivalent length of all fittings in the line. The equivalent length of the fittings can be taken from Table 22-4.

TABLE 22-4—EQUIVALENT FEET OF PIPE FOR VALVES AND FITTINGS

Line Size IPS	3/8	1/2	3/4	1	1 1/4	1 1/2	2	2 1/2	3	3 1/2	4	5	6	8	10	12
In Inches OD	1/2	5/8	7/8	1 1/8	1 3/8	1 5/8	2 1/8	2 5/8	3 1/8	3 5/8	4 1/8	5 1/8	6 1/8	8 1/8	10 1/8	12 1/8
Globe Valve (Open)	14	16	22	28	36	42	57	69	83	99	118	138	168	225	280	335
Angle Valve	7	9	12	15	18	21	28	34	42	49	57	70	83	117	140	165
Elbow	1	2	2	3	4	4	5	7	8	10	12	14	16	20	26	31
Tee (Through Side)	3	4	5	6	8	9	12	14	17	20	22	28	34	44	56	65

From ACRMA Eqpt. Std. 510

Example 22-2.—Choose the lines for Example 22-1 by the pressure drop method instead of by the velocity method.

The following data is picked directly from Fig. 22-6.

LINE SIZES		PRESSURE DROPS
Suction	2 1/8 in	0.97 psi per 100 ft
Discharge	1 5/8 in	1.4 psi per 100 ft
Liquid	7/8 in	1.6 psi per 100 ft

Although the 7/8 in. liquid line seems to have a small pressure drop for a liquid line, a 5/8 in. tubing shows a drop of 10 psi per 100 ft which is too great. Notice that by this method, we are able to use a smaller suction line but should use a larger liquid line than when figured by the velocity method. Longer lines or colder temperatures might well figure the same size suction line or even a larger one. But by figuring by this method pressure drops, which should be the determining factor, are used. So this is the better way of figuring.

Example 22-3.—A three ton Refrigerant 12 job works at a 0 F evaporator and a 110 F condenser. It is so placed that 30 ft of liquid and suction line must be run from the compressor to the evaporator. Each line contains four ells and one shut off valve (globe valve type). What sized lines should be chosen, and what is the expected pressure drop in each?

A 1 5/8 in suction line gives a pressure drop of 0.80 psi per 100 ft. The equivalent length of the 1 5/8 in line is figured as follows.

4 ells at 4 ft per ell	16 ft
1 shut off valve	42 ft
Length of tubing	30 ft
Total equivalent length	88 ft

Pressure drop in the suction line:

$$\frac{88}{100} \times 0.80 = 0.704 \text{ psi}$$

A ⅞ in discharge line gives a 4.5 psi per 100 ft pressure drop. If this is a short line from the compressor to the condenser, this will be satisfactory. But if the equivalent length is over 20 ft, a 1⅛ in discharge line should be used.

A ½ in liquid line will give a drop of 4.8 psi per 100 ft. The equivalent length would be:

4 ells at 1 ft per ell	4 ft
1 shut off valve	14 ft
Length of tubing	30 ft
Total equivalent length	48 ft

Pressure drop in the liquid line:

$$\frac{48}{100} \times 4.8 = 2.3 \text{ psi}$$

Effect of Changing Conditions of Flow.—A few general rules regarding piping and friction should be pointed out before leaving the subject. First, the cross sectional area of a pipe varies as the square of the diameter. That is, if the diameter of the pipe is doubled, the area is increased 4 times; if the diameter is tripled, the area is increased 9 times. An increase of 50 percent in diameter gives a little more than twice the area.

The velocity is inversely proportional to the area. Thus, if the area was doubled, the velocity would be half the original. If this is combined with the above data on diameter, twice the pipe size gives one fourth the velocity.

The friction in a pipe varies as the square of the velocity. Thus, if the velocity is doubled, the pressure drop is increased 4 times. If twice as much gas is forced through a given sized pipe, the pressure drop increases 4 times. So, since so many of these changes vary results so quickly, small changes in pipe sizes or in amounts of gas handled can have astonishing results. If lines are large enough, the savings made by larger sizes are insignificant. But if the size is reduced, pressure drops rise very rapidly. So if there is any doubt in choosing pipe sizes, it is always better to choose the larger size.

One further point to consider; all the above figures were made up on the basis of pure refrigerants without oil. The presence of oil in the lines or in the refrigerant increases the friction considerably. But since the percent of oil circulating is never accurately known, it can hardly be figured. But this is still another good reason for always erring toward larger rather than smaller pipe.

QUESTIONS

22-1. An ammonia plant is operating with a 0 F evaporator and an 8 psi suction line drop. What is the percent loss in capacity of the compressor due to the suction line loss?

22-2. If Example 22-3 was Refrigerant 22 instead of Refrigerant 12, what would be the required line sizes? Figure by the pressure loss method.

22-3. If Example 22-2 was Refrigerant 22 with a —40 F evaporator, what would be the required line sizes? Use the pressure loss

22-4. A 50 ton ammonia plant operates with a 0 F evaporator. The discharge line is 25 ft long, and contains 3 ells and one globe valve. The liquid and suction lines are 65 ft long, and contain 4 ells and a globe valve each. Choose suitable line sizes.

22-5. An additional 15 ton evaporator is added to Question 22-4. How much does this increase the pressure drops if no change is made in line sizes?

CHAPTER 23

BRINE IN REFRIGERATION

General.—All the previously described refrigeration systems have been direct systems. An indirect system is illustrated in Fig. 23-1. Here a brine or other anti-freeze solution is chilled, then pumped around to do the required cooling. Its biggest disadvantage is the fact that lower suction pressures are usually needed to main-

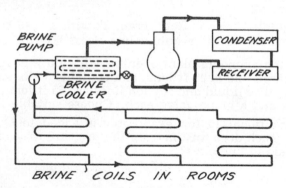

Fig. 23-1. Indirect refrigeration system.

tain a required room temperature. Comparable figures are shown in Fig. 23-2 and Table 23-1. Another disadvantage of a brine system is the corrosion caused by the brine. But a brine system has many advantages, too. All the refrigerant containing equipment is in the engine room directly under the supervision of the engineer. A leak in any other part of the building will leak only brine. This will cause considerable less damage than a refrigerant leak, particularly if that refrigerant is ammonia. If there is a leak in the ammonia side of the system, since it is where it will be discovered, steps can be taken to remedy it immediately.

An indirect system has considerable hold over capacity. In case of temporary shut downs, the cold brine will continue to hold temperatures for a short time. This is not only used in case of certain repairs that will not take too long. If sufficient brine is used, refrigeration equipment can be operated during the day to refrigerate the brine, then turned off and the brine depended on to hold temperatures over night. A circulating brine pump is usually left in operation, but such may be operated with little or no attention.

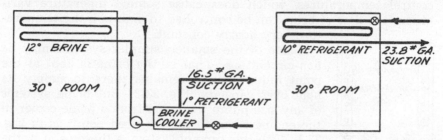

Fig. 23-2. Diagram of direct expansion vs. brine.

TABLE 23-1—TYPICAL COIL TEMPERATURES FOR DIFFERENT ROOM TEMPERATURES

Room Temperature	Direct Expansion Suction Temperature	Indirect System	
		Brine Temperature	Suction Temperature
40°	16°	20°	8°
30°	10°	12°	1°
20°	3°	4°	− 6°
10°	− 5°	− 4°	−13°
0°	−12°	−12°	−20°
−10°	−20°	−20°	−27°
−20°	−30°	−28°	−34°

Such a method makes it unnecessary to have operating engineers on the job 24 hours a day. Such systems were very common in small applications before the development of present automatic control equipment. It is less used at the present time on stationary applications because of the greater simplicity of automatic equipment. But it is still used in special applications.

Another application where brine works well is in storing refrigeration for heavy intermittent loads. Milk cooling loads or something similar may be only required once or twice a day, but an enormous amount of product must be cooled at one time. A direct system would have to be very large in size, which means expensive. Yet it would be idle the greater part of the day. A smaller unit can be chosen to run steadily, or on an average of 16 hours out of the 24. During the time no refrigeration is required, the capacity of the machine is used to chill brine. Then the cold brine plus the machine can be used on the load when required.

Brine is also used in some applications because refrigeration from it is considered steadier. Instead of cycling the machine to control temperatures, which does cause some temperature variations, the flow of brine can be controlled to maintain the temperature very nearly constant.

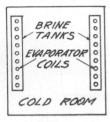

Fig. 23-3. Non-circulating brine system.

Some of the smaller, simpler systems may be non-circulating. That is, the brine is kept at the point required, and remains there to supply its hold over capacity, Fig. 23-3. But brine systems of any size pump the brine from a brine cooler in the engine room to the required point, as in Fig. 23-1. With this type of system, a thermostat in the room can be made to control a throttling type valve in the brine line. This does not close completely, but increases or decreases the flow of brine as required to meet the imposed heat load.

Brines used for hold over jobs where a large refrigeration capacity is needed are sometimes frozen. Such is mostly used in a non circulating system such as Fig. 23-3. Occasionally where ice water temperatures are suitable, as in an air conditioning system, water ice may be used instead of a frozen brine, Fig. 23-4. Such a system does not work so well with brine for reasons given later. By using some form of freezing, the latent heat of fusion can be taken advantage of, and a larger refrigeration capacity obtained with less brine and a smaller brine tank.

Brine Chemistry.—To fully understand the use of brine we should know something of its chemical behavior. Pure water freezes at 32 F. As any soluable salt is dissolved in the water, its freezing temperature is lowered. The greater the amount of salt dissolved, the lower the freezing point. This is illustrated by the freezing line of Fig. 23-5. But when freezing starts, the mixture of salt and water does not form ice. It is the water alone that starts to freeze leaving the salt behind. This salt forced into the remaining water increases its concentration which further lowers its freezing point. Thus, the freezing temperature of a brine continually gets colder as more of it is frozen. This pure water which freezes out of the brine forms separate ice crystals which float in the brine. If it is not cooled to the final freezing point, these ice crystals form a slush in the brine instead of freezing into a solid cake.

The limiting point of this gradual reduction in freezing temperature is the solubility of the particular salt used. Refer to the solubility line of Fig. 23-5. The colder the temperature, the less salt can be dissolved. As temperatures go lower a point is reached

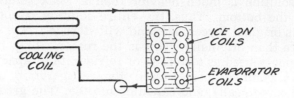

Fig. 23-4. Ice storage for hold over capacity.

where the solubility line crosses the freezing line. Below this intersection point any further salt rejected from the freezing fluid is not soluble, so the freezing point is not further lowered. At this point the entire mass begins to freeze solid. This point is called the

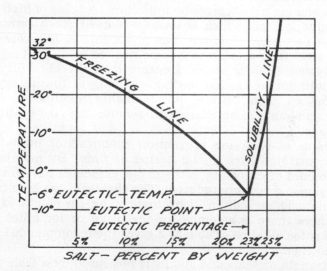

Fig. 23-5. Sodium chloride brine chart (illustrating eutectic point).

eutectic point, and a solution of the proper percent of salt to give this condition is a eutectic solution. Notice the eutectic point is the lowest possible freezing point for the brine considered.

Even when freezing at the eutectic point, there is still separation of the salt and water. This gives complications when the frozen brine is thawed. Since the salt is no longer in solution it drops to the bottom of the tank or container. Here it is very slow in redissolving in the cold solution. Unless agitation is very thorough, the salt may eventually saturate the solution at the bottom. Since the saturated solution is much heavier than a weak solution, it will remain on the bottom. Thus, the entire solution is not reconcentrated at its original percentage, and will start to freeze at a higher temperature than originally. This is the reason frozen brine is not more commonly used as a storage of refrigeration capacity.

The two common brines used for refrigeration are sodium chloride (common salt), and calcium chloride. The greatest difference between them is the sodium chloride has a eutectic point of —6 F, and the calcium chloride a eutectic of —60 F. Sodium chloride brine is usually preferred where the temperature range is above 0 F. Below 0 F, calcium chloride brine is usually used. Either brine will cause corrosion if it is not properly controlled.

Corrosion Control.—There are three basic factors in brine corrosion control methods. These are control of the brine density and alkalinity and the use of corrosion inhibitors. A brine of high density will dissolve less air which is usually blamed for a considerable amount of corrosion. A brine that is alkaline is less corrosive to iron and steel than a brine that is neutral or acid.

In a system such as an ice freezing tank the alkalinity of the brine should not be carried too high as long as the ice cans have galvanizing on them. Brine that is highly alkaline or contains significant amounts of ammonia will remove the zinc coating from the ice cans.

The value of corrosion prevention chemicals or inhibitors has been demonstrated over a long period of time. By maintaining a certain amount of chromate in the brine, engineers have found that the corrosion and rust are reduced. The chromate can be introduced as chromic acid or sodium dichromate. The chromic acid is preferred where there is amomnia in the brine or for other reasons the brine is too alkaline. Table 23-2 gives the recommended dosages of chrome chemicals.

The strength of acids and alkalis is measured by a scale running from 1 to 14. This is called the pH scale. A pH of 1 means the strongest acid, a pH of 7 which is the center point is neutral, and a pH of 14 is the strongest alkali. Various vegetable dyes or indicators are available which show different colors in different pH solutions. For a test, a few drops of the indicator solution are dropped into a test tube of the brine to be checked. For rough checks the colors are gauged by sight and memory. But for the most accurate work, color standards are available with which to make direct comparisons. Phenolphthalein is a common indicator used. This is colorless up to a pH of 8 and red at a pH of 10. From 8 up to 10 it goes from a pale pink to a darker pink and finally red. Litmus is another common indicator. It is red up to a pH of 4.5 and blue

TABLE 23-2—CHROMATE DOSAGES FOR BRINE TREATMENT IN POUNDS PER 1,000 CU FT OF BRINE

Neutral treatment
12 lb chromic acid plus 9.6 lb caustic soda
is equal to
18 lb sodium dichromate plus 4.8 lb caustic soda

To neutralize brine contaminated by ammonia
2.9 lb of chromic acid neutralizes 1 lb ammonia
8.8 lb of sodium dichromate neutralizes 1 lb ammonia

—K. M. Holaday in 1947, Operating Data Book

at a pH of 8.5. Table 23-3 gives a list of some of the common indicators and their color changes. It is recommended that the brine be maintained at a pH of 7.5 to 8.5 with an average of about 8.0 in ordinary brine systems. Below 7.0 it becomes more active against iron and steel. Above 8.0 it becomes active against brass or galvanizing (zinc). Ice freezing tanks contain galvanized cans, as well as uncoated steel. For overall corrosion control the pH is held

TABLE 23-3—COLOR RANGE OF pH INDICATORS

Indicator	pH Range	Color Change
Litmus	4.5 to 8.5	Red—Blue
Phenolphthalein	8.0 to 10.0	Clear—Red
Bromthymol Blue	6.0 to 7.6	Yellow—Blue
Phenol Red	6.8 to 8.4	Yellow—Red
Cresol Red	7.2 to 8.8	Yellow—Red
Thymol Blue	8.0 to 9.6	Yellow—Blue

between 7.2 and 7.5. Sometimes where no galvanizing is present, or has all been corroded away, the pH is carried up to 9 or 9.5. This seems to give better protection for the iron and steel parts, but may cause pitting if allowed to go higher.

When the pH must be changed, to increase it a caustic or alkali must be added to the brine. Slacked lime or caustic soda may be used. To decrease the pH, muriatic acid, or chromic acid may be used. Chromic acid at the same time inhibits corrosion directly. In any addition of acids or alkalis, they should be added very slowly and cautiously with good circulation maintained. Checks must be made to see that correction is not carried too far. Too much acid, or too rapid an addition of acid at one point will cause more corrosion than if no correction had been attempted. If too much alkali is added to a calcium brine, the calcium chloride may precipitate out which will allow the brine to freeze up.

TABLE 23-4—PROPERTIES OF SODIUM CHLORIDE BRINE
PURE ANHYDROUS SALT NaCl

Percent Pure Sodium Chloride By Weight	Specific Gravity	Beume Scale	Specific Heat B.T.U. Per Pound	Freezing Point Deg. Fahr.	Weight Per Gallon Pounds	Weight Per Cubic Foot Pounds	Corresponding NH₃ Suction Pres. Gage
0	1.000	0.00	1.000	32.0	8.34	62.4	47.6
5	1.035	5.1	0.938	27.0	8.65	64.6	41.4
6	1.043	6.1	0.927	25.5	8.71	65.1	39.6
7	1.050	7.0	0.917	24.0	8.76	65.5	37.9
8	1.057	8.0	0.907	23.2	8.82	66.0	37.0
9	1.065	9.0	0.897	21.8	8.89	66.5	35.6
10	1.072	10.1	0.888	20.4	8.95	66.9	34.1
11	1.080	10.8	0.879	18.5	9.02	67.4	32.0
12	1.087	11.8	0.870	17.2	9.08	67.8	30.6
13	1.095	12.7	0.862	15.5	9.14	68.3	28.9
14	1.103	13.6	0.854	13.9	9.22	68.8	27.4
15	1.111	14.5	0.847	12.0	9.28	69.3	25.6
16	1.118	15.4	0.840	10.2	9.33	69.8	24.0
17	1.126	16.3	0.833	8.2	9.40	70.3	22.3
18	1.134	17.2	0.826	6.1	9.47	70.8	20.5
19	1.142	18.1	0.819	4.0	9.54	71.3	18.8
20	1.150	19.0	0.813	1.8	9.60	71.8	17.1
21	1.158	19.9	0.807	− 0.8	9.67	72.3	15.1
22	1.166	20.8	0.802	− 3.0	9.74	72.8	13.6
*23	1.175	21.7	0.796	− 6.0	9.81	73.3	11.6
24	1.183	22.5	0.791	+ 3.8	9.88	73.8	18.6
25	1.191	23.4	0.786	+16.1	9.95	74.3	29.5

* Eutectic point.   Specific gravity and weights at 59 F.   Referred to water at 39 F.   Specific heat at 59 F.

An operating engineer can learn to make the above checks of the condition of his brine, and to maintain it at approximately the proper condition. But on many larger systems it is considered worth while to engage the services of an industrial chemist who makes periodic checks of samples furnished. From checks on these samples he can prescribe the proper treatment. More accurate control of the chemical condition of the brine can be kept in this way. On large plants the greater life of all metal parts in contact with the brine well repays such a service. The operator must still be able to intelligently follow the instructions of the chemist to get proper results.

Brine Concentrations.—The actual choice of the proper brine concentration involves several factors. Table 23-4 and Table 23-5

TABLE 23-5—PROPERTIES OF CALCIUM CHLORIDE BRINE
PURE ANHYDROUS SALT $CaCl_2$

Percent Pure Calcium Chloride By Weight	Specific Gravity	Beaume Scale	Specific Heat B.T.U. Per Pound	Freezing Point Deg. Fahr.	Weight Per Gallon Pounds	Weight Per Cubic Foot Pounds	Corresponding NH_3 Suction Pres. Gage
0	1.000	0.00	1.000	32.0	8.34	62.4	47.6
5	1.044	6.1	0.9246	29.0	8.717	65.15	43.8
6	1.050	7.0	0.9143	28.0	8.760	65.52	42.6
7	1.060	8.2	0.8984	27.0	8.851	66.14	41.4
8	1.069	9.3	0.8842	25.5	8.926	66.70	39.0
9	1.078	10.4	0.8699	24.0	9.001	67.27	37.9
10	1.087	11.6	0.8556	23.0	9.076	67.83	36.8
11	1.096	12.6	0.8429	21.5	9.143	68.33	35.0
12	1.105	13.8	0.8284	19.0	9.227	68.95	32.5
13	1.114	14.8	0.8166	17.0	9.302	69.51	30.4
14	1.124	15.9	0.8043	14.5	9.377	70.08	28.0
15	1.133	16.9	0.7930	12.5	9.452	70.64	26.0
16	1.143	18.0	0.7798	9.5	9.536	71.26	23.4
17	1.152	19.1	0.7672	6.5	9.619	71.89	20.8
18	1.162	20.2	0.7566	3.0	9.703	72.51	18.0
19	1.172	21.3	0.7460	0.0	9.786	73.13	15.7
20	1.182	22.1	0.7375	− 3.0	9.853	73.63	13.6
21	1.192	23.0	0.7290	− 5.5	9.928	74.19	11.9
22	1.202	24.4	0.7168	−10.5	10.037	75.00	8.8
23	1.212	25.5	0.7076	−15.5	10.120	75.63	5.9
24	1.223	26.4	0.6979	−20.5	10.212	76.32	3.4
25	1.233	27.4	0.6899	−25.0	10.295	76.94	1.3
26	1.244	28.3	0.6820	−30.0	10.379	77.56	* 1.6
27	1.254	29.3	0.6735	−36.0	10.471	78.25	* 6.1
28	1.265	30.4	0.6657	−43.5	10.563	78.94	*10.6
29	1.276	31.4	0.6584	−53.0	10.655	79.62	*15.7
29.5	1.280	31.7	0.6557	−58.0	10.688	79.87	*17.8

* Inches vacuum. Specific gravity and weights at 60 F. Referred to water at 39 F. Specific heat at 60 F.

give the properties of sodium chloride and calcium chloride brines respectively. If insurance against freezing was the only require-ment, the brine could be kept as strong as possible up to the eutectic percentage. But the stronger the brine, the heavier it is. Also the less is its specific heat. When its specific heat is less, more of it must be circulated to do a given refrigeration job. When it is heavier, more pumping power must be used to circulate it. Therefore the stronger the brine, the greater will be the pumping costs. For this reason the brine should be kept only strong enough that it will not freeze out against the refrigerated surfaces in the brine cooler.

A higher density brine is less corrosive. In ice freezing tanks it is customary to hold brine density at the maximum which can be carried without floating the cans.

Occasionally a brine spray system is used to help the control of humidity. A weak brine (near its freezing point) will tend to keep air in contact with it nearly saturated. If a small temperature difference is used, such a system will maintain high humidity. If a strong concentration of brine is used, it will absorb moisture from the air and lower its humidity. Refer again to Fig. 11-6 for one form of brine spray system. Fig. 23-6 shows a system commonly used in meat packing houses. The spray pans help guide the air flow like the baffles of Fig. 5-17. The brine sprays act as injectors to help force the circulation of air.

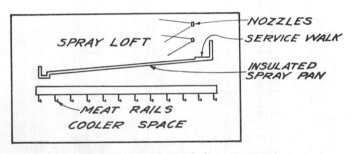

Fig. 23-6. Packing house brine spray system.

Example 23-1.—A single room has a load of 6 tons of refrigeration. It is to be refrigerated by brine coils with not over 6 F rise in brine temperature. What would be the difference between the use of a calcium chloride brine with a specific gravity of 1.14 and a gravity of 1.23?

From Table 23-5 the following data is found.

Specific gravity	1.14	1.23
Freezing point	10 F	23.5 F
Percent	16%	25%
Specific heat	0.784	0.692

The formula:

H = Quantity of heat, $H = W\,S\,(t_2 - t_1)$
can be rearranged as follows to solve for the weight of brine to be circulated.

$$W = \frac{H}{S\,(t_2 - t_1)}.$$

Six tons of refrigeration is
$$H = 6 \times 200 = 1200 \text{ Btu per min.}$$
For the 1.14 gravity brine, the circulation would be

$$W = \frac{1200}{0.784 \times 6} = 255 \text{ lb of brine per min}$$

For the 1.23 gravity brine, the circulation would be

$$W = \frac{1200}{0.692 \times 6} = 289 \text{ lb of brine per min.}$$

The latter figure is 13 percent greater than the former. The pumping cost is proportional to the weight, so the 1.23 gravity brine would require 13 percent more power for pumping.

Example 23-2.—A small ice maker, Fig. 25-17, uses ice cans setting in a refrigerated brine. This icemaker holds 250 gallons of brine. For fast ice freezing, the brine might be wanted as low as 0 F. To get this, the coils will have to be down to about —5 F. To prevent freezing out on the coils, the freezing point of the brine must be below this temperature.

(a) What type of brine should be used?
(b) What strength of brine should be used?
(c) How many pounds of salt would be necessary to mix this brine?

(a). Calcium chloride brine must be used to get below —5 F without freezing.
(b). From Table 23-5, the brine should have a strength of 22 percent or a gravity of 1.20 to get a freezing point safely below —5 F.
(c). From Table 23-5, the weight of a gallon of 22 percent brine is 10.0 lb. Twenty two percent of 10 lb is 2.2 lb per gallon.

2.2 × 250 = 550 lb of calcium chloride salt needed.

Example 23-3.—A certain system holds 12,700 gallons of calcium chloride brine. It is supposed to be maintained at 25 percent strength. A hydrometer reading shows a gravity of 1.22. How much calcium chloride should be added?

The required brine of 25 percent strength weighs 10.295 lb per gal.

0.25 × 10.295 = 2.574 lb of salt per gal required.

Brine with a gravity of 1.22 is 23.8 percent and weighs 10.19 lb per gal.

0.238 × 10.19 = 2.425 lb per gal now in brine.
2.574 — 2.425 = 0.149 lb per gal to be added.
0.149 × 12,700 = 1892 lb of salt needed.
This is practically nineteen 100 lb sacks.

Example 23-4.—Five hundred gallons of milk are to be cooled twice a day on a dairy. The milk will be cooled to 70 F with water, and from 70 F to 40 F with refrigeration on a surface cooler similar to Fig. 24-9. The milk has to be cooled within two hours from milking time. Milking takes about two hours, so this gives four hours total time in which to cool the 500 gallons.

(a) What size condensing unit would be required if direct expansion was used?

(b) What sized condensing unit would be required if a brine storage system was used?

(c) What type and density of brine should be used?

(d) How much brine would be required to store the refrigeration required for (b)?

(e) How much salt would be required to mix the brine?

(f) How large a brine storage tank would be required?

From Table A-2 in the Appendix the specific heat of milk is 0.92, and its weight per gal is 8.6 lb.

500 × 8.6 = 4300 lb of milk per cooling. Heat to be removed:

$$H = W S (t_2 — 2_1)$$
$$= 4300 × 0.92 (70 — 40) = 119,000 \text{ Btu to remove.}$$

If this is to be done by direct expansion, the compressor can be allowed to run steady for the four hour cooling period.

$$\frac{119,000}{4} = 29,700 \text{ Btu per hr cooling required.}$$

Since there is no safety factor in the running time, at least 15 percent should be added to this for a factor of safety.

1.15 × 29,700 = 34,200 Btu per hr equipment capacity.
This is

$$\frac{34,200}{12,000} = 2.84 \text{ tons of refrigeration.}$$

(b) If a brine storage system is used, the total cooling for the two milkings per day is

2 × 119,000 = 238,000 Btu per day.
On the basis of 16 hour running time this would be

$$\frac{238,000}{16} = 14,900 \text{ Btu per hr.}$$

$$\frac{14,900}{12,000} = 1.24 \text{ tons of refrigeration.}$$

Thus, a little less than half as large a condensing unit would be required if a brine system was to be used.

(c) For milk cooling, brine cannot be run too cold or there will be trouble with freezing the milk on the edges of the lower tubes. To get an adequate temperature difference in the milk cooler, a brine will be chosen that will be cooled to 25 F to begin the milk cooling, and will be allowed to heat to 35 F at the end of the cooling period. To cool the brine to 25 F, a refrigerant temperature as low as 15 F might be used. A 14 percent sodium chloride brine will be satisfactory for this.

(d) To give sufficient brine with some factor of safety, the help from the condensing unit during the milk cooling period will be neglected. This will require the total 116,000 Btu stored in the brine. The weight required is:

$$W = \frac{H}{S\,(t_2 - t_1)},$$

$$= \frac{119,000}{0.854 \times (35 - 25)} = 13,950 \text{ lb of brine.}$$

Brine at 14 percent weighs 9.22 lb per gal.
$$\frac{13,950}{9.22} = 1512 \text{ gal of brine required.}$$

(e) Fourteen percent of 13,950 is
$$0.14 \times 13,950 = 1950 \text{ lb of salt required.}$$

(f) One cubic foot of 14 percent brine weighs 68.8 lb. Therefore the size of 13,950 lb is
$$\frac{13,950}{68.8} = 203 \text{ cu ft tank required.}$$

Congealing Tanks—Eutectic Plates.—As previously mentioned, ordinary congealing tanks have not been too successful because on thawing, the salt separates and settles out. But a eutectic mixture held in a jelled solution holds the salt whether it separates or not. The salt will not settle out of the jelly, and has a better chance of re-dissolving. Fig. 23-7 illustrates such a tank called a hold over plate. Different salts are chosen to give different eutectic temperatures. Thus, tanks can be supplied having different congealing temperatures. These eutectic plates are commonly used in truck refrigeration for daytime deliveries.

Two general systems are used. The first uses a condensing unit mounted on the truck, but driven by 110 volt or 220 volt power. This is plugged into the required power source when the truck is garaged for the night. The unit freezes the brine in the plates. When the truck leaves for daytime deliveries, the unit is disconnected from its power supply, but the frozen plates supply the required refrigeration. The second system leaves the entire condensing unit in the garage. Flexible liquid and suction lines are connected to the truck by a special connecting block which can be quickly connected or disconnected. This system saves the weight of the condensing unit on the truck, making that much more pay load possible. But refrigerant losses, and air leakage into the lines through improperly closed valves are often very troublesome. This latter system, therefore, requires much more checking and more servicing.

—Kold-Hold Manufacturing Co. photo

Fig. 23-7. Eutectic hold over plates in a truck.

Eutectic plates must be chosen with two requirements in mind; surface and storage capacity. The heat transfer is usually low due to no circulation within the tank, and usually due to small temperature differences between the brine and the room. The latent heat of the brine is less than for water. It varies for different substances, but if definite data is not available on the particular substance used, about 110 Btu per lb is a good average.

Example 23-5.—An ice cream delivery truck is to be maintained at 0 F with congealing plates having a eutectic temperature of —18 F. The total refrigeration load on the truck body is estimated to be 3000 Btu per hr. Capacity is wanted to last 12 hours to give a factor of safety over a normal 8 hour shift. What area and weight of plates are necessary?

The area is found from the formula:

$$A = \frac{H}{K\,(t_2 - t_1)}$$

From Table A-12 in the appendix K is found to be 2.25 Btu per sq ft.

$$A = \frac{3000}{18 \times 2.25} = 74 \text{ sq ft}$$

The required weight is found by dividing the total load by the latent heat of one pound of the brine.

$$\frac{3000 \times 12}{110} = 327 \text{ lb of brine}$$

Therefore tanks must be selected having a total area of at least 74 sq ft, and a total weight of at least 327 pounds. In the sizes available, at least three tanks would probably have to be chosen to get these totals.

QUESTIONS

23-1. What is the difference between a direct and an indirect refrigeration system?

23-2. Give some of the advantages and the disadvantages of a brine system?

23-3. Do salt solutions necessarily have a constant freezing point?

23-4. What is a eutectic brine?

23-5. What is an inhibitor?

23-6. What effect has the pH of a brine on its corrosive properties?

23-7. An ice cream popsicle tank is to be maintained at —20 F. What type and strength of brine would be chosen?

23-8. A room has a heat load of 52,000 Btu per hr. It is cooled with an 18 percent sodium chloride brine. The temperature rise of the brine is not to be over 4 F. How much brine must be circulated?

23-9. Twenty five hundred gallons of sodium chloride brine is to be maintained at 20 percent strength. A hydrometer reading shows it to have a gravity of 1.14. How much salt must be added?

23-10. Rework example 23-4 with the following changes:
300 gallons of milk cooled twice a day.
Total cooling period to be not over 3 hours.

CHAPTER 24

LIQUID COOLING

Beverage Cooling Requirements.—Water or other fluids are often cooled for beverage purposes. For drinking, water should not be cooler than 45 F. If colder than this, enough of it cannot be drunk to quench thirst. For factory work, or other places where people are hot and sweaty, even 50 F water is too cold. This should be taken into account when putting in bubbling cups where water is drunk directly.

If the water is to be served in glasses, as in a restaurant, it may be cooled to 40 F. The glass is usually warmer than this, and it sets in a warm room after filling but before drinking. This gives the water a chance to warm up to a satisfactory temperature. Beverages which are intended to be slowly sipped could be cooled below 40 F without objection, but usually are not. Soft drinks, beer, etc. are usually cooled to 40 F. Water cooling requirements, both quantities and recommended temperatures are listed in Table 24-1.

Water Coolers.—Water coolers are made in a great variety of sizes and shapes. The simplest type of cooler is illustrated in Fig. 24-1. A small sealed condensing unit in the base supplies the required

TABLE 24-1—DRINKING WATER TABLE

USAGE	TEMP. F.	TOTAL WATER USED AND WASTED
Office Bldg—Employees	50	1/8 gal per hr per person
Office Bldg—Transients	50	1/2 gal per hr per 250 persons per day
Light Manufacturing	50—55	1/5 gal per hr per person
Heavy Manufacturing	50—55	1/4 gal per hr per person
Restaurants	45—50	1/10 gal per hr per person
Cafeteria	45—50	1/12 gal per hr per person
Hotel	50	1/2 gal per hr per room
Theater	50	1 gal per hr per 75 seats
Stores	50	1 gal per hr per 100 customers
Schools	50—55	1/8 gal per hr per student
Hospitals	45—50	1/12 gal per day per bed

—Courtesy Temprite Cooler Corp.

refrigeration. The cooler usually is a storage type. It chills and holds in reserve a small tank of water. The refrigeration coil may be fed by a thermostatic expansion valve, automatic expansion valve, or capillary tube. Some older models were fed by high side float valves. A constant pressure valve is usually placed in the suction line. This is set at a sufficiently high pressure that there is no danger of freezing the water. To freeze up a cooler may burst it. The outlet of the cooler may be a bubbling cup or a glass filler. A thermostatic control with the bulb in a well in the tank is usually used to control temperature.

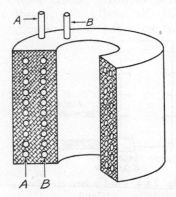

Fig. 24-2. Instantaneous remote water cooler. Coil A is evaporator coil. Coil B is water coil. Both are embedded in aluminum casting to give good heat transfer between them.

—Frigidaire Division photo

Fig. 24-1. Self contained water cooler.

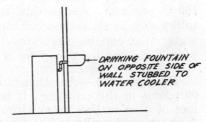

Fig. 24-3. Remote bubbler from cooler.

Fig. 24-2 illustrates an instantaneous, remote type cooler. It is remote because refrigerant lines are piped to it from a remote condensing unit. It is an instantaneous type because it holds only a small amount of water at a time, but depends on adequate surface and rapid refrigerant evaporation to chill the water as needed. It may be fed with a thermostatic expansion valve. Either a storage or an instantaneous cooler may be used with either the self contained or remote type.

Fig. 24-3 illustrates how a remote bubbler is sometimes connected to a cooler. This makes it possible to supply cold water at two points with one cooler. Remote bubblers should only be a short distance from the cooler to prevent excessive use of both water and refrigeration. The water in the line will heat up to room temperature when not circulating. Users soon learn to let the water run until it gets cold. Naturally, the remote bubbler should be placed at the point that gets the least demand.

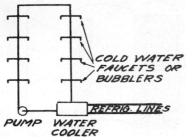

COLD WATER FAUCETS OR BUBBLERS

REFRIG. LINES

PUMP   WATER COOLER

Fig. 24-4. Cold water circulating system.

Where cold water is required at many different points, such as in every room of a hotel, a circulating water system such as Fig. 24-4 is usually used. Refrigeration losses are greater with the cold water flowing through the pipes at all times. But it is the only type of system that has proved satisfactory for such an installation. Such a system is designed so the water will not pick up over 5 F on its circuit. Heat losses from various sized pipe can be taken from Table A-16 in the appendix. Ice water thickness insulation is usually used. To work out such a problem, a pipe size must be assumed, then worked out to see if it is satisfactory. The speed of flow through the pipes is limited to 180 ft per min. Above this, the churning action turns the water milky due to entrained bubbles. Table 24-2 shows the amount of water that can be circulated through different sized pipes at this speed, and the heat load for a 5 F temperature rise.

Example 24-1.—An office building is to have running ice water to 60 rooms in the building. It is estimated there will be 1800 lineal feet of pipe in the water circuit. The design temperature is 90 F. A check shows city water temperatures to be 70 F in the summer time. What sized pipe is recommended, and what are the refrigeration requirements?

From Table 24-1, we find ⅛ gallon per person per hour is required. This table also gives a required temperature of 50 F. A recheck of the job should be made to check the average number of persons per office. In this case, assume we find an average of six persons. So a total of

6 × 60 × ⅛ = 45 gal per hr required to be cooled.

TABLE 24-2—WATER COOLING TABLE

The quantity of water that will pick up 5F at a velocity of 180 ft per min for different sized pipes, and the refrigeration load for this 5F rise.

Pipe Size Inches	Volume		Heat Load Btu per hr
	cu ft per min	gal per min	
½	0.380	2.79	7,100
¾	0.668	5.00	12,500
1	1.08	8.10	20,250
1¼	1.87	14.0	35,000
1½	2.54	19.0	47,500
2	4.20	31.5	78,500

If we assume a ½ in pipe, Table 24-2 shows a circulation of 2.79 gal per min gives a heat load of 7100 Btu per hr. From Table A-16 the heat picked up by a ½ in pipe with ice water insulation is 0.132 Btu per hr per degree per lineal ft. An average temperature of 50 F in a 90 F ambient will give a temperature difference of 40 F. Therefore the total heat transfer to the water is

$0.132 \times 1800 \times 40 = 9500$ Btu per hr.

This is more than the 7100 Btu that would cause a 5 F rise, so would raise the water temperature more than is permissible. Therefore a ½ in pipe would be unsatisfactory. A ¾ in gives a heat load of 12,500 Btu per hr to heat the water 5 F. The heat transfer is

$0.140 \times 1800 \times 40 = 10,100$ Btu per hr.

This is less than the 12,500 Btu above, so will not heat the water quite 5 F. Therefore the ¾ in pipe is satisfactory.

The total refrigeration load will be made up as follows.
Cooling 45 gal of make up water. Heat removed:

$H = W \times S (t_2 - t_1)$
$= (45 \times 8.34) \times 1 \times (70 - 50) = 7500$ Btu per hr
Heat leakage through pipe $\qquad$ 10,100 Btu per hr
Total $\qquad$ 17,600 Btu per hr

To correct this for running time:
$1.5 \times 17,600 = 26,400$ Btu per hr
Therefore, a condensing unit and a water cooler having a capacity of 26,400 Btu per hr must be chosen.

Water or brine coolers for industrial purposes usually require greater quantities and greater loads than beverage requirements. Two general types of coolers are available, the open type and the

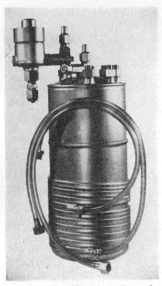

Fig. 24-5. Combination cooler for beer and water.

shell and tube type. Fig. 24-5 shows a combined beer and water cooler. The refrigerant circulates in the shell. Beer coils are inside and water coils around the outside. This design works well on small and intermediate sizes.

Fig. 5-6 illustrates a shell and tube cooler. It is just a shell and tube condenser in reverse. The refrigerant is in the shell space, and the liquid to be cooled is in the tubes. The flow of liquid through the tubes, and the rapid boiling of the refrigerant with complete separation of the vapor from the liquid gives excellent heat transfer. Such coolers are usually preferred on intermediate and large sized jobs.

Beer Coolers.—Fig. 24-6 illustrates the common method of handling draft beer. The keg is kept in a refrigerated compartment. This may be a section of the bar, or may be a walk in cooler. The cooler should be either near by or in the basement directly under the bar. Which of the above systems used depends on the amount of beer handled and sold. If the separate cooler is used, as in Fig. 24-6-B better results are obtained by using a refrigerated tunnel to the bar rather than by using insulated lines. Regardless of the amount of insulation, the beer in the line will eventually warm up to the surrounding temperature when there is no flow. With beer, this not only increases the final cooling problem, but complicates the control of foam or head.

From the keg, the beer is piped to a beverage cooler similar to the instantaneous water cooler of Fig. 24-2. Here, its temperature is brought down to 40 F as it is delivered to the glass.

Beside the temperature, the control of foam, or head, or bead as it is variously called, offers quite a problem in the dispensing of beer. This foam is caused by bubbles of carbon dioxide. The beer in the keg is under a carbon dioxide pressure which keeps a certain percent dissolved in the beer. It is this carbon dioxide that gives beer its sharp taste. Beer which has lost its carbon dioxide is flat. When the pressure is released, some of the carbon dioxide is released. That released under the surface forms bubbles in the beer. The beer is thick or sticky enough that instead of rising to the top and breaking as in soda pop, the bubbles remain as foam. It is exactly the same kind of action that causes oil foaming when a refrigerant pressure is released on the oil.

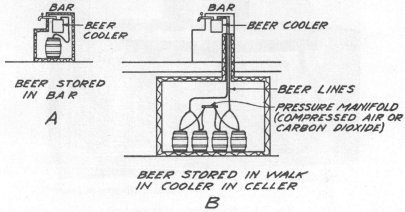

Fig. 24-6. Beer cooling systems.

Sales appeal requires a certain amount of foam to be served with the beer. But too much foam is a waste. A glass of only foam cannot be served a customer. Yet when a keg is first opened, several glasses or pitchers of foam must sometimes be drawn before beer begins to flow. Also the last beer remaining when the keg is nearly empty may be nearly all foam. Also, every bit of foam formed flattens the beer, in that less of the carbon dioxide "tang" is left.

This foam can be controlled by a combination of two methods, temperature and pressure. An increase in pressure reduces the foam, at least until it gets in the glass. A reduction in temperature also decreases the foam, since the carbon dioxide remains in solution better at lower temperatures. Some of the simpler bars as in Fig. 24-6-A do not use pressure, but depend entirely on temperature. But better control is obtained by adding pressure to the keg as well as keeping the temperature down. This pressure may be applied by a tank of carbon dioxide through a pressure reducing valve.

Charged Water—Soda Water.—Charged water, either for soda fountains or for bottling plants requires refrigeration. The water may be cooled by any of the other previously mentioned water bottling works by any of the other previously mentioned water coolers. It is then put through a carbonator which agitates the cold water under a carbon dioxide pressure. The cold water, under pressure will absorb some of the carbon dioxide. Again, as in the case of beer, the lower the temperature and the higher the pressure, the greater the carbon dioxide absorption.

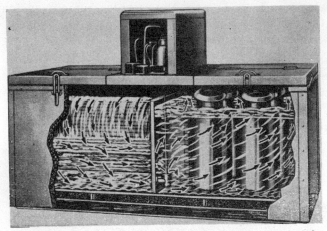

—*Wilson Refrigeration, Inc. photo*

Fig. 24-7. Water bath milk cooler.

Milk Coolers.—Milk may be cooled in a number of· ways. The simplest milk cooler suitable for cooling a few cans of milk on the farm is a sweet water bath, Fig. 24-7. The cooling coil may be either in one end, or may be wrapped around the entire inner liner. A small agitator or pump is usually used to improve the heat transfer. Such coolers are manufactured in sizes suitable for 2 to 12 cans of milk. Or they may be constructed on the job in a concrete tank.

—*Creamery Package Mfg. Co. photo*

Fig. 24-8. Baudelot or surface cooler.

One of the early methods of cooling milk and other fluids is over a Baudelot or surface cooler, Fig. 24-8. The milk is put in the top tank which distributes it evenly over the top tube. It trickles down over this, then from tube to tube until it reaches the bottom. It is cooled to the required temperature by the time it leaves the last tube. The entire cooler may be chilled by direct expansion or by chilled water. Or the top sec-

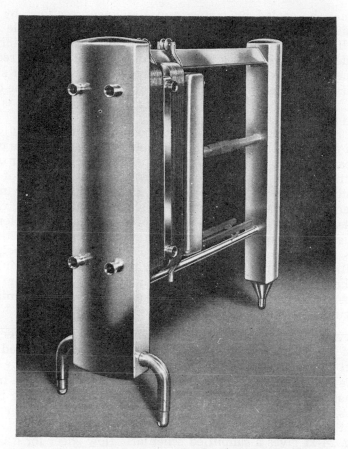

—*Creamery Package Mfg. Co. photo*

Fig. 24-9. Plate type milk cooler.

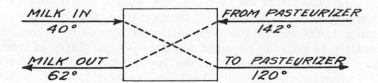

Fig. 24-10. Plate cooler as intercooler in flash pasteurizing.

tions may be cooled by water, and the lower sections by direct expansion. Such coolers are made small enough to handle only a few gallons per minute for farm use. Their size may be increased as needed for large dairies to handle any amount of milk required.

Some of the older coolers of this type were tin plated steel or brass. But nearly all modern ones are of stainless steel. The outside surface is the only one that touches the milk, and this is easily cleaned and sterilized.

The most recent design is a plate cooler, Fig. 24-9. This is made of thin plates of stainless steel, so formed that passages are created. The headers are so formed and connected that cooling water or brine flows through the passages formed by every other pair of plates. The milk flows through the alternate passages. Thus, the milk has a water cooled stainless steel wall on each side of it. Excellent, rapid heat transfer is obtained by this method. Such coolers have been used as intercoolers between flash pasteurizers and the milk coolers, Fig. 24-10. The hot milk from the pasteurizers helps heat the milk going to the pasteurizer, and the cool milk entering helps cool the milk leaving. After use, the plate type cooler can be opened up so each individual plate is exposed for cleaning and sterilizing.

Brewery Refrigeration.—The brewing industry is a very large user of industrial refrigeration. The design of the required refrigeration equipment so ties in with the actual design of the rest of the brewing equipment, that design data could hardly be included in a book of this scope. However, a brief outline of the brewing process, and its use of refrigeration will be of help to anyone in contact with the brewing industry.

Fig. 24-11 gives a simplified schematic flow sheet for a brewery. A mash, made chiefly of grains, is cooked in a brew kettle to form a *wort*. Only one batch a day is cooked up, so it must be the entire daily production. This wort is allowed to cool over night. This is done in open pans in a carefully controlled or air conditioned atmosphere. The following morning, the wort is put through a cooler to bring it down to fermenting temperature, then pumped to fermenting tanks. Here the fermenting temperature is maintained accurately to give the required results. Temperatures of from 45 F to 55 F are used, depending on the type of beer or ale to be made. This fermentation generates heat and carbon dioxide. After fermentation, the beer is further cooled, and pumped to aging tanks. It is aged for several weeks at about 34 F for beer or 45 F for ale. It is then sent to the racking room for barreling or bottling. It is mainly by an accurate control of temperature that the brewmaster gets the results he is after. Therefore, all temperatures are specified by him, and when need be, altered by him.

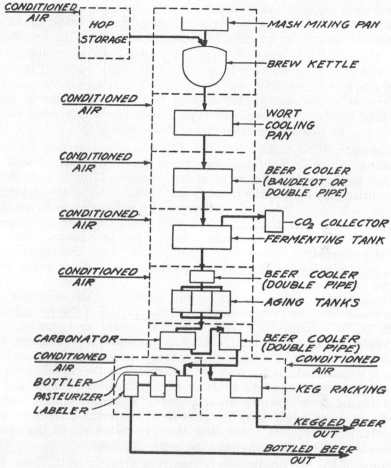

CONDITIONED AIR

HOP STORAGE

MASH MIXING PAN

BREW KETTLE

CONDITIONED AIR

WORT COOLING PAN

CONDITIONED AIR

BEER COOLER (BAUDELOT OR DOUBLE PIPE)

CONDITIONED AIR

CO_2 COLLECTOR

FERMENTING TANK

CONDITIONED AIR

BEER COOLER (DOUBLE PIPE)

AGING TANKS

CARBONATOR

BEER COOLER (DOUBLE PIPE)

CONDITIONED AIR

CONDITIONED AIR

BOTTLER
PASTEURIZER
LABELER

KEG RACKING

KEGGED BEER OUT

BOTTLED BEER OUT

Fig. 24-11. Schematic flow sheet of a brewery.

Operating costs are, in a brewery, probably more than in any other industry, dependent on the design of equipment based on the proper heat balance. It lends itself well to steam power for driving mechanical equipment, with exhaust steam used for cooking and heating. Even where the convenience of push button electric power is desired, a steam driven generator is sometimes installed to furnish the electric power. Heat exchangers between the brew kettle and the first wort cooler are used to reduce the heating requirements for the batch being prepared, and to reduce the cooling requirements for the batch being cooled. Water cooling, usually with water from a cooling tower is used wherever possible. Refrigeration takes up where the water cooling leaves off. Heavy peak loads like wort cooling and cooling between fermenting and aging are staggered to reduce total demand loads. Where heavy demands excessively increase equipment cost or power cost, water tanks, brine tanks or congealing tanks may be used to store refrigeration for the peaks.

Any cooling that might be necessary in the air conditioning of the wort pans after cooking is usually done with water. The wort cooling before fermenting, may be done on a baudelet cooler similar to the milk cooler of Fig. 24-8, or may be in a double pipe or shell and tube cooler. If an enclosed type cooler is used, it must be so that it can be opened for cleaning and sterilizing.

The fermenting room offers two problems, cooling and air conditioning. Since fermentation generates heat, this heat as well as leakage to the room or tanks must be absorbed. This is sometimes done entirely by coils in the room, but is better done by *attemperator* coils in each fermenting tank. Attemperator coils are merely cooling coils inside the tank through which refrigerated water is pumped. The water flow can be accurately controlled to maintain the required temperature. Even with attemperator coils the fermenting room is also refrigerated. This keeps down the heat transfer load on the tanks.

Fermentation also produces carbon dioxide. If something is not done about this, the carbon dioxide concentration of the fermenting room would increase to a point where it would be hazardous for workmen. This carbon dioxide may or may not be reclaimed, but there is always enough that adequate ventilation is necessary to reduce its concentration. Any air delivered to the room must be cooled to room temperature. It is also particularly important to keep this air clean. Fermentation requires the maintenance of conditions that are conducive to the growth of bacteria. Therefore it is important to keep the room, and the air delivered to the room, clean enough that it cannot contaminate the beer.

Some of the carbon dioxide is dissolved directly in the beer, but the beer is often further charged with carbon dioxide when bottled or kegged. Therefore, the carbon dioxide escaping is often reclaimed and stored for further use. It may be stored as gas, but this requires gas holders of large volume. Much space can be saved by liquifying the carbon dioxide. This is done by increasing its pressure, and reducing its temperature by refrigeration.

After fermentation, the temperature must be further dropped as the beer goes to aging tanks. At this point the beer cannot be aerated, so an enclosed cooler must be used. Either the double pipe or the shell and tube cooler may be used. Fermentation is completed by this time, so attemperator coils are not necessary. The rooms are kept at aging temperature to reduce heat transfer to the beer.

After aging, the beer is pumped to the racking room to be bottled or put in kegs. The racking room is usually kept at about aging temperature to keep the temperature of beer from rising. If the beer is to be put in kegs, it is usually first put through a small double pipe or shell type cooler, and its temperature reduced 2 F or 3 F. This offsets any temperature rise due to the handling and pumping. If the beer is to be bottled or canned, it is first pasteurized, then cooled to a low temperature. Heat exchangers are commonly used here to save refrigeration and heat requirements. Whether put in kegs, bottles or cans, the filling is usually done in a carbon dioxide atmosphere or under a carbon dioxide pressure. This helps maintain its sharpness. This is where the carbon dioxide from the fermentation is used.

Beside the above direct requirements of refrigeration, two important ingredients require careful storage at reduced temperatures. Hops, which help flavor the wort are often purchased soon after harvest time in the fall. They must then be stored under proper conditions to prevent spoilage. About 34 F at a humidity of 65 percent has proved best for this. The other important ingredient is yeast. This must be kept at reduced temperatures, usually about 38 F. It must also be kept in a clean atmosphere to prevent contamination from any air born organisms.

Refrigeration in Wine Making.—In recent years an increasing amount of refrigeration is being used in the making and aging of wine. Here, as in the brewery, fermentation generates heat. This fermentation can be more accurately controlled by controlling the temperature. This is usually at a temperature high enough that water from a cooling tower is sufficient.

The aging can be greatly speeded up by refrigeration. The purpose of aging is to allow time for the precipitation of sediments. The clear wine can then be filtered or drawn off and it will then remain clear. Wine that has not been properly aged will precipitate and become cloudy in the bottle. This aging process used to take several years. By using refrigeration, fall wine can be made ready for the Christmas market.

One of two methods may be used. The wine may be cooled to within about a degree of its congealing point, then held for two weeks or more. The second method is to congeal the wine, and hold it for several days, then allow it to thaw. In either method, the wine may be allowed to stand in tanks so the precipitate will settle out. Or it may be pumped through a filter. Some wine makers feel one such treatment, if accurately controlled, is sufficient. Others cool and filter the wine as many as five times. It is possible, according to some authorities, to force precipitation so far that the wine loses some of its bouquet.

The aging wine is stored in large tanks. Its chilling may be done in three different ways. Direct expansion or brine coils may be placed inside the tanks. This method gives the poorest control because of lack of agitation, temperature variations throughout the tank, and sometimes freezing out on the coils.

The second, and probably the commonest method, is to have an external cooler, usually a double pipe or shell type cooler. Aerating coolers cannot be used because the wine must be protected from the oxygen in the air to prevent secondary fermentation or spoilage. Coolers are usually made of stainless steel. A single central cooler may be arranged with lines and valves to it, so it can be operated on one tank at a time. The wine is pumped from the tank, through the cooler, and back to the tank. This circulation is kept up continuously until the tank temperature is brought down to the desired point. Then the valves and pipes or hoses can be used to transfer the cooler to another tank.

The third method is to have all the tanks in a room refrigerated to the desired aging temperature. This alone is too slow to be satisfactory. But when this method is combined with an external cooler it gives the most accurate and best controlled results.

The temperature required depends on the type of wine, and whether it is to be aged at above or below freezing. Table or dry wines will freeze at temperatures from 20 F to 22 F. Sweet or fortified wines will freeze at temperatures from 7 F to 12 F.

One other practice requiring refrigeration commonly used with sparkling wines is to do the final aging in bottles. While aging, the bottles are set upside down. This allows the sediment to settle against the cork. To remove this sediment, the neck of the bottle is frozen by immersing it in refrigerated brine. The cork is then removed with the bottle upright. The sediment is frozen to the cork, so comes out with it. The bottle is then recorked and is ready for market.

QUESTIONS

24- 1. a. What is the coldest temperature water should be cooled for drinking?

b. What temperatures are recommended for drinking water?

24- 2. What is the difference between a remote and a self contained water cooler?

24- 3. What is the difference between a storage and an instantaneous type cooler?

24- 4. A circulating water system in a hotel has cold water outlets in 80 rooms. The water circuit is to be 1200 lineal feet. The design temperature is 95 F. The summer water temperature is 70 F.
   a. What size circulating pipe should be used?
   b. What is the total refrigeration load?

24- 5. Why is a pressure sometimes used in beer dispensing?

24- 6. Why is soda water chilled before charging with carbon dioxide, even though it will be allowed to warm up again after bottling?

24- 7. Can Baudelot coolers be used satisfactorily to cool milk? Wort? Aged beer? Wine?

24- 8. What is the biggest advantage of a Baudelot cooler over the enclosed type?

24- 9. What is a plate cooler?

24-10. Of what materials are most modern milk coolers made?

24-11. List the different places in a brewery requiring the cooling of a liquid.

24-12. List the different places in a brewery requiring room refrigeration.

24-13. Why is aging wine refrigerated?

24-14. What three methods are used in cooling wine?

CHAPTER 25

COMPLETE SYSTEMS

Commercial Multiplexing.—The past chapters have all dealt more with individual parts of a refrigeration system. In this chapter, these parts are put together as an integrated whole. Most present day domestic and small commercial equipment is made up entirely of factory assembled units. Therefore, all that need be done to install them is to move them into place and connect them up to electric power, and sometimes water lines and drains. But any but the simplest commercial equipment usually leads to multiplexing, that is, connecting several cabinets or fixtures to the same compressor.

Where all fixtures are to operate at the same temperature, this is no problem. But if different temperatures are wanted, a few general rules should be kept in mind to prevent faulty temperature regulation. These rules are as follows.

1. Place auxiliary valves such as solenoid valves or constant pressure valves in the lines of the warmer fixtures.

2. Place a check valve in the suction line of the coldest fixture.

3. Do not connect fixtures having too great a temperature difference to a single compressor.

4. Do not connect fixtures having too great a difference in peak loads to a single compressor.

5. Have at least one third of the total load open to the compressor with no auxiliary valves. (This must be the suction from the coldest evaporator).

6. Choose a condensing unit with a capacity equal the sum of all the fixtures to be connected, and at the suction temperature of the coldest fixture.

The reason for the first and second rules were covered in Chapter 9. Too wide a temperature variation should not be allowed because any condition that maintains the load on the higher temperature fixtures will maintain such a high suction pressure that refrigeration on the low temperature fixtures will be unsatisfactory. If there is a large variation in peak loads, steady compressor operation caused by a large load on one fixture may cause too much refrigeration on lighter loaded units. At least one third of the total load must be open to the compressor at all times. If auxiliary valves close more than this off, the large compressor on the small remaining load will cause short cycling. The condensing unit must have capacity to handle the total load if it is to satisfactorily refrigerate it all. It must be able to handle this total load at the lowest suction pressure because the auxiliary valves usually throttle the higher pressure down to the lower pressure. Some typical examples illustrate these rules.

Example 25-1.—A system such as Fig. 25-1 is to be multiplexed. The figures give the calculated heat load for each fixture without a correction for running time. Work out the material list required.

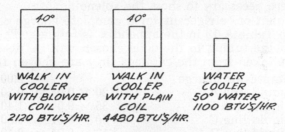

Fig. 25-1. Example 1.

The blower coil is usually operated at about a 10 F temperature difference. It must work on a defrosting cycle to prevent plugging up the coil with frost. A solenoid valve operated from a pressure control set for pressures to give temperatures of about 24 F and 36 F would give this. The natural convection coil will operate at about 20 F temperature difference. This will require a refrigerant temperature of 20 F, which is the coldest of the entire group. So the back pressure control on the condensing unit would be set to give this average temperature. Also this is the biggest part of the load, so falls within our rule of having at least one third of the capacity open to the condensing unit. The water cooler will probably run with about a 5 F temperature difference, so its suction temperature will be about 45 F. This could be obtained with a constant pressure valve.

The required coil sizes will each be 50 percent larger than the data of Fig. 25-1 to allow for running time. Therefore the coils and their loads will be tabulated as follows.

Blower Coil	3180	Btu per hr at 10 F T D
Natural Convection Coil	6720	Btu per hr at 20 F T D
Water Cooler	1650	Btu per hr
Total	11550	Btu per hr

Therefore a condensing unit of 11,550 Btu per hr at a 20 F suction temperature would be chosen.

The line sizes are chosen from these loads and Fig. 22-7, assuming Freon 12 is the refrigerant and 100 F condensing temperature. To keep the pressure drops within the proper limits, the following line sizes will be chosen.

	Suction line	Liquid line
Line A	⅝ in	¼ in
Line B	⅞ in	⅜ in
Line C	½ in	¼ in
Line D	1⅛ in	⅜ in

Fig. 25-2 gives a complete schematic diagram of the installation with settings required, etc. For simplicity liquid lines are omitted except where necessary to show the solenoid.

The amount of refrigerant for a complete charge could be estimated from Table A-13 in the appendix as follows. The length and diameter of the tubing in the coils chosen will be needed for this. This can be taken from the catalogs they are chosen from.

Compressor charge		=	2.00 lb
Liquid line A	20×0.01 =		0.20 lb
Liquid line B	35×0.04 =		1.40 lb
Liquid line C	50×0.01 =		0.50 lb
Liquid line D	12×0.04 =		0.48 lb
Blower coil	90×0.03 =		2.70 lb
Natural Convection Coil	120×0.03 =		3.60 lb
Water cooler[1]	21×0.01 =		0.21 lb
Total			11.09 lb

Additional refrigerant should be available for purging, possible losses or variations in estimate. Figure 15 pound total.

All this information could be brought together in a bill of materials necessary for the job.

1 Condensing unit complete with motor starter. 11,500 capacity at 20 F suction temperature.

1 Blower coil. 3180 Btu capacity at 10 F temperature difference.

1 Natural convection coil, 6720 Btu capacity at 20 F temperature difference.[2]

1 Water cooler. 1100 Btu capacity.[3]

1 Thermostatic expansion valve. ¾ ton capacity.[4]

[1] A flooded type water cooler may take 5 lbs. or more of refrigerant so one should be sure and check the type of cooler furnished.

[2] The size and shape of this coil must fit the cabinet.

[3] The water cooler may be furnished with the other fixtures. Water coolers are usually rated in gallons of water per hour, but the Btu load is used here for convenience.

[4] Thermostatic expansion valves are occasionally furnished with blower coils or water coolers.

2 Thermostatic expansion valves. ½ ton capacity.[5] [4]
2 Back pressure controls
1 Solenoid valve
1 Constant pressure valve
1 Check valve
1 Suction manifold with the following hand valves
    1 ½ in. Valve
    1 ⅝ in. Valve
    1 ⅞ in. Valve
1 Liquid manifold with the following hand valves
    2 ¼ in. Valves
    1 ⅜ in. Valve

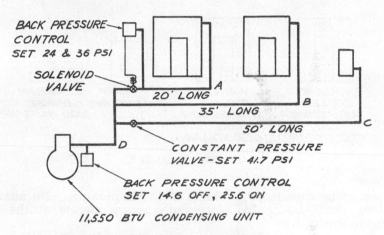

Fig. 25-2. Example 1, completed.

90 ft ¼ in. Copper tubing[6]
75 ft ⅜ in. Copper tubing[6]
65 ft ½ in. Copper tubing[6]
25 ft ⅝ in. Copper tubing[6]
60 ft ⅞ in. Copper tubing[6]
    Miscellaneous fittings for all above tubing sizes[7]

15 Lb Refrigerant 12
¼ gal Refrigerant 12 compressor oil

[5]The smallest size of most manufacturer's valves are good up to at least ½ ton.
[6]Tubing figures are all about 25% more than than the estimated lengths required, to allow for short ends and other waste.
[7]Among required fittings may be required reducers to adapt the size tubing used to the available valves, and to the condensing unit liquid and suction valves.

Electric wiring and plumbing are usually sublet, or in a large organization figured by separate departments. Therefore such data is not included.

Example 25-2.—A system as outlined in Fig. 25-3 is to be multiplexed. Work out the required details for this job.

Such a system as this will best be operated from two condensing units for two reasons. First, there is too great a difference between temperatures. Second, the colder part of the load does not make up one third of the total load.

The two walk in coolers would be hooked together on one condensing unit. This should have a refrigeration capacity of
1.5 (4750 + 6250) = 16,500 Btu per hr

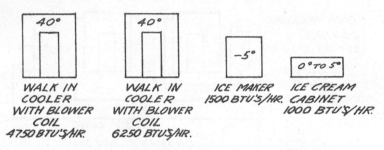

Fig. 25-3. Example 2.

It would be chosen for a 30 F suction temperature. No auxiliary valves would be needed since both boxes operate at the same temperature.

The ice maker and the ice cream cabinet would be hooked up to a second compressor having a capacity of
1.5 (1500 + 1000) = 3750 Btu per hr

This should be chosen with a suction temperature of 0 F. These units might be operated together with no auxiliary valves. But if it was felt that maximum capacity might be wanted for ice freezing, the customer might want the freezer set colder than the ice cream cabinet. In that case a constant pressure valve is put in the suction line from the ice cream cabinet.

The line sizes would be as follows.

	Suction line	Liquid line
Line A	7/8 in.	3/8 in.
Line B	7/8 in.	3/8 in.
Line C	1 1/8 in.	1/2 in.
Line D	7/8 in.	1/4 in.
Line E	7/8 in.	1/4 in.
Line F	7/8 in.	3/8 in.

Fig. 25-4 illustrates the assembly of the parts necessary to make up the complete system.

Example 25-3.—Fig. 25-5 shows a job typical of a large restaurant, or an institution such as a boarding school or a hospital. Work out the required details for this job.

Again, the load will best be divided into two groups with the storage boxes on one condensing unit, and the ice and ice cream equipment on the other. But to give greater flexibility and standby service, these condensing units will be cross connected, Fig. 25-6. These cross connections would normally be left closed, but in case of failure of one compressor, the other could help hold the other load temporarily. The required capacity of the first condensing unit would be

1.5 (14,000 + 12,000 + 8000 + 1200) = 52,800 Btu per hr at 0 F (meat box evaporator).

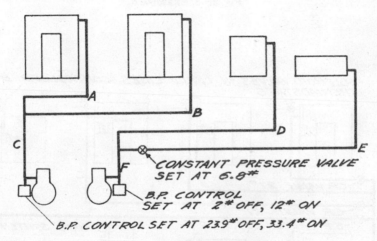

Fig. 25-4. Example 2, completed.

The ice cream freezer would not be operated continuously. This might be furnished with its own condensing unit. If not, no provision for running time would have to be made, since it will only run a few hours a day anyway. Therefore, the capacity of the second condensing unit would be

1.5 (1800 + 1500) + 2000 = 6950 Btu per hr at —10 F.

The temperature of each box or fixture will be regulated by a thermostat which operates a solenoid. When there is a possibility of having a suction pressure lower than desired when the solenoid is open, a constant pressure valve is used also. Fig. 25-6 illustrates

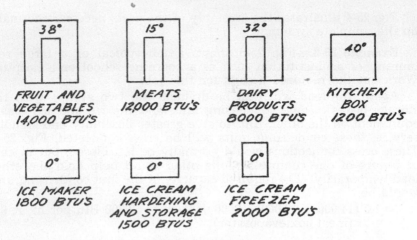

FRUIT AND VEGETABLES 14,000 BTU'S

MEATS 12,000 BTU'S

DAIRY PRODUCTS 8000 BTU'S

KITCHEN BOX 1200 BTU'S

ICE MAKER 1800 BTU'S

ICE CREAM HARDENING AND STORAGE 1500 BTU'S

ICE CREAM FREEZER 2000 BTU'S

Fig. 25-5. Example 3.

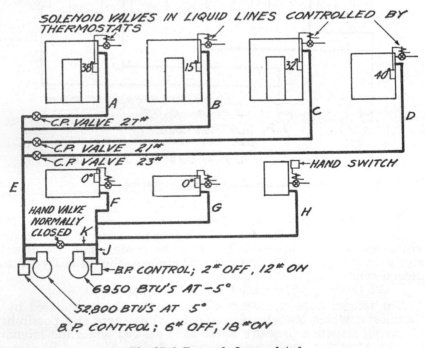

SOLENOID VALVES IN LIQUID LINES CONTROLLED BY THERMOSTATS

C.P. VALVE 27#

C.P. VALVE 21#

C.P. VALVE 23#

HAND SWITCH

HAND VALVE NORMALLY CLOSED

B.P. CONTROL; 2# OFF, 12# ON

6950 BTU'S AT -5°

52,800 BTU'S AT 5°

B.P. CONTROL; 6# OFF, 18# ON

Fig. 25-6. Example 3, completed.

the valving and control of this system. The line sizes would be as follows.

	Suction line	Liquid line
Line A	1⅛ in.	½ in.
Line B	1⅜ in.	½ in.
Line C	1⅛ in.	⅜ in.
Line D	½ in.	¼ in.
Line E	2⅛ in.	⅝ in.
Line F	⅞ in.	¼ in.
Line G	⅞ in.	¼ in.
Line H	⅝ in.	¼ in.
Line J	1⅛ in.	⅜ in.
Line K	1⅛ in.	⅜ in.

The cross over lines K need not be any larger than the lines J, for this is the maximum capacity that would flow through them if either compressor was down. Naturally, the small compressor could not carry the load of the big one. But careful conservation of the temperatures already down, would make it possible to hold them for a short time.

Cold Storage.—Cold storage warehouses have always been one of the major applications of refrigeration. A cold storage plant may be a refrigerated collecting station on a large ranch, or a small cooperative warehouse which acts as a collecting station for all the growers of a community. Or it may be a large industrial warehouse of many floors covering one or more city blocks. It may be built with only one type of local commodity in mind, or it may precool, freeze, or store all types of perishable commodities required in a large city.

Any refrigeration warehouse, whether large or small, should be designed and built with the following considerations in mind.

1. Who will use it?

2. How will users deliver commodities to it, and how will they be shipped out?

3. Is water for cooling and a suitable fuel or power available?

4. What is the cost of land, construction, etc.?

5. What type of commodity or commodities will users want to store?

6. How much commodity will probably be stored at a time?

7. For what length of time will these commodities require storage?

8. What temperatures and humidities will be required for these commodities?

9. Should an ice plant or other load equalizing factor be included?

The first four of the above items will dictate the location of the warehouse. It must be conveniently reached by those using it. It must have proper truck loading docks. These should be so located that unloading trucks will not block traffic, either in the street or trying to reach other parts of the plant. Nearly all cases call for a railroad siding. Some plants that felt they would always depend on trucks have since regretted the omission of this.

The other five items listed will determine the type and size of building, and the economics of the entire project. Ice plants have often been incorporated in a warehouse to give a steadier annual load, and to help the total income. More recently, locker plants have been included. First costs and estimated operating costs must be justified by estimated income.

Example 25-4.—A small cold storage plant is for the purpose of collecting, precooling and packing local fruits. Apricots, peaches and pears are expected. The cold storage part of the building is shown in Fig. 25-7. Four inches of insulation is to be used. It is desired to be able to precool 60,000 pounds of fruit per day. The local design temperature is 90 F. Work out the refrigeration requirements for this job.

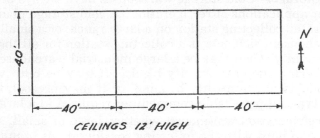

CEILINGS 12' HIGH

Fig. 25-7. Example 4.

A 35 F cooler temperature is common for such fruit. The heat transfer load would be as follows:

Roof area
$$40 \times 120 = 4800 \text{ sq ft}$$

Roof temperature difference including sun effect.
$$(90 - 35) + 30 = 85 \text{ F}$$

Heat leakage through roof
$$H = \frac{Ak(t_2 - t_1)}{x}$$
$$= \frac{4800 \times 0.3 \times 85}{4} \qquad = 30,600 \text{ Btu per hr}$$

Floor leakage. The floor is up off the ground to give an air space under it.

$$H = \frac{4800 \times 0.3 \times 55}{4} \qquad = \quad 19,800 \text{ Btu per hr}$$

Heat leakage through south wall.

$$H = \frac{1440 \times 0.3 \times 65}{4} \qquad = \quad 7,020 \text{ Btu per hr}$$

Heat leakage through north wall.

$$H = \frac{1440 \times 0.3 \times 55}{4} \qquad = \quad 5,940 \text{ Btu per hr}$$

Heat leakage through west wall.

$$H = \frac{480 \times 0.3 \times 75}{4} \qquad = \quad 2,700 \text{ Btu per hr}$$

Heat leakage through east wall.

$$H = \frac{480 \times 0.3 \times 55}{4} \qquad = \quad 1,980 \text{ Btu per hr}$$

Total heat leakage $= \quad 68,040$ Btu per hr

Estimated loss due to door openings, ventilation, etc. at 15% of leakage $= \quad 10,206$ Btu per hr

Heat load of 10 workmen in rooms
10×600 $= \quad 6,000$ Btu per hr

Lights estimated at ½ watt per sq ft floor area
$½ \times 4800 \times 3.41$ $= \quad 8,200$ Btu per hr

Total daily steady load $92,446$ Btu per hr

The product load would be as follows:
$$H = \frac{WS (t_2 - t_1)}{time}$$
$$= \frac{60,000 \times 0.92 \times 55}{24} \qquad = \quad 126,500 \text{ Btu per hr}$$

Total leakage and product load $= 218,946$ Btu per hr

Add 25% for safety factor $54,736$ Btu per hr

Total capacity of equipment required $273,682$ Btu per hr

To choose the required coils for each room it will be assumed that one-third of this total load is in each room.

$$\frac{273,682}{3} \quad 91,227 \text{ Btu per hr}$$

If 1¼ inch iron pipe coils are used at a 20 F temperature difference:

$$A = \frac{H}{K (t_2 - t_1)} = \frac{91,227}{2.5 \times 20} = 1825 \text{ sq ft of surface required}$$

From the tables, there is 2.3 lineal feet of 1¼ inch pipe per sq ft of surface.

$$2.3 \times 1825 = 4200 \text{ lineal feet of pipe per room.}$$

The total refrigeration load will be

$$\frac{273,682}{12,000} = 22.8 \text{ tons}$$

The leakage load will vary somewhat with various outside temperatures. The product load will only be required when products are being cooled. Therefore, the compressor capacity should be divided. A system of this size is more or less on the dividing line between ammonia equipment and Freon 12 equipment. This case assumes ammonia equipment chosen. The load will be divided into two compressors, one to take care of the leakage load, and one to take care of the product load. Two compressors of 11.4 tons each at a 15 F suction and 85 F condenser will be chosen. Fig. 20-10 gives the required displacement per ton, 2.8 cu ft per min. Fig. 20-4 gives the volumetric efficiency; for a compression ratio of 3.85 it is 82 percent. This will require a compressor with an actual displacement of

$$\frac{11.4 \times 2.8}{0.82} = 38.9 \text{ cu ft per min}$$

From Table 20-2 a 4½ in $\times$ 4½ in compressor gives a displacement of 8.282 cu ft per min per 100 R P M.

$$\frac{38.9}{8.282} = 470 \text{ rpm}$$

Therefore two 4¼ $\times$ 4½ two cylinder compressors turning 470 rpm would handle this job. From Fig. 20-12 the required power per ton is 0.82 hp. Since this is a theoretical figure, this is increased by 50 percent to take care of losses and to give a safe reserve. Thus, the required motor size would be

$$1.5 \times 11.4 \times 0.82 = 14.0 \text{ hp}$$

A 15 hp motor is the nearest standard size to this. A single condenser with a capacity of 22.8 tons capacity could be chosen. The entire system would be assembled as in Fig. 25-8.

Locker Plants.—A locker plant is actually a cold storage warehouse. It has been said that a cold storage warehouse is something like a bank. One puts certain valuable products there for safekeeping. The difference between a bank and a cold storage warehouse is that in the bank, the customer is satisfied to withdraw any money similar to that deposited. In the warehouse, the customer wants to withdraw exactly the same product he deposited. It is fairly simple to keep each customers product segregated where the quantities are large. But if each customer has, at the most, only a few hundred pounds, and this is apt to be deposited or withdrawn only a few pounds at a time; the segregation and book keeping necessary would be so involved as to cost more than the actual storage costs.

Locker plants are an answer to this problem. Each customer rents a separate locker in which he keeps his valuable food products. It acts more like the safe deposit vault of a bank. Food is brought to the locker plant by the customer. It may be prepared and packaged at home, but this is more often done right at the plant. The packages are frozen, then transferred to the customers locker. From here, the customer may withdraw them as required.

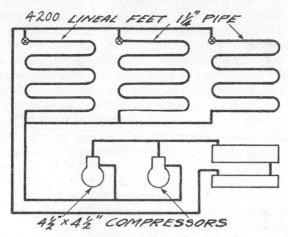

Fig. 25-8. Example 4, completed.

The size of the locker plant and the type of facilities to be included will depend on the probable patronage. All the requirements listed for a good cold storage warehouse should be considered. A locker plant of less than 400 to 500 lockers is not usually financially self supporting. If built in conjunction with a meat market, cold storage plant, ice plant, or other similar establishment, it may well pay for the part time attention it requires. Few locker plants of any size are successful if locker rentals alone are depended on. Processing charges are made for all goods processed and frozen in the plant. Sufficient food should be moved through the plant to make these processing charges pay for the time and labor of the men who must be available to do this work.

Regardless of size, locker plants are most successful in rural communities where the farmer or grower can use it to preserve food for his personal or family requirements, or where town dwellers may purchase directly from the farmer and put up their own requirements. In cities where the customers can only buy food through regular retail channels, the savings is not great enough or the food turn over not fast enough to make the plant very successful either from the standpoint of the patron or the operator.

Usually, more meat goes through a locker plant than any other commodity. Therefore a good locker plant becomes a miniature meat packing plant. Pens and slaughtering chutes may or may not be included. The slaughtering is often done on the farm anyway. But provision must be made for a chill room, aging room and cutting room, as well as the freezer and the locker room. Besides this, it is desirable to have equipment for making sausage, rendering lard, smoking, pickling, etc. An experienced butcher either as a part time or full time employee, depending on the size of the plant is absolutely necessary. Beside the meat handling equipment, any but the smallest plants usually make provision for cleaning, preparing, and packaging fruits and vegetables. Washing tables and trays, with hot and cold water, and provisions for blanching, either with boiling water or steam are usually all that is required for this.

The amount of food that must be handled in a locker plant will naturally be based on the number of lockers, and to a certain extent on the requirements of the patrons and the local products. But averages can be worked out from the fact that the average locker of 6 cubic feet capacity will hold about 250 pounds of food, and may be filled an estimated three times a year. Thus, for each locker, the plant must be able to handle

$$3 \times 250 = 750 \text{ lb of food a year}$$

This, based on a five day week is

$$\frac{750}{5 \times 52} = 2.9 \text{ lb per day per locker}$$

Due to the fact that this load is not evenly spread out over the entire year, this should be increased by about 50 percent. This will require the freezing of approximately 4.5 lb per day per locker. If the freezer is filled once in the morning and once in the evening, this will cut the size of the freezer in half, so it must be large enough to hold 2.25 lb of food per locker.

A fair estimate is that three fourths of the 4.5 lb is meat, so facilities for handling about 3.4 lb of meat per day per locker, and 1.1 lb of fruit and vegetables per day per locker would give a basis for designing the food handling equipment. All meat must be chilled. It will take two days to completely chill large carcasses. Therefore, the chill room must be able to hold

$$2 \times 3.4 = 6.8 \text{ lb per locker}$$

The types of meat will depend largely on what is raised locally, but beef is often 50 percent or more of the meat handled. This will amount to approximately 2 pounds per locker. If beef is to be aged for two weeks, aging space must be made for

$$2 \times 14 = 28 \text{ lb per locker}$$

This data is summarized in Table 25-1.

TABLE 25-1—SIZE OF LOCKER PLANT FACILITIES REQUIRED PER LOCKER

	Room Size, Floor Area or Volume	Cu Ft of Food Products	Pounds of Food Products Per Loading	Days Between Loading Periods	Lb. Food per Day to be Refrigerated or Handled	Recommended Temp. F.
Locker Room	1.3 to 1.6 sq ft	6	250			0
Chill Room	.09 to .13 sq ft	.163	6.8	2	3.4	35
Aging Room	.38 to .55 sq ft	.672	28	14	2	35
Freezer	.08 to .11 cu ft	.054	2.25	½	4.5	−15 to −40
Meat Cutting Room and Facilities					3.4	Room Temp.
Fruit and Vegetable Preparing Facilities					1.1	Room Temp.

Chill rooms and aging rooms should be maintained at about 35 F. Blower coils are favored. Cutting rooms and fruit and vegetable preparing rooms are at normal room temperature. Shelf freezers in a relatively small cabinet are favored at the present time. But

TABLE 25-2—APPROXIMATE STORAGE PERIOD FOR FROZEN FOODS IN LOCKERS. (FROM ASRE)

	Approximate Storage Period, Months		
	at 0F	at 5F	at 10F
Fruit, vegetables, beef, veal	10 to 12	8 to 10	3 to 4
Lamb, mutton, poultry, eggs	8 to 10	6 to 8	3 to 4
Pork, butter	6 to 8	4 to 6	2 to 3
Ground meat (unsalted), cream	4 to 6	3 to 4	1 to 2
Bacon and ham (Mild cured, not smoked)	4 to 5	3 to 4	1 to 2
Fish, ground meat with salt in seasoning	3 to 4	2 to 3	1 to 2

air blast freezers have had considerable use. Either shelf or air blast freezers may be run from —20 F to —40 F. Some freezers have been operated as high as 0 F, but they do not give as satisfactory results. The locker rooms should be held about 0 F, see Table 25-2. Blower coils, pipe coils, and plate coils have all had considerable use. Defrosting is a problem here that must not be overlooked. Blower coils are usually defrosted daily. Water defrost, electric heat, and hot gas defrost have all been used successfully. If pipe coils or plate coils are used, they are usually grouped over the aisles. This gives better air distribution to all the lockers. It also allows the frost to drop into the aisles instead of on the tops of the lockers when defrosting. Pipe and plate coils are defrosted as needed, usually at intervals of several months.

Fig. 25-9, 25-10, and 25-11 illustrate three typical locker plant layouts suggested by the American Society of Refrigerating Engineers. Fig. 25-9 is for a small plant that could be used as part of another store or establishment. All parts of this plant have been reduced to an irreducible minimum.

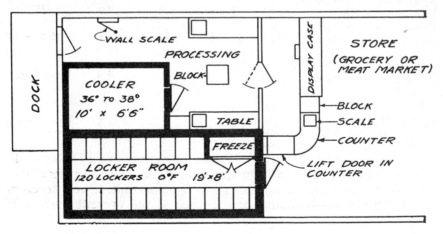

Fig. 25-9. Frozen food locker plant combined with grocery and meat market. (From A.S.R.E. Data Book.)

Fig. 25-10 could be operated in conjunction with another business such as an ice plant, or it could be built as a separate establishment. Fig. 25-11 is a larger and more elaborate plant.

Calculations for the plant shown for Fig. 25-10 will be typical of a locker plant problem. In this case 12 inches of insulation is to be used around the locker room, and 6 inches of insulation around the chill room and aging room. Six inches will also be used in the walls between the aging room and the locker room. A design temperature of 95 F is assumed.

Locker room load.

Roof leakage

$$H = \frac{(16 \times 30.5) \times 0.3(95 - 0 + 30)}{12} = 1530 \text{ Btu per hr}$$

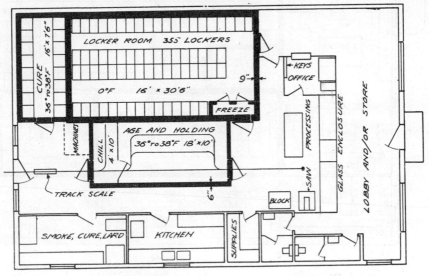

Fig. 25-10. Typical frozen food locker plant. (From A.S.R.E. Data Book.)

Floor leakage
$$H = \frac{(16 \times 30.5) \times 0.3(95 - 0)}{12} = 1160 \text{ Btu per hr}$$

Wall leakage (North wall)
$$H = \frac{(30.5 \times 12) \times 0.3(95 - 0)}{12} = 869 \text{ Btu per hr}$$

Wall leakage between locker room and curing room.
$$H = \frac{(16 \times 12) \times 0.3(35 - 0)}{6} = 336 \text{ Btu per hr}$$

Wall leakage between locker room and aging room.
$$H = \frac{(18 \times 12) \times 0.3(35 - 0)}{6} = 378 \text{ Btu per hr}$$

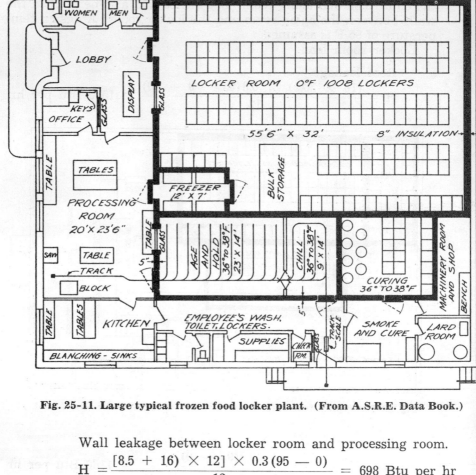

Fig. 25-11. Large typical frozen food locker plant. (From A.S.R.E. Data Book.)

Wall leakage between locker room and processing room.

$$H = \frac{[8.5 + 16) \times 12] \times 0.3\,(95 - 0)}{12} = 698 \text{ Btu per hr}$$

Heat load from lights.

$\frac{1}{2} \times 16 \times 30.5 \times 3.41$ =   832 Btu per hr

Heat load from two people.

2×600 =   1200 Btu per hr

Total   7003 Btu per hr

50 percent addition for running time   3501 Btu per hr

Total capacity required for locker room   10,504 Btu per hr

Freezer load. Assume food precooled to 35 F.

To cool from 35 F to 28 F

0.8 × 7	=	5.6 Btu
To Freeze	=	100 Btu
To cool to 0 F		
0.4 × (28 — 0)	=	11.2 Btu
Total per lb of food	=	116.8

355 lockers at 4.5 lb per locker
355 × 4.5 = 1600 lb per day
1600 × 116.8 = 186,900 Btu freezer load per day.
On the basis of 16 hr running time

$$\frac{186,900}{16} = 11,680 \text{ But per hr}$$

The leakage of the freezer cabinet is so small compared to this total load that with the correction for running time, it may be neglected.

Chill room load.

Roof leakage.
$$\frac{(4 \times 10) \times 0.3(95 - 35 + 30)}{6} \qquad = 180 \text{ Btu per hr}$$

Floor leakage
$$\frac{(4 \times 10) \times 0.3(95 - 35)}{6} \qquad = 120 \text{ Btu per hr}$$

Exposed wall leakage
$$\frac{[12 \times (10 + 4)] \times 0.3(95 - 35)}{6} \qquad = 504 \text{ Btu per hr}$$

Total leakage   804 Btu per hr

50% additional for running time   402 Btu per hr

Product load
355 lockers at 3.4 lb per locker
1210 × 0.8(95 — 35) = 58,000 Btu
On the basis of 16 hr run time

$$\frac{58,000}{16} \qquad = 3620 \text{ Btu per hr}$$

Total chill room load   4826 Btu per hr

Aging room load.
Roof leakage
$$\frac{(18 \times 10) \times 0.3(95 - 35 + 30)}{6} \qquad = 810 \text{ Btu per hr}$$

Floor leakage
$$\frac{(18 \times 10) \times 0.3(95 - 35)}{6}$$ = 540 Btu per hr

Wall leakage
$$\frac{[12(18 + 10)] \times 0.3(95 - 35)}{6}$$ = 1,010 Btu per hr

Total leakage   2,360 Btu per hr

Correct for running time
1.5 × 2360   = 3,540 Btu per hr

Since all chilling is done in the chill room, the product load in the aging room should be negligible. Any that might be there could be taken care of by the extra capacity added for the running time correction.

Curing room load

Roof leakage
$$\frac{(16 \times 7.5) \times 0.3(95 - 35 + 30)}{6}$$ = 540 Btu per hr

Floor leakage
$$\frac{(16 \times 7.5) \times 0.3(95 - 35)}{6}$$ = 360 Btu per hr

North wall and inside wall
$$\frac{[(7.5 + 7.5) \times 12] \times 0.3(95 - 35)}{6}$$ = 540 Btu per hr

West wall
$$\frac{(16 \times 12) \times 0.3(95 - 35 + 20)}{6}$$ = 768 Btu per hr

Total leakage   2,208 Btu per hr

50% additional for running time   1,104 Btu per hr

For curing estimate one pound per locker.
355 × 0.8(95 — 35) = 17,000 Btu
On the basis of 16 hr run time

$$\frac{17,000}{16} = 1060 \text{ Btu per hr}$$

Total curing room load   = 4372 Btu per hr

These loads are summarized as follows.

Locker room	10,504 Btu per hr	—10 F Suction
Freezer	11,680 Btu per hr	—30 F Suction
Chill room	4,826 Btu per hr	25 F Suction
Aging room	3,540 Btu per hr	25 F Suction
Curing room	4,372 Btu per hr	25 F Suction

Various condensing unit combinations are possible, from a single unit large enough for the whole load to individual units on each separate load. But usually the simplest set up is to group similar temperature loads together. This is done here. Water cooled condensing units are most desirable on jobs of this size. Proper grouping with horse power ratings from a catalog follow.

Locker room	10,504 Btu per hr	—10 F Suction	2 hp
Freezer	11,680 Btu per hr	—30 F Suction	3 hp
Chill, age and			
cure rooms	12,738 Btu per hr	25 F Suction	1½ hp

The freezer unit could be turned off during times freezing is not needed. The units should be cross connected so that in case of failure of any one, its load could, with some favoring, be carried by the others.

The chill room requires a high humidity and rapid heat transfer. The aging room requires a high humidity. Forced draft coils do the best job for these loads. A forced draft coil would also be very satisfactory for the curing room. These rooms will require the following.

Chill room	Blower coil 4,826 Btu per hr at 10 F T D
Aging room	Blower coil 3,540 Btu per hr at 10 F T D
Curing room	Blower coil 4,372 Btu per hr at 10 F T D

The above three rooms will best be controlled by thermostats in each room. These thermostats will control solenoid valves in the liquid lines to their respective coils. A back pressure control on the condensing unit will turn it off if all solenoids are closed.

The freezer should have a capacity of approximately

$$0.10 \times 355 = 35.5 \text{ cu ft.}$$

Refrigeration will be produced by plate coils that will be arranged as freezing shelves. One square foot of freezer plate for every five lockers has been found to give a satisfactory ratio.

$$\frac{355}{5} = 71 \text{ sq ft}$$

Plates 22 in $\times$72 in having an area of 11 sq ft are a standard size. This would require 7 freezer plates.

For a 10 F temperature difference between the refrigerant and the locker room, the coil area required for natural convection coils would be:

$$A = \frac{10,504}{10 \times 2.5} = 420 \text{ sq ft}$$

If freezer plates are used to supply the cold surface in the locker room, both sides of the plates would be effective. Therefore 210 sq ft of plate surface would be required. If the same sized plates are used as were chosen for the freezer cabinet, the number required would be

$$\frac{210}{11} = 19 \text{ plates}$$

Twenty plates would divide nicely into four banks of five plates each.

This job has been figured much more liberally, and larger sized equipment chosen than some designers would do. But other types of refrigeration plants are usually figured with a factor of safety that is adequate to take care of unusual or peak load conditions. The author believes this same factor of safety should be applied to locker plants.

Air Conditioning.—Air conditioning is a use of refrigeration which has been greatly popularized in recent years. However, it should be recognized that refrigeration is only a part of air conditioning. Air conditioning is heating and ventilating with refinements. Complete air conditioning means controlling temperature, heating or cooling as required; controlling humidity, adding or extracting moisture; controlling air distribution, and controlling air purity. So an air conditioning man must know more than refrigeration. However, refrigeration is an important part of summer air conditioning, both to cool the air, and to chill it below the dew point to reduce the humidity. The control of humidity cannot be treated in detail in a book of this scope. However, if the principles given in Chapter 19 are kept in mind, some understanding of the humidity problem is possible. Briefly, the lower the coil temperature the drier the air. Or the warmer the coil temperature, the less the air is dehumidified. It is important to choose a type of coil and operate it at such a temperature that the required dehumidification is accomplished while getting exactly the right amount of air cooling.

Air conditioning loads are different than common refrigeration loads in several respects. Evaporator temperatures are higher. Thirty-five to 45 F or sometimes even 50 F is used. The evaporator cannot go as low as 32 F because it would plug with frost. With these higher evaporator temperatures, more refrigeration is produced per cubic foot displacement of the compressor, and per horse power. This means more refrigeration and a larger motor for a given sized machine than the average refrigeration man is used to.

Another difference is that centrifugal blowers can deliver an enormous amount of air with a very large heat load to an air conditioning coil. Air conditioning loads are surprisingly large to a refrigeration man. At times, when there is a great deal of humidity in the air, there can be very heavy refrigeration loads with very little air cooling.

—*Fedders Quigan Corp. photo*

Fig. 25-12. (Above) Self contained window type room air conditioner.

Air conditioning equipment may be self contained or remote. Fig. 25-12 shows a small self contained window type room air conditioner. Such equipment is commonly built in ½ hp to 1½ hp sizes. The units are designed to set in the window so outside air can be used for condensing purposes.

Not only are these units being used for residential and conditioning, but many of the older commercial buildings, hotels and motels have found these individual units enabled them to use air conditioning without major reconstruction costs which would be required if a central air conditioning system was installed.

Fig. 25-13 shows a larger type of self contained room cooler. These are commonly made in 3 hp and 5 hp sizes, and some manufacturers make them up to 10 or 20 hp. This is a type commonly installed in small stores or suites of offices. Such a conditioner may include a steam or hot water coil for heating when required. Naturally, such a coil must be supplied by a separate boiler. Fig. 25-14 shows different ways such a conditioner can be installed.

Many air conditioners are now built which chill water in a coil similar to Fig. 5-6. This chilled water is then pumped to the air cooling coil.

Remote units for either domestic or commercial applications are available. The section containing the evaporator and blower may be designed to fit directly into a duct system. Or it may go in an ornamental cabinet that sets directly in the room to be conditioned. The condensing unit may be designed with either an air cooled or water cooled condenser. It may be installed in a basement, back room, outside "dog house" or any other convenient location.

An interesting development for heating is the reverse cycle air conditioning system or heat pump. A special valve reverses the refrigerant flow so the condenser and evaporator trade functions. In the summer, the unit cools the room or building. In the winter, the valves are reversed and the room coil becomes the condenser, thus, heating the air blown over it.

The advantages of such a system can be better understood if reference is made to the coefficient of performance in Chapter 2, and to the total heat in the condenser compared to the motor power of Fig. 20-8. By this method from three to six times as much heat can be obtained as by consuming the same amount of power in standard electric heaters. The extra heat comes from the heat in outside air which is refrigerated, then rejected to the outside again. In some commercial plants, the efficiency has been increased by placing this heat absorbing evaporator in a duct of exhausting warm air.

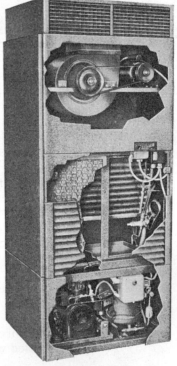

These systems should have a high speed defrost system on the outside coil. If plugged with frost, there is no heating effect available.

Such systems can best be applied to areas where the heat load in the winter is not more than 25% above the cooling load in the summer; and where electric power costs are quite reasonable compared to other fuels. Misapplication of this, or any other special system, will leave reputations which will hurt sales in areas where they may economically fit.

Fig. 25-15 illustrates a central station type conditioner, which is a larger and more elaborate remote type. Sometimes the air washer is omitted. Where

—United Conditioning Corp. photo

Fig. 25-13. Vertical floor model room cooler.

the air washer is used, the water temperature may be heated or cooled as required to add to or reduce the moisture content of the air. Or the temperature of the air entering the washer may be so controlled as to give the required condition leaving the washer.

Units such as Fig. 25-12 or 25-13 may be operated by a simple three point switch with a point for off, a point for fan only, and a point for cooling. Both the fan and the compressor operate on this last point. If this is all the control used, the unit is often small enough that it is impossible to get too much cooling. Or the machine may be turned off manually if it does get too cold.

The simplest automatic control is temperature control. The bulb is usually in the stream of room air drawn into the conditioner. On larger systems, a back pressure control is usually added to eliminate the possibility of too cold a coil.

The control of central station systems is more elaborate. Controls operated by compressed air instead of electricity are common. Air controls can be modulating where required. That is, they can open or close valves or dampers to any required point without necessarily being wide open or completely closed.

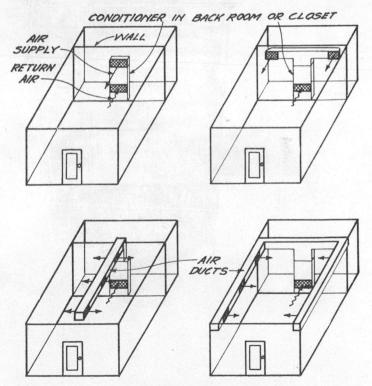

Fig. 25-14. Different methods of installing vertical floor coolers.

—*Carrier Corporation photo*

Fig. 25-15. Central station air conditioning unit.

Ice Making.—Natural ice or snow has been used in limited amounts since ancient times to aid in the preservation of food or to chill drinks. Since colonial times, natural ice has been harvested in this country. That is, where frozen on ponds or rivers in the winter it was sawed into blocks. These were packed in sawdust in barns or warehouses to keep until needed later in the year. During the first half of the nineteenth century, American clipper ships carried natural New England ice to many other parts of the world.

But manufactured ice is still an easy, convenient way of obtaining refrigeration or cooling. It may be used for cooling anything from a glass of water (or other beverage) to refrigerator cars and fishing boats. If it is purchased, there is need for little or no investment in equipment. Others would rather install their own equipment than purchase ice.

—*Peerless of America photo*

Fig. 25-16. Ice making evaporator.

The ice cube trays of a domestic refrigerator are miniature ice plants. Ice cubes for bars, restaurants, and similar establishments are often made similarly in larger ice making evaporators, Fig. 25-16. Or they may be purchased from ice companies who make them by cutting up large ice blocks.

Many firms have developed automatic ice makers which pump or circulate water through refrigerated ice trays or tubes, then automatically thaw the ice to release it. The finished cubes either drop, or are carried into a separate storage bin. When the bin fills to the top, ice cubes in contact with a thermostatic bulb automatically shut down the machine. Some of these ice makers are more or less miniature models of the tube ice maker described further on in the chapter.

The next size ice maker for comparatively small quantities is illustrated in Fig. 25-17. An insulated tank of brine is refrigerated to below freezing temperatures. Cans of fresh water are submerged in the brine, and the water freezes. Cans of 25 pound or 50 pound capacity are commonly used to make it possible to handle them without hoisting equipment.

Fig. 25-18 illustrates the production side of an ice plant. This particular plant has loose cans and the ammonia coils run between the rows of cans. In this respect it represents plants erected up to about 1925 although many like this remain in operation. Later designs utilize cans fastened in steel frames (baskets) so that from 4 to 24 or more are lifted from the brine at one time. The brine is refrigerated by flooded coolers of the type shown in Figs. 4-5, 4-6 or 5-8.

In late designs the brine is circulated by vertical shaft propellors (agitators) which do not have to project through the tank and insulation. Also where the cans are in baskets the tank cover sections are supported by the cans and the wood framework is largely eliminated. Steel partitions direct the flow of brine through the tank and a velocity of about 30 ft per min must be maintained to secure proper freezing speed. Air is introduced at the bottom of the cans or through drop tubes down the center to keep the ice clear as it freezes. The production of clear ice by well operated air agitation, water conditioning and freezing speed is a specialty in itself.

Some ice plants have storage rooms only large enough to take a few days supply, and will only make what can be immediately sold. Others make room for thousands of tons, so peak season requirements can be built up ahead when sales are light. The ice storage room is maintained at about 24 to 28 F. This prevents meltage and keeps the ice perfectly dry. Scoring, crushing, or cubing equipment may be installed in the storage room or out on the loading platform. The ice going to retail sales is usually scored, which marks it for 25 pound or 50 pound cuts. This is done in a jig or guide with circular saws. Where cubes are required, the cakes are run through a cuber which saws or cuts them up into small sized ice cubes. More of the ice may be crushed for sale where that type of ice is desired. The crushed ice is usually run through a sizer which grades it according to size. Thus, coarse, fine or snow ice can be supplied separately.

After dumping, the cans are turned upright. Directly over them are outlets from measuring cans. A lever is pulled which opens valves and each can in the basket is filled the required amount. They are then taken back and replaced in the ice tank. The baskets are pulled in rotation, so the entire tank is covered. Each can remains in place anywhere from 30 to 60 hours to freeze completely.

If plain water was frozen without treatment, the ice would be white; marble ice it is sometimes called. Much of the ice made for car icing and similar applications is made this way. If made for retail sales, a crystal clear ice is desired. To make clear ice, the water must first be treated chemically to precipitate dissolved solids or minerals. This is done in a tank large enough to give these solids time to settle out. The water is then run through a sand filter to catch anything that had not settled. The type of treatment used

—*Recold Corporation photo*

Fig. 25-17. One ton daily capacity ice freezing tank with 100 lb. cans.

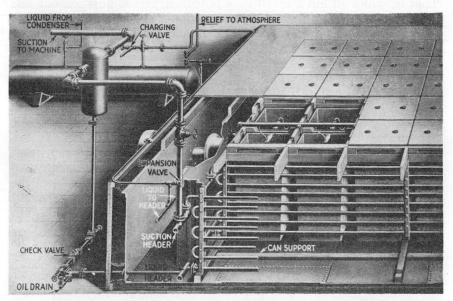

—*Frick Company photo*

Fig. 25-18. Cross section of large ice freezing tank showing general design and ammonia and air connections.

should be specified by an industrial chemist for the type of mineral in the local water. A combination of lime and alum is the most common treatment. The lime precipitates the calcium and magnesium carbonates which are the common form of mineral found in most waters. The alum coagulates the precipitates so they better settle or filter out.

Even this water will not make clear ice if there is no further treatment because all solids are not removed. Also any water contains dissolved gases, particularly air. These gases separate out in freezing, to make millions of tiny bubbles, which give the ice its white color. Anything that will keep the water agitated will break these bubbles loose from the surface of the ice as they form. The simplest method of agitation found has been an air tube in each can. Air bubbling through the water stirs it up enough to break loose any new bubbles forming.

All this treatment would give an ice that is clear except for the core. It has not been economically feasible until recently to eliminate all mineral from the water except by distillation. In the can, pure water freezes first, and the remaining minerals are concentrated in the unfrozen water at the center. If allowed to freeze, this would give a dirty, cloudy core. This is eliminated by coring the ice. That is, when all but a small core is frozen, this is pumped out and the space refilled with fresh treated water. This will then produce ice with only a thin "feather" down the center. Recently water demineralizing systems have been used to produce water which requires no coreing or air agitation.

The air drop tubes are removed before the block freezes solid, or a "needle" or thin tube carrying steam or hot water is inserted inside the drop tube so the latter is melted out. Freezing cans with fixed tubes eliminate these operations but the agitating air must be dehydrated.

The refrigeration load for an ice plant is figured like any other freezing load. To freeze ice, water must first be cooled to 32 F, then the 144 Btu of latent heat removed. This, plus heat losses from the ice tank make necessary roughly 1.5 tons of refrigeration for every ton of ice produced. Table 25-3 gives the required refrigeration per ton of ice at different water temperatures.

The time necessary to freeze ice can be calculated from the formula

$$T = \frac{C\ x^2}{32 - t_b}$$

where T = time in hours
C = a constant, 5.5 to 7
x = thickness in inches
32 = freezing point of ice
t_b = brine temperature

The constant C will vary with the condition of the plant. The can submergence and brine velocity have the most effect on it. For older plants, a C of 7 is a good figure to use. The best modern plants have brought this down to 5.5. The thickness x is the total thickness of the ice block. Average freezing time and other related data are given in Table 25-4. Late design plants reduce these freezing time figures.

TABLE 25-3—TONS OF REFRIGERATION PER TON OF ICE WITH DIFFERENT INITIAL WATER TEMPERATURE

Initial Water Temperature	Tons of Refrigeration Per Ton of Ice
40 F	1.39 Tons
50 F	1.46 Tons
60 F	1.53 Tons
70 F	1.60 Tons
80 F	1.67 Tons
90 F	1.74 Tons

TABLE 25-4—FREEZING TIME AND CANS PER TON OF ICE

Brine Temp.	Freezing Time 11″ Ice	Freezing Time 11½″ Ice	No. of 11″ 300 Lb. Cans Per Ton Ice	No. of 11″ 400 Lb. Cans Per Ton Ice	No. of 11½″ 300 Lb. Cans Per Ton Ice	No. of 11½″ 400 Lb. Cans Per Ton Ice
10	34.4	37.6	9.55	7.17	10.46	7.84
11	36.0	39.4	10.00	7.50	10.94	8.21
12	37.8	41.4	10.50	7.88	11.50	8.62
13	39.8	43.5	11.05	8.31	12.08	9.06
14	42.0	46.0	11.66	8.75	12.77	9.58
15	44.5	48.7	12.36	9.27	13.52	10.15
16	47.2	51.6	13.11	9.84	14.34	10.75
17	50.4	55.1	14.00	10.50	15.30	11.48
18	54.0	59.1	15.00	11.25	16.41	12.31
19	58.2	63.6	16.15	12.13	17.66	13.25
20	63.0	68.9	17.50	13.12	19.14	14.36

Notice the colder the brine, the quicker the freezing. But if brine temperature goes too low, the ice gets very brittle and is difficult to handle without cracking. Beside making it unfit for block trade it is dangerous if a man is handling it or pulling on it with ice tongs. Special chemicals have been added to the water to toughen the ice and make lower brine temperatures practical. Also notice the time increases as the square of the thickness of the cans. By modifying the constant, this formula can be used to estimate the freezing time of any product. A test under known conditions should establish this constant for those conditions. Then it is easy to make corrections for changes in thickness or temperature differences.

Example 25-5.—How long should a 300 lb cake of ice take to freeze with a 16 F brine temperature?
Assume C = 6.

$$T = \frac{C\ x^2}{32 - t_b}$$

$$= \frac{6 \times 11^2}{32 - 16} = 45.3 \text{ hours.}$$

Faster Ice Freezing Methods.—The large investment for buildings and equipment, and the length of time required for the can system has encouraged designers to look for other ways of producing ice. Several excellent systems have been developed to give ice in snow, flake, cube or briquette form, which will start producing ice within a few minutes after refrigeration is applied.

—*York Corporation photo*

Fig. 25-19. FlakIce Machine, 20 tons daily.

The *FlakIce* machine is one of these, Fig. 25-19. The inner drum, which is filled with refrigerated brine, rotates slowly in a bath of water. The water freezes to the bare metal in narrow ribbons, which are separated from each other by rubber bands around the drum. The drum is distorted out of round at the top sufficiently that the ice ribbons peel off over an apron, and then drop down into a storage chamber. They are thin enough that they break up in this peeling and dropping to form small flakes of ice, hence its name.

The *Pak-Ice* machine makes ice in snow or crystal form, Fig. 25-20. This machine is very similar in construction to an ice cream freezer. Water is sprayed onto the inside surface, and scraper blades scrape it off and out the end. Each ring of this freezer will make five tons of ice a day. Up to six rings can be assembled in one unit to give greater capacity. In case the ice is required in solid form, a briquette press can be installed on the ice outlet. This compresses the loose snow into hard briquettes which are still small enough to

—*Vilter Manufacturing Co. photo*

Fig. 25-20. Pack-Ice Machine, 30 tons daily.

be stored in bins or handled by small conveyors or chutes.

The *Tube-Ice* machine is a vertical shell and tube cooler operated as a freezer, Fig. 5-9. This works in cycles controlled by an automatic timer. During the freezing cycle water is pumped from the sump to the top of the freezer where it circulates down through the tubes. These tubes are submerged in the liquid ammonia so the water freezes to the sides of the tubes. At the end of the freezing cycle head pressure is admitted to the ammonia side. This forces the liquid ammonia out into the auxiliary drum, and the warm discharge gas thaws the ice loose. The ice drops from the tubes and a revolving cutter cuts it off in short lengths. By changing the time of the freezing cycle anything from a very thin shell which breaks up into a flake ice, to a solid cylindrical ice cube can be produced.

QUESTIONS

25–1. Work out a system and bill of materials for Fig. 25-21.

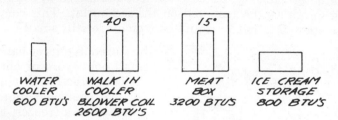

Fig. 25-21. Question 1.

25–2. A 30 ft by 30 ft by 10 ft building with 6 inches of insulation is to be used as an egg collecting station at a location having a design temperature of 105 F. Cooling capacity to handle 800 cases of eggs a day is required.
  a. What is the leakage load?
  b. What is the product load?
  c. What would be the additional load for lights and two work-men
  d. What size ammonia compressor operating at what speed should be chosen?
  e. How many lineal feet of 1½ inch pipe should be used for evaporator surface?

25–3. Work out the size equipment needed for Fig. 25-9. Assume 8 inches of corkboard in the locker room, 5 inches in the aging room, and 5 inches between the two rooms. The refrigerated rooms are protected from sun by other parts of the building. Assume a design temperature of 90 F.

25-4. Briefly describe the can ice making system.

25-5. What other ice making methods are available?

25-6. What is the difference between white ice and clear ice?

25-7. How is this difference obtained in the manufacture of ice?

CHAPTER 26

CARBON DIOXIDE—DRY ICE

Carbon Dioxide Refrigeration.—Until the time the fluorocarbons proved themselves, carbon dioxide was the only available refrigerant that was safe. This led to many installations in hospitals, prisons, passenger ships, and other similar applications. A review of Table 3-1 shows that at 5 F and 86 F, carbon dioxide pressures are 320 psig and 1024 psig. Such pressures require double extra heavy piping throughout. Also compressors, condensers, receivers, etc. must be designed to stand such pressures. Its power per ton is 1.78 hp; 78 percent greater than other common refrigerants. Its critical temperature is 88 F. Therefore, if an adequate amount of low temperature cooling water is not available, carbon dioxide cannot be properly condensed. All these factors have discouraged the installation of new carbon dioxide equipment when compared to fluorocarbon equipment.

Manufacture of Dry Ice.—The manufacture of dry ice requires carbon dioxide refrigeration equipment. Dry ice is carbon dioxide snow compressed under a tremendous pressure into blocks. The triple point of carbon dioxide is 60 psig and —70 F temperature. At any pressure less than 60 psig carbon dioxide cannot exist as a liquid. Any substance which evaporates and melts has such a range. But with most familiar substances, this only happens at a high vacuum. The triple point of water, for instance, is 29.74 in of vacuum. Actually the boiling point of water is reduced to 32 F at this pressure, but the freezing point does not change. Therefore water could not exist as a liquid at a higher vacuum than 29.74 in. It would be either ice or vapor. With carbon dioxide, this triple point is above atmospheric pressure. Therefore at atmospheric pressure it cannot exist as a liquid. Only a dry gas is given off with no liquid to soak into the product being cooled, or to have to be drained from the refrigerated space. The gas given off has low toxicity and is not injurious to commonly stored food products in low concentrations. It should be recognized, however, that carbon dioxide is a heavy gas that will settle into low places or closed rooms and reach a concentration hazardous to life. Thus, care should always be used in entering any place where carbon dioxide may be concentrated, especially because these is no warning odor.

The sources of carbon dioxide to make dry ice are varied. In some places it comes from wells, either in free form or dissolved in water. It is a by product from many chemical processes such as fermentation or burning carbonates. It is present in all flue gases. By building a plant at the location of wells or chemical plants, the cost of the carbon dioxide may be little or nothing. But the temperature of dry ice is such that there is considerable loss if it must be stored for any length of time, or shipped for any great distance. And with the power costs necessary to produce it, it is certainly not cheap after it is in frozen form. Therefore, it is usually as economical to manufacture near its point of ultimate consumption from more expensive sources of carbon dioxide.

An interesting type of plant burns coal, oil, or gas under a boiler. The carbon dioxide in the flue gas is taken to make the dry ice. The steam from the boiler drives the compression equipment necessary to freeze the dry ice.

Where the carbon dioxide comes from wells in pure or nearly pure form, it can be run directly to the compressor. If dissolved in water, heat is all that is needed to separate it. If mixed with flue gases, air, or other contaminating substances, it is dissolved by a caustic solution, then separated from the caustic by heat, Fig. 26-1.

To compress the carbon dioxide from atmospheric pressure to a condensing pressure of about 1000 psig, is a compression ratio of almost 70 to 1. A few cascade systems have been used with ammonia to condense the carbon dioxide and hold its pressure down. What is more commonly used is a three stage carbon dioxide system, Fig. 26-2.

The first stage raises the pressure to about 70 psig, the second to about 300 psig, and the third to full condensing temperature. Between the first and second stages is a purifier and drier. It is placed here instead of ahead of the first stage because the gas is easier to dry and purify at higher pressure. Naturally, there is also an intercooler between each stage to remove the heat of compression. Expansion is also done in three stages. The flash gas formed at each expansion is carried back to the proper compressor stage. In this way one third of the flash gas only need be compressed from 300 psig to 1000 psig, the second third from 70 psig to 1000 psig, and only the remaining third need be compressed through the entire 70 to 1 compression ratio.

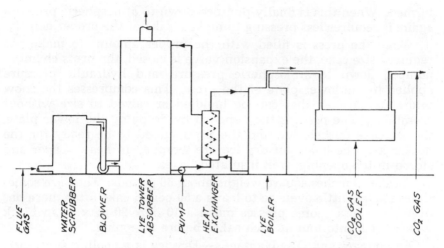

Fig. 26-1. Carbon dioxide absorption equipment.

The low pressure receiver is a storage for the liquid carbon dioxide ready for the snow press. The snowing period is run intermittently. With the press closed, the expansion valve to it is opened. The liquid flows into the press chamber forming flash gas and snow. The pressure in the press gradually rises during this period. Sometimes the press or operating cycle is so designed that the pressure gets above the 60 psig critical, toward the end of the snowing period. Then liquid carbon dioxide flows into the snow already

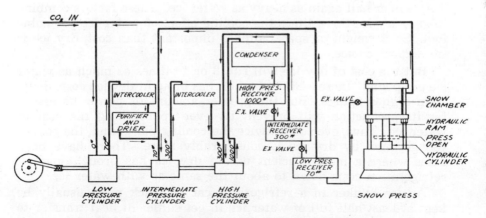

Fig. 26-2. Three stage carbon dioxide compression system.

formed. When this is finally pumped down to atmospheric pressure again, it requires less pressing to make a cake of the proper density.

When the press is filled with the proper amount to make the required size cake, the expansion valve is closed, the press chamber pumped down to atmospheric pressure, and hydraulic pressure applied to the lower plate of the press. This compresses the snow into a dense mass that can be handled or sawed to size without crumbling. The press is then opened by dropping the lower plate, the ice cake pushed out, and the press closed to be ready for the next cake. The blocks of dry ice are wrapped in heavy paper and stored in top opening, well insulated boxes.

A cake 10 inches square weighs about 50 pounds. They are sometimes made a little oversize to leave a 50 pound cake after there has been some loss. Some presses make a 10 in x 20 in x 20 in block which is cut into four 10 inch cakes before wrapping.

Advantages and Disadvantages.—Dry ice is a cooling substance, in some respects similar to water ice and in other respects quite different. Its greatest difference is its temperature. In its own carbon dioxide atmosphere it is 109.4 F below 0 F. In an atmosphere of air it will go below —200 F. This is a decided advantage for keeping things that must be kept frozen, or for producing sub-zero temperatures in small quantities. It can be a disadvantage where freezing the product can damage it, if its cooling effect is not properly regulated or controlled. Its latent heat is 246.3 Btu per lb. If the sublimed gas is allowed to heat up to 32 F before escaping, this will give an additional 28 Btu of cooling effect, or a total of 274.3 Btu. Thus, dry ice has nearly twice the cooling effect per pound of water ice. The density of dry ice runs from 90 to 95 lb per cu ft. This is over half again as heavy as water ice. These factors combine to give dry ice three times the cooling effect of water ice per cubic foot. So if weight or space is more important than cost, dry ice is the logical choice.

But the cost of dry ice will run 8 or 10 times as much as water ice per pound. Increased production has brought dry ice costs down from higher figures. But the greater amount of power necessary for its production will prevent its ever approaching the cost of water ice. Thus, even with twice the cooling per pound, the cost of refrigeration by dry ice is considerably more. There have been cases where a more efficient use of dry ice has brought overall refrigeration costs down to about the same as with water ice.

An ice bunker in a refrigerator car or truck must usually be kept at least half full of water ice to get sufficient heat transfer to maintain temperatures. This means bunkers half full of ice must be wasted at the end of the trip. Also cars can often be loaded heavier and still maintain satisfactory temperatures where dry ice is used. Combining these factors has brought the total refrigeration costs per ton of produce shipped with dry ice down to a figure comparable with that of water ice in some cases. Because of the number of variables, exact comparison is hard to make for a new set of conditions. All factors must be considered, and often test runs made before a dependable comparison can be made.

TABLE 26-1—ICE CREAM PACKING CHART

Based on standard ice cream (average 10 to 12 percent butter fat content) packed at 0 F for summer temperatures (75 F to 100 F) and on 200 lb test single corrugated shipping cartons with double corrugated liners. See variations below for climatic differences.

Outside temperature 0 F to 40 F. Chart amounts, less 30 percent
Outside temperature 50 F to 74 F. Chart amounts, less 10 percent.
Outside temperature 75 F to 100 F. As shown.

Other variations to be considered are consistency and flavor of ice cream; packing temperatures of ice cream above or below zero; care used in sealing cartons; method of handling after packing, and quality of cartons.

| | | Pounds dry ice required to carry package | | | | | | |
		4 hrs	8 hrs	12 hrs	16 hrs	20 hrs	24 hrs	36 hrs
1 qt	top	1	1½	1½	2½	3½	4	6½
	bottom	0	0	½	1	1	2	3
4 qt	top	2	2	2½	3½	4½	6	8
brick	bottom	0	½	1	1	1½	2	2½
8 qt	top	2	3	4	6	7	8	12
brick	center	0	0	0	0	1	1	2
	bottom	1	1	1	2	2½	3½	4½
20 qt	top	3	5	6½	8½	12	15	18
brick	center	1	1	2	2	3	4	5
	bottom	1½	3	3½	4½	5½	7	9
medium	top	1½	3½	5	6½	7½	9½	14
cake	bottom	½	1	1½	2½	3¼	4	6
1 gal	top	2	2	2½	3½	4½	6	8
bulk	bottom	0	½	1	1	1½	2	2½
5 gal	top	3½	5	6½	8	10	12	15
bulk	bottom	1	2	2½	3	4	5	7

—From table, Copyright 1937—Liquid Carbonic Corp.

All molds should be iced top and bottom.

Use of Dry Ice.—A great deal of dry ice is used in shipping small packages or shipments requiring refrigeration. The 10 inch square blocks are usually sawed into one inch thick slabs, then ripped once down the center. This gives a slab 1 in x 5 in x 10 in which weighs approximately 2.5 pounds. This is easily broken into smaller pieces if needed. Flowers or other highly perishable products are shipped in corrugated cardboard cartons with false bottoms and covers to hold the dry ice. It is a natural for shipping ice cream. Table 26-1 gives quantities of dry ice required for ice cream shipments under different conditions.

Fig. 26-3 shows a simple system used to refrigerate both boxes and truck bodies. A refrigerated container suitable for L C L freight shipments is made similar to this. The metal plate on the bottom of the dry ice bunker is designed with the proper area to balance the leakage into the box. Notice there would be little difference in the refrigeration produced by this plate surface whether the bunker is full of dry ice, or only contains enough to keep it covered.

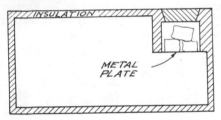

Fig. 26-3. Box or truck body with dry ice bunker.

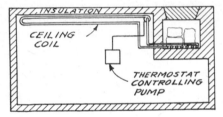

Fig. 26-4. Box or truck body with coil and dry ice bunker.

Fig. 26-4 illustrates a system giving more accurate temperature control. In the bunker is a coil that contains a non-freezing solution such as alcohol or a suitable glycol. This is circulated through a coil in the box or truck body, either by gravity or by a pump. The circulation can be controlled by a thermostat that either controls the flow through a valve or controls the operation of the pump.

QUESTIONS

26-1. Why has carbon dioxide been used as a refrigerant in certain applications in the past?

26-2. What refrigerant has replaced it?

26-3. Explain what dry ice is.

26-4. Under what conditions could dry ice melt to a liquid?

26-5. Describe the manufacturing of dry ice.

26-6. List the advantages and disadvantages of dry ice over water ice.

26-7. Why is dry ice used in spite of being much more expensive than water ice.

26-8. At five cents per lb for dry ice, how much would it cost to pack two gallons of brick ice cream for a 24 hour trip.

CHAPTER 27

ALTITUDE AND ITS EFFECT

OUR studies up to this point have made clear the importance of pressure and its measurement in refrigeration. Gage pressure, which is the difference between atmospheric pressure and the pressure in the system, is the pressure considered by the practical man. Yet much engineering information is given in terms of absolute pressure, the pressure above a perfect vacuum. This is because boiling temperatures are always the same for the same absolute pressure, but this is not always true for gage pressures.

For those whose entire work will be at elevations less than 2000 feet, these variations need not concern them. At elevations above 2000 feet, errors introduced are large enough that they should be taken into account. Certain parts of the United States are well above this elevation, and other parts are near enough to mountain areas that refrigeration men may be called to work on resort, hotel or other equipment at such elevations.

In Chapter 1 it was stated that an absolute pressure could be obtained by adding 14.7 to the gage pressure. This is only true at sea level. The air pressure is approximately 1 inch or ½ psi less for every 1000 rise in elevation. These figures are close enough for practical purposes. Fig. 27-1 compares them with the actual variation. Notice that the error is not more than ¼ psi or ½ inch until above 10,000 feet. This is an elevation above any normal refrigeration job found unless in aircraft.

The greatest effect of altitude is the apparent variation in saturation pressure. Ammonia boils at 5 F at 34.3 psia and 19.6 psig at sea level. At 6000 feet elevation it still boils at 34.3 psia. But atmospheric pressure at 6000 feet is 3 psi less than at sea level, or

$$14.7 - 3 = 11.7 \text{ psi.}$$

Therefore, to get a 5 F evaporator, the low pressure gage would have to show

$$34.3 - 11.7 = 22.6 \text{ psig pressure.}$$

This is 3 psi more than the 19.6 psig at sea level.

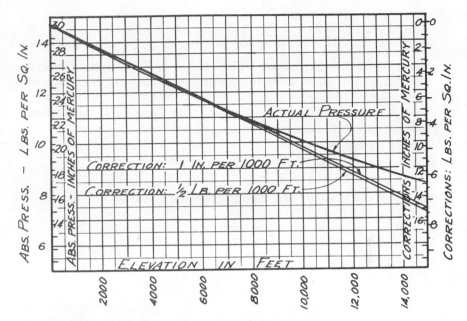

Fig. 27-1. Pressure variations with altitude.

Thus *at an elevation greater than sea level, the correction must be added to the sea level gage pressure,* to get the corresponding temperature. It is important to realize that 22.6 psig at 6000 feet is not a different pressure. The ammonia pressure inside the system is identical to that at sea level. It is the air pressure surrounding the gage that is different, see Fig. 27-2. For the same reason, the condensing pressure at 86 F at 6000 feet would be

154.5 + 3 = 157.5 psig.

Example 27-1.—A Refrigerant 12 system is to have the back pressure control set for 0 F and 25 F at 5000 feet elevation. What are the gage pressure settings?

FIRST METHOD.—A gage pressure table made up for sea level gives pressures of 9.2 psig and 24.6 psig for these temperatures. The corrections at ½ psi per 1000 feet is 2.5 psi. Therefore the required pressures are as follows.

Cut out point: 9.2 + 2.5 = 11.7 psig
Cut in point: 24.6 + 2.5 = 27.1 psig

SECOND METHOD.—An absolute pressure table gives 23.9 psia and 39.3 psia. The atmospheric pressure is

14.7 — 2.5 = 12.2 psi

Therefore the required gage pressures are as follows:
    Cut out point: 23.9 — 12.2 = 11.7 psig
    Cut in point: 39.3 — 12.2 = 27.1 psig

Example 27-2.—Settings of —35 F and —10 F are asked for on a Refrigerant 12 job at 6000 feet of elevation. What are the required gage pressure settings?

FIRST METHOD.—The pressure correction is 3 psi. The table gives gage pressures of 8.3 inches and 4.5 psig at sea level.

The 8.3 inches is —4.1 psi.

Cut out point: —4.1 + 3 = —1.1 psi or 2.2 inches.

Cut in point: 4.5 + 3 = 7.5 psig

SECOND METHOD.—The atmospheric pressure at 6000 feet is
        14.7 — 3 = 11.7 psi

The absolute pressures from the table are 10.6 psia and 19.2 psia.

Cut out point: 10.6 — 11.7 = — 1.1 psi or 2.2 inches

Cut in point: 19.2 — 11.7 = 7.5 psig

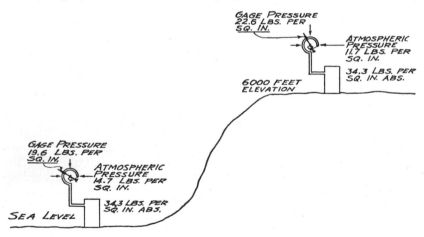

Fig. 27-2. Effect of altitude and air pressure on a pressure gage.

Men working at elevations high enough to make corrections necessary, often make up their own gage pressure tables accurate for that altitude. It is well worth the energy necessary to do this, because each value is figured only once, then a record made of it for future use.

Beside the above changes in gage pressures, altitude also affects equipment with a bellows or diaphragm if reached by air pressure. If such equipment is set to gage pressure readings, the above mentioned corrections are all that are necessary. But some controls have temperature or pressure scales indicated directly on them. Whether a temperature or a pressure control, these will be in error[1]. In Fig. 27-3, notice how the air pressure surrounding the bellows helps compress the bellows. If this air pressure is reduced, the spring pressure opposing the bellows must be increased. Controls with a temperature scale will operate colder than the markings show if not readjusted. Controls known to be adjusted to a certain temperature in factory tests will operate at a lower temperature at an altitude.

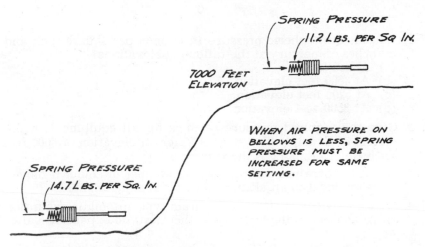

SPRING PRESSURE
11.2 LBS. PER SQ IN.

7000 FEET ELEVATION

WHEN AIR PRESSURE ON BELLOWS IS LESS, SPRING PRESSURE MUST BE INCREASED FOR SAME SETTING.

SPRING PRESSURE
14.7 LBS. PER SQ. IN.

Fig. 27-3. Effect of altitude and air pressure on a bellows.

Automatic expansion valves are also affected by altitude. Again, if set to a correct gage setting, they will operate properly. But this setting will be different than the same valve set at sea level. Notice in Fig. 4-14 and 4-15 how air pressure helps the spring oppose the diaphragm or bellows. Thermostatic expansion valves of the diaphram type have a refrigerant pressure on each side of the diaphram. Therefore air pressure will not affect their setting. But the double bellows type is affected. Such valves with a proper factory adjustment will require readjusting at an elevation.

Constant pressure valves are operated by a bellows or diaphragm, so are affected by altitude. In Chapter 24 it was mentioned that with water coolers, a constant pressure valve is sometimes used as a temperature limiting valve. These valves are factory adjusted to the

---

[1]One manufacturer makes a control which depends on the expansion and contraction of a liquid with temperature changes. Such a control is not affected by altitude.

required setting, then soldered over so the adjustment cannot be changed in the field. Therefore, if such equipment is to be used at an elevation over 2000 feet, this must be specified to get the proper factory setting.

QUESTIONS

27–1. What is atmospheric pressure in pounds per square inch and in inches of mercury at the following elevations?
   (a) At sea level.
   (b) At 3600 feet elevation.
   (c) At 5200 feet elevation.
   (d) At 8500 feet elevation.

27–2. Give the required pressure settings for all equipment in the system of Example 25-1, page 377, for an elevation of 6600 feet with Refrigerant 12 as the refrigerant.

27–3. Will a temperature control operate warmer or colder if moved from sea level to an altitude without readjustment?

27–4. Why does altitude affect a diaphram type automatic expansion valve and not a diaphram type thermostatic expansion valve.

CHAPTER 28

ABSORPTION SYSTEMS

Simple, Intermittent Absorption System.—In the early development of ammonia refrigeration, the absorption system had considerable use. But due to certain difficulties, as the compression system was improved, the absorption system dropped out of the picture. In recent years, improved designs which will work automatically have begun to stage a comeback. One such system uses ammonia and water. Others use water as the refrigerant and a special salt brine as an absorbent.

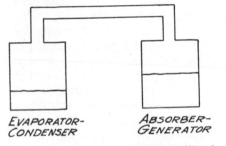

EVAPORATOR-
CONDENSER

ABSORBER-
GENERATOR

Fig. 28-1. An elementary, intermittent absorption system.

In its simplest form, an intermittent absorption system can be made up of two tanks connected with an open pipe, Fig. 28-1. Liquid ammonia is in the left tank and water in the right one. Ammonia vapor is so highly soluble in water that the vapor over the water is absorbed. This lowers the pressure in the right tank which causes more vapor to flow from the connecting tube, which in turn is absorbed. This constant absorption of vapor is just as effective as if it was being removed by the suction side of a compressor. A refrigerating cycle is started with the left tank as an evaporator, and the right tank or absorber taking the place of the compressor. This produces refrigeration in the left tank.

Eventually, the water in the absorber will become saturated with ammonia, and will fail to absorb more vapor. If it is then heated, and the left tank placed in cooling water, the ammonia is distilled from the right tank, and condensed in the left tank. This makes a generator out of the right tank, and a condenser out of the left tank, to complete the refrigerating cycle.

Such a system was once built for domestic use where electric power was not available. The evaporator hung inside an insulated box and produced refrigeration for about 24 hours. Once a day the entire "dumbell" was removed from the box. The evaporator-condenser was placed in a bucket of water and the absorber-generator heated with a special burner supplied with the unit. This recharged it so the system was ready to produce refrigeration for another 24 hours. Such a system was simple, and needed no other source of power. But the quality of refrigeration was poor by present standards.

Other intermittent systems were designed which did not require the removal of the unit from the cabinet. A burner in the unit with a measured amount of kerosene was lighted each day. This charged the unit so it would give approximately 24 hours of cooling.

Continuous Ammonia System.—Fig. 28-2 shows in the simplest form, a continuous absorption refrigeration system. The condenser, receiver, and evaporator are identical to those on compression system. The ammonia vapor from the evaporator is piped to the absorber where it is absorbed by water or weak liquor to form strong liquor. Heat is generated in this absorption process, so a water coil in the absorber keeps the temperature down.

The lower the temperature of the absorber, the more vapor can be absorbed, and the more concentrated the solution of strong liquor can be made. The generator is at high pressure, so a mechanical pump must be used to pump the strong liquor to the generator against this pressure. In the generator, heat is applied, usually by a steam coil. The temperature can be controlled by controlling the steam pressure. The weak liquor is heavier than the strong liquor, so will sink to the bottom. A drain is taken from the bottom of the generator, which returns the weak liquor back to the absorber. It passes through a pressure reducing valve to maintain the difference in pressure between the two chambers. The ammonia vapor distilled from the generator passes to the condenser, which acts just as in the compression system.

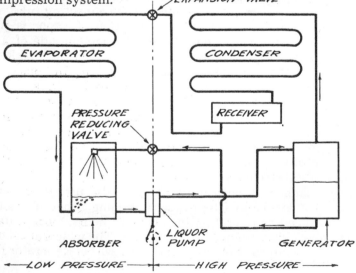

Fig. 28-2. Simplified continuous absorption system.

Fig. 28-6 schematically outlines the absorption cycle beside a compression cycle. Note there are two circulating fluids in the absorption system. From the absorber to the generator, they circulate together. From the generator, they divide, and the water returns to the absorber. The ammonia travels through the rest of the cycle exactly like in the compression system. Thus, the absorber, generator, liquor pump group is just another device to raise low pressure ammonia vapor to a high pressure.

A system such as Fig. 28-2 would operate, but not very economically and not without trouble. Fig. 28-3 is a complete absorption system. Between the absorber and generator is a heat exchanger. This warms the strong liquor before it reaches the generator, so less heat is required at the generator. It cools the weak liquor before it reaches the absorber, so less cooling water is required to bring it

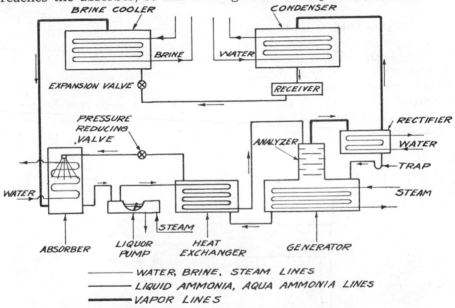

Fig. 28-3. Complete industrial absorption system.

down to a temperature that will absorb a satisfactory amount of ammonia vapor. After leaving the heat exchanger, the strong liquor goes to an analyzer. Here it is of sufficient strength that the hot vapors from the generator separate some of the vapor from it, which saves more heat in the generator. Also, some water vapor is evaporated from the liquor in the generator. The cooler strong liquor entering the analyzer condenses some of this water vapor and carries it back to the generator. Any additional water vapor in the ammonia vapor is condensed out in the rectifier. This must be kept under close control to return practically all the water vapor without condensing and returning liquid refrigerant to the generator. From here on, the system is identical to a compression system.

The industrial ammonia absorption system has been applied to large jobs of 600 to 1000 or more tons capacity. This system works best at comparatively steady loads. The only mechanically rotating or moving parts are circulating pumps. The rest of the system is made up of pipes and tank shells, so can go either outdoors or indoors.

This type of absorption system particularly fits applications where steam is a cheaper source of energy than mechanical power. It usually does not pay to install boilers for no other purpose than to operate an absorption system. But where boilers must be installed for other processes; where the refrigeration loads are steady; and where fuel is cheap, they have found some use. Some oil companies favor the absorption system in their refinery operations requiring refrigeration.

Water Absorption System.—An intermittent system such as Fig. 28-1 would also work with water in the evaporator-condenser and a strong salt brine in the absorber-generator. The brine would absorb the water vapor, and produce cooling in the evaporator. Heating the generator-absorber, and cooling the evaporator-condenser would drive the water back for reuse. Of course the system would have to work at refrigeration temperatures above 32 F. And it would work at a high vacuum, see Fig. 3-1.

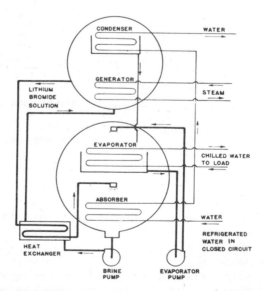

Fig. 28-4. Lithium bromide-water absorption system

Continuous systems of the same principle as Fig. 28-2 using water and salt have been developed. One design places the evaporator and absorber in a single chamber, and the condenser and generator in a second chamber, Fig. 28-4. These chambers or tanks, with the necessary pumps and a purge unit, are mounted as a single assembly. Lithium bromide is the salt used. It is a simple system with only pumps requiring mechanical power. It is vibration free and makes very little noise. It may be mounted indoors or out. Such have been installed on the roof of office buildings.

This system does require a source of steam for power. It will use from 17 to 20 pounds of steam per hour per ton, depending on conditions. A boiler may be used all year around, for heating in the winter and cooling in the summer. Thus more use is made of boiler investment.

The system is used particularly for air conditioning applications. But it can be used anywhere a large amount of chilled water is required. It is made in sizes from 100 to over 700 tons capacity.

A smaller, direct gas fired system has also been designed for domestic applications. It works on the same general principle as the above system. It is assembled with a gas furnace to give both summer and winter conditioning from the same unit.

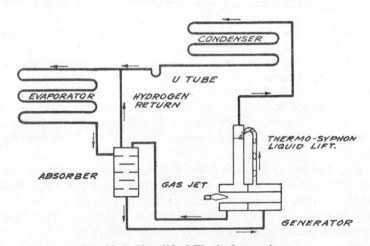

Fig. 28-5. Simplified Electrolux system.

The Diffusion-Absorption System.—An interesting modification of the absorption system eliminates the need of a mechanical pump. It is sometimes called a diffusion-absorption system. A simplified diagram of this system is shown in Fig. 28-5. Instead of an expansion valve there is a U tube filled with liquid ammonia. On the condenser side of the U tube is the ammonia condenser pressure, usually 200 psig or higher with an air cooled condenser. On the evaporator side, this pressure is balanced by a hydrogen pressure, so there is the same total pressure on each side of the U tube. Thus, any liquid condensed flows into the U tube and out into the evaporator. But the liquid filled U tube prevents the hydrogen from backing up into the condenser.

The liquid ammonia in an atmosphere of hydrogen will evaporate and cause cooling just as water can evaporate in an atmosphere of air. The ammonia gas diffuses into the hydrogen, thus the name diffusion-absorption.

The evaporating temperature of the ammonia depends on the partial pressure of the ammonia vapor which mixes with the hydrogen as it evaporates. The evaporated ammonia mixed with the hydrogen flows to the absorber. Here, the ammonia gas is soluble in water but the hydrogen is not. Therefore the ammonia is dissolved leaving almost pure hydrogen. Hydrogen is a much lighter gas than ammonia. Therefore, the column of hydrogen is lighter than the column of ammonia and hydrogen. This causes the hydrogen to rise to the top of the evaporator as the heavier mixture of the two gases settles from the evaporator to the absorber.

The generator is made in two sections. The first section is the lowest point and the second is the highest point containing liquid in the system. The liquor is lifted from the first to the second section by the heat and boiling action through the thermo-syphon. It works exactly like the coffee in a coffee percolator. From the second section of the generator, the liquid flows to the absorber, over the absorber plates, then back to the first section of the generator by gravity. Since there is no difference in total pressure, a pump and reducing valve is not necessary. The hydrogen from the absorber cannot get over to the generator because all lines are filled with liquid.

Fig. 28-6 compares the flow of the compressor system, absorption, and diffusion-absorption system. Where the simple absorption system has two fluids, the diffusion-absorption has three. The absorber is the only place where all three fluids are together. The hydrogen is present in what would normally be the low side.

The rate of cooling of this system is controlled by the rate of circulation. This is controlled by the amount of heat applied to the generator. Heat is usually applied by a gas burner. The temperature control operates by throttling the gas flowing to the burner. This is set to a minimum which prevents it from getting so low there is danger of going out. Thus, it acts as its own pilot light. A thermostatic safety control is included which prevents the gas valve from opening if the blaze should go out. For anything other than the minimum setting, an increase in cooling requirements is transferred by a diaphragm to open the gas valve wider. Thus, the system works by increasing or decreasing a steady production of refrigeration, rather than by cycling as a compression system does.

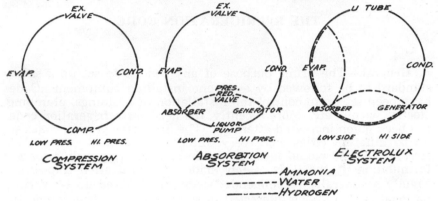

Fig. 28-6. Different refrigeration cycles.

QUESTIONS

28-1. Why is ammonia used as the refrigerant even in domestic equipment with the absorption system?

28-2. How is ammonia vapor removed from the evaporator in the absorption system?

28-3. What is the difference between the intermittent and the continuous absorption system?

28-4. What parts of the absorption cycle are identical to the compression cycle?

28-5. What parts of the absorption cycle are different from the compression cycle?

28-6. Why are not more absorption systems used at the present time in larger than domestic equipment?

28-7. What takes the place of the expansion valve in the diffusion-absorption system?

28-8. What is the purpose of the hydrogen in the Electrolux system?

28-9. What is the relationship between Dalton's Law of Partial Pressures and the diffusion-absorption system?

28-10. What are the advantages and disadvantages of the water-lithium bromide absorption system?

CHAPTER 29

THE REFRIGERATION CODE

General.—The prime purpose of any code is to set up a safety standard to be followed by everyone installing equipment. Codes have been set up to control the installation of buildings, plumbing, electric wiring, etc. More recently, the need for refrigeration codes has been given increased attention. The first refrigeration codes set up by different cities were very different from each other. Each stressed the individual ideas of the individuals responsible for the formulation of the code. Such made standardization impossible. Finally a generally recommended code was worked up by various national organizations interested in safety and in refrigeration, the American Standard Safety Code for Mechanical Refrigeration. It has been classified by the American Standards Association as ASA B9. It has been revised from time to time as needed and the number usually carries the date of the last revision, such as ASA B9-53.

This code is not a national law enforced throughout the country, but a model for cities setting up their own codes. It should bear the same relationship to the refrigeration industry as the National Electric Code has to the electric industry. It has been adopted by many cities. Some have adopted part of it, but kept part of their old code along with it. Some states have tied it in with contracting or licensing laws.

For any who are not working under the jurisdiction of the code it should be considered a minimum good practice guide. For all, it should be recognized as a minimum acceptable standard of quality. To brag that a job is "according to code" is to state that it is the least acceptable quality that will get by.

It is highly recommended that everyone in the refrigeration industry push for general adoption of this code. First, a good code does not hurt the legitimate refrigeration contractor. But it does protect him and the customer against price cutting jobs in which more or less essential equipment is omitted to meet cost limits.

This particular code should be adopted for two reasons. First, it is a code worked out by committees of experts from all branches of the field. Therefore, it is a much better code than could possibly be worked out by one man. Also a code so worked up is protection against individual preferences or prejudices. Such preferences or prejudices are often honestly believed by single individuals who might be instrumental in working up a new code. Such are probably more common in refrigeration than in older and better established industries or trades where traditions of custom or good practice have been built up.

The second reason for adopting the code is to make it standard throughout the country. Certainly what is safe in one city is safe in another. If this is the case there is no reason for making a workman memorize a separate set of rules every time he moves from one city to another. This can be particularly troublesome and sometimes costly where one organization does business in several cities grouped together.

The latest copy of the complete code may be secured from the American Society of Heating, Refrigerating and Air-Conditioning Engineers (ASHRAE), 345 E. 47th St., New York 17, N.Y. Every refrigerating engineer should have a copy of this code and familiarize himself with it. The questions in this chapter will assist him in his study of the code.

QUESTIONS

29-1. What are the properties of Group 1 refrigerants?

29-2. What are the properties of Group 2 refrigerants?

29-3. What are the properties of Group 3 refrigerants?

29-4. In which group do each of the common refrigerants belong?

29-5. When are Group 1 refrigerants except carbon dioxide considered as belonging to Group 2?

29-6. Are flames from matches and cigarette lighters considered open flames?

29-7. What is an Institutional Occupancy? Give examples.

29-8. What is a Commercial Occupancy? Give examples.

29-9. What is a Residential Occupancy? Give examples.

29-10. What is a Public Assembly Occupancy? Give examples.

29-11. What is the difference between an ordinary machinery room and a Class T machinery room?

29-12. What is the difference between a direct and an indirect refrigeration system?

29-13. What is the largest size flare connections permissible?

29-14. According to the code, what is the difference between brazing and soldering?

29-15. Where are stop valves required on systems having from 50 to 100 pounds of Group 1 refrigerant; 6 to 100 pounds of other refrigerant?

29-16. Where are stop valves required on systems having 100 pounds or more of refrigerant?

29-17. What valves should be labeled?

29-18. What is a pressure relief device?

29-19. What is a pressure limiting device?

29-20. What containers require a pressure relief device?

29-21. Where may a fusible plug be substituted for a pressure relief device?

29-22. What compressors require a pressure relief device?

29-23. At what pressure shall pressure relief devices be set?

29-24. May pressure relief devices be set in the field?

29-25. What relief devices shall be piped to discharge outside the building?

29-26. On what air cooled jobs shall pressure limiting devices be used?

29-27. On what water cooled jobs shall pressure limiting devices be used?

29-28. At what pressure shall pressure limiting devices be set?

APPENDIX

The following pages contain helpful tables, references, explanations, including the refrigerant tables—all collected in one section for ready reference.

For the refrigerant charts and the charts on refrigerant flow in tubes and pipes, see cover pocket.

Complete tables and Mollier diagrams not found in this book are available in the "Data Book, Design Volume" published by the American Society of Heating, Refrigerating and Air-Conditioning Engineers. Or tables and charts for individual refrigerants are available from manufacturers and suppliers.

TABLE A-1—WEIGHTS AND SPECIFIC HEATS OF VARIOUS SUBSTANCES

Material	Weight lbs. per cu. ft.	Specific Heat Btu per lb.
Air (At 70 F)	0.075	0.24
Alcohol	49.6	0.60
Aluminum	166.5	0.214
Bakelite	86.0	0.35
Brass	511 to 536	0.094
Bronze	531 to 538	0.090
Copper	552	0.094
Concrete	147	0.19
Cork	15	0.48
Glass (Common)	164	0.199
Glycerine		0.576
Ice	57.5	0.504
Iron	480	0.118
Lead	710	0.030
Masonry (Brick)	112	0.200
Mercury	847	0.033
Oil (Machine)	57.5	0.400
Paper (Cardboard)	58	0.324
Rubber	59	0.48
Sand	100	0.195
Steel	492	0.117
Stone	135 to 200	0.20
Tar	75	0.35
Water	62.4	1.000
Wood		
Fir	37	0.65
Oak	48	0.57
Pine	38	0.47
Zinc	446	0.096

TABLE A-2—PROPERTIES OF FOOD PRODUCTS

Commodity	Water Content Percent	Specific Heat Above Freezing Btu/lb.	Specific Heat Below Freezing Btu/lb.	Freezing Temp. F	Latent Heat Btu/lb.	Storage Temp. F	Storage Humidity Percent	Storage Life
FRUITS								
Apples	84	.92	.39	28.4	120	30-32	85-88	2 to 7 mo
Apricots	85	.92	.46	28.1	122	31-32	80-85	1 to 2 wk
Avocados	65-82	.91	.49	27.2	136	40-55	85-90	4 to 8 wk
Bananas	75	.80	.43	26-30	108	56-60	90	7 to 10 da
Blackberries	85	.92	.46	28.9	124	31-32	80-85	7 to 10 da
Cherries	83	.85	.45	24-28	118	31-32	80-85	10 to 14 da
Cranberries	88	.91	.47	27.3	128	36-40	85-90	1 to 3 mo
Currants	85			30.2	123	32	80-85	10 to 14 da
Dewberries	85	.92	.46	29.2	124	31-32	80-85	7 to 10 da
Dried Fruits	15-30		.29-.47	21-32	21 to 43	26-32	70-75	9 to 12 mo
Figs, Dry	24	.47	.32		43	40-45	65-75	9 to 12 mo
Figs, Fresh	78	.88	.48	27.1	116	28-32	65-75	5 to 7 da
Gooseberries	88	.92	.47	28.9	130	31-32	80-85	3 to 4 wk
Grapefruit	89	.92	.49	28.4	128	32-55	85-90	6 to 8 wk
Grapes	82	.92	.37	27.5	83	31-32	80-85	3 to 8 wk
Lemons	89	.91	.39	28.1	126	55-58	85-90	1 to 4 wk
Limes	86	.91	.49	29.3	126	45-48	85-90	6 to 8 wk
Melons Casaba, Persian						36-40		4 to 6 wk
Honey Dew, Honey Ball				29.0		36-38	75-85	2 to 4 wk
Muskmelons	81	.92	.34	29.0	128	32-34	75-85	7 to 10 da
Watermelons	92	.92	.47	29.2	135	36-40	75-85	2 to 3 wk
Nuts, Dried	3-6	.21-.29	.19-.24	19-24	4 to 14	32-50	65-75	8 to 12 mo
Olives, Fresh	75			28.5		45-50	85-90	4 to 6 wk

TABLE A-2—PROPERTIES OF FOOD PRODUCTS—CONTINUED

Commodity	Water Content Percent	Specific Heat — Above Freezing Btu/lb.	Specific Heat — Below Freezing Btu/lb.	Freezing Temp. F	Latent Heat Btu/lb.	Storage Temp. F	Storage Humidity Percent	Storage Life
Oranges	87	.89	.39	28.0	125	34–38	85–90	8 to 10 wk
Peaches	87	.92	.42	29.4	106	31–32	80–85	2 to 4 wk
Pears								
Bartlett	83	.90	.43	28.5	109	29–31	85–90	1 to 3 mo
Fall and Winter	82	.90	.43	27–28	108	29–31	85–90	2 to 7 mo
Persimmons	78	.80	.46	28.3	96	31–32	85–90	2 to 3 wk
Pineapples								
Mature Green	85–89	.90	.46	29.1	128	50–60	85–90	3 to 4 wk
Ripe				29.9		40–45	85–90	2 to 4 wk
Plums } Fresh Prunes	78	.83		28.0		31–32	80–85	3 to 8 wk
Quinces	85			28.1		31–32	80–85	2 to 3 mo
Raisins						40–45	50–60	9 to 12 mo
Raspberries	82–86	.89		30.0		31–32	80–85	7 to 10 da
Strawberries	90	.92		29.9		31–32	80–85	7 to 10 da
VEGETABLES								
Artichokes								
Globe	84	.90	.49	29.1	134	31–32	90–95	1 to 2 wk
Jerusalem	79			27.5		31–32	90–95	2 to 5 mo
Asparagus	93	.95	.48	29.8	134	32	85–90	3 to 4 wk
Beans, Dried	12	.30	.24		17	32–36	75	
Beans, Green	89	.91	.47	29.7	128	32–40	85–90	2 to 4 wk
Beans, Lima	66	.89	.41	30.1	100	32–40	85–90	2 to 4 wk
Beets, Bunched	88					32	85–90	10 to 14 da
Beets, Topped	90	.90	.48	26.9	129	32	95–98	1 to 3 mo
Broccoli		.93	.48	29.2	135	32–35	90–95	7 to 10 da
Brussels Sprouts	85	.91	.49	31.0	136	32–35	90–95	3 to 4 wk

Table A-2—Properties of Food Products—Continued

Commodity	Water Content Percent	Specific Heat Above Freezing Btu/lb.	Specific Heat Below Freezing Btu/lb.	Freezing Temp. F	Latent Heat Btu/lb.	Storage Temp. F	Storage Humidity Percent	Storage Life
Cabbage	92	.93	.47	31.2	131	32	90–95	3 to 4 mo
Carrots								
Bunched	88	.87	.45	29.6	119	32	85–90	10 to 14 da
Topped	93	.94	.48	30.1		32	95–98	4 to 5 mo
Cauliflower	94	.95	.48	29.7	135	32	85–90	2 to 3 wk
Celery	74	.80	.43	28.9ᵉ	108	31–32	90–95	2 to 4 mo
Corn, Green	95	.93	.48	30.5	137	31–32	90–95	1 to 2 wk
Cucumbers	93	.91	.45	30.4	132	45–50	80–85	10 to 14 da
Eggplant	74			25.4		45–50	85–90	7 to 10 da
Garlic, Dry	74			26.4		32	70–75	6 to 8 mo
Horseradish	73			30.0		32	95–98	10 to 12 mo
Kohlrabi	90			29.2		32	85–90	2 to 4 wk
Leek, Green	88					32	85–90	1 to 3 mo
Lettuce	94	.95	.48	31.2	135	32	90–95	2 to 3 wk
Mushrooms	91	.90	.47	30.2	126	32–35	80–85	2 to 3 da
Onions	88	.91	.46	30.1	126	32	70–75	6 to 8 mo
Parsnips	79	.86	.45	28.9	119	32	90–95	2 to 4 mo
Peas, Green	74	.85	.42	30.0	107	32	85–90	1 to 2 wk
Peppers, Green	92	.90	.46	30.1		32	85–90	4 to 6 wk
Peppers, Chili						32–50	50–75	6 to 9 mo
Potatoes	79	.79	.42	28.9	106	38–50	85–90	5 to 12 mo
Pumpkins } Squash	90	.90	.43	29–30	127	50–55	70–75	2 to 6 mo
Radishes	91	.90	.48	28.4	132	32	95–98	2 to 4 mo
Rhubarb	95	.90	.46	29.5	134	32	90–95	2 to 3 wk
Rutabagas	89					32	95–98	2 to 4 mo
Spinach	93	.92	.51	30.3	129	32	90–95	10 to 14 da
Sweet Potatoes	78	.86	.42	28.5	102	55–60	75–80	4 to 6 mo
Tomatoes								
Mature Green	95	.92	.46	30.4	132	55–70	85–90	3 to 5 wk
Ripe	94	.92	.46	30.4	132	50	85–90	7 to 10 da
Turnips	91	.90	.45	30.5	128	32	95–98	4 to 5 mo

TABLE A-2—PROPERTIES OF FOOD PRODUCTS—CONTINUED

MEATS & FISH							
Beef	62–77	.77	28–29	98	32–40	88–92	1 to 6 wk
Fish, Fresh	65–83	.82	28	101	33–40	90–95	5 to 20 da
Fish, Dried	45	.56		65	23–25	70–75	2 to 4 mo
Fish, Smoked					23–25	70–75	2 to 4 mo
Fish, Brined					26–28	85	2 to 6 mo
Lamb	60–70	.66	28–29	83	32–34	85–90	5 to 12 da
Poultry	60–65	.80	27	86	32	80	1 wk
Pork, Fresh	35–46	.51–.68	28–29	86	32–34	85–90	3 to 7 da
Pork, Cured } Ham, Bacon, Etc.	20	.50	27	116	32–40	70–80	2 to 4 mo
Oysters, Shell	80	.84	27	125	33–35	90	30 to 60 da
Oysters, Tub	87	.90			32	90	10 to 15 da
Rabbits					32–34	90–95	1 to 5 da
Veal	70–80	.70	28–29		32–34	90–95	5 to 10 da
DAIRY PRODUCTS							
Butter	10	.64	30–0	15	See below	65–70	10–12 da
Cheese	35–38	.64	4–18	86	32–34		
Cream	59	.87	28	84	30–33	85–90	8–10 mo
Eggs	68–73	.76	28	100	29–31		
Ice Cream	67	.80	28	96			
Milk	87	.92	31	124	36–38		

FROZEN FOOD STORAGE

Commodity	Storage Temperature, F.	Storage Life
Fruits	0 or Below	12 month plus
Vegetables	0 or Below	12 month plus
Meats	0 or Below	6 to 8 month
Poultry	−10 or Below	12 month
Fish	0 or Below	12 month
Butter	0 or Below	8 to 12 month
Eggs	0 or Below	12 month plus

TABLE A-3—SIZES AND WEIGHTS OF FOOD CONTAINERS

Commodity	Container	Size in Inches			Approximate Weight in Lb.		Minimum Car Lb.	Notes
		Depth	Width	Length	Gross	Tare		
FRUITS								
Apples	Box	10½	11½	19¾	49	5½		
Apricots	Flat Box	5	16	17½	24	3		
	Lug Box	8	14½	23	55	5		
Bananas	Bunch				50		21,000	
Berries	Barrel				500		60,000	Frozen
Cherries	Flat Box	2¾	9	19¾	11	1		
	Lug Box	8	14½	23	55	5		
Grapes	Flat Box	5¾	13½	17½	33	4	34,255	
	Single Flat	5	16	17½	28	3		
Grapefruit	Std. Box	11½	11½	24	68	4	35,112	
Lemons	Std. Box	10	13	25	84	4		
	No. 2 Jumbo	11⅛	13½	25	92	4½		
Melons								
Cantaloup	Flat Box	4½	13½	23½	28	3		
	Std. Box	12	12	23½	68	5		
	Jumbo	15	14	23½	32	4		
	Jumbo	13	13	23½	78	7		
Honey Dew	Flat Box	5¾	14½	23½	35	3½		
	Std. Box	6½	16¼	23½	40	4		
	Jumbo	7½	16¼	23½	45	4½		
Oranges	Std. Box	11½	11½	24	78	7	48,195	
	No. 2 Jumbo	11½	12½	24	82	7½		
Peaches	Flat Box	5	11½	19½	21½	3	29,400	
	Lug Box	8	14½	23	55	5		
Pears	Std. Box	9	11½	19¾	50	4	37,200	
Plums	Flat Box	5	16	17½	46	4	27,500	

VEGETABLES								
Broccoli	Crate	8½	16	24	48	6		
Carrots	Crate	13	18	24½	122	8	31,494	Gross wt. includes 30 lb ice
Cauliflower	Crate	8½	16	24	48	6	21,504	
Celery	Crate	20	20¼	24¾	140	13		
Lettuce	Crate	13	18	23⅛	92	8	23.712	Gross wt. includes 30 lb ice
Onions	Sack				50		30,300	
Peas	Crate	10	18	24½	88	7	22,400	
	Pony Crate	8½	18	24½	62	6½		Gross wt. includes 30 lb ice
Potatoes	Sack				101		36,360	
Rutabagas	Sack				50½		36,360	
Tomatoes	Box	6½	13½	17½	34	4		

Commodity	Container	Contents	Size Dia. or Width Inches	Height Inches	Approx. Weight of Container Lb. unless Otherwise Noted	Notes
DAIRY PRODUCTS						
Milk	Can	10 gal.	13	25	26	Milk weighs 8.6 lb per gal
	Can	5 gal.	10½	19½	15	
	Can	3 gal.	9	19½	5	
	Bottle	1 qt.	4	9½	1½	
	Bottle	1 pt.	3¼	8½	1	
	Bottle	½ pt.	2¾	6¾		
	Carton	1 qt.	2¾	8 or 9	3 oz.	
	Carton	1 pt.	2¼	6½		Square top
			2¾	5½	1 oz.	Pinch top
	Carton	½ pt.	2¼	3½	¾ oz.	

TABLE A-3—SIZES AND WEIGHTS OF FOOD CONTAINERS—CONTINUED

Commodity	Container	Contents	Depth	Width	Length		Notes
Milk	Case	12 qt.	10¾	14	18½	16	
	Case	20 pt.	9	14½	18½	14	
	Case	30½ pt.	6¾	14½	18½	11	
				Dia.	Height		
Ice Cream	Can	5 gal.		9	21½	12	
	Can	2½		9	11	7	
	Carton	5 gal.		9	19	1¾	
		2½		9	10	1	
			Depth	Width	Length		
Eggs	Crates	30 doz.	12	13½	25½	8½	Net wt of eggs 42 to 44 lb 400 Crates to a carload.
	Cartons	15 doz.	12	12	13	1½	

Approximate Weights

Commodity	Minimum	Maximum	Average	Notes
MEAT				
Beef	400	1000	500	Handled in halves
Lamb	20	120	40	
Pork	90	450	180	
Veal	70	275	150	

TABLE A-4—ENERGY CONVERSION EQUIVALENTS

1 Horsepower	=	33000 ft lb per min
	=	550 ft lb per sec
	=	746 watts
	=	2545 Btu per hr
	=	42.42 Btu per min
1 Horsepower-hour	=	1 horsepower for 1 hour
	=	746 watt-hours
	=	0.746 kilowatt-hours
	=	2545 Btu
1 kilowatt	=	1000 watts
	=	1.34 horsepower
1 kilowatt-hour	=	1 kilowatt for 1 hour
	=	1000 watt-hours
	=	1.34 horsepower-hours
	=	3415 Btu
1 Btu.	=	778 ft. lbs.
1 ton of refrigeration	=	288000 Btu. per day
	=	12000 Btu. per hr
	=	200 Btu. per min
	=	83.3 lb IME

TABLE A-5—PRESSURE RATIOS

1 psi	=	0.068 atmospheres
	=	2.04 inches of mercury
	=	2.31 feet of water
	=	27.7 inches of water
1 oz per sq in.	=	0.128 inches of mercury
	=	1.73 inches of water
1 inch of mercury	=	0.0334 atmospheres
	=	0.491 psi
	=	1.13 feet of water
	=	13.6 inches of water
1 foot of water	=	0.0295 atmospheres
	=	0.433 psi
	=	62.4 lb per sq ft
	=	0.883 inches of mercury
1 atmosphere	=	29.92 inches of mercury
	=	33.94 feet of water
	=	14.696 psi

TABLE A-6. WEIGHTS AND MEASURES

WEIGHTS	LINEAR MEASURE
7000 grains equals 1 pound	12 inches equals 1 foot
16 ounces equals 1 pound	3 feet equals 1 yard
2000 pounds equals 1 ton	2.54 centimeters equals 1 inch
2.2 pounds equals 1 kilogram	

SQUARE MEASURE (FOR MEASURING AREAS)

144 square inches equals 1 square foot
9 square feet equals 1 square yard

Area of a rectangle equals length times width
$A = LW$

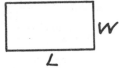

Area of a triangle equals half the base times height
$$A = \frac{BH}{2}$$

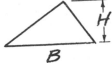

Area of a trapazoid equals average length times height
$$A = \frac{ab}{2} H$$

 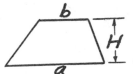

Area of a circle equals 3.1416 times radius squared or .7854 times diameter squared
$$A = \pi R^2$$
$$= .7854 \, D^2$$

CUBIC MEASURE (FOR MEASURING VOLUMES)

1728 cubic inches equals 1 cubic foot
27 cubic feet equals 1 cubic yard

Volume of rectangular solid equals length times width times height.
$V = LWH$

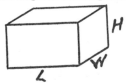

Volume of cylinder equals 3.1416 times radius squared times height or .7854 times diameter squared times height
$$V = \pi R^2 H$$
$$= .7854 \, D^2 H$$

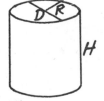

TABLE A-6. WEIGHTS AND MEASURES—Continued

LIQUID MEASURE	REFRIGERATION MEASURE
(FOR MEASURING VOLUME OF LIQUID)	

LIQUID MEASURE
(FOR MEASURING VOLUME OF LIQUID)

16 ounces equals 1 pint
2 pints equals 1 quart
32 ounces equals 1 quart
4 quarts equals 1 gallon
8 pints equals 1 gallon
231 cubic inches equals 1 gallon
7.48 gallons equals 1 cubic foot
8.34 pounds of water equals 1 gallon

REFRIGERATION MEASURE

200 Btu per minute equals 1 ton of refrigeration
12,000 Btu per hour equals 1 ton of refrigeration
288,000 Btu per day equals 1 ton of refrigeration

Table A-7—Soft Drawn Copper Tubing

Outside Diam.	Wall Thickness	Inside Diam.	Weight lb per ft	Length Per sq ft External Surface	Sectional area Internal		External Sq In	Contents per lineal ft in Cu Ft
					Sq In	Sq Ft		
3/16¹	.035	.1175	.065	20.6	.0108	.0000750	.0276	.0000750
1/4	.035	.180	.0916	15.3	.0254	.000176	.0491	.000176
5/16¹	.035	.2425	.118	12.2	.0462	.000321	.0767	.000321
3/8	.035	.305	.145	10.2	.0731	.000508	.110	.000508
1/2	.035	.430	.198	7.64	.1452	.00101	.196	.00101
5/8	.035	.555	.251	6.11	.242	.00168	.307	.00168
3/4	.035	.680	.305	5.10	.363	.00252	.442	.00252

¹These sizes used on some domestic units, but not commercial jobs.

Type K Copper Tube (For Working Pressures up to 400 lb per sq in)

Outside Diam.	Wall Thickness	Inside Diam.	Weight lb per ft	Length Per sq ft External Surface	Sectional area Internal		External Sq In	Contents per lineal ft in Cu Ft
					Sq In	Sq Ft		
3/8	.032	.311	.134	10.2	.076	.000527	.110	.000527
1/2	.049	.402	.269	7.64	.127	.000882	.196	.000882
5/8	.049	.527	.344	6.11	.218	.001514	.307	.001514
3/4	.049	.652	.418	5.10	.334	.00232	.442	.00232
7/8	.065	.745	.641	4.37	.436	.00303	.601	.00303
1 1/8	.065	.995	.839	3.40	.778	.00540	.994	.00540
1 3/8	.065	1.245	1.04	2.78	1.217	.00845	1.485	.00845
1 5/8	.072	1.481	1.36	2.35	1.722	.01195	2.07	.01195
2 1/8	.083	1.959	2.06	1.80	3.014	.0209	3.55	.0209
2 5/8	.095	2.435	2.93	1.46	4.656	.0323	5.41	.0323
3 1/8	.109	2.907	4.00	1.22	6.637	.0471	7.67	.0471
3 5/8	.120	3.385	5.12	1.05	9.00	.0625	10.32	.0625
4 1/8	.134	3.857	6.51	.927	11.68	.0811	13.36	.0811
5 1/8	.160	4.805	9.67	.746	18.13	.1259	20.63	.1259
6 1/8	.192	5.741	13.87	.625	25.9	.1795	29.5	.1795
8 1/8	.271	7.583	25.92	.470	45.2	.313	51.8	.313
10 1/8	.338	9.449	40.28	.387	70.1	.487	80.5	.487
12 1/8	.405	11.315	57.80	.316	100.5	.698	115.5	.698

TYPE L COPPER TUBE (For Working Pressures up to 300 lb per sq in)

Size								
3/8	.030	.315	.126	10.2	.078	.00054	.110	.00054
1/2	.035	.430	.198	7.64	.146	.00101	.196	.00101
5/8	.040	.545	.285	6.11	.233	.00162	.307	.00162
3/4	.042	.666	.362	5.10	.348	.00242	.442	.00242
7/8	.045	.785	.455	4.37	.484	.00336	.601	.00336
1 1/8	.050	1.025	.655	3.40	.825	.00572	.994	.00572
1 3/8	.055	1.265	.884	2.78	1.256	.00872	1.485	.00872
1 5/8	.060	1.505	1.14	2.35	1.78	.01235	2.07	.01235
2 1/8	.070	1.985	1.75	1.80	3.09	.0215	3.55	.0215
2 5/8	.080	2.465	2.48	1.46	4.77	.0331	5.41	.0331
3 1/8	.090	2.945	3.33	1.22	6.81	.0473	7.67	.0473
3 5/8	.100	3.425	4.29	1.05	9.21	.0640	10.32	.0640
4 1/8	.110	3.905	5.38	.927	11.97	.0831	13.36	.0831
5 1/8	.125	4.875	7.61	.746	18.67	.1295	20.63	.1295
6 1/8	.140	5.845	10.20	.625	26.83	.1862	29.46	.1862
8 1/8	.200	7.725	19.30	.470	46.87	.325	51.85	.325
10 1/8	.250	9.625	30.06	.387	72.76	.505	80.52	.505
12 1/8	.280	11.56	40.39	.316	105.0	.729	115.5	.729

TYPE M (For Working Pressures up to 250 lbs per sq in)

Size								
3/8	.025	.325	.107	10.2	.083	.000576	.110	.000576
1/2	.025	.450	.145	7.64	.159	.00110	.196	.00110
5/8	.028	.569	.204	6.11	.254	.00176	.307	.00176
3/4	.030	.690	.263	5.10	.374	.00260	.442	.00260
7/8	.032	.811	.328	4.37	.516	.00359	.601	.00359
1 1/8	.035	1.055	.465	3.40	.874	.00606	.994	.00606
1 3/8	.042	1.291	.682	2.78	1.309	.00908	1.485	.00908
1 5/8	.049	1.527	.940	2.35	1.831	.0127	2.07	.0127
2 1/8	.058	2.009	1.46	1.80	3.17	.0220	3.55	.0220
2 5/8	.065	2.495	2.03	1.46	4.89	.0339	5.41	.0339
3 1/8	.072	2.981	2.68	1.22	6.98	.0484	7.67	.0484
3 5/8	.083	3.459	3.58	1.05	9.40	.0652	10.32	.0652
4 1/8	.095	3.935	4.66	.927	12.16	.0868	13.36	.0868
5 1/8	.109	4.907	6.66	.746	18.91	.1313	20.63	.1313
6 1/8	.122	5.881	8.92	.625	27.16	.1885	29.46	.1885
8 1/8	.170	7.785	16.47	.470	47.6	.330	51.85	.330
10 1/8	.212	9.701	25.59	.387	73.9	.513	80.52	.513
12 1/8	.254	11.617	36.72	.316	105.6	.733	115.5	.743

TABLE A-8—DIMENSIONS OF STANDARD WEIGHT IRON PIPE

Size Inches	Diameters		Nominal Weight Per Ft Plain Ends lb	Length Per sq ft External Surface, Feet	Sectional Area Internal		Contents of Pipe per Lineal Foot	
	Exter. Inches	Approx. Inter. Inches			Square Inch	Square Feet	Gal.	Cu ft
1/8	.405	.269	.244	9.431	.056	.0004	.003	.0004
1/4	.540	.364	.424	7.073	.102	.0007	.005	.0007
3/8	.675	.493	.567	5.658	.191	.0013	.010	.0013
1/2	.840	.622	.850	4.547	.300	.0021	.016	.0021
3/4	1.050	.824	1.130	3.637	.530	.0037	.027	.0037
1	1.315	1.049	1.678	2.904	.854	.0060	.044	.0060
1 1/4	1.660	1.380	2.272	2.301	1.482	.0104	.077	.0104
1 1/2	1.900	1.610	2.717	2.010	2.020	.0141	.105	.0141
2	2.875	2.067	3.652	1.608	3.334	.0233	.174	.0233
2 1/2	2.875	2.469	5.793	1.328	4.775	.0332	.248	.0332
3	3.500	3.068	7.575	1.091	7.348	.0513	.384	.0513
3 1/2	4.000	3.548	9.109	.954	9.833	.0687	.513	.0687
4	4.500	4.026	10.790	.848	12.667	.0887	.661	.0887
5	5.563	5.047	14.617	.686	19.921	.1389	1.039	.1389
6	6.625	6.065	18.974	.576	28.779	.2006	1.500	.2006
8	8.625	7.981	28.554	.442	50.027	.3474	2.598	.3474
10	10.750	10.020	40.483	.355	78.618	.5476	4.096	.5476
12	12.750	12.000	49.562	.299	113.087	.7854	5.875	.7854

TABLE A-9—THERMAL CONDUCTIVITY OF VARIOUS MATERIALS

Material	Weight lbs per cu ft	Conductivity k, Btu/hr/sq ft/in./deg.
Aluminum foil		
Spaced	2.36	0.22
Crumpled	0.196	0.28
Asbestos		
Packed	43.8	1.52
Loose	29.3	0.94
Corrugated paper	16.2	0.58
Bagasse	2.4	0.25
"	8.9	0.30
Coconut husk fiber	3.0	0.33
Corkboard, average	10.5	0.28
Light	6.5	0.25
Cork, granulated	8.1	0.34
Corn Stalk Pulp	3.86	0.26
" " "	6.44	0.31
Cotton	5.0	0.39
Eel grass mats	9.4	0.31
Eiderdown	4.92	0.33
Felt	16.9	0.25
Glass wool	4.0	0.29
Hulls		
Buckwheat	12.24	0.32
Cotton seed	4.43	0.31
Kapok, loose	0.87	0.24
Lith board	12.5	0.38
Magnesium 85%, Asbestos 15%	17.4	0.50
Mineral wool, loose	12.0	0.26
" " packed	21.2	0.29
Paper, cardboard	43.0	0.49
Redwood bark, shredded	5.04	0.25
Rock wool	6.0	0.26
" "	18.0	0.29
Rubber		
Hard	74.3	1.10
Soft	68.6	1.21
Sponge	14.0	0.37
Cellular	3.7 to 7.5	0.25
Sawdust, pine	18.76	0.57
Shavings	8.74	0.40
Sisal	6.84	0.24
Steel plates, polished	6.0	0.22
Straw		
Wheat	4.56	0.27
Pressed	8.67	0.31
Wood pulp	4.92	0.26
" "	9.0	0.28
Wool	4.99	0.26
Wood		
Balsa	7.05	0.32
Cypress	28.7	0.67
Fir	34.1	0.97
Mahogany	34.3	1.48
Maple	44.3	1.10
Oak	51.5	1.45

TABLE A-9—THERMAL CONDUCTIVITY OF VARIOUS MATERIALS—CONTINUED

Material	Weight lbs per cu ft	Conductivity k, Btu/hr/sq ft/in./deg.
Wood—Continued		
Pine, Virginia	34.3	0.96
Pine, white	31.2	0.78
Pine, Oregon	37.0	0.80
Redwood	22.0	0.70
Brick		
Average wall	93.0	5.0
Fire	145	9.0
Concrete, Average	150	12.0
" Cinder	110	4.9
" Sawdust		0.97
Glass	164	5.5
Gypsum plaster		5.0
Mortar, cement	103	2.3
Mortar, lime	90	3.3
Porcelain	250	10.0
Stone		
Granite	179	13.0
Limestone	160	5.8
Marble	170	3.4
Quartz	165	6.0
Sandstone	145	8.5
Slate	175	10.4

Material	Conductivity K factors Btu's per hr. per sq. ft. per deg. (Not per inch thick)
Air Space (More than ⅜")	1.1
Single glass	1.13
Double glass	0.46
Triple glass	0.29
4 Pane glass	0.21

TABLE A-10—OTHER HEAT LOADS: SUN EFFECTS (TO BE ADDED TO TD)

	Dark °F	Average °F	Aluminum paint °F
Roof	45	30	15
E or W Wall	30	20	10
S Wall	15	10	5

Electric loads	3.41	Btu per watt hr
Mechanical loads	2545	Btu per hp hr
Occupants	600	Btu per person

TABLE A-11—COOLER USAGE FACTORS (DO NOT USE FOR OVER 1500 CU FT)

Usage	Usage factor Btu per hr per cu ft per deg. Reach in cabinets	Walk in cabinets
Light	0.18	0.06
Medium	0.22	0.08
Heavy	0.30	0.12

TABLE A-12—HEAT TRANSFER IN REFRIGERATION EQUIPMENT
Conductivity K in Btu per sq ft per degree per hour

COOLING AIR

	Still air	200	300	Air velocity in fpm 400	500	600	700	800
Direct Expansion Coil	2.5	5.0	5.8	6.6	7.7	8.3	8.9	9.3
Brine Coil	3.0	8.5	10.0	11.0	12.0	12.8	13.2	13.6
Hold Over Brine Tank	2.25							

COOLING LIQUID: REFRIGERATION COIL IN LIQUID TANK

	Still liquid	20	Agitated liquid-velocity in fpm 30	40	50	100	150
Direct expansion	12	18	22	25	28	40	49

BRINE COOLERS

Velocity fpm	Shell and tube	Double pipe
50	55	
100	80	75
150	100	85
200	115	97.5
250	125	110
300		120
400		135
Congealing Tank, Still Brine		8
Shell and Coil Liquid Ammonia Cooler		45

BAUDELOT COOLERS

Water or milk, direct expansion	60
Water or milk, brine	80
Cream, direct expansion	50
Oil, direct expansion	10

CONDENSER DATA

Velocity fpm	Horizontal Shell and tube	Double pipe	Shell and coil	Atmospheric gpm/ft. length		Vertical shell and tube Water flow gpm/tube	2" tube	2½" tube
50	75	125	160	1	78	1	115	80
100	120	195	225	2	124	2	175	120
150	150	235	260	3	153	3	235	150
200	175	260	285	4	170	4	290	185
250	190	280	305	5	180	5		215
300	210	290	320			6		245
350	220		335			7		280
400	225							

Evaporative Condenser 125 to 250	
Shell and Tube Desuperheater	25
Double Pipe Heat Exchanger	80

TABLE A-13—REFRIGERANT REQUIRED TO CHARGE A SYSTEM
Pounds of refrigerant per lineal foot of Type L copper tubing

Pipe Size, in.	Liquid line			Evaporator coil					
				Dry expansion (25% liquid)			Flooded (50% liquid)		
	CH₃Cl	F-12	F-22	CH₃Cl	F-12	F-22	CH₃Cl	F-12	F-22
¼	.01	.01	.01						
⅜	.03	.04	.04	.01	.01	.01	.02	.02	.02
½	.06	.08	.08	.02	.02	.02	.03	.04	.04
⅝	.09	.13	.12	.02	.03	.03	.04	.06	.06
⅞	.19	.27	.25	.05	.07	.06	.10	.14	.12
1⅛	.32	.47	.42	.08	.12	.10	.16	.24	.21
1⅜	.49	.71	.65	.12	.18	.16	.25	.36	.82
1⅝	.70	1.01	.92	.18	.25	.23	.35	.50	.46
2⅛	1.21	1.75	1.59	.30	.44	.40	.60	.88	.80
2⅝	1.88	2.70	2.46	.47	.68	.62	.94	1.35	1.23
3⅛	2.68	3.86	3.51	.67	.96	.88	1.34	1.93	1.76
3⅝	3.62	5.23	4.76	.90	1.31	1.19	1.81	2.62	2.38
4⅛	4.66	6.72	6.12	1.16	1.68	1.53	2.33	3.36	3.06
5⅛	7.36	10.60	9.67	1.84	2.65	2.42	3.68	5.30	4.84
6⅛	10.50	15.10	13.80	2.62	3.78	3.45	5.25	7.55	6.90

Pounds of refrigerant per lineal foot of iron pipe

Pipe Size,	Liquid Line			Evaporator Coil					
				Dry Expansion (25% liquid)			Flooded (50% liquid)		
	F-12	F-22	NH₃	F-12	F-22	NH₃	F-12	F-22	NH₃
¼ X	.04	.04	.02						
¼ Std.	.06	.05	.03						
⅜ X	.08	.07	.04						
⅜ Std.	.11	.10	.05						
½ X	.13	.12	.06						
½ Std.	.17	.16	.08	.04	.04	.02	.08	.08	.04
¾ X	.24	.22	.11	.06	.06	.03	.12	.11	.05
¾ Std.	.30	.27	.14	.08	.07	.04	.15	.13	.07
1 X	.40	.37	.19	.10	.09	.05	.20	.18	.10
1 Std.	.49	.44	.22	.12	.11	.06	.24	.22	.11
1¼ X	.72	.66	.33	.18	.16	.08	.36	.33	.16
1¼ Std.	.86	.77	.39	.22	.19	.10	.43	.38	.20
1½ X	1.00	.90	.46	.25	.22	.12	.50	.45	.23
1½ Std.	1.15	1.04	.53	.29	.26	.13	.58	.52	.26
2 X	1.67	1.52	.77	.42	.38	.19	.84	.76	.38
2 Std.	1.90	1.72	.87	.48	.43	.22	.95	.86	.44
2½ X	2.40	2.17	1.10	.60	.54	.28	1.20	1.08	.55
2½ Std.	2.70	2.46	1.24	.68	.62	.31	1.35	1.23	.62
3 X	3.73	3.40	1.71	.92	.85	.43	1.86	1.70	.86
3 Std.	4.19	3.80	1.92	1.05	.95	.48	2.10	1.90	.96
3½ X	5.00	4.57	2.30				2.50	2.28	1.15
3½ Std.	5.58	5.10	2.57				2.79	2.55	1.28
4 X	6.50	5.91	2.99				3.25	2.96	1.50
4 Std.	7.21	6.58	3.31				3.60	3.29	1.66
4½ Std.	9.05	8.24	4.15				4.52	4.12	2.08
5 X	10.2	9.37	4.71						
5 Std.	11.3	10.3	5.20						
6 X	14.7	13.4	6.78						
6 Std.	16.3	14.9	7.53						
8 X			10.85						
8 Std.			13.00						
10 X			19.35						
10 Std.			20.50						

TABLE A-14—LOG. MEAN TEMPERATURE DIFFERENCE

D_1 or D_2	1	2	3	4	5	6	7	8	9	10	11	12	13	14	15	16	17	18	19	20
1	1.00	1.44	1.82	2.16	2.48	2.79	3.08	3.37	3.64	3.91	4.17	4.43	4.68	4.93	5.17	5.41	5.65	5.88	6.11	6.34
2	1.44	2.00	2.47	2.89	3.28	3.64	3.99	4.33	4.65	4.97	5.28	5.58	5.88	6.17	6.45	6.73	7.01	7.28	7.55	7.82
3	1.82	2.47	3.00	3.51	3.95	4.33	4.73	5.10	5.40	5.82	6.17	6.49	6.82	7.15	7.46	7.77	8.08	8.37	8.67	8.95
4	2.16	2.89	3.51	4.00	4.48	4.93	5.36	5.77	6.17	6.55	6.92	7.28	7.64	8.00	8.32	8.66	8.98	9.31	9.63	9.94
5	2.48	3.28	3.95	4.48	5.00	5.49	5.94	6.38	6.81	7.21	7.61	8.00	8.37	8.74	9.10	9.46	9.81	10.15	10.49	10.82
6	2.79	3.64	4.33	4.93	5.49	6.00	6.37	7.01	7.40	7.85	8.27	8.70	9.08	9.47	9.98	10.22	10.61	10.96	11.30	11.67
7	3.08	3.99	4.73	5.36	5.94	6.37	7.00	7.63	8.00	8.49	8.87	9.67	10.52	10.86	11.26	11.65	12.04	12.37
8	3.37	4.33	5.10	5.77	6.38	7.01	7.63	8.00	8.49	8.96	9.42	9.86	10.30	10.72	11.13	11.54	11.94	12.33	12.72	13.10
9	3.64	4.65	5.40	6.17	6.81	7.40	8.00	8.49	9.00	9.58	10.06	10.52	10.97	11.24	11.70	12.14	12.57	12.99	13.39	13.92
10	3.91	4.97	5.82	6.55	7.21	7.85	8.49	8.96	9.58	10.00	10.49	10.97	11.43	11.89	12.33	12.77	13.19	13.61	14.02	14.43
11	4.17	5.28	6.17	6.92	7.61	8.27	8.87	9.42	10.06	10.49	11.00	11.49	11.96	12.42	12.94	13.33	13.79	14.22	14.65	15.06
12	4.43	5.58	6.49	7.28	8.00	8.70	9.32	9.86	10.52	10.97	11.49	12.00	12.50	12.99	13.45	13.90	14.45	14.80	15.23	15.66
13	4.68	5.88	6.82	7.64	8.37	9.08	9.67	10.30	10.97	11.43	11.96	12.50	13.00	13.48	13.91	14.44	14.90	15.35	15.80	16.26
14	4.93	6.17	7.15	8.00	8.74	9.47	10.10	10.72	11.24	11.89	12.42	12.99	13.48	14.00	14.58	14.93	15.46	15.80	16.38	16.81
15	5.17	6.45	7.46	8.32	9.10	9.98	10.52	11.13	11.70	12.33	12.94	13.45	13.91	14.58	15.00	15.87	16.00	16.45	16.90	17.39
16	5.41	6.73	7.77	8.66	9.46	10.22	10.86	11.54	12.14	12.77	13.33	13.90	14.44	14.93	15.87	16.00	16.29	16.98	17.31	17.93
17	5.65	7.01	8.08	8.98	9.81	10.61	11.26	11.94	12.57	13.19	13.79	14.45	14.90	15.46	16.46	16.29	17.00	17.51	18.07	18.51
18	5.88	7.28	8.37	9.31	10.15	10.96	11.65	12.33	12.99	13.61	14.22	14.80	15.35	14.93	16.90	16.98	17.51	18.00	18.35	18.99
19	6.11	7.55	8.67	9.63	10.49	11.30	12.04	12.72	13.39	14.02	14.65	15.23	15.80	16.38	17.39	17.31	18.07	18.35	19.00	19.23
20	6.34	7.82	8.95	9.94	10.82	11.67	12.37	13.10	13.92	14.43	15.06	15.66	16.26	16.81	15.00	17.93	18.51	18.99	19.23	20.00
21	6.57	8.08	9.25	10.25	11.15	12.00	12.74	13.47	14.19	14.83	15.47	16.08	16.69	17.26	17.83	18.35	18.96	19.43	20.24	20.49
22	6.79	8.34	9.54	10.56	11.47	12.35	13.11	13.84	14.57	15.22	15.87	16.50	17.11	17.71	18.28	18.84	19.40	19.96	20.45	20.99
23	7.02	8.60	9.82	10.86	11.79	12.68	13.79	14.20	14.89	15.61	16.27	16.92	17.53	18.12	18.72	19.27	19.90	20.38	20.90	21.46
24	7.24	8.85	10.10	11.16	12.11	13.02	13.79	14.56	15.27	15.99	16.64	17.31	17.95	18.55	19.15	19.73	20.33	20.86	21.48	21.94
25	7.46	9.11	10.38	11.46	12.43	13.34	14.14	14.92	15.65	16.37	17.05	17.66	18.35	18.95	19.58	20.14	20.76	21.30	21.86	22.41
26	7.67	9.36	10.65	11.75	12.74	13.67	14.46	15.26	16.02	16.75	17.43	18.11	18.76	19.38	20.01	20.60	21.20	21.77	22.34	22.87
27	7.89	9.61	10.92	12.05	13.05	13.99	14.81	15.62	16.38	17.11	17.82	18.50	19.20	19.79	20.42	21.01	21.63	22.19	22.76	23.33
28	8.10	9.85	11.19	12.33	13.35	14.31	15.15	15.96	16.75	17.48	18.20	18.89	19.55	20.20	20.83	21.44	22.04	22.62	23.20	23.77
29	8.32	10.01	11.46	12.62	13.65	14.63	15.49	16.31	17.10	17.85	18.57	19.27	19.94	20.60	21.24	21.85	22.49	23.07	23.66	24.22
30	8.53	10.34	11.73	12.90	13.95	14.94	15.79	16.64	17.46	18.20	18.94	19.64	20.33	20.99	21.64	22.27	22.90	23.48	24.08	24.66
31	8.74	10.58	11.98	13.19	14.25	15.25	16.12	16.98	17.81	18.56	19.31	20.01	20.71	21.27	22.09	22.67	23.31	23.92	24.50	25.10
32	8.94	10.82	12.26	13.47	14.55	15.57	16.45	17.31	18.11	18.91	19.66	20.39	21.11	21.77	22.45	23.08	23.72	24.33	24.94	25.53
33	9.15	11.06	12.51	13.74	14.84	15.87	16.75	17.64	18.46	19.26	20.03	20.76	21.47	22.18	22.83	23.47	24.13	24.75	25.35	25.96
34	9.36	11.29	12.76	14.02	15.13	16.18	17.08	17.97	18.80	19.61	20.37	21.12	21.85	22.53	23.22	23.88	24.53	25.15	25.79	26.39
35	9.56	11.53	13.03	14.29	15.47	16.48	17.40	18.29	19.14	19.96	20.72	21.48	22.22	22.92	23.60	24.27	24.94	25.58	26.19	26.80
36	9.77	11.76	13.28	14.56	15.70	16.77	17.71	18.62	19.48	20.30	21.08	21.85	22.58	23.30	23.99	24.66	25.33	25.97	26.62	27.22
37	9.97	12.00	13.53	14.83	15.99	17.07	18.01	18.94	19.81	20.64	21.43	22.25	22.95	23.66	24.37	25.04	25.72	26.36	27.01	27.63
38	10.17	12.23	13.78	15.10	16.27	17.36	18.31	19.25	20.14	20.97	21.78	22.55	23.30	24.05	24.73	25.43	26.11	26.77	27.41	28.04
39	10.37	12.45	14.04	15.37	16.55	17.67	18.63	19.57	20.47	21.31	22.13	22.91	23.67	24.41	25.12	25.81	26.50	27.16	27.80	28.45
40	10.57	12.68	14.29	15.63	16.83	17.95	18.92	19.88	20.80	21.64	22.46	23.26	24.02	24.77	25.49	26.19	26.89	27.56	28.21	28.86

D_1 or D_2

—Courtesy McQuay Incorporated

TABLE A-15. SATURATED AMMONIA-TEMPERATURE TABLE

Temp. °F.	Pressure.		Volume vapor. ft³/lb.	Density vapor. lbs./ft.³	Heat content.		Latent heat. Btu./lb.	Entropy.		Temp. °F.
	Absolute. lbs./in.²	Gage. lbs./in.²			Liquid. Btu./lb.	Vapor. Btu./lb.		Liquid. Btu./lb.°F.	Vapor. Btu./lb.°F.	
t	p	g. p.	V	1/V	h	H	L	s	S	t
−60	5.55	*18.6	44.73	0.02235	−21.2	589.6	610.8	−0.0517	1.4769	−60
−59	5.74	*18.2	43.37	.02306	−20.1	590.0	610.1	−.0490	.4741	−59
−58	5.93	*17.8	42.05	.02378	−19.1	590.4	609.5	−.0464	.4713	−58
−57	6.13	*17.4	40.79	.02452	−18.0	590.8	608.8	−.0438	.4686	−57
−56	6.33	*17.0	39.56	.02528	−17.0	591.2	608.2	−.0412	.4658	−56
−55	6.54	*16.6	38.38	0.02605	−15.9	591.6	607.5	−0.0386	1.4631	−55
−54	6.75	*16.2	37.24	.02685	−14.8	592.1	606.9	.0360	.4604	−54
−53	6.97	*15.7	36.15	.02766	−13.8	592.4	606.2	−.0334	.4577	−53
−52	7.20	*15.3	35.09	.02850	−12.7	592.9	605.6	−.0307	.4551	−52
−51	7.43	*14.8	34.06	.02936	−11.7	593.2	604.9	−.0281	.4524	−51
−50	7.67	*14.3	33.08	0.03023	−10.6	593.7	604.3	−0.0256	1.4497	−50
−49	7.91	*13.8	32.12	.03113	−9.6	594.0	603.6	−.0230	.4471	−49
−48	8.16	*13.3	31.20	.03205	−8.5	594.4	602.9	−.0204	.4445	−48
−47	8.42	*12.8	30.31	.03299	−7.4	594.9	602.3	−.0179	.4419	−47
−46	8.68	*12.2	29.45	.03395	−6.4	595.2	601.6	−.0153	.4393	−46
−45	8.95	*11.7	28.62	0.03494	−5.3	595.6	600.9	−0.0127	1.4368	−45
−44	9.23	*11.1	27.82	.03595	−4.3	596.0	600.3	−.0102	.4342	−44
−43	9.51	*10.6	27.04	.03698	−3.2	596.4	599.6	−.0076	.4317	−43
−42	9.81	*10.0	26.29	.03804	−2.1	596.8	598.9	−.0051	.4292	−42
−41	10.10	*9.3	25.56	.03912	−1.1	597.2	598.3	−.0025	.4267	−41
−40	10.41	*8.7	24.86	0.04022	0.0	597.6	597.6	0.0000	1.4242	−40
−39	10.72	*8.1	24.18	.04135	1.1	598.0	596.9	.0025	.4217	−39
−38	11.04	*7.4	23.53	.04251	2.1	598.3	596.2	.0051	.4193	−38
−37	11.37	*6.8	22.89	.04369	3.2	598.7	595.5	.0076	.4169	−37
−36	11.71	*6.1	22.27	.04489	4.3	599.1	594.8	.0101	.4144	−36
−35	12.05	*5.4	21.68	0.04613	5.3	599.5	594.2	0.0126	1.4120	−35
−34	12.41	*4.7	21.10	.04739	6.4	599.9	593.5	.0151	.4096	−34
−33	12.77	*3.9	20.54	.04868	7.4	600.2	592.8	.0176	.4072	−33
−32	13.14	*3.2	20.00	.04999	8.5	600.6	592.1	.0201	.4048	−32
−31	13.52	*2.4	19.48	.05134	9.6	601.0	591.4	.0226	.4025	−31
−30	13.90	*1.6	18.97	0.05271	10.7	601.4	590.7	0.0250	1.4001	−30
−29	14.30	*0.8	18.48	.05411	11.7	601.7	590.0	.0275	.3978	−29
−28	14.71	0.0	18.00	.05555	12.8	602.1	589.3	.0300	.3955	−28
−27	15.12	0.4	17.54	.05701	13.9	602.5	588.6	.0325	.3932	−27
−26	15.55	0.8	17.09	.05850	14.9	602.8	587.9	.0350	.3909	−26
−25	15.98	1.3	16.66	0.06003	16.0	603.2	587.2	0.0374	1.3886	−25
−24	16.42	1.7	16.24	.06158	17.1	603.6	586.5	.0399	.3863	−24
−23	16.88	2.2	15.83	.06317	18.1	603.9	585.8	.0423	.3840	−23
−22	17.34	2.6	15.43	.06479	19.2	604.3	585.1	.0448	.3818	−22
−21	17.81	3.1	15.05	.06644	20.3	604.6	584.3	.0472	.3796	−21
−20	18.30	3.6	14.68	0.06813	21.4	605.0	583.6	0.0497	1.3774	−20
−19	18.79	4.1	14.32	.06985	22.4	605.3	582.9	.0521	.3752	−19
−18	19.30	4.6	13.97	.07161	23.5	605.7	582.2	.0545	.3729	−18
−17	19.81	5.1	13.62	.07340	24.6	606.1	581.5	.0570	.3708	−17
−16	20.34	5.6	13.29	.07522	25.6	606.4	580.8	.0594	.3686	−16
−15	20.88	6.2	12.97	0.07709	26.7	606.7	580.0	0.0618	1.3664	−15
−14	21.43	6.7	12.66	.07898	27.8	607.1	579.3	.0642	.3643	−14
−13	21.99	7.3	12.36	.08092	28.9	607.5	578.6	.0666	.3621	−13
−12	22.56	7.9	12.06	.08289	30.0	607.8	577.8	.0690	.3600	−12
−11	23.15	8.5	11.78	.08490	31.0	608.1	577.1	.0714	.3579	−11
−10	23.74	9.0	11.50	0.08695	32.1	608.5	576.4	0.0738	1.3558	−10

* Inches of mercury below one standard atmosphere (29.92 in.).

TABLE A-15. SATURATED AMMONIA-TEMPERATURE TABLE

Temp. °F.	Pressure.		Volume vapor. ft³/lb.	Density vapor. lbs./ft.³	Heat content.		Latent heat. Btu./lb.	Entropy.		Temp. °F.
	Absolute. lbs./in.²	Gage. lbs./in.²			Liquid. Btu./lb.	Vapor. Btu./lb.		Liquid. Btu./lb.°F.	Vapor. Btu./lb.°F.	
t	p	$'g. p.$	V	$1/V$	h	H	L	s	S	t
−10	23.74	9.0	11.50	0.08695	32.1	608.5	576.4	0.0738	1.3558	−10
−9	24 35	9.7	11.23	.08904	33.2	608.8	575.6	.0762	.3537	−9
−8	24.97	10.3	10.97	.09117	34.3	609.2	574.9	.0786	.3516	−8
−7	25.61	10.9	10.71	.09334	35.4	609.5	574.1	.0809	.3495	−7
−6	26.26	11.6	10.47	.09555	36.4	609.8	573.4	.0833	.3474	−6
−5	26.92	12.2	10.23	0.09780	37.5	610.1	572.6	0.0857	1.3454	−5
−4	27.59	12.9	9.991	.1001	38.6	610.5	571.9	.0880	.3433	−4
−3	28.28	13.6	9.763	.1024	39.7	610.8	571.1	.0904	.3413	−3
−2	28.98	14.3	9.541	.1048	40.7	611.1	570.4	.0928	.3393	−2
−1	29.69	15.0	9.326	.1072	41.8	611.4	569.6	.0951	.3372	−1
0	30.42	15.7	9.116	0.1097	42.9	611.8	568.9	0.0975	1.3352	0
1	31.16	16.5	8.912	.1122	44.0	612.1	568.1	.0998	.3332	1
2	31.92	17.2	8.714	.1148	45.1	612.4	567.3	.1022	.3312	2
3	32.69	18.0	8.521	.1174	46.2	612.7	566.5	.1045	.3292	3
4	33.47	18.8	8.333	.1200	47.2	613.0	565.8	.1069	.3273	4
5	34.27	19.6	8.150	0.1227	48.3	613.3	565.0	0.1092	1.3253	5
6	35.09	20.4	7.971	.1254	49.4	613.6	564.2	.1115	.3234	6
7	35.92	21.2	7.798	.1282	50.5	613.9	563.4	.1138	.3214	7
8	36.77	22.1	7.629	.1311	51.6	614.3	562.7	.1162	.3195	8
9	37.63	22.9	7.464	.1340	52.7	614.6	561.9	.1185	.3176	9
10	38.51	23.8	7.304	0.1369	53.8	614.9	561.1	0.1208	1.3157	10
11	39.40	24.7	7.148	.1399	54.9	615.2	560.3	.1231	.3137	11
12	40.31	25.6	6.996	.1429	56.0	615.5	559.5	.1254	.3118	12
13	41.24	26.5	6.847	.1460	57.1	615.8	558.7	.1277	.3099	13
14	42.18	27.5	6.703	.1492	58.2	616.1	557.9	.1300	.3081	14
15	43.14	28.4	6.562	0.1524	59.2	616.3	557.1	0.1323	1.3062	15
16	44.12	29.4	6.425	.1556	60.3	616.6	556.3	.1346	.3043	16
17	45.12	30.4	6.291	.1590	61.4	616.9	555 5	.1369	.3025	17
18	46.13	31.4	6.161	.1623	62.5	617.2	554.7	.1392	.3006	18
19	47.16	32.5	6.034	.1657	63.6	617.5	553.9	.1415	.2988	19
20	48.21	33.5	5.910	0.1692	64.7	617.8	553.1	0.1437	1.2969	20
21	49.28	34.6	5.789	.1728	65.8	618.0	552.2	.1460	.2951	21
22	50.36	35.7	5.671	.1763	66.9	618.3	551.4	.1483	.2933	22
23	51.47	36.8	5.556	.1800	68.0	618.6	550.6	.1505	.2915	23
24	52.59	37.9	5.443	.1837	69.1	618.9	549.8	.1528	.2897	24
25	53.73	39.0	5.334	0.1875	70.2	619.1	548.9	0.1551	1.2879	25
26	54.90	40.2	5.227	.1913	71.3	619.4	548.1	.1573	.2861	26
27	56.08	41.4	5.123	.1952	72.4	619.7	547.3	.1596	.2843	27
28	57.28	42.6	5.021	.1992	73.5	619.9	546.4	.1618	.2825	28
29	58.50	43.8	4.922	.2032	74.6	620.2	545.6	.1641	.2808	29
30	59.74	45.0	4.825	0.2073	75.7	620.5	544.8	0.1663	1.2790	30
31	61.00	46.3	4.730	.2114	76.8	620.7	543.9	.1686	.2773	31
32	62.29	47.6	4.637	.2156	77.9	621.0	543.1	.1708	.2755	32
33	63.59	48.9	4.547	.2199	79.0	621.2	542.2	.1730	.2738	33
34	64.91	50.2	4.459	.2243	80.1	621.5	541.4	.1753	.2721	34
35	66.26	51.6	4.373	0.2287	81.2	621.7	540.5	0.1775	1.2704	35
36	67.63	52.9	4.289	.2332	82.3	622.0	539.7	.1797	.2686	36
37	69.02	54.3	4.207	.2377	83.4	622.2	538.8	.1819	.2669	37
38	70.43	55.7	4.126	.2423	84.6	622.5	537.9	.1841	.2652	38
39	71.87	57.2	4.048	.2470	85.7	622.7	537.0	.1863	.2635	39
40	73.32	58.6	3.971	0.2518	86.8	623.0	536.2	0.1885	1,2618	40

TABLE A-15. SATURATED AMMONIA-TEMPERATURE TABLE

Temp. °F.	Pressure.		Volume vapor. ft.³/lb.	Density vapor. lbs./ft.³	Heat content.		Latent heat. Btu./lb.	Entropy.		Temp. °F.
	Absolute. lbs./in.³	Gage. lbs./in.²			Liquid. Btu./lb.	Vapor. Btu./lb.		Liquid. Btu./lb.°F.	Vapor. Btu./lb.°F.	
t	p	g. p.	V	1/V	h	H	L	s	S	t
40	73.32	58.6	3.971	0.2518	86.8	623.0	536.2	0.1885	1.2618	**40**
41	74.80	60.1	3.897	.2566	87.9	623.2	535.3	.1908	.2602	41
42	76.31	61.6	3.823	.2616	89.0	623.4	534.4	.1930	.2585	42
43	77.83	63.1	3.752	.2665	90.1	623.7	533.6	.1952	.2568	43
44	79.38	64.7	3.682	.2716	91.2	623.9	532.7	.1974	.2552	44
45	80.96	66.3	3.614	0.2767	92.3	624.1	531.8	0.1996	1.2535	**45**
46	82.55	67.9	3.547	.2819	93.5	624.4	530.9	.2018	.2519	46
47	84.18	69.5	3.481	.2872	94.6	624.6	530.0	.2040	.2502	47
48	85.82	71.1	3.418	.2926	95.7	624.8	529.1	.2062	.2486	48
49	87.49	72.8	3.355	.2981	96.8	625.0	528.2	.2083	.2469	49
50	89.19	74.5	3.294	0.3036	97.9	625.2	527.3	0.2105	1.2453	**50**
51	90.91	76.2	3.234	.3092	99.1	625.5	526.4	.2127	.2437	51
52	92.66	78.0	3.176	.3149	100.2	625.7	525.5	.2149	.2421	52
53	94.43	79.7	3.119	.3207	101.3	625.9	524.6	.2171	.2405	53
54	96.23	81.5	3.063	.3265	102.4	626.1	523.7	.2192	.2389	54
55	98.06	83.4	3.008	0.3325	103.5	626.3	522.8	0.2214	1.2373	**55**
56	99.91	85.2	2.954	.3385	104.7	626.5	521.8	.2236	.2357	56
57	101.8	87.1	2.902	.3446	105.8	626.7	520.9	.2257	.2341	57
58	103.7	89.0	2.851	.3508	106.9	626.9	520.0	.2279	.2325	58
59	105.6	90.9	2.800	.3571	108.1	627.1	519.0	.2301	.2310	59
60	107.6	92.9	2.751	0.3635	109.2	627.3	518.1	0.2322	1.2294	**60**
61	109.6	94.9	2.703	.3700	110.3	627.5	517.2	.2344	.2278	61
62	111.6	96.9	2.656	.3765	111.5	627.7	516.2	.2365	.2262	62
63	113.6	98.9	2.610	.3832	112.6	627.9	515.3	.2387	.2247	63
64	115.7	101.0	2.565	.3899	113.7	628.0	514.3	.2408	.2231	64
65	117.8	103.1	2.520	0.3968	114.8	628.2	513.4	0.2430	1.2216	**65**
66	120.0	105.3	2.477	.4037	116.0	628.4	512.4	.2451	.2201	66
67	122.1	107.4	2.435	.4108	117.1	628.6	511.5	.2473	.2186	67
68	124.3	109.6	2.393	.4179	118.3	628.8	510.5	.2494	.2170	68
69	126.5	111.8	2.352	.4251	119.4	628.9	509.5	.2515	.2155	69
70	128.8	114.1	2.312	0.4325	120.5	629.1	508.6	0.2537	1.2140	**70**
71	131.1	116.4	2.273	.4399	121.7	629.3	507.6	.2558	.2125	71
72	133.4	118.7	2.235	.4474	122.8	629.4	506.6	.2579	.2110	72
73	135.7	121.0	2.197	.4551	124.0	629.6	505.6	.2601	.2095	73
74	138.1	123.4	2.161	.4628	125.1	629.8	504.7	.2622	.2080	74
75	140.5	125.8	2.125	0.4707	126.2	629.9	503.7	0.2643	1.2065	**75**
76	143.0	128.3	2.089	.4786	127.4	630.1	502.7	.2664	.2050	76
77	145.4	130.7	2.055	.4867	128.5	630.2	501.7	.2685	.2035	77
78	147.9	133.2	2.021	.4949	129.7	630.4	500.7	.2706	.2020	78
79	150.5	135.8	1.988	.5031	130.8	630.5	499.7	.2728	.2006	79
80	153.0	138.3	1.955	0.5115	132.0	630.7	498.7	0.2749	1.1991	**80**
81	155.6	140.9	1.923	.5200	133.1	630.8	497.7	.2769	.1976	81
82	158.3	143.6	1.892	.5287	134.3	631.0	496.7	.2791	.1962	82
83	161.0	146.3	1.861	.5374	135.4	631.1	495.7	.2812	.1947	83
84	163.7	149.0	1.831	.5462	136.6	631.3	494.7	.2833	.1933	84
85	166.4	151.7	1.801	0.5552	137.8	631.4	493.6	0.2854	1.1918	**85**

TABLE A-15. SATURATED AMMONIA-TEMPERATURE TABLE

Temp. °F.	Pressure.		Volume vapor. ft.³/lb.	Density vapor. lbs./ft.³	Heat content.		Latent heat. Btu./lb.	Entropy.		Temp. °F.
	Absolute. lbs./in.³	Gage. lbs./in.³			Liquid. Btu./lb.	Vapor. Btu./lb.		Liquid. Btu./lb.°F.	Vapor. Btu./lb.°F.	
t	p	g. p.	V	1/V	h	H	L	s	S	t
85	166.4	151.7	1.801	0.5552	137.8	631.4	493.6	0.2854	1.1918	85
86	169.2	154.5	1.772	.5643	138.9	631.5	492.6	.2875	.1904	86
87	172.0	157.3	1.744	.5735	140.1	631.7	491.6	.2895	.1889	87
88	174.8	160.1	1.716	.5828	141.2	631.8	490.6	.2917	.1875	88
89	177.7	163.0	1.688	.5923	142.4	631.9	489.5	.2937	.1860	89
90	180.6	165.9	1.661	0.6019	143.5	632.0	488.5	0.2958	1.1846	90
91	183.6	168.9	1.635	.6116	144.7	632.1	487.4	.2979	.1832	91
92	186.6	171.9	1.609	.6214	145.8	632.2	486.4	.3000	.1818	92
93	189.6	174.9	1.584	.6314	147.0	632.3	485.3	.3021	.1804	93
94	192.7	178.0	1.559	.6415	148.2	632.5	484.3	.3041	.1789	94
95	195.8	181.1	1.534	0.6517	149.4	632.6	483.2	0.3062	1.1775	95
96	198.9	184.2	1.510	.6620	150.5	632.6	482.1	.3083	.1761	96
97	202.1	187.4	1.487	.6725	151.7	632.8	481.1	.3104	.1747	97
98	205.3	190.6	1.464	.6832	152.9	632.9	480.0	.3125	.1733	98
99	208.6	193.9	1.441	.6939	154.0	632.9	478.9	.3145	.1719	99
100	211.9	197.2	1.419	0.7048	155.2	633.0	477.8	0.3166	1.1705	100
101	215.2	200.5	1.397	.7159	156.4	633.1	476.7	.3187	.1691	101
102	218.6	203.9	1.375	.7270	157.6	633.2	475.6	.3207	.1677	102
103	222.0	207.3	1.354	.7384	158.7	633.3	474.6	.3228	.1663	103
104	225.4	210.7	1.334	.7498	159.9	633.4	473.5	.3248	.1649	104
105	228.9	214.2	1.313	0.7615	161.1	633.4	472.3	0.3269	1.1635	105
106	232.5	217.8	1.293	.7732	162.3	633.5	471.2	.3289	.1621	106
107	236.0	221.3	1.274	.7852	163.5	633.6	470.1	.3310	.1607	107
108	239.7	225.0	1.254	.7972	164.6	633.6	469.0	.3330	.1593	108
109	243.3	228.6	1.235	.8095	165.8	633.7	467.9	.3351	.1580	109
110	247.0	232.3	1.217	0.8219	167.0	633.7	466.7	0.3372	1.1566	110
111	250.8	236.1	1.198	.8344	168.2	633.8	465.6	.3392	.1552	111
112	254.5	239.8	1.180	.8471	169.4	633.8	464.4	.3413	.1538	112
113	258.4	243.7	1.163	.8600	170.6	633.9	463.3	.3433	.1524	113
114	262.2	247.5	1.145	.8730	171.8	633.9	462.1	.3453	.1510	114
115	266.2	251.5	1.128	0.8862	173.0	633.9	460.9	0.3474	1.1497	115
116	270.1	255.4	1.112	.8996	174.2	634.0	459.8	.3495	.1483	116
117	274.1	259.4	1.095	.9132	175.4	634.0	458.6	.3515	.1469	117
118	278.2	263.5	1.079	.9269	176.6	634.0	457.4	.3535	.1455	118
119	282.3	267.6	1.063	.9408	177.8	634.0	456.2	.3556	.1441	119
120	286.4	271.7	1.047	0.9549	179.0	634.0	455.0	0.3576	1.1427	120
121	290.6	275.9	1.032	.9692	180.2	634.0	453.8	.3597	.1414	121
122	294.8	280.1	1.017	.9837	181.4	634.0	452.6	.3618	.1400	122
123	299.1	284.4	1.002	.9983	182.6	634.0	451.4	.3638	.1386	123
124	303.4	288.7	0.987	1.0132	183.9	634.0	450.1	.3659	.1372	124
125	307.8	293.1	0.973	1.028	185.1	634.0	448.9	0.3679	1.1358	125

TABLE A-15. PROPERTIES OF LIQUID AMMONIA

Temp. °F.	Pressure (abs.). lbs./in.²	Volume. ft.³/lb.	Density. lbs./ft.³	Specific heat. Btu./lb. °F.	Heat content. Btu./lb.	Latent heat. Btu./lb.	Latent heat of pressure variation. Btu./lb. lb./in.²	Variation of h with p (t constant). Btu./lb. lb./in.²	Compressibility. per lb./in.³×10⁶	Temp. °F.
t	p	v	$\frac{1}{v}$	c	h	L	l	$\left(\frac{\partial h}{\partial p}\right)_t$	$-\frac{1}{v}\left(\frac{\partial v}{\partial p}\right)_t$	t
Triple point. {	...... 0.88	0.01961* .02182	51.00* 45.83	....	....	....	....	....	....	-107.86
-100	1.24	0.02197	45.52	(1.040)	(-63.0)	(633)	......	......	......	-100
-95	1.52	.02207	45.32	(1.042)	(-57.8)	(631)	......	......	......	-95
-90	1.86	.02216	45.12	(1.043)	(-52.6)	(628)	......	......	......	-90
-85	2.27	.02226	44.92	(1.045)	(-47.4)	(625)	......	......	......	-85
-80	2.74	.02236	44.72	(1.046)	(-42.2)	(622)	......	......	......	-80
-75	3.29	0.02246	44.52	(1.048)	(-36.9)	(619)	......	......	......	-75
-70	3.94	.02256	44.32	(1.050)	(-31.7)	(616)	......	......	......	-70
-65	4.69	.02267	44.11	(1.052)	(-26.4)	(613)	......	......	......	-65
-60	5.55	.02278	43.91	1.054	-21.18	610.8	-0.0016	0.0026	4.4	-60
-55	6.54	.02288	43.70	1.056	-15.90	607.5	-.0016	.0026	4.5	-55
-50	7.67	0.02299	43.49	1.058	-10.61	604.3	-0.0017	0.0026	4.6	-50
-45	8.95	.02310	43.28	1.060	-5.31	600.9	-.0017	.0026	4.7	-45
-40	10.41	.02322	43.08	1.062	0.00	597.6	-.0018	.0025	4.8	-40
-35	12.05	.02333	42.86	1.064	+5.32	594.2	-.0018	.0025	5.0	-35
-30	13.90	.02345	42.65	1.066	10.66	590.7	-.0019	.0025	5.1	-30
-25	15.98	0.02357	42.44	1.068	16.00	587.2	-0.0019	0.0024	5.2	-25
-20	18.30	.02369	42.22	1.070	21.36	583.6	-.0020	.0024	5.4	-20
-15	20.88	.02381	42.00	1.073	26.73	580.0	-.0020	.0024	5.5	-15
-10	23.74	.02393	41.78	1.075	32.11	576.4	-.0021	.0023	5.7	-10
-5	26.92	.02406	41.56	1.078	37.51	572.6	-.0022	.0023	5.8	-5
0	30.42	0.02419	41.34	1.080	42.92	568.9	-0.0022	0.0022	6.0	0
5	34.27	.02432	41.11	1.083	48.35	565.0	-.0023	.0022	6.2	5
10	38.51	.02446	40.89	1.085	53.79	561.1	-.0024	.0021	6.4	10
15	43.14	.02460	40.66	1.088	59.24	557.1	-.0025	.0021	6.6	15
20	48.21	.02474	40.43	1.091	64.71	553.1	-.0025	.0020	6.8	20
25	53.73	0.02488	40.20	1.094	70.20	548.9	-0.0026	0.0020	7.0	25
30	59.74	.02503	39.96	1.097	75.71	544.8	-.0027	.0019	7.3	30
35	66.26	.02518	39.72	1.100	81.23	540.5	-.0028	.0019	7.5	35
40	73.32	.02533	39.49	1.104	86.77	536.2	-.0029	.0018	7.8	40
45	80.96	.02548	39.24	1.108	92.34	531.8	-.0030	.0017	8.1	45
50	89.19	0.02564	39.00	1.112	97.93	527.3	-0.0031	0.0017	8.4	50
55	98.06	.02581	38.75	1.116	103.54	522.8	-.0032	.0016	8.8	55
60	107.6	.02597	38.50	1.120	109.18	518.1	-.0033	.0015	9.1	60
65	117.8	.02614	38.25	1.125	114.85	513.4	-.0034	.0014	9.5	65
70	128.8	.02632	38.00	1.129	120.54	508.6	-.0035	.0013	10.0	70
75	140.5	0.02650	37.74	1.133	126.25	503.7	-0.0037	0.0012	10.4	75

*Properties of solid ammonia at the triple point (-107.86 °F.)

TABLE A-15. PROPERTIES OF LIQUID AMMONIA

Temp. °F.	Pressure (abs.). lbs./in.²	Volume. ft.³/lb.	Density. lbs./ft.³	Specific heat. Btu./lb. °F	Heat content. Btu./lb.	Latent heat. Btu./lb.	Latent heat of pressure variation. Btu./lb. lb./in.²	Variation of h with p (t constant). Btu./lb. lb./in.²	Compressibility. per lb./in.²×10⁶	Temp. °F.
t	p	v	$\frac{1}{v}$	c	h	L	l	$\left(\dfrac{\partial h}{\partial p}\right)_t$	$-\dfrac{1}{v}\left(\dfrac{\partial v}{\partial p}\right)_t$	
75	140. 5	0. 02650	37. 74	1. 133	126. 25	503. 7	−0. 0037	0. 0012	10. 4	75
80	153. 0	. 02668	37. 48	1. 138	131. 99	498. 7	− . 0038	. 0011	10. 9	80
85	166. 4	. 02687	37. 21	1. 142	137. 75	493. 6	− . 0040	. 0010	11. 4	85
90	180. 6	. 02707	36. 95	1. 147	143. 54	488. 5	− . 0041	. 0009	12. 0	90
95	195. 8	. 02727	36. 67	1. 151	149. 36	483. 2	− . 0043	. 0008	12. 6	95
100	211. 9	0. 02747	36. 40	1. 156	155. 21	477. 8	−0. 0045	0. 0006	13. 3	100
105	228. 9	. 02769	36. 12	1. 162	161. 09	472. 3	− . 0047	. 0005	14. 1	105
110	247. 0	. 02790	35. 84	1. 168	167. 01	466. 7	− . 0049	. 0003	14. 9	110
115	266. 2	. 02813	35. 55	1. 176	172. 97	460. 9	− . 0051	. 0001	15. 8	115
120	286. 4	. 02836	35. 26	1. 183	178. 98	455. 0	− . 0053	. 0000	16. 7	120
125	307. 8	0. 02860	34. 96	(1. 189)	(185)	(449)	....	....	....	125
130	330. 3	. 02885	34. 66	(1. 197)	(191)	(443)	....	....	....	130
135	354. 1	. 02911	34. 35	(1. 205)	(197)	(436)	....	....	....	135
140	379. 1	. 02938	34. 04	(1. 213)	(203)	(430)	....	....	....	140
145	405. 5	. 02966	33. 72	(1. 222)	(210)	(423)	....	....	....	145
150	433. 2	0. 02995	33. 39	(1. 23)	(216)	(416)	....	....	....	150
155	462. 3	. 03025	33. 06	(1. 24)	(222)	(409)	....	....	....	155
160	492. 8	. 03056	32. 72	(1. 25)	(229)	(401)	....	....	....	160
165	524. 8	. 03089	32. 37	(1. 26)	(235)	(394)	....	....	....	165
170	558. 4	. 03124	32. 01	(1. 27)	(241)	(386)	....	....	....	170
175	593. 5	0. 03160	31. 65	(1. 29)	(248)	(377)	....	....	....	175
180	630. 3	. 03198	31. 27	(1. 30)	(255)	(369)	....	....	....	180
185	668. 7	. 03238	30. 88	(1. 32)	(262)	(360)	....	....	....	185
190	708. 9	. 03281	30. 48	(1. 34)	(269)	(351)	....	....	....	190
195	750. 9	. 03326	30. 06	(1. 36)	(276)	(342)	....	....	....	195
200	794. 7	0. 03375	29. 63	(1. 38)	(283)	(332)	....	....	....	200
210	888. 1	. 03482	28. 72	(1. 43)	(297)	(310)	....	....	....	210
220	989. 5	. 0361	27. 7	(1. 49)	(313)	(287)	....	....	....	220
230	1099. 5	. 0376	26. 6	(1. 57)	(329)	(260)	....	....	....	230
240	1218. 5	. 0395	25. 3	(1. 70)	(346)	(229)	....	....	....	240
250	1347	. 0422	23. 7	(1. 90)	(365)	(192)	....	....	....	250
260	1486	. 0463	21. 6	(2. 30)	(387)	(142)	....	....	....	260
270	1635	. 0577	17. 3	(5. 30)	(419)	(52)	....	....	....	270
Critical.	1657	. 0686	14. 6	∞	(433)	0	− ∞	− ∞	∞	271. 4

NOTE.—The figures in parentheses were calculated from empirical equations given in Bureau of Standards Scientific Papers Nos. 313 and 315 and represent values obtained by extrapolation beyond the range covered in the experimental work.

TABLE A-15. PROPERTIES OF SUPERHEATED AMMONIA VAPOR

(V = volume in ft ³/lb; H = heat content in Btu/lb;
S = entropy in Btu/lb °F)

Temp. °F.	Absolute pressure in lbs./in.² (Saturation temperature in italics.)									Temp. °F.
	5 −63.11°			6 −57.64°			7 −52.38°			
	V	H	S	V	H	S	V	H	S	
Sat.	49.31	588.3	1.4587	41.59	590.8	1.4703	36.01	592.5	1.4574	Sat.
−50	51.05	595.2	1.5025	42.44	594.6	1.4803	36.29	594.0	1.4611	−50
−40	52.36	600.3	.5149	43.55	599.8	.4928	37.25	599.3	.4739	−40
−30	53.67	605.4	.5269	44.64	604.9	.5049	38.19	604.5	.4861	−30
−20	54.97	610.4	.5385	45.73	610.0	.5166	39.13	609.6	.4979	−20
−10	56.26	615.4	.5498	46.82	615.1	.5280	40.07	614.7	.5094	−10
0	57.55	620.4	1.5608	47.90	620.1	1.5391	41.00	619.8	1.5206	0
10	58.84	625.4	.5716	48.98	625.2	.5499	41.93	624.9	.5314	10
20	60.12	630.4	.5821	50.05	630.2	.5605	42.85	629.9	.5421	20
30	61.41	635.4	.5925	51.12	635.2	.5708	43.77	635.0	.5525	30
40	62.69	640.4	.6026	52.19	640.2	.5810	44.69	640.0	.5627	40
50	63.96	645.5	1.6125	53.26	645.2	1.5910	45.61	645.0	1.5727	50
60	65.24	650.5	.6223	54.32	650.3	.6008	46.53	650.1	.5825	60
70	66.51	655.5	.6319	55.39	655.3	.6104	47.44	655.2	.5921	70
80	67.79	660.6	.6413	56.45	660.4	.6199	48.36	660.2	.6016	80
90	69.06	665.6	.6506	57.51	665.5	.6292	49.27	665.3	.6110	90
100	70.33	670.7	1.6598	58.58	670.6	1.6384	50.18	670.4	1.6202	100
110	71.60	675.8	.6689	59.64	675.7	.6474	51.09	675.5	.6292	110
120	72.87	680.9	.6778	60.70	680.8	.6563	52.00	680.7	.6382	120
130	74.14	686.1	.6865	61.76	685.9	.6651	52.91	685.8	.6470	130
140	75.41	691.2	.6952	62.82	691.1	.6738	53.82	691.0	.6557	140
150	76.68	696.4	.7038	63.87	696.3	1.6824	54.73	696.2	1.6643	150
160	77.95	701.6	.7122	64.93	701.5	.6909	55.63	701.4	.6727	160
170	79.21	706.8	.7206	65.99	706.7	.6992	56.54	706.6	.6811	170
180	80.48	712.1	.7289	67.05	712.0	.7075	57.45	711.9	.6894	180

Temp. °F.	10 −41.34°			11 −38.14°			12 −35.16°			Temp. °F.
	V	H	S	V	H	S	V	H	S	
Sat.	25.81	597.1	1.4276	23.61	598.3	1.4196	21.77	599.4	1.4124	Sat.
−30	26.58	603.2	1.4420	24.12	602.7	1.4300	22.07	602.3	1.4190	−30
−20	27.26	608.5	.4542	24.74	608.1	.4423	22.64	607.7	.4314	−20
−10	27.92	613.7	.4659	25.35	613.3	.4542	23.20	613.0	.4434	−10
0	28.58	618.9	1.4773	25.95	618.5	1.4656	23.75	618.2	1.4549	0
10	29.24	624.0	.4884	26.55	623.7	.4768	24.31	623.4	.4661	10
20	29.90	629.1	.4992	27.15	628.9	.4876	24.86	628.6	.4770	20
30	30.55	634.2	.5097	27.74	634.0	.4982	25.41	633.7	.4877	30
40	31.20	639.3	.5200	28.34	639.1	.5085	25.95	638.9	.4980	40
50	31.85	644.4	1.5301	28.93	644.2	1.5187	26.49	644.0	1.5082	50
60	32.49	649.5	.5400	29.52	649.3	.5286	27.03	649.1	.5182	60
70	33.14	654.6	.5497	30.10	654.4	.5383	27.57	654.3	.5279	70
80	33.78	659.7	.5593	30.69	659.6	.5479	28.11	659.4	.5375	80
90	34.42	664.8	.5687	31.28	664.7	.5573	28.65	664.5	.5470	90
100	35.07	670.0	1.5779	31.86	669.8	1.5666	29.19	669.7	1.5562	100
110	35.71	675.1	.5870	32.44	675.0	.5757	29.72	674.8	.5654	110
120	36.35	680.3	.5960	33.03	680.1	.5847	30.26	680.0	.5744	120
130	36.99	685.4	.6049	33.61	685.3	.5936	30.79	685.2	.5833	130
140	37.62	690.6	.6136	34.19	690.5	.6023	31.33	690.4	.5920	140
150	38.26	695.8	1.6222	34.77	695.7	1.6109	31.86	695.6	1.6006	150
160	38.90	701.1	.6307	35.35	700.9	.6194	32.39	700.8	.6092	160
170	39.54	706.3	.6391	35.93	706.2	.6278	32.92	706.1	.6176	170
180	40.17	711.6	.6474	36.51	711.5	.6362	33.46	711.4	.6259	180
190	40.81	716.9	.6556	37.09	716.8	.6444	33.99	716.7	.6341	190
200	41.45	722.2	1.6637	37.67	722.1	1.6525	34.52	722.0	1.6422	200

TABLE A-15. PROPERTIES OF SUPERHEATED AMMONIA VAPOR

(V = volume in ft ^{3}/lb; H = heat content in Btu/lb;
S = entropy in Btu/lb °F)

Temp. °F.	Absolute pressure in lbs./in.² (Saturation temperature in italics.)									Temp. °F.
	8 *−48.64°*			9 *−44.38°*			10 *−41.34°*			
	V	H	S	V	H	S	V	H	S	
Sat.	*31.79*	*594.2*	*1.4462*	*28.48*	*595.7*	*1.4363*	*25.81*	*597.1*	*1.4276*	*Sat.*
−50										**−50**
−40	32.52	598.8	1.4573	28.85	598.3	1.4426	25.90	597.8	1.4293	−40
−30	33.36	604.1	.4697	29.59	603.6	.4551	26.58	603.2	.4420	−30
−20	34.19	609.3	.4816	30.34	608.9	.4672	27.26	608.5	.4542	−20
−10	35.01	614.4	.4932	31.07	614.0	.4788	27.92	613.7	.4659	−10
0	35.83	619.5	1.5044	31.80	619.2	1.4902	28.58	618.9	1.4773	0
10	36.64	624.6	.5154	32.53	624.3	.5012	29.24	624.0	.4884	10
20	37.45	629.7	.5261	33.26	629.4	.5119	29.90	629.1	.4992	20
30	38.26	634.7	.5365	33.98	634.5	.5224	30.55	634.2	.5097	30
40	39.07	639.8	.5467	34.70	639.5	.5327	31.20	639.3	.5200	40
50	39.88	644.8	1.5568	35.42	644.6	1.5427	31.85	644.4	1.5301	50
60	40.68	649.9	.5666	36.13	649.7	.5526	32.49	649.5	.5400	60
70	41.48	655.0	.5763	36.85	654.8	.5623	33.14	654.6	.5497	70
80	42.28	660.1	.5858	37.56	659.9	.5718	33.78	659.7	.5593	80
90	43.08	665.2	.5952	38.27	665.0	.5812	34.42	664.8	.5687	90
100	43.88	670.3	1.6044	38.98	670.1	1.5904	35.07	670.0	1.5779	100
110	44.68	675.4	.6135	39.70	675.3	.5995	35.71	675.1	.5870	110
120	45.48	680.5	.6224	40.40	680.4	.6085	36.35	680.3	.5960	120
130	46.27	685.7	.6312	41.11	685.6	.6173	36.99	685.4	.6049	130
140	47.07	690.9	.6399	41.82	690.7	.6260	37.62	690.6	.6136	140
150	47.87	696.1	1.6485	42.53	695.9	1.6346	38.26	695.8	1.6222	150
160	48.66	701.3	.6570	43.24	701.2	.6431	38.90	701.1	.6307	160
170	49.46	706.5	.6654	43.95	706.4	.6515	39.54	706.3	.6391	170
180	50.25	711.8	.6737	44.65	711.7	.6598	40.17	711.6	.6474	180

Temp. °F.	13 *−32.37°*			14 *−29.76°*			15 *−27.29°*			Temp. °F.
	V	H	S	V	H	S	V	H	S	
Sat.	*20.20*	*600.5*	*1.4057*	*18.85*	*601.4*	*1.3996*	*17.87*	*602.4*	*1.3938*	*Sat.*
−30	20.33	601.8	1.4088							−30
−20	20.86	607.2	.4213	19.33	606.8	1.4119	18.01	606.4	1.4031	−20
−10	21.38	612.6	.4334	19.82	612.2	.4241	18.47	611.9	.4154	−10
0	21.90	617.9	1.4450	20.30	617.6	1.4358	18.92	617.2	1.4272	0
10	22.41	623.1	.4563	20.78	622.8	.4472	19.37	622.5	.4386	10
20	22.92	628.3	.4672	21.26	628.0	.4582	19.82	627.8	.4497	20
30	23.43	633.5	.4779	21.73	633.2	.4688	20.26	633.0	.4604	30
40	23.93	638.6	.4883	22.22	638.4	.4793	20.70	638.2	.4709	40
50	24.43	643.8	1.4985	22.67	643.6	1.4896	21.14	643.4	1.4812	50
60	24.94	648.9	.5085	23.14	648.7	.4996	21.58	648.5	.4912	60
70	25.43	654.1	.5183	23.60	653.9	.5094	22.01	653.7	.5011	70
80	25.93	659.2	.5279	24.06	659.0	.5191	22.44	658.9	.5108	80
90	26.43	664.4	.5374	24.53	664.2	.5285	22.88	664.0	.5203	90
100	26.93	669.5	1.5467	24.99	669.4	1.5378	23.31	669.2	1.5296	100
110	27.42	674.7	.5558	25.45	674.5	.5470	23.74	674.4	.5388	110
120	27.92	679.9	.5649	25.91	679.7	.5560	24.17	679.6	.5478	120
130	28.41	685.1	.5737	26.37	884.9	.5649	24.60	684.8	.5567	130
140	28.90	690.3	.5825	26.83	690.1	.5737	25.03	690.0	.5655	140
150	29.40	695.5	1.5911	27.29	695.4	1.5824	25.46	695.3	1.5742	150
160	29.89	700.7	.5997	27.74	700.6	.5909	25.88	700.5	.5827	160
170	30.38	706.0	.6081	28.20	705.9	.5993	26.31	705.8	.5911	170
180	30.87	711.3	.6164	28.66	711.2	.6076	26.74	711.1	.5995	180
190	31.36	716.6	.6246	29.11	716.5	.6159	27.16	716.4	.6077	190
200	31.85	721.9	1.6328	29.57	721.8	1.6240	27.59	721.7	1.6158	200

TABLE A-15. PROPERTIES OF SUPERHEATED AMMONIA VAPOR

(V = volume in ft ^{3}/lb; H = heat content in Btu/lb;
S = entropy in Btu/lb °F)

Temp. °F.	15 −27.89° V	15 H	15 S	16 −24.95° V	16 H	16 S	17 −22.73° V	17 H	17 S	Temp. °F.
Sat.	17.67	608.4	1.3358	16.64	605.2	1.3385	15.72	604.0	1.3335	Sat.
−20	18.01	606.4	1.4031	16.86	606.0	1.3948	15.83	605.6	1.3870	−20
−10	18.47	611.9	.4154	17.29	611.5	.4072	16.24	611.1	.3994	−10
0	18.92	617.2	1.4272	17.72	616.9	1.4191	16.65	616.6	1.4114	0
10	19.37	622.5	.4386	18.14	622.2	.4306	17.05	621.9	.4230	10
20	19.82	627.8	.4497	18.56	627.5	.4417	17.45	627.2	.4342	20
30	20.26	633.0	.4604	18.97	632.7	.4525	17.84	632.5	.4450	30
40	20.70	638.2	.4709	19.39	638.0	.4630	18.23	637.7	.4556	40
50	21.14	643.4	1.4812	19.80	643.2	1.4733	18.62	642.9	1.4659	50
60	21.58	648.5	.4912	20.21	648.3	.4834	19.01	648.1	.4761	60
70	22.01	653.7	.5011	20.62	653.5	.4933	19.39	653.3	.4860	70
80	22.44	658.9	.5108	21.03	658.7	.5030	19.78	658.5	.4957	80
90	22.88	664.0	.5203	21.43	663.9	.5125	20.16	663.7	.5052	90
100	23.31	669.2	1.5296	21.84	669.1	1.5218	20.54	668.9	1:5146	100
110	23.74	674.4	.5388	22.24	674.3	.5310	20.92	674.1	.5238	110
120	24.17	679.6	.5478	22.65	679.5	.5401	21.30	679.3	.5328	120
130	24.60	684.8	.5567	23.05	684.7	.5490	21.68	684.5	.5418	130
140	25.03	690.0	.5655	23.45	689.9	.5578	22.06	689.8	.5506	140
150	25.46	695.3	1.5742	23.86	695.1	1.5665	22.44	695.0	1.5593	150
160	25.88	700.5	.5827	24.26	700.4	.5750	22.82	700.3	.5678	160
170	26.31	705.8	.5911	24.66	705.7	.5835	23.20	705.6	.5763	170
180	26.74	711.1	.5995	25.06	711.0	.5918	23.58	710.9	.5846	180
190	27.16	716.4	.6077	25.46	716.3	.6001	23.95	716.2	.5929	190
200	27.59	721.7	1.6158	25.86	721.6	1.6082	24.33	721.5	1.6010	200
220	28.44	732.4	.6318	26.66	732.3	.6242	25.08	732.2	.6170	220

Temp. °F.	20 −16.64° V	20 H	20 S	21 −14.78° V	21 H	21 S	22 −12.93° V	22 H	22 S	Temp. °F.
Sat.	13.50	606.2	1.3700	12.90	606.3	1.3659	12.35	607.4	1.3621	Sat.
−10	13.74	610.0	1.3784	13.06	609.6	1.3720	12.45	609.2	1.3659	−10
0	14.09	615.5	1.3907	13.40	615.2	1.3844	12.77	614.8	1.3784	0
10	14.44	621.0	.4025	13.73	620.7	.3962	13.09	620.4	.3903	10
20	14.78	626.4	.4138	14.06	626.1	.4077	13.40	625.8	.4018	20
30	15.11	631.7	.4248	14.38	631.5	.4187	13.71	631.2	.4129	30
40	15.45	637.0	.4356	14.70	636.8	.4295	14.02	636.6	.4237	40
50	15.78	642.3	1.4460	15.02	642.1	1.4400	14.32	641.9	1.4342	50
60	16.12	647.5	.4562	15.34	647.3	.4502	14.63	647.1	.4445	60
70	16.45	652.8	.4662	15.65	652.6	.4602	14.93	652.4	.4545	70
80	16.78	658.0	.4760	15.97	657.8	.4700	15.23	657.7	.4643	80
90	17.10	663.2	.4856	16.28	663.1	.4796	15.53	662.9	.4740	90
100	17.43	668.5	1.4950	16.59	668.3	1.4891	15.83	668.1	1.4834	100
110	17.76	673.7	.5042	16.90	673.5	.4983	16.12	673.4	.4927	110
120	18.08	678.9	.5133	17.21	678.8	.5075	16.42	678.6	.5019	120
130	18.41	684.1	.5223	17.52	684.0	.5165	16.72	683.9	.5109	130
140	18.73	689.4	.5312	17.83	689.3	.5253	17.01	689.2	.5197	140
150	19.05	694.7	1.5399	18.14	694.6	1.5340	17.31	694.4	1.5285	150
160	19.37	700.0	.5485	18.44	699.8	.5426	17.60	699.7	.5371	160
170	19.70	705.3	.5569	18.75	705.1	.5510	17.89	705.0	.5456	170
180	20.02	710.6	.5653	19.06	710.5	.5595	18.19	710.4	.5539	180
190	20.34	715.9	.5736	19.36	715.8	.5678	18.48	715.7	.5622	190
200	20.66	721.2	1.5817	19.67	721.1	1.5759	18.77	721.1	1.5704	200
220	21.30	732.0	.5978	20.28	731.9	.5920	19.35	731.8	.5865	220
240	21.94	742.8	.6135	20.89	742.7	.6077	19.94	742.7	.6022	240

TABLE A-15. PROPERTIES OF SUPERHEATED AMMONIA VAPOR

(V = volume in ft ^{3}/lb; H = heat content in Btu/lb;
S = entropy in Btu/lb °F)

Temp. °F	Absolute pressure in lbs./in.^{2} (Saturation temperature in italics.)									Temp °F
	18 −20.81°			19 −18.58°			20 −16.64°			
	V	H	S	V	H	S	V	H	S	
Sat.	14.90	604.8	1.3787	14.17	605.5	1.3748	13.50	606.2	1.3700	Sat.
−20	14.93	605.1	1.3795							−20
−10	15.32	610.7	.3921	14.49	610.3	1.3851	13.74	610.0	1.3784	−10
0	15.70	616.2	1.4042	14.85	615.9	1.3973	14.09	615.5	1.3907	0
10	16.08	621.6	.4158	15.21	621.3	.4090	14.44	621.0	.4025	10
20	16.46	626.9	.4270	15.57	626.7	.4203	14.78	626.4	.4138	20
30	16.83	632.2	.4380	15.93	632.0	.4312	15.11	631.7	.4248	30
40	17.20	637.5	.4486	16.28	637.3	.4419	15.45	637.0	.4356	40
50	17.57	642.7	1.4590	16.63	642.5	1.4523	15.78	642.3	1.4460	50
60	17.94	647.9	.4691	16.98	647.7	.4625	16.12	647.5	.4562	60
70	18.30	653.1	.4790	17.33	653.0	.4724	16.45	652.8	.4662	70
80	18.67	658.4	.4887	17.67	658.2	.4822	16.78	858.0	.4760	80
90	19.03	663.6	.4983	18.02	663.4	.4918	17.10	663.2	.4856	90
100	19.39	668.8	1.5077	18.36	668.6	1.5012	17.43	668.5	1.4950	100
110	19.75	674.0	.5169	18.70	673.8	.5104	17.76	673.7	.5042	110
120	20.11	679.2	.5260	19.04	679.1	.5195	18.08	678.9	.5133	120
130	20.47	684.4	.5349	19.38	684.3	.5285	18.41	684.2	.5223	130
140	20.83	689.7	.5438	19.72	689.5	.5373	18.73	689.4	.5312	140
150	21.19	694.9	1.5525	20.06	694.8	1.5460	19.05	694.7	1.5399	150
160	21.54	700.2	.5610	20.40	700.1	.5546	19.37	700.0	.5485	160
170	21.90	705.5	.5695	20.74	705.4	.5631	19.70	705.3	.5569	170
180	22.26	710.8	.5778	21.09	710.7	.5714	20.02	710.6	.5653	180
190	22.61	716.1	.5861	21.42	716.0	.5797	20.34	715.9	.5736	190
200	22.97	721.4	1.5943	21.75	721.3	1.5878	20.66	721.2	1.5817	200
220	23.68	732.2	.6103	22.43	732.1	.6039	21.30	732.0	.5978	220

Temp. °F	23 −11.85°			24 −9.58°			25 −7.96°			Temp °F
	V	H	S	V	H	S	V	H	S	
Sat.	11.85	608.1	1.3584	11.39	608.6	1.3549	10.96	609.1	1.3515	Sat.
−10	11.89	608.8	1.3600							−10
0	12.20	614.5	1.3726	11.67	614.1	1.3670	11.19	613.8	1.3616	0
10	12.50	620.0	.3846	11.96	619.7	.3791	11.47	619.4	.3738	10
20	12.80	625.5	.3961	12.25	625.2	.3907	11.75	625.0	.3855	20
30	13.10	630.9	.4073	12.54	630.7	.4019	12.03	630.4	.3967	30
40	13.40	636.3	.4181	12.82	636.1	.4128	12.30	635.8	.4077	40
50	13.69	641.6	1.4287	13.11	641.4	1.4234	12.57	641.2	1.4183	50
60	13.98	646.9	.4390	13.39	646.7	.4337	12.84	646.5	.4287	60
70	14.27	652.2	.4491	13.66	652.0	.4438	13.11	651.8	.4388	70
80	14.56	657.5	.4589	13.94	657.3	.4537	13.37	657.1	.4487	80
90	14.84	662.7	.4686	14.22	662.6	.4634	13.64	662.4	.4584	90
100	15.13	668.0	1.4780	14.49	667.8	1.4729	13.90	667.7	1.4679	100
110	15.41	673.2	.4873	14.76	673.1	.4822	14.17	673.0	.4772	110
120	15.70	678.5	.4965	15.04	678.4	.4914	14.43	678.2	.4864	120
130	15.98	683.8	.5055	15.31	683.6	.5004	14.69	683.5	.4954	130
140	16.26	689.0	.5144	15.58	688.9	.5093	14.95	688.8	.5043	140
150	16.55	694.3	1.5231	15.85	694.2	1.5180	15.21	694.1	1.5131	150
160	16.83	699.6	.5317	16.12	699.5	.5266	15.47	699.4	.5217	160
170	17.11	704.9	.5402	16.39	704.8	.5352	15.73	704.7	.5303	170
180	17.39	710.3	.5486	16.66	710.2	.5436	15.99	710.1	.5387	180
190	17.67	715.6	.5569	16.93	715.5	.5518	16.25	715.4	.5470	190
200	17.95	721.0	1.5651	17.20	720.9	1.5600	16.50	720.8	1.5552	200
220	18.51	731.7	.5812	17.73	731.7	.5761	17.02	731.6	.5713	220
240	19.07	742.6	.5969	18.27	742.6	.5919	17.53	742.5	.5870	240

TABLE A-15. PROPERTIES OF SUPERHEATED AMMONIA VAPOR

(V = volume in ft ^{3}/lb; H = heat content in Btu/lb;
S = entropy in Btu/lb °F)

Temp. °F.	Absolute pressure in lbs./in.² (Saturation temperature in italics.)									Temp. °F.
	25 −7.96°			26 −6.39°			27 −4.87°			
	V	H	S	V	H	S	V	H	S	
Sat.	10.96	609.1	1.3515	10.56	609.7	1.3482	10.20	610.2	1.3451	Sat.
0	11.19	613.8	1.3616	10.74	613.4	1.3564	10.33	613.0	1.3513	0
10	11.47	619.4	.3738	11.01	619.1	.3686	10.59	618.8	.3637	10
20	11.75	625.0	.3855	11.28	624.7	.3804	10.85	624.4	.3755	20
30	12.03	630.4	.3967	11.55	630.2	.3917	11.11	629.9	.3869	30
40	12.30	635.8	.4077	11.81	635.6	.4027	11.37	635.4	.3979	40
50	12.57	641.2	1.4183	12.08	641.0	1.4134	11.62	640.8	1.4087	50
60	12.84	646.5	.4287	12.34	646.3	.4238	11.87	646.1	.4191	60
70	13.11	651.8	.4388	12.59	651.6	.4339	12.12	651.5	.4292	70
80	13.37	657.1	.4487	12.85	656.9	.4439	12.37	656.8	.4392	80
90	13.64	662.4	.4584	13.11	662.2	.4536	12.61	662.1	.4489	90
100	13.90	667.7	1.4679	13.36	667.5	1.4631	12.86	667.4	1.4585	100
110	14.17	673.0	.4772	13.61	672.8	.4725	13.10	672.7	.4679	110
120	14.43	678.2	.4864	13.87	678.1	.4817	13.34	678.0	.4771	120
130	14.69	683.5	.4954	14.12	683.4	.4907	13.59	683.3	.4861	130
140	14.95	688.8	.5043	14.37	688.7	.4996	13.83	688.6	.4950	140
150	15.21	694.1	1.5131	14.62	694.0	1.5084	14.07	693.9	1.5038	150
160	15.47	699.4	.5217	14.87	699.3	.5170	14.31	699.2	.5125	160
170	15.73	704.7	.5303	15.12	704.6	.5256	14.55	704.5	.5210	170
180	15.99	710.1	.5387	15.37	710.0	.5340	14.79	709.9	.5295	180
190	16.25	715.4	.5470	15.62	715.3	.5423	15.03	715.2	.5378	190
200	16.50	720.8	1.5552	15.86	720.7	1.5505	15.27	720.6	1.5460	200
220	17.02	731.6	.5713	16.36	731.5	.5666	15.75	731.4	.5621	220
240	17.53	742.5	.5870	16.85	742.4	.5824	16.23	742.3	.5779	240
260	18.04	753.4	.6025	17.35	753.3	.5978	16.70	753.2	.5933	260
	30 −0.57°			31 +0.79°			32 +2.11°			
Sat.	9.236	611.6	1.3364	8.955	612.0	1.3338	8.693	612.4	1.3310	Sat.
10	9.492	617.8	1.3497	9.173	617.4	1.3453	8.874	617.1	1.3411	10
20	9.731	623.5	.3618	9.405	623.2	.3574	9.099	622.9	.3532	20
30	9.966	629.1	.3733	9.633	628.8	.3691	9.321	628.5	.3649	30
40	10.20	634.6	.3845	9.858	634.4	.3803	9.540	634.1	.3762	40
50	10.43	640.1	1.3953	10.08	639.9	1.3912	9.757	639.6	1.3871	50
60	10.65	645.5	.4059	10.30	645.3	.4017	9.972	645.1	.3977	60
70	10.88	650.9	.4161	10.52	650.7	.4120	10.18	650.5	.4080	70
80	11.10	656.2	.4261	10.74	656.1	.4221	10.40	655.9	.4181	80
90	11.33	661.6	.4359	10.96	661.4	.4319	10.61	661.2	.4280	90
100	11.55	666.9	1.4456	11.17	666.7	1.4415	10.81	666.6	1.4376	100
110	11.77	672.2	.4550	11.38	672.1	.4510	11.02	671.9	.4470	110
120	11.99	677.5	.4642	11.60	677.4	.4602	11.23	677.3	.4563	120
130	12.21	682.9	.4733	11.81	682.7	.4693	11.44	682.6	.4655	130
140	12.43	688.2	.4823	12.02	688.1	.4783	11.64	687.9	.4744	140
150	12.65	693.5	1.4911	12.23	693.4	1.4871	11.85	693.3	1.4833	150
160	12.87	698.8	.4998	12.44	698.7	.4958	12.05	698.6	.4920	160
170	13.08	704.2	.5083	12.66	704.1	.5044	12.26	704.0	.5006	170
180	13.30	709.6	.5168	12.87	709.5	.5129	12.46	709.4	.5090	180
190	13.52	714.9	.5251	13.07	714.8	.5212	12.66	714.7	.5174	190
200	13.73	720.3	1.5334	13.28	720.2	1.5294	12.86	720.1	1.5256	200
220	14.16	731.1	.5495	13.70	731.1	.5456	13.27	731.0	.5418	220
240	14.59	742.0	.5653	14.12	742.0	.5614	13.67	741.9	.5576	240
260	15.02	753.0	.5808	14.53	752.9	.5769	14.08	752.9	.5731	260
280	15.45	764.1	.5960	14.95	764.0	.5921	14.48	763.9	.5883	280

TABLE A-15. PROPERTIES OF SUPERHEATED AMMONIA VAPOR

(V = volume in ft ^{3}/lb; H = heat content in Btu/lb;
S = entropy in Btu/lb °F)

Temp. °F.	Absolute pressure in lbs./in.² (Saturation temperature in italics.)									Temp. °F.
	28 −3.40°			**29** −1.97°			**30** −0.57°			
	V	H	S	V	H	S	V	H	S	
Sat.	*9.853*	*610.7*	*1.3421*	*9.534*	*611.1*	*1.3392*	*9.236*	*611.6*	*1.3364*	Sat.
0	9. 942	612. 7	1. 3465	9. 584	612. 3	1. 3417	9. 250	611. 9	1. 3371	0
10	10. 20	618. 4	. 3589	9. 834	618. 1	. 3542	9. 492	617. 8	. 3497	10
20	10. 45	624. 1	. 3708	10. 08	623. 8	. 3662	9. 731	623. 5	. 3618	20
30	10. 70	629. 6	. 3822	10. 32	629. 4	. 3777	9. 966	629. 1	. 3733	30
40	10. 95	635. 1	. 3933	10. 56	634. 9	. 3888	10. 20	634. 6	. 3845	40
50	11. 19	640. 5	1. 4041	10. 80	640. 3	1. 3996	10. 43	640. 1	1. 3953	50
60	11. 44	645. 9	. 4145	11. 03	645. 7	. 4101	10. 65	645. 5	. 4059	60
70	11. 68	651. 2	. 4247	11. 26	651. 1	. 4204	10. 88	650. 9	. 4161	70
80	11. 92	656. 6	. 4347	11. 50	656. 4	. 4304	11. 10	656. 2	. 4261	80
90	12. 15	661. 9	. 4445	11. 73	661. 7	. 4401	11. 33	661. 6	. 4359	90
100	12. 39	667. 2	1. 4540	11. 96	667. 1	1. 4497	11. 55	666. 9	1. 4456	100
110	12. 63	672. 5	. 4634	12. 18	672. 4	. 4591	11. 77	672. 2	. 4550	110
120	12. 86	677. 8	. 4726	12. 41	677. 7	. 4684	11. 99	677. 5	. 4642	120
130	13. 10	683. 1	. 4817	12. 64	683. 0	. 4775	12. 21	682. 9	. 4733	130
140	13. 33	688. 4	. 4906	12. 86	688. 3	. 4864	12. 43	688. 2	. 4823	140
150	13. 56	693. 7	1. 4994	13. 09	693. 6	1. 4952	12. 65	693. 5	1. 4911	150
160	13. 80	699. 1	. 5081	13. 31	699. 0	. 5039	12. 87	698. 8	. 4998	160
170	14. 03	704. 4	. 5167	13. 54	704. 3	. 5124	13. 08	704. 2	. 5083	170
180	14. 26	709. 8	. 5251	13. 76	709. 7	. 5209	13. 30	709. 6	. 5168	180
190	14. 49	715. 1	. 5334	13. 99	715. 0	. 5292	13. 52	714. 9	. 5251	190
200	14. 72	720. 5	1. 5416	14. 21	720. 4	1. 5374	13. 73	720. 3	1. 5334	200
220	15. 18	731. 3	. 5578	14. 65	731. 2	. 5536	14. 16	731. 1	. 5495	220
240	15. 64	742. 2	. 5736	15. 10	742. 2	. 5694	14. 59	742. 0	. 5653	240
260	16. 10	753. 2	. 5890	15. 54	753. 1	. 5848	15. 02	753. 0	. 5808	260
	33 *3.40°*			**34** *4.66°*			**35** *5.89°*			
Sat.	*8.445*	*612.8*	*1.3285*	*8.211*	*613.2*	*1.3260*	*7.991*	*613.6*	*1.3236*	Sat.
10	8. 592	616. 8	1. 3369	8. 328	616. 4	1. 3328	8. 078	616. 1	1. 3289	10
20	8. 812	622. 6	. 3492	8. 542	622. 3	. 3452	8. 287	622. 0	. 3413	20
30	9. 028	628. 3	. 3609	8. 753	628. 0	. 3570	8. 493	627. 7	. 3532	30
40	9. 242	633. 9	. 3722	8. 960	633. 6	. 3684	8. 695	633. 4	. 3646	40
50	9. 452	639. 4	1. 3832	9. 166	639. 2	1. 3793	8. 895	638. 9	1. 3756	50
60	9. 661	644. 9	. 3938	9. 369	644. 7	. 3900	9. 093	644. 4	. 3863	60
70	9. 868	650. 3	. 4042	9. 570	650. 1	. 4004	9. 289	649. 9	. 3967	70
80	10. 07	655. 7	. 4143	9. 770	655. 5	. 4105	9. 484	655. 3	. 4069	80
90	10. 28	661. 1	. 4241	9. 969	660. 9	. 4204	9. 677	660. 7	. 4168	90
100	10. 48	666. 4	1. 4338	10. 17	666. 3	1, 4301	9. 869	666. 1	1. 4265	100
110	10. 68	671. 8	. 4433	10. 36	671. 6	. ′396	10. 06	671. 5	. 4360	110
120	10. 88	677. 1	. 4526	10. 56	677. 0	. 4489	10. 25	676. 8	. 4453	120
130	11. 08	682. 5	. 4617	10. 75	682. 3	. 4581	10. 44	682. 2	. 4545	130
140	11. 28	687. 8	. 4707	10. 95	687. 7	. 4671	10. 63	687. 6	. 4635	140
150	11. 48	693. 2	1. 4795	11. 14	693. 0	1. 4759	10. 82	692. 9	1. 4724	150
160	11. 68	698. 5	. 4883	11. 33	698. 4	. 4846	11. 00	698. 3	. 4811	160
170	11. 88	703. 9	. 4968	11. 53	703. 8	. 4932	11. 19	703. 7	. 4897	170
180	12. 08	709. 3	. 5053	11. 72	709. 2	. 5017	11. 38	709. 1	. 4982	180
190	12. 27	714. 6	. 5137	11. 91	714. 5	. 5101	11. 56	714. 5	. 5066	190
200	12. 47	720. 0	1. 5219	12. 10	720. 0	1. 5183	11. 75	719. 9	1. 5148	200
220	12. 86	730. 9	. 5381	12. 48	730. 8	. 5346	12. 12	730. 7	. 5311	220
240	13. 26	741. 8	. 5540	12. 86	741. 7	. 5504	12. 49	741. 7	. 5469	240
260	13. 65	752. 8	. 5695	13. 24	752. 7	. 5659	12. 86	752. 7	. 5624	260
280	14. 04	763. 9	. 5846	13. 62	763. 8	. 5811	13. 23	763. 7	. 5776	280

TABLE A-15. PROPERTIES OF SUPERHEATED AMMONIA VAPOR

(V = volume in ft ^{3}/lb; H = heat content in Btu/lb;
S = entropy in Btu/lb °F)

Temp. °F.	Absolute pressure in lbs./in.³ (Saturation temperature in italics.)									Temp. °F.
	35 *5.89°*			36 *7.06°*			37 *8.27°*			
	V	*H*	*S*	*V*	*H*	*S*	*V*	*H*	*S*	
Sat.	*7.991*	*615.6*	*1.3256*	*7.782*	*614.0*	*1.3215*	*7.584*	*614.3*	*1.3190*	*Sat.*
10	8.078	616.1	1.3289	7.842	615.7	1.3250	7.619	615.4	1.3212	10
20	8.287	622.0	.3413	8.046	621.7	.3375	7.819	621.4	.3333	20
30	8.493	627.7	.3532	8.247	627.4	.3494	8.015	627.2	.3458	30
40	8.695	633.4	.3646	8.445	633.1	.3609	8.208	632.9	.3573	40
50	8.895	638.9	1.3756	8.640	638.7	1.3720	8.398	638.5	1.3684	50
60	9.093	644.4	.3863	8.833	644.2	.3827	8.587	644.0	.3792	60
70	9.289	649.9	.3967	9.024	649.7	.3932	8.773	649.5	.3897	70
80	9.484	655.3	.4069	9.214	655.2	.4033	8.958	655.0	.3999	80
90	9.677	660.7	.4168	9.402	660.6	.4133	9.142	660.4	.4098	90
100	9.869	666.1	1.4265	9.589	666.0	1.4230	9.324	665.8	1.4196	100
110	10.06	671.5	.4360	9.775	671.3	.4325	9.506	671.2	.4291	110
120	10.25	676.8	.4453	9.961	676.7	.4419	9.686	676.6	.4385	120
130	10.44	682.2	.4545	10.15	682.1	.4510	9.866	681.9	.4477	130
140	10.63	687.6	.4635	10.33	687.4	.4601	10.05	687.3	.4567	140
150	10.82	692.9	1.4724	10.51	692.8	1.4689	10.22	692.7	1.4656	150
160	11.00	698.3	.4811	10.69	698.2	.4777	10.40	698.1	.4744	160
170	11.19	703.7	.4897	10.88	703.6	.4863	10.58	703.5	.4830	170
180	11.38	709.1	.4982	11.06	709.0	.4948	10.76	708.9	.4915	180
190	11.56	714.5	.5066	11.24	714.4	.5032	10.93	714.3	.4999	190
200	11.75	719.9	1.5148	11.42	719.8	1.5115	11.11	719.7	1.5082	200
220	12.12	730.7	.5311	11.78	730.6	.5277	11.46	730.6	.5244	220
240	12.49	741.7	.5469	12.14	741.6	.5436	11.81	741.5	.5403	240
260	12.86	752.7	.5624	12.50	752.6	.5591	12.16	752.5	.5558	260
280	13.23	763.7	.5776	12.86	763.7	.5743	12.51	763.6	.5710	280
	40 *11.66°*			42 *13.81°*			44 *15.88°*			
Sat.	*7.047*	*615.4*	*1.3185*	*6.751*	*616.0*	*1.3084*	*6.442*	*616.6*	*1.3048*	*Sat.*
20	7.203	620.4	1.3231	6.842	619.8	1.3164	6.513	619.1	1.3099	20
30	7.387	626.3	.3353	7.019	625.8	.3287	6.663	625.2	.3224	30
40	7.568	632.1	.3470	7.192	631.6	.3405	6.850	631.1	.3343	40
50	7.746	637.8	1.3583	7.363	637.3	1.3519	7.014	636.8	1.3457	50
60	7.922	643.4	.3692	7.531	643.0	.3628	7.176	642.5	.3567	60
70	8.096	648.9	.3797	7.697	648.5	.3734	7.336	648.1	.3674	70
80	8.268	654.4	.3900	7.862	654.1	.3838	7.494	653.7	.3778	80
90	8.439	659.9	.4000	8.026	659.5	.3939	7.650	659.2	.3880	90
100	8.609	665.3	1.4098	8.188	665.0	1.4037	7.806	664.7	1.3978	100
110	8.777	670.7	.4194	8.349	670.4	.4133	7.960	670.1	.4075	110
120	8.945	676.1	.4288	8.510	675.9	.4228	8.114	675.6	.4170	120
130	9.112	681.5	.4381	8.669	681.3	.4320	8.267	681.0	.4263	130
140	9.278	686.9	.4471	8.828	686.7	.4411	8.419	686.4	.4354	140
150	9.444	692.3	1.4561	8.986	692.1	1.4501	8.570	691.9	1.4444	150
160	9.609	697.7	.4648	9.144	697.5	.4589	8.721	697.3	.4532	160
170	9.774	703.1	.4735	9.301	702.9	.4676	8.871	702.7	.4619	170
180	9.938	708.5	.4820	9.458	708.3	.4761	9.021	708.1	.4704	180
190	10.10	714.0	.4904	9.614	713.8	.4845	9.171	713.6	.4789	190
200	10.27	719.4	1.4987	9.770	719.2	1.4928	9.320	719.0	1.4872	200
220	10.59	730.3	.5150	10.08	730.1	.5091	9.617	730.0	.5035	220
240	10.92	741.3	.5309	10.39	741.1	.5251	9.913	741.0	.5195	240
260	11.24	752.3	.5465	10.70	752.2	.5406	10.21	752.0	.5350	260
280	11.56	763.4	.5617	11.01	763.3	.5559	10.50	763.1	.5503	280
300	11.88	774.6	.5766	11.31	774.5	.5708	10.80	774.3	.5652	300

TABLE A-15. PROPERTIES OF SUPERHEATED AMMONIA VAPOR

(V = volume in ft ³/lb; H = heat content in Btu/lb; S = entropy in Btu/lb °F)

Temp. °F.	Absolute pressure in lbs./in.² (Saturation temperature in italics.)									Temp. °F.
	38 9.42°			39 10.55°			40 11.66°			
	V	H	S	V	H	S	V	H	S	
Sat.	7.396	614.7	1.3168	7.217	615.0	1.3146	7.047	615.4	1.3125	S-t.
10	7.407	615.0	1.3175	....	....	....	....	....	....	10
20	7.603	621.0	.3301	7.398	620.7	1.3266	7.203	620.4	1.3231	20
30	7.795	626.9	.3422	7.586	626.6	.3387	7.387	626.3	.3353	30
40	7.983	632.6	.3538	7.770	632.4	.3504	7.568	632.1	.3470	40
50	8.170	638.3	1.3650	7.952	638.0	1.3616	7.746	637.8	1.3583	50
60	8.353	643.8	.3758	8.132	643.6	.3724	7.922	643.4	.3692	60
70	8.535	649.3	.3863	8.310	649.1	.3830	8.096	648.9	.3797	70
80	8.716	654.8	.3965	8.486	654.6	.3932	8.268	654.4	.3900	80
90	8.895	660.2	.4065	8.661	660.1	.4032	8.439	659.9	.4000	90
100	9.073	635.6	1.4163	8.835	665.5	1.4130	8.609	665.3	1.4098	100
110	9.250	671.0	.4258	9.008	670.9	.4226	8.777	670.7	.4194	110
120	9.426	676.4	.4352	9.179	676.3	.4320	8.945	676.1	.4288	120
130	9.602	681.8	.4444	9.351	681.7	.4412	9.112	681.5	.4381	130
140	9.776	687.2	.4534	9.521	687.1	.4503	9.278	686.9	.4471	140
150	9.950	692.6	1.4623	9.691	692.5	1.4592	9.444	692.3	1.4561	150
160	10.12	698.0	.4711	9.860	697.8	.4679	9.609	697.7	.4648	160
170	10.30	703.3	.4797	10.03	703.2	.4766	9.774	703.1	.4735	170
180	10.47	708.7	.4883	10.20	708.6	.4851	9.938	708.5	.4820	180
190	10.64	714.2	.4966	10.36	714.1	.4935	10.10	714.0	.4904	190
200	10.81	719.6	1.5049	10.53	719.5	1.5018	10.27	719.4	1.4987	200
220	11.16	730.5	.5212	10.87	730.4	.5181	10.59	730.3	.5150	220
240	11.50	741.4	.5371	11.20	741.3	.5340	10.92	741.3	.5309	240
260	11.84	752.4	.5526	11.53	752.4	.5495	11.24	752.3	.5465	260
280	12.18	763.5	.5678	11.86	763.5	.5647	11.56	763.4	.5617	280

Temp. °F.	46 17.87°			48 19.80°			50 21.67°			Temp. °F.
	V	H	S	V	H	S	V	H	S	
Sat.	6.177	617.2	1.3009	5.954	617.7	1.2975	5.710	618.2	1.2939	Sat.
20	6.213	618.5	1.3036	5.937	617.8	1.2976	....	....	....	20
30	6.377	624.6	.3102	6.096	624.0	.3103	5.838	623.4	1.3046	30
40	6.538	630.5	.3283	6.251	630.0	.3223	5.988	629.5	.3169	40
50	6.696	636.4	1.3398	6.404	635.9	1.3341	6.135	635.4	1.3286	50
60	6.851	642.1	.3509	6.554	641.6	.3453	6.280	641.2	.3399	60
70	7.005	647.7	.3617	6.702	647.3	.3561	6.423	646.9	.3508	70
80	7.157	653.3	.3721	6.848	652.9	.3666	6.564	652.6	.3613	80
90	7.308	658.9	.3823	6.993	658.5	.3768	6.704	658.2	.3716	90
100	7.457	664.4	1.3922	7.137	664.0	1.3868	6.843	663.7	1.3816	100
110	7.605	669.8	.4019	7.280	669.5	.3965	6.980	669.2	.3914	110
120	7.753	675.3	.4114	7.421	675.0	.4061	7.117	674.7	.4009	120
130	7.899	680.7	.4207	7.562	680.5	.4154	7.252	680.2	.4103	130
140	8.045	686.2	.4299	7.702	685.9	.4246	7.387	685.7	.4195	140
150	8.190	691.6	1.4389	7.842	691.4	1.4336	7.521	691.1	1.4286	150
160	8.335	697.1	.4477	7.981	696.8	.4425	7.655	696.6	.4374	160
170	8.479	702.5	.4564	8.119	702.3	.4512	7.788	702.1	.4462	170
180	8.623	707.9	.4650	8.257	707.7	.4598	7.921	707.5	.4548	180
190	8.766	713.4	.4735	8.395	713.2	.4683	8.053	713.0	.4633	190
200	8.909	718.8	1.4818	8.532	718.7	1.4766	8.185	718.5	1.4716	200
220	9.194	729.8	.4981	8.805	729.6	.4930	8.448	729.4	.4880	220
240	9.477	740.8	.5141	9.077	740.6	.5090	8.710	740.5	.5040	240
260	9.760	751.9	.5297	9.348	751.7	.5246	8.970	751.6	.5197	260
280	10.04	763.0	.5450	9.619	762.9	.5399	9.230	762.7	.5350	280
300	10.32	774.2	1.5599	9.888	774.1	1.5548	9.489	774.0	1.5500	300

TABLE A-15. PROPERTIES OF SUPERHEATED AMMONIA VAPOR

(V = volume in ft ³/lb; H = heat content in Btu/lb;
S = entropy in Btu/lb °F)

Temp. °F.	Absolute pressure in lbs./in.² (Saturation temperatures in italics.)									Temp. °F.
	50 *21.67°*			**52** *23.48°*			**54** *25.23°*			
	V	H	S	V	H	S	V	H	S	
Sat.	*5.710*	*618.2*	*1.2929*	*5.502*	*618.7*	*1.2906*	*5.309*	*619.5*	*1.2875*	*Sat.*
30	5.838	623.4	1.3046	5.599	622.8	1.2991	5.378	622.2	1.2937	30
40	5.988	629.5	.3169	5.744	629.0	.3114	5.519	628.4	.3062	40
50	6.135	635.4	1.3286	5.887	634.9	1.3233	5.657	634.4	1.3181	50
60	6.280	641.2	.3399	6.027	640.8	.3346	5.793	640.3	.3295	60
70	6.423	646.9	.3508	6.165	646.5	.3456	5.927	646.1	.3406	70
80	6.564	652.6	.3613	6.302	652.2	.3562	6.059	651.8	.3513	80
90	6.704	658.2	.3716	6.437	657.8	.3665	6.190	657.5	.3616	90
100	6.843	663.7	1.3816	6.571	663.4	1.3766	6.319	663.1	1.3717	100
110	6.980	669.2	.3914	6.704	668.9	.3864	6.447	668.6	.3816	110
120	7.117	674.7	.4009	6.835	674.4	.3960	6.575	674.2	.3912	120
130	7.252	680.2	.4103	6.966	679.9	.4054	6.701	679.7	.4006	130
140	7.387	685.7	.4195	7.096	685.4	.4146	6.827	685.2	.4099	140
150	7.521	691.1	1.4286	7.225	690.9	1.4237	6.952	690.7	1.4190	150
160	7.655	696.6	.4374	7.354	696.4	.4326	7.076	696.1	.4279	160
170	7.788	702.1	.4462	7.483	701.8	.4413	7.200	701.6	.4367	170
180	7.921	707.5	.4548	7.611	707.3	.4500	7.323	707.1	.4453	180
190	8.053	713.0	.4633	7.738	712.8	.4585	7.446	712.6	.4538	190
200	8.185	718.5	1.4716	7.865	718.3	1.4668	7.569	718.1	1.4622	200
210	8.317	724.0	.4799	7.992	723.8	.4751	7.691	723.6	.4705	210
220	8.448	729.4	.4880	8.118	729.3	.4833	7.813	729.1	.4787	220
240	8.710	740.5	.5040	8.370	740.3	.4993	8.056	740.2	.4947	240
260	8.970	751.6	.5197	8.621	751.4	.5149	8.298	751.3	.5104	260
280	9.230	762.7	1.5350	8.871	762.6	1.5303	8.539	762.5	1.5257	280
300	9.489	774.0	.5500	9.120	773.8	.5453	8.779	773.7	.5407	300
	60 *30.21°*			**62** *31.78°*			**64** *33.31°*			
	V	H	S	V	H	S	V	H	S	
Sat.	*4.805*	*620.5*	*1.2787*	*4.658*	*620.9*	*1.2759*	*4.519*	*621.3*	*1.2733*	*Sat.*
40	4.933	626.8	1.2913	4.762	626.2	1.2866	4.602	625.6	1.2820	40
50	5.060	632.9	1.3035	4.886	632.4	1.2989	4.723	631.9	1.2944	50
60	5.184	639.0	.3152	5.007	638.5	.3107	4.842	638.0	.3063	60
70	5.307	644.9	.3265	5.127	644.4	.3220	4.958	644.0	.3177	70
80	5.428	650.7	.3373	5.244	650.3	.3330	5.072	649.9	.3287	80
90	5.547	656.4	.3479	5.360	656.0	.3435	5.185	655.7	.3393	90
100	5.665	662.1	1.3581	5.474	661.7	1.3538	5.296	661.4	1.3496	100
110	5.781	667.7	.3681	5.588	667.4	.3638	5.406	667.1	.3597	110
120	5.897	673.3	.3778	5.700	673.0	.3736	5.516	672.7	.3695	120
130	6.012	678.9	.3873	5.811	678.6	.3831	5.624	678.3	.3791	130
140	6.126	684.4	.3966	5.922	684.2	.3925	5.731	683.9	.3885	140
150	6.239	689.9	1.4058	6.032	689.7	1.4017	5.838	689.5	1.3977	150
160	6.352	695.5	.4148	6.142	695.2	.4107	5.944	695.0	.4067	160
170	6.464	701.0	.4236	6.250	700.8	.4195	6.050	700.5	.4156	170
180	6.576	706.5	.4323	6.359	706.3	.4282	6.155	706.1	.4243	180
190	6.687	712.0	.4409	6.467	711.8	.4368	6.260	711.6	.4329	190
200	6.798	717.5	1.4493	6.574	717.3	1.4453	6.364	717.2	1.4413	200
210	6.909	723.1	.4576	6.681	722.9	.4536	6.468	722.7	.4497	210
220	7.019	728.6	.4658	6.788	728.4	.4618	6.572	728.3	.4579	220
230	7.129	734.1	.4739	6.895	734.0	.4699	6.675	733.8	.4660	230
240	7.238	739.7	.4819	7.001	739.5	.4779	6.778	739.4	.4741	240
260	7.457	750.9	1.4976	7.213	750.7	1.4937	6.984	750.6	1.4898	260
280	7.675	762.1	.5130	7.424	761.9	.5091	7.188	761.8	.5052	280
300	7.892	773.3	.5281	7.634	773.2	.5241	7.392	773.1	.5203	300

TABLE A-15. PROPERTIES OF SUPERHEATED AMMONIA VAPOR

(V = volume in ft ^{3}/lb; H = heat content in Btu/lb;
S = entropy in Btu/lb °F)

Temp. °F.	Absolute pressure in lbs./in.² (Saturation temperature in italics.)									Temp. °F.
	56 *26.94°*			58 *28.59°*			60 *30.21°*			
	V	H	S	V	H	S	V	H	S	
Sat.	*5.129*	*619.7*	*1.2844*	*4.962*	*620.1*	*1.2815*	*4.805*	*620.5*	*· 1.2787*	Sat.
30	5.172	621.6	1.2884	4.981	621.0	1.2834				30
40	5.310	627.9	.3011	5.115	627.3	.2961	4.933	626.8	1.2913	40
50	5.444	633.9	1.3131	5.245	633.4	1.3082	5.060	632.9	1.3035	50
60	5.576	639.9	.3246	5.373	639.4	.3199	5.184	639.0	.3152	60
70	5.706	645.7	.3357	5.499	645.3	.3310	5.307	644.9	.3265	70
80	5.834	651.4	.3465	5.624	651.1	.3418	5.428	650.7	.3373	80
90	5.960	657.1	.3569	5.746	656.8	.3523	5.547	656.4	.3479	90
100	6.085	662.7	1.3670	5.868	662.4	1.3625	5.665	662.1	1.3581	100
110	6.209	668.3	.3769	5.988	668.0	.3724	5.781	667.7	.3681	110
120	6.333	673.9	.3866	6.107	673.6	.3821	5.897	673.3	.3778	120
130	6.455	679.4	.3961	6.226	679.1	.3916	6.012	678.9	.3873	130
140	6.576	684.9	.4053	6.343	684.7	.4009	6.126	684.4	.3966	140
150	6.697	690.4	1.4144	6.460	690.2	1.4100	6.239	689.9	1.4058	150
160	6.817	695.9	.4234	6.577	695.7	.4190	6.352	695.5	.4148	160
170	6.937	701.4	.4322	6.692	701.2	.4278	6.464	701.0	.4236	170
180	7.056	706.9	.4408	6.808	706.7	.4365	6.576	706.5	.4323	180
190	7.175	712.4	.4494	6.923	712.2	.4450	6.687	712.0	.4409	190
200	7.294	717.9	1.4578	7.037	717.7	1.4535	6.798	717.5	1.4493	200
210	7.412	723.4	.4661	7.151	723.2	.4618	6.909	723.1	.4576	210
220	7.529	728.9	.4743	7.265	728.8	.4700	7.019	728.6	.4658	220
240	7.764	740.0	.4903	7.492	739.9	.4860	7.238	739.7	.4819	240
260	7.998	751.1	.5060	7.718	751:0	.5017	7.457	750.9	.4976	260
280	8.230	762.3	1.5213	7.943	762.2	.5171	7.675	762.1	1.5130	280
300	8.462	773.6	.5364	8.167	773.5	.5321	7.892	773.3	.5281	300

Temp. °F.	66 *34.81°*			68 *36.27°*			70 *37.70°*			Temp. °F.
	V	H	S	V	H	S	V	H	S	
Sat.	*4.589*	*621.7*	*1.2707*	*4.467*	*622.0*	*1.2682*	*4.351*	*622.4*	*1.2658*	Sat.
40	4.452	625.1	1.2775	4.310	624.5	1.2731	4.177	623.9	1.2688	40
50	4.570	631.4	1.2900	4.426	630.9	1.2858	4.290	630.4	1.2816	50
60	4.686	637.6	.3020	4.539	637.1	.2978	4.401	636.6	.2937	60
70	4.799	643.6	.3135	4.650	643.2	.3094	4.509	642.7	.3054	70
80	4.910	649.5	.3245	4.758	649.1	.3205	4.615	648.7	.3166	80
90	5.020	655.3	.3352	4.865	655.0	.3312	4.719	654.6	.3274	90
100	5.129	661.1	1.3456	4.971	660.7	1.3417	4.822	660.4	1.3378	100
110	5.236	666.8	.3557	5.075	666.5	.3518	4.924	666.1	.3480	110
120	5.342	672.4	.3655	5.179	672.1	.3617	5.025	671.8	.3579	120
130	5.447	678.0	.3751	5.281	677.8	.3713	5.125	677.5	.3676	130
140	5.552	683.6	.3846	5.383	683.4	.3807	5.224	683.1	.3770	140
150	5.656	689.2	1.3938	5.484	689.0	1.3900	5.323	688.7	1.3863	150
160	5.759	694.8	.4028	5.585	694.5	.3991	5.420	694.3	.3954	160
170	5.862	700.3	.4117	5.685	700.1	.4080	5.518	699.9	.4043	170
180	5.964	705.9	.4205	5.784	705.7	.4167	5.615	705.5	.4131	180
190	6.066	711.4	.4291	5.883	711.2	.4254	5.711	711.0	.4217	190
200	6.167	717.0	1.4375	5.982	716.8	1.4338	5.807	716.6	1.4302	200
210	6.268	722.5	.4459	6.080	722.3	.4422	5.902	722.2	.4386	210
220	6.369	728.1	.4541	6.179	727.9	.4505	5.998	727.7	.4469	220
230	6.470	733.7	.4623	6.275	733.5	.4586	6.093	733.3	.4550	230
240	6.570	739.2	.4703	6.373	739.1	.4666	6.187	738.9	.4631	240
260	6.769	750.4	1.4861	6.567	750.3	1.4824	6.376	750.1	1.4789	260
280	6.968	761.7	.5015	6.760	761.5	.4979	6.563	761.4	.4943	280
300	7.165	773.0	.5166	6.952	772.8	.5130	6.750	772.7	.5095	300

TABLE A-15. PROPERTIES OF SUPERHEATED AMMONIA VAPOR

(V = volume in ft ^{3}/lb; H = heat content in Btu/lb; S = entropy in Btu/lb °F)

Temp. °F.	Absolute pressure in lbs./in.² (Saturation temperature in italics.)									Temp. °F.
	75 *41.13°*			80 *44.40°*			85 *47.50°*			
	V	H	S	V	H	S	V	H	S	
Sat.	*3.887*	*683.2*	*1.2599*	*3.855*	*684.0*	*1.2545*	*3.449*	*684.7*	*1.2494*	*Sat.*
50	3.982	629.1	1.2715	3.712	627.7	1.2619	3.473	626.4	1.2527	**50**
60	4.087	635.5	2839	3.812	634.3	.2745	3.569	633.0	.2656	60
70	4.189	641.7	2957	3.909	640.6	.2866	3.662	639.5	.2779	70
80	4.289	647.7	3071	4.005	646.7	.2981	3.753	645.7	2896	80
90	4.388	653.7	3180	4.098	652.8	.3092	3.842	651.8	.3008	90
100	4.485	659.6	1.3286	4.190	658.7	1.3199	3.930	657.8	1.3117	**100**
110	4.581	665.4	.3389	4.281	664.6	.3303	4.016	663.8	.3221	110
120	4.676	671.1	.3489	4.371	670.4	.3404	4.101	669.6	.3323	120
130	4.770	676.8	3586	4.460	676.1	.3502	4.186	675.4	.3422	130
140	4.863	682.5	.3682	4.548	681.8	3598	4.269	681.2	.3519	140
150	4.956	688.1	1.3775	4.635	687.5	1.3692	4.352	686.9	1.3614	**150**
160	5.048	693.7	.3866	4.722	693.2	.3784	4.434	692.6	.3706	160
170	5.139	699.3	3956	4.808	698.8	.3874	4.515	698.2	.3797	170
180	5.230	704.9	.4044	4.893	704.4	.3963	4.596	703.9	.3886	180
190	5.320	710.5	.4131	4.978	710.0	.4050	4.677	709.5	.3974	190
200	5.410	716.1	1.4217	5.063	715.6	1.4136	4.757	715.2	1.4060	**200**
210	5.500	721.7	.4301	5.147	721.3	.4220	4.836	720.8	.4145	210
220	5.589	727.3	.4384	5.231	726.9	.4304	4.916	726.4	.4228	220
230	5.678	732.9	.4466	5.315	732.5	.4386	4.995	732.1	.4311	230
240	5.767	738.5	.4546	5.398	738.1	.4467	5.074	737.7	.4392	240
250	5.855	744.1	1.4625	5.482	743.8	1.4547	5.152	743.4	1.4472	**250**
260	5.943	749.8	.4705	5.565	749.4	.4626	5.230	749.0	.4551	260
280	6.119	761.1	.4860	5.730	760.7	.4781	5.386	760.4	.4707	280
300	6.294	772.4	.5011	5.894	772.1	.4933	5.541	771.8	.4859	300

Temp.	100 *56.06°*			105 *58.67°*			110 *61.21°*			Temp.
Sat.	*2.952*	*686.5*	*1.2356*	*2.817*	*687.0*	*1.2314*	*2.693*	*687.5*	*1.2275*	*Sat.*
70	3.068	636.0	1.2539	2.907	634.9	1.2464	2.761	633.7	1.2392	**70**
80	3.149	642.6	2661	2.985	641.5	2589	2.837	640.5	.2519	80
90	3.227	649.0	.2778	3.061	648.0	2708	2.910	647.0	.2640	90
100	3.304	655.2	1.2891	3.135	654.3	1.2822	2.981	653.4	1.2755	**100**
110	3.380	661.3	.2999	3.208	660.5	.2931	3.051	659.7	.2866	110
120	3.454	667.3	.3104	3.279	666.6	3037	3.120	665.8	.2972	120
130	3.527	673.3	.3206	3.350	672.6	.3139	3.188	671.9	3076	130
140	3.600	679.2	.3305	3.419	678.5	3239	3.255	677.8	.3176	140
150	3.672	685.0	1.3401	3.488	684.4	1.3336	3.321	683.7	1.3274	**150**
160	3.743	690.8	.3495	3.556	690.2	.3431	3.386	689.6	.3370	160
170	3.813	696.6	.3588	3.623	696.0	.3524	3.451	695.4	.3463	170
180	3.883	702.3	.3678	3.690	701.8	.3615	3.515	701.2	.3555	180
190	3.952	708.0	.3767	3.757	707.5	.3704	3.579	707.0	.3644	190
200	4.021	713.7	1.3854	3.823	713.3	1.3792	3.642	712.8	1.3732	**200**
210	4.090	719.4	.3940	3.888	719.0	.3878	3.705	718.5	.3819	210
220	4.158	725.1	.4024	3.954	724.7	.3963	3.768	724.3	.3904	220
230	4.226	730.8	.4108	4.019	730.4	.4046	3.830	730.0	.3988	230
240	4.294	736.5	.4190	4.083	736.1	.4129	3.892	735.7	.4070	240
250	4.361	742.2	1.4271	4.148	741.9	1.4210	3.954	741.5	1.4151	**250**
260	4.428	747.9	.4350	4.212	747.6	.4290	4.015	747.2	.4232	260
270	4.495	753.6	.4429	4.276	753.3	.4369	4.076	752.9	.4311	270
280	4.562	759.4	.4507	4.340	759.0	.4447	4.137	758.7	.4389	280
290	4.629	765.1	.4584	4.403	764.8	.4524	4.198	764.5	.4466	290
300	4.695	770.8	1.4660	4.466	770.5	1.4600	4.259	770.2	1.4543	**300**

TABLE A-15. PROPERTIES OF SUPERHEATED AMMONIA VAPOR

(V = volume in ft ^{3}/lb; H = heat content in Btu/lb;
S = entropy in Btu/lb °F)

Temp. °F.	Absolute pressure in lbs./in.² (Saturation temperature in italics.)									Temp. °F.
	90 *50.47°*			**95** *53.32°*			**100** *56.05°*			
	V	H	S	V	H	S	V	H	S	
Sat.	*3.266*	*625.3*	*1.2445*	*3.101*	*625.9*	*1.2399*	*2.952*	*626.5*	*1.2356*	Sat.
50	....	....	....	3.160	630.5	1.2489	2.985	629.3	1.2409	50
60	3.353	631.8	1.2571	3.160	630.5	1.2489	2.985	629.3	1.2409	60
70	3.442	638.3	.2695	3.245	637.2	.2616	3.068	636.0	.2539	70
80	3.529	644.7	.2814	3.329	643.6	.2736	3.149	642.6	.2661	80
90	3.614	650.9	.2928	3.411	649.9	.2852	3.227	649.0	.2778	90
100	3.698	657.0	1.3038	3.491	656.1	1.2963	3.304	655.2	1.2891	100
110	3.780	663.0	.3144	3.570	662.1	.3070	3.380	661.3	.2999	110
120	3.862	668.9	.3247	3.647	668.1	.3174	3.454	667.3	.3104	120
130	3.942	674.7	.3347	3.724	674.0	.3275	3.527	673.3	.3206	130
140	4.021	680.5	.3444	3.799	679.8	.3373	3.600	679.2	.3305	140
150	4.100	686.3	1.3539	3.874	685.6	1.3469	3.672	685.0	1.3401	150
160	4.178	692.0	.3633	3.949	691.4	.3562	3.743	690.8	.3495	160
170	4.255	697.7	.3724	4.022	697.1	.3654	3.813	696.6	.3588	170
180	4.332	703.4	.3813	4.096	702.8	.3744	3.883	702.3	.3678	180
190	4.408	709.0	.3901	4.168	708.5	.3833	3.952	708.0	.3767	190
200	4.484	714.7	1.3988	4.241	714.2	1.3919	4.021	713.7	1.3854	200
210	4.560	720.4	.4073	4.313	719.9	.4005	4.090	719.4	.3940	210
220	4.635	726.0	.4157	4.384	725.6	.4089	4.158	725.1	.4024	220
230	4.710	731.7	.4239	4.455	731.3	.4172	4.226	730.8	.4108	230
240	4.785	737.3	.4321	4.526	736.9	.4254	4.294	736.5	.4190	240
250	4.859	743.0	1.4401	4.597	742.6	1.4334	4.361	742.2	1.4271	250
260	4.933	748.7	.4481	4.668	748.3	.4414	4.428	747.9	.4350	260
280	5.081	760.0	.4637	4.808	759.7	.4570	4.562	759.4	.4507	280
300	5.228	771.5	.4789	4.947	771.2	.4723	4.695	770.8	.4660	300

Temp. °F.	**115** *63.86°*			**120** *66.02°*			**125** *68.31°*			Temp. °F.
Sat.	*2.580*	*628.2*	*1.2237*	*2.476*	*628.4*	*1.2201*	*2.380*	*628.8*	*1.2166*	Sat.
70	2.628	632.5	1.2323	2.505	631.3	1.2255	2.392	630.0	1.2189	70
80	2.701	639.4	.2451	2.576	638.3	.2386	2.461	637.2	.2322	80
90	2.772	646.0	.2574	2.645	645.0	.2510	2.528	644.0	.2448	90
100	2.841	652.5	1.2690	2.712	651.6	1.2628	2.593	650.7	1.2568	100
110	2.909	658.8	.2802	2.778	658.0	.2741	2.657	657.1	.2682	110
120	2.975	665.0	.2910	2.842	664.2	.2850	2.719	663.5	.2792	120
130	3.040	671.1	.3015	2.905	670.4	.2956	2.780	669.7	.2899	130
140	3.105	677.2	.3116	2.967	676.5	.3058	2.840	675.8	.3002	140
150	3.168	683.1	1.3215	3.029	682.5	1.3157	2.900	681.8	1.3102	150
160	3.231	689.0	.3311	3.089	688.4	.3254	2.958	687.8	.3199	160
170	3.294	694.9	.3405	3.149	694.3	.3348	3.016	693.7	.3294	170
180	3.355	700.7	.3497	3.209	700.2	.3441	3.074	699.6	.3387	180
190	3.417	706.5	.3587	3.268	706.0	.3531	3.131	705.5	.3478	190
200	3.477	712.3	1.3675	3.326	711.8	1.3620	3.187	711.3	1.3567	200
210	3.538	718.1	.3762	3.385	717.6	.3707	3.243	717.2	.3654	210
220	3.598	723.8	.3847	3.442	723.4	.3793	3.299	723.0	.3740	220
230	3.658	729.6	.3931	3.500	729.2	.3877	3.354	728.8	.3825	230
240	3.717	735.3	.4014	3.557	734.9	.3960	3.409	734.5	.3908	240
250	3.776	741.1	1.4096	3.614	740.7	1.4042	3.464	740.3	1.3990	250
260	3.835	746.8	.4176	3.671	746.5	.4123	3.519	746.1	.4071	260
270	3.894	752.6	.4256	3.727	752.2	.4202	3.573	751.9	.4151	270
280	3.952	758.4	.4334	3.783	758.0	.4281	3.627	757.7	.4230	280
290	4.011	764.1	.4411	3.839	763.8	.4359	3.681	763.5	.4308	290
300	4.069	769.9	1.4488	3.895	769.6	1.4435	3.735	769.3	1.4385	300

TABLE A-15. PROPERTIES OF SUPERHEATED AMMONIA VAPOR

(V = volume in ft ³/lb; H = heat content in Btu/lb; S = entropy in Btu/lb °F)

Temp. °F.	Absolute pressure in lbs./in.² (Saturation temperature in italics.)									Temp. °F.
	125 68.31°			130 70.53°			135 73.69°			
	V	H	S	V	H	S	V	H	S	
Sat.	2.380	688.3	1.2166	2.291	689.2	1.2133	2.209	689.8	1.2100	Sat.
80	2.461	637.2	1.2322	2.355	636.0	1.2260	2.257	634.9	1.2199	80
90	2.528	644.0	.2448	2.421	643.0	.2388	2.321	642.0	.2329	90
100	2.593	650.7	1.2568	2.484	649.7	1.2509	2.382	648.8	1.2452	100
110	2.657	657.1	.2682	2.546	656.3	.2625	2.442	655.4	.2569	110
120	2.719	663.5	.2792	2.606	662.7	.2736	2.501	661.9	.2681	120
130	2.780	669.7	.2899	2.665	668.9	.2843	2.559	668.2	.2790	130
140	2.840	675.8	.3002	2.724	675.1	.2947	2.615	674.4	.2894	140
150	2.900	681.8	1.3102	2.781	681.2	1.3048	2.671	680.5	1.2996	150
160	2.958	687.8	.3199	2.838	687.2	.3146	2.726	686.6	.3094	160
170	3.016	693.7	.3294	2.894	693.2	.3241	2.780	692.6	.3191	170
180	3.074	699.6	.3387	2.949	699.1	.3335	2.834	698.6	.3284	180
190	3.131	705.5	.3478	3.004	705.0	.3426	2.887	704.5	.3376	190
200	3.187	711.3	1.3567	3.059	710.9	1.3516	2.940	710.4	1.3466	200
210	3.243	717.2	.3654	3.113	716.7	.3604	2.992	716.2	.3554	210
220	3.299	723.0	.3740	3.167	722.5	.3690	3.044	722.1	.3641	220
230	3.354	728.8	.3825	3.220	728.3	.3775	3.096	727.9	.3726	230
240	3.409	734.5	3908	3.273	734.1	3858	3.147	733.7	3810	240
250	3.464	740.3	1.3990	3.326	739.9	1.3941	3.198	739.6	1.3893	250
260	3.519	746.1	.4071	3.379	745.7	.4022	3.249	745.4	.3974	260
270	3.573	751.9	.4151	3.431	751.5	.4102	3.300	751.2	.4054	270
280	3.627	757.7	↑4230	3.483	757.3	.4181	3.350	757.0	.4133	280
290	3.681	763.5	.4308	3.535	763.1	.4259	3.400	762.8	.4212	290
300	3.735	769.3	1.4385	3.587	769.0	1.4336	3.450	768.6	1.4289	300
320	3.842	780.9	.4536	3.690	780.6	.4487	3.550	780.3	.4441	320

Temp. °F.	150 78.81°			160 83.84°			170 86.29°			Temp. °F.
	V	H	S	V	H	S	V	H	S	
Sat.	1.994	690.5	1.2009	1.872	691.1	1.1958	1.764	691.8	1.1900	Sat.
90	2.061	638.8	1.2161	1.914	636.6	1.2055	1.784	634.4	1.1952	90
100	2.118	645.9	1.2289	1.969	643.9	1.2186	1.837	641.9	1.2087	160
110	2.174	652.8	.2410	2.023	651.0	.2311	1.889	649.1	.2215	110
120	2.228	659.4	.2526	2.075	657.8	.2429	1.939	656.1	.2336	120
130	2.281	665.9	.2638	2.125	664.4	.2542	1.988	662.8	.2452	130
140	2.334	672.3	.2745	2.175	670.9	.2652	2.035	669.4	.2563	140
150	2.385	678.6	1.2849	2.224	677.2	1.2757	2.081	675.9	1.2669	150
160	2.435	684.8	.2949	2.272	683.5	.2859	2.127	682.3	.2773	160
170	2.485	690.9	.3047	2.319	689.7	.2958	2.172	688.5	.2873	170
180	2.534	696.9	.3142	2.365	695.8	.3054	2.216	694.7	.2971	180
190	2.583	702.9	.3236	2.411	701.9	.3148	2.260	700.8	.3066	190
200	2.631	708.9	1.3327	2.457	707.9	1.3240	2.303	706.9	1.3159	200
210	2.679	714.8	.3416	2.502	713.9	.3331	2.346	713.0	.3249	210
220	2.726	720.7	.3504	2.547	719.9	.3419	2.389	719.0	.3338	220
230	2.773	726.6	.8590	2.591	725.8	.3506	2.431	724.9	.3426	230
240	2.820	732.5	.3675	2.635	731.7	.3591	2.473	730.9	.3512	240
250	2.866	738.4	1.3758	2.679	737.6	1.3675	2.514	736.8	1.3596	250
260	2.912	744.3	.3840	2.723	743.5	.3757	2.555	742.8	.3679	260
270	2.958	750.1	.3921	2.766	749.4	.3838	2.596	748.7	.3761	270
280	3.004	756.0	.4001	2.809	755.3	.3919	2.637	754.6	.3841	280
290	3.049	761.8	.4079	2.852	761.2	.3998	2.678	760.5	.3921	290
300	3.095	767.7	1.4157	2.895	767.1	1.4076	2.718	766.4	1.3999	300
320	3.185	779.4	.4310	2.980	778.9	.4229	2.798	778.3	.4153	320
340	3.274	791.2	.4459	3.064	790.7	.4379	2.878	790.1	.4303	340

TABLE A-15. PROPERTIES OF SUPERHEATED AMMONIA VAPOR

(V = volume in ft ³/lb; H = heat content in Btu/lb; S = entropy in Btu/lb °F)

Temp. °F.	Absolute pressure in lbs./in.² (Saturation temperature in Italics.)									Temp. °F.
	140 74.79°			145 76.85°			150 78.81°			
	V	H	S	V	H	S	V	H	S	
Sat.	3.132	629.9	1.2068	3.061	630.2	1.2055	2.994	630.5	1.2009	Sat.
80	2.166	633.8	1.2140	2.080	632.6	1.2082	2.001	631.4	1.2025	80
90	2.228	640.9	.2272	2.141	639.9	.2216	2.061	638.8	.2161	90
100	2.288	647.8	1.2396	2.200	646.9	1.2342	2.118	645.9	1.2289	100
110	2.347	654.5	.2515	2.257	653.6	.2462	2.174	652.8	.2410	110
120	2.404	661.1	.2628	2.313	660.2	.2577	2.228	659.4	.2526	120
130	2.460	667.4	.2738	2.368	666.7	.2687	2.281	665.9	.2638	130
140	2.515	673.7	.2843	2.421	673.0	.2793	2.334	672.3	.2745	140
150	2.569	679.9	1.2945	2.474	679.2	1.2896	2.385	678.6	1.2849	150
160	2.622	686.0	.3045	2.526	685.4	.2996	2.435	684.8	.2949	160
170	2.675	692.0	.3141	2.577	691.4	.3093	2.485	690.9	.3047	170
180	2.727	698.0	.3236	2.627	697.5	.3188	2.534	696.9	.3142	180
190	2.779	704.0	.3328	2.677	703.4	.3281	2.583	702.9	.3236	190
200	2.830	709.9	1.3418	2.727	709.4	1.3372	2.631	708.9	1.3327	200
210	2.880	715.8	.3507	2.776	715.3	.3461	2.679	714.8	.3416	210
220	2.931	721.6	.3594	2.825	721.2	.3548	2.726	720.7	.3504	220
230	2.981	727.5	.3679	2.873	727.1	.3634	2.773	726.6	.3590	230
240	3.030	733.3	.3763	2.921	732.9	.3718	2.820	732.5	.3675	240
250	3.080	739.2	1.3846	2.969	738.8	1.3801	2.866	738.4	1.3758	250
260	3.129	745.0	.3928	3.017	744.6	.3883	2.912	744.3	.3840	260
270	3.179	750.8	.4008	3.064	750.5	.3964	2.958	750.1	.3921	270
280	3.227	756.7	.4088	3.111	756.3	.4043	3.004	756.0	.4001	280
290	3.275	762.5	.4166	3.158	762.2	.4122	3.049	761.8	.4079	290
300	3.323	768.3	1.4243	3.205	768.0	1.4199	3.095	767.7	1.4157	300
320	3.420	780.0	.4395	3.298	779.7	.4352	3.185	779.4	.4310	320

Temp. °F.	180 89.78°			190 93.15°			200 96.34°			Temp. °F.
	V	H	S	V	H	S	V	H	S	
Sat.	1.867	638.0	1.1850	1.581	638.4	1.1892	1.502	638.7	1.1756	Sat.
90	1.668	632.2	1.1853	....			....			90
100	1.720	639.9	1.1992	1.615	637.8	1.1899	1.520	635.6	1.1809	100
110	1.770	647.3	.2123	1.663	645.4	.2034	1.567	643.4	.1947	110
120	1.818	654.4	.2247	1.710	652.6	.2160	1.612	650.9	.2077	120
130	1.865	661.3	.2364	1.755	659.7	.2281	1.656	658.1	.2200	130
140	1.910	668.0	.2477	1.799	666.5	.2396	1.698	665.0	.2317	140
150	1.955	674.6	1.2586	1.842	673.2	1.2506	1.740	671.8	1.2429	150
160	1.999	681.0	.2691	1.884	679.7	.2612	1.780	678.4	.2537	160
170	2.042	687.3	.2792	1.925	686.1	.2715	1.820	684.9	.2641	170
180	2.084	693.6	.2891	1.966	692.5	.2815	1.859	691.3	.2742	180
190	2.126	699.8	.2987	2.005	698.7	.2912	1.897	697.7	.2840	190
200	2.167	705.9	1.3081	2.045	704.9	1.3007	1.935	703.9	1.2935	200
210	2.208	712.0	.3172	2.084	711.1	.3099	1.972	710.1	.3029	210
220	2.248	718.1	.3262	2.123	717.2	.3189	2.009	716.3	.3120	220
230	2.288	724.1	.3350	2.161	723.2	.3278	2.046	722.4	.3209	230
240	2.328	730.1	.3436	2.199	729.3	.3365	2.082	728.4	.3296	240
250	2.367	736.1	1.3521	2.236	735.3	1.3450	2.118	734.5	1.3382	250
260	2.407	742.0	.3605	2.274	741.3	.3534	2.154	740.5	.3467	260
270	2.446	748.0	.3687	2.311	747.3	.3617	2.189	746.5	.3550	270
280	2.484	753.9	.3768	2.348	753.2	.3698	2.225	752.5	.3631	280
290	2.523	759.9	.3847	2.384	759.2	.3778	2.260	758.5	.3712	290
300	2.561	765.8	1.3926	2.421	765.2	1.3857	2.295	764.5	1.3791	300
320	2.637	777.7	.4081	2.493	777.1	.4012	2.364	776.5	.3947	320
340	2.713	789.6	.4231	2.565	789.0	.4163	2.432	788.5	.4099	340

Table A-15. Properties of Superheated Ammonia Vapor

(V = volume in ft ^{3}/lb; H = heat content in Btu/lb;
S = entropy in Btu/lb °F)

Temp. °C.	Absolute pressure in lbs./in.^{2} (Saturation temperature in italics.)									Temp. °F.
	200 *96.34°*			**210** *99.45°*			**220** *102.42°*			
	V	*H*	*S*	*V*	*H*	*S*	*V*	*H*	*S*	
Sat.	*1.502*	*652.7*	*1.1756*	*1.451*	*653.0*	*1.1715*	*1.367*	*653.2*	*1.1671*	*Sat.*
110	1.567	643.4	1.1947	1.480	641.5	1.1863	1.400	639.4	1.1781	110
120	1.612	650.9	.2077	1.524	649.1	.1996	1.443	647.3	.1917	120
130	1.656	658.1	.2200	1.566	656.4	.2121	1.485	654.8	.2045	130
140	1.698	665.0	.2317	1.608	663.5	.2240	1.525	662.0	.2167	140
150	1.740	671.8	1.2429	1.648	670.4	1,2354	1.564	669.0	1.2281	**150**
160	1.780	678.4	.2537	1.687	677.1	.2464	1.601	675.8	.2394	160
170	1.820	684.9	.2641	1.725	683.7	.2569	1.638	682.5	.2501	170
180	1.859	691.3	72742	1.762	690.2	.2672	1.675	689.1	.2604	180
190	1.897	697.7	.2840	1.799	696.6	.2771	1.710	695.5	.2704	190
200	1.935	703.9	1.2935	1.836	702.9	1.2867	1.745	701.9	1.2801	**200**
210	1.972	710.1	.3029	1.872	709.2	.2961	1.780	708.2	.2896	210
220	2.009	716.3	.3120	1.907	715.3	.3053	1.814	714.4	.2989	220
230	2.046	722.4	.3209	1.942	721.5	.3143	1.848	720.6	.3079	230
240	2.082	728.4	.3296	1.977	727.6	.3231	1.881	726.8	.3168	240
250	2.118	734.5	1.3382	2.011	733.7	1.3317	1.914	732.9	1.3255	**250**
260	2.154	740.5	.3467	2.046	739.8	.3402	1.947	739.0	.3340	260
270	2.189	746.5	.3550	2.080	745.8	.3486	1.980	745.1	.3424	270
280	2.225	752.5	.3631	2.113	751.8	.3568	2.012	751.1	.3507	280
290	2.260	758.5	.3712	2.147	757.9	.3649	2.044	757.2	.3588	290
300	2.295	764.5	1.3791	2.180	763.9	1.3728	2.076	763.2	1.3668	**300**
320	2.364	776.5	.3947	2.246	775.9	.3884	2.140	775.3	.3825	320
340	2.432	788.5	.4099	2.312	787.9	.4037	2.203	787.4	.3978	340
360	2.500	800.5	.4247	2.377	800.0	.4186	2.265	799.5	.4127	360
380	2.568	812.5	.4392	2.442	812.0	.4331	2.327	811.6	.4273	380

Temp. °C.	**250** *110.80°*			**260** *113.42°*			**270** *115.97°*			Temp. °F.
Sat.	*1.202*	*653.2*	*1.1555*	*1.155*	*653.9*	*1.1518*	*1.112*	*653.9*	*1.1483*	*Sat.*
120	1.240	641.5	1.1690	1.182	639.5	1.1617	1.128	637.5	1.1544	120
130	1.278	649.6	.1827	1.220	647.8	.1757	1.166	645.9	.1689	130
140	1.316	657.2	.1956	1.257	655.6	.1889	1.202	653.9	.1823	140
150	1.352	664.6	1.2078	1.292	663.1	1.2014	1.236	661.6	1.1950	**150**
160	1.386	671.8	.2195	1.326	670.4	.2132	1.269	669.0	.2071	160
170	1.420	678.7	.2306	1.359	677.5	.2245	1.302	676.2	.2185	170
180	1.453	685.5	.2414	1.391	684.4	.2354	1.333	683.2	.2296	180
190	1.486	692.2	.2517	1.422	691.1	.2458	1.364	690.0	.2401	190
200	1.518	698.8	1.2617	1.453	697.7	1.2560	1.394	696.7	1.2504	**200**
210	1.549	705.3	.2715	1.484	704.3	.2658	1.423	703.3	.2603	210
220	1.580	711.7	.2810	1.514	710.7	.2754	1.452	709.8	.2700	220
230	1.610	718.0	.2902	1.543	717.1	.2847	1.481	716.2	.2794	·230
240	1.640	724.3	.2993	1.572	723.4	.2938	1.509	722.6	.2885	240
250	1.670	730.5	1.3081	1.601	729.7	1.3027	1.537	728.9	1.2975	**250**
260	1.699	736.7	.3168	1.630	736.0	.3115	1.565	735.2	.3063	260
270	1.729	742.9	.3253	1.658	742.2	.3200	1.592	741.4	.3149	270
280	1.758	749.1	.3337	1.686	748.4	.3285	1.620	747.7	.3234	280
290	1.786	755.2	.3420	1.714	754.5	.3367	1.646	753.9	.3317	290
300	1.815	761.3	1.3501	1.741	760.7	1.3449	1.673	760.0	1.3399	**300**
320	1.872	773.5	.3659	1.796	772.9	.3608	1.726	772.3	.3559	320
340	1.928	785.7	.3814	1.850	785.2	.3763	1.778	784.6	.3714	340
360	1.983	797.9	.3964	1.904	797.4	.3914	1.830	796.9	.3866	360
380	2.038	810.1	.4111	1.957	809.6	.4062	1.881	809.1	.4014	380
400	2.093	822.3	1.4255	2.009	821.9	1.4206	1.932	821.4	1.4158	**400**

TABLE A-15. PROPERTIES OF SUPERHEATED AMMONIA VAPOR

(V = volume in ft ^{3}/lb; H = heat content in Btu/lb;
S = entropy in Btu/lb °F)

Temp. °F.	Absolute pressure in lbs./in.² (Saturation temperature in italics.)									Temp. °F.
	230 *105.30°*			240 *108.09°*			250 *110.80°*			
	V	*H*	*S*	*V*	*H*	*S*	*V*	*H*	*S*	
Sat.	*1.307*	*635.4*	*1.1651*	*1.253*	*635.6*	*1.1592*	*1.202*	*635.8*	*1.1555*	*Sat.*
110	1.328	637.4	1.1700	1.261	635.3	1.1621				110
120	1.370	645.4	.1840	1.302	643.5	.1764	1.240	641.5	1.1690	120
130	1.410	,653.1	.1971	1.342	651.3	.1898	1,278	649.6	.1827	130
140	1.449	660.4	.2095	1.380	658.8	.2025	1.316	657.2	.1956	140
150	1.487	667.6	1.2213	1.416	666.1	1.2145	1.352	664.6	1,2078	150
160	1.524	674.5	.2325	1.452	673.1	.2259	1.386	671.8	.2195	160
170	1.559	681.3	.2434	1.487	680.0	.2369	1.420	678.7	.2306	170
180	1.594	687.9	.2538	1.521	686.7	.2475	1.453	685.5	.2414	180
190	1.629	694.4	.2640	1.554	693.3	.2577	1.486	692.2	.2517	190
200	1.663	700.9	1.2738	1.587	699.8	1.2677	1.518	698.8	1.2617	200
210	1.696	707.2	.2834	1.619	706.2	.2773	1.549	705.3	.2715	210
220	1.729	713.5	.2927	1.651	712.6	.2867	1.580	711.7	.2810	220
230	1.762	719.8	.3018	1.683	718.9	.2959	1.610	718.0	.2902	230
240	1.794	726.0	.3107	1.714	725.1	.3049	1.640	724.3	.2993	240
250	1.826	732.1	1.3195	1.745	731.3	1.3137	1.670	730.5	1.3081	250
260	1.857	738.3	.3281	1.775	737.5	.3224	1.699	736.7	.3168	260
270	1.889	744.4	.3365	1.805	743.6	.3308	1.729	742.9	.3253	270
280	1.920	750.5	.3448	1.835	749.8	.3392	1.758	749.1	.3337	280
290	1.951	756.5	.3530	1.865	755.9	.3474	1.786	755.2	.3420	290
300	1.982	762.6	1.3610	1.895	762.0	1.3554	1.815	761.3	1.3501	300
320	2.043	774.7	.3767	1.954	774.1	.3712	1.872	773.5	.3659	320
340	2.103	786.8	.3921	2.012	786.3	.3866	1.928	785.7	.3814	340
360	2.163	798.9	.4070	2.069	798.4	.4016	1.983	797.9	.3964	360
380	2.222	811.1	.4217	2.126	810.6	.4163	2.038	810.1	.4111	380

Temp. °F.	280 *118.45°*			290 *120.86°*			300 *123.21°*			Temp. °F.
	V	*H*	*S*	*V*	*H*	*S*	*V*	*H*	*S*	
Sat.	*1.072*	*634.0*	*1.1449*	*1.034*	*634.0*	*1.1415*	*0.999*	*634.0*	*1.1383*	*Sat.*
120	1.078	635.4	1.1473							120
130	1.115	644.0	.1621	1.068	642.1	1.1554	1.023	640.1	1.1487	130
140	1.151	652.2	.1759	1.103	650.5	.1695	1.058	648.7	.1632	140
150	1.184	660.1	1.1888	1.136	658.5	1.1827	1.091	656.9	1.1767	150
160	1.217	667.6	.2011	1.168	666.1	.1952	1.123	664.7	.1894	160
170	1.249	674.9	.2127	1.199	673.5	.2070	1.153	672.2	.2014	170
180	1.279	681.9	.2239	1.229	680.7	.2183	1.183	679.5	.2129	180
190	1.309	688.9	.2346	1.259	687.7	.2292	1.211	686.5	.2239	190
200	1.339	695.6	1.2449	1.287	694.6	1.2396	1.239	693.5	1.2344	200
210	1.367	702.3	.2550	1.315	701.3	.2497	1.267	700.3	.2447	210
220	1.396	708.8	.2647	1,343	707.9	.2596	1.294	706.9	.2546	220
230	1.424	715.3	.2742	1.370	714.4	.2691	1.320	713.5	.2642	230
240	1.451	721.8	.2834	1.397	720.9	.2784	1.346	720.0	.2736	240
250	1.478	728.1	1.2924	1.423	727.3	1.2875	1.372	726.5	1.2827	250
260	1.505	734.4	.3013	1.449	733.7	.2964	1.397	732.9	.2917	260
270	1.532	740.7	.3099	1.475	740.0	.3051	1.422	739.2	.3004	270
280	1.558	747.0	.3184	1.501	746.3	.3137	1.447	745.5	.3090	280
290	1.584	753.2	.3268	1.526	752.5	.3221	1.472	751.8	.3175	290
300	1.610	759.4	1.3350	1.551	758.7	1.3303	1.496	758.1	1.3257	300
320	1.661	771.7	.3511	1.601	771.1	.3464	1.544	770.5	.3419	320
340	1.712	784.0	.3667	1.650	783.5	.3621	1.592	782.9	.3576	340
360	1.762	796.3	.3819	1.698	795.8	.3773	1.639	795.3	.3729	360
380	1.811	808.7	.3967	1.747	808.2	.3922	1.686	807.7	.3878	380
400	1.861	821.0	1.4112	1.794	820.5	1.4067	1.732	820.1	1.4024	400

TABLE A-15. REFRIGERANT 11, TRICHLOROMONOFLUOROMETHANE (CCl$_3$F)
PROPERTIES OF SATURATED VAPOR

Temp.	Pressure		Volume		Density		Heat Content from —40°			Entropy from —40°		Temp.
°F.	Abs. lb./in.²	Gage lb./in.²	Liquid ft.³/lb.	Vapor ft.³/lb.	Liquid lb./ft.³	Vapor lb./ft.³	Liquid Btu./lb.	Latent Btu./lb.	Vapor Btu./lb.	Liquid Btu./lb.°F.	Vapor Btu./lb.°F.	°F.
t	p	p_d	v_f	v_g	1/v_f	1/v_g	h_f	h	h_g	s_f	s_g	t
—40	0.7391	28.42*	0.00988	44.21	101.25	0.02262	0.00	87.48	87.48	0.0000	0.2085	—40
—38	0.7916	28.31*	.00989	41.47	101.10	.02411	0.39	87.33	87.72	.0009	.2081	—38
—36	0.8471	28.20*	.00991	38.93	100.96	.02569	0.79	87.17	87.96	.0019	.2076	—36
—34	0.9060	28.08*	.00992	36.57	100.81	.02735	1.18	87.02	88.20	.0028	.2072	—34
—32	0.9682	27.95*	.00993	34.37	100.66	.02910	1.58	86.86	88.44	.0037	.2068	—32
—30	1.034	27.81*	0.00995	32.33	100.52	0.03093	1.97	86.70	88.67	0.0046	0.2064	—30
—28	1.103	27.67*	.00996	30.44	100.37	.03285	2.36	86.55	88.91	.0055	.2060	—28
—26	1.176	27.53*	.00998	28.68	100.22	.03487	2.75	86.40	89.15	.0064	.2057	—26
—24	1.253	27.37*	.00999	27.03	100.07	.03700	3.15	86.24	89.39	.0073	.2053	—24
—22	1.334	27.20*	.01001	25.50	99.92	.03922	3.55	86.08	89.63	.0082	.2049	—22
—20	1.420	27.03*	0.01002	24.06	99.77	0.04157	3.94	85.93	89.87	0.0091	0.2046	—20
—18	1.510	26.85*	.01004	22.72	99.63	.04401	4.33	85.78	90.11	.0100	.2043	—18
—16	1.605	26.65*	.01005	21.47	99.48	.04658	4.73	85.62	90.35	.0109	.2040	—16
—14	1.705	26.45*	.01007	20.30	99.33	.04927	5.12	85.47	90.59	.0118	.2036	—14
—12	1.810	26.24*	.01008	19.20	99.18	.05209	5.52	85.31	90.83	.0127	.2033	—12
—10	1.920	26.01*	0.01010	18.17	99.03	0.05503	5.91	85.16	91.07	0.0136	0.2030	—10
— 8	2.035	25.78*	.01011	17.21	98.87	.05810	6.31	85.00	91.31	.0145	.2027	— 8
— 6	2.156	25.53*	.01013	16.32	98.72	.06129	6.70	84.85	91.55	.0153	.2024	— 6
— 4	2.283	25.27*	.01015	15.47	98.57	.06464	7.10	84.69	91.79	.0162	.2021	— 4
— 2	2.416	25.00*	.01016	14.68	98.42	.06813	7.49	84.54	92.03	.0171	.2018	— 2
0	2.555	24.72*	0.01018	13.94	98.27	0.07176	7.89	84.38	92.27	0.0179	0.2015	0
2	2.700	24.42*	.01019	13.24	98.11	.07554	8.28	84.23	92.51	.0188	.2013	2
4	2.852	24.11*	.01021	12.58	97.96	.07949	8.68	84.07	92.75	.0197	.2010	4
5†	2.931	23.95*	.01022	12.27	97.88	.08152	8.88	84.00	92.88	.0201	.2009	5†
6	3.012	23.79*	.01022	11.96	97.81	.08361	9.08	83.92	93.00	.0205	.2008	6
8	3.179	23.45`	.01024	11.38	97.65	.08790	9.48	83.76	93.24	.0213	.2005	8
10	3.352	23.10*	0.01026	10.83	97.50	0.09233	9.88	83.60	93.48	0.0222	0.2003	10
12	3.534	22.73*	.01027	10.31	97.34	.09697	10.28	83.45	93.72	.0231	.2000	12
14	3.724	22.34*	.01029	9.823	97.19	.1018	10.68	83.29	93.97	.0239	.1998	14
16	3.923	21.94*	.01031	9.359	97.03	.1068	11.07	83.14	94.21	.0248	.1996	16
18	4.129	21.52*	.01032	8.925	96.88	.1120	11.47	82.98	94.45	.0256	.1993	18
20	4.342	21.08*	0.01034	8.519	96.72	0.1174	11.87	82.82	94.69	0.0264	0.1991	20
22	4.567	20.62*	.01036	8.129	96.57	.1230	12.27	82.66	94.94	.0273	.1989	22
24	4.801	20.15*	.01037	7.760	96.41	.1289	12.68	82.50	95.18	.0281	.1987	24
26	5.043	19.66*	.01039	7.414	96.25	.1349	13.08	82.34	95.42	.0289	.1985	26
28	5.294	19.14*	.01041	7.087	96.10	.1411	13.48	82.18	95.66	.0297	.1983	28
30	5.557	18.61*	0.01042	6.776	95.94	0.1476	13.88	82.03	95.91	0.0306	0.1981	30
32	5.830	18.05*	.01044	6.481	95.78	.1543	14.28	81.87	96.15	.0314	.1979	32
34	6.115	17.47*	.01046	6.200	95.62	.1613	14.68	81.71	96.39	.0322	.1977	34
36	6.411	16.87*	.01048	5.934	95.46	.1685	15.08	81.55	96.63	.0330	.1976	36
38	6.718	16.25*	.01049	5.682	95.30	.1760	15.49	81.38	96.87	.0338	.1974	38
40	7.032	15.61*	0.01051	5.447	95.14	0.1836	15.89	81.22	97.11	0.0346	0.1972	40
42	7.362	14.94*	.01053	5.220	94.98	.1916	16.30	81.06	97.36	.0354	.1970	42
44	7.702	14.24*	.01055	5.006	94.82	.1998	16.70	80.90	97.60	.0362	.1969	44
46	8.055	13.52*	.01056	4.802	94.66	.2083	17.11	80.73	97.84	.0370	.1967	46
48	8.422	12.78*	.01058	4.607	94.50	.2170	17.52	80.57	98.08	.0378	.1966	48
50	8.804	12.00*	0.01060	4.421	94.34	0.2262	17.92	80.40	98.32	0.0386	0.1964	50
52	9.199	11.20*	.01062	4.245	94.18	.2356	18.33	80.24	98.56	.0394	.1963	52
54	9.605	10.37*	.01064	4.078	94.02	.2452	18.74	80.07	98.81	.0402	.1961	54
56	10.02	9.53*	.01066	3.921	93.85	.2550	19.15	79.90	99.05	.0410	.1960	56
58	10.45	8.65*	.01067	3.770	93.69	.2652	19.56	79.73	99.29	.0418	.1959	58
60	10.90	7.73*	0.01069	3.626	93.53	0.2758	19.96	79.57	99.53	0.0426	0.1958	60
62	11.37	6.78*	.01071	3.487	93.36	.2868	20.37	79.40	99.77	.0434	.1956	62
64	11.85	5.80*	.01073	3.356	93.20	.2980	20.78	79.23	100.01	.0442	.1955	64
66	12.35	4.78*	.01075	3.229	93.04	.3097	21.19	79.06	100.25	.0450	.1954	66
68	12.87	3.72*	.01077	3.107	92.87	.3219	21.61	78.88	100.49	.0457	.1953	68
70	13.40	2.64†	0.01079	2.993	92.71	0.3342	22.02	78.71	100.73	0.0465	0.1951	70
72	13.95	1.53*	.01081	2.883	92.54	.3469	22.43	78.54	100.97	.0473	.1950	72
74	14.51	0.39*	.01083	2.779	92.38	.3598	22.84	78.37	101.21	.0481	.1949	74
76	15.09	0.39	.01085	2.679	92.21	.3732	23.26	78.19	101.45	.0489	.1948	76
78	15.69	0.99	.01086	2.584	92.04	.3870	23.68	78.01	101.69	.0496	.1947	78

* Inches of mercury below one atmosphere.
† Standard ton temperature

TABLE A-15. REFRIGERANT 11, TRICHLOROMONOFLUOROMETHANE (CCl₃F)
PROPERTIES OF SATURATED VAPOR

Temp.	Pressure		Volume		Density		Heat Content from −40°			Entropy from −40°		Temp
°F.	Abs. lb./in.²	Gage lb./in.²	Liquid ft.³/lb.	Vapor ft.³/lb.	Liquid lb./ft.³	Vapor lb./ft.³	Liquid Btu./lb.	Latent Btu./lb.	Vapor Btu./lb.	Liquid Btu./lb.°F.	Vapor Btu./lb.°F.	°F.
t	p	p_d	v_f	v_g	1/v_f	1/v_g	h_f	h	h_g	s_f	s_g	t
80	16.31	1.61	0.01088	2.492	91.88	0.4012	24.09	77.84	101.93	0.0504	0.1947	80
82	16.94	2.24	.01090	2.406	91.71	.4157	24.51	77.66	102.17	.0512	.1946	82
84	17.60	2.90	.01092	2.322	91.54	.4307	24.93	77.48	102.41	.0519	.1945	84
86†	18.28	3.58	.01094	2.242	91.38	.4461	25.34	77.31	102.65	.0527	.1944	86†
88	18.97	4.27	.01096	2.165	91.21	.4619	25.76	77.13	102.89	.0535	.1943	88
90	19.69	4.99	0.01098	2.091	91.04	0.4783	26.18	76.95	103.12	0.0542	0.1942	90
92	20.43	5.73	.01101	2.020	90.87	.4950	26.60	76.76	103.36	.0550	.1941	92
94	21.19	6.49	.01103	1.952	90.70	.5122	27.01	76.58	103.59	.0557	.1941	94
96	21.97	7.27	.01105	1.887	90.53	.5299	27.43	76.40	103.83	.0565	.1940	96
98	22.77	8.07	.01107	1.825	90.36	.5480	27.85	76.21	104.07	.0572	.1939	98
100	23.60	8.90	0.01109	1.765	90.19	0.5666	28.27	76.03	104.30	0.0580	0.1938	100
102	24.45	9.75	.01111	1.707	90.02	.5857	28.70	75.84	104.54	.0587	.1938	102
104	25.33	10.63	.01113	1.652	89.85	.6054	29.12	75.65	104.77	.0595	.1937	104
106	26.23	11.53	.01115	1.599	89.68	.6256	29.54	75.46	105.00	.0602	.1937	106
108	27.15	12.45	.01117	1.548	89.51	.6461	29.97	75.27	105.24	.0610	.1936	108
110	28.09	13.39	0.01119	1.499	89.34	0.6671	30.40	75.08	105.47	0.0617	0.1935	110
112	29.05	14.35	.01122	1.452	89.16	.6885	30.82	74.89	105.71	.0625	.1935	112
114	30.04	15.34	.01124	1.407	88.99	.7107	31.24	74.70	105.9₀	.0632	.1935	114
116	31.07	16.37	.01126	1.363	88.82	.7335	31.67	74.50	106.17	.0639	.1934	116
118	32.11	17.41	.01128	1.321	88.65	.7570	32.10	74.30	106.40	.0647	.1933	118
120	33.20	18.50	0.01130	1.281	88.47	0.7808	32.53	74.10	106.63	0.0654	0.1933	120
122	34.29	19.59	.01133	1.243	88.30	.8049	32.95	73.91	106.86	.0661	.1932	122
124	35.42	20.72	.01135	1.206	88.12	.8296	33.38	73.71	107.09	.0669	.1932	124
126	36.56	21.86	.01137	1.170	87.95	.8550	33.81	73.51	107.32	.0676	.1931	126
128	37.74	23.04	.01139	1.135	87.77	.8811	34.24	73.31	107.55	.0683	.1931	128
130	38.96	24.26	0.01142	1.101	87.60	0.9080	34.67	73.11	107.78	0.0691	0.1931	130
132	40.23	25.53	.01144	1.068	87.42	.9361	35.10	72.90	108.00	.0698	.1930	132
134	41.50	26.80	.01146	1.037	87.25	.9646	35.54	72.69	108.23	.0705	.1929	134
136	42.80	28.10	.01149	1.007	87.07	0.9927	35.97	72.49	108.46	.0712	.1929	136
138	44.12	29.42	.01151	.9785	86.88	1.022	36.40	72.28	108.68	.0719	.1929	138
140	45.50	30.80	0.01154	0.9505	86.69	1.052	36.84	72.07	108.91	0.0727	0.1929	140
142	46.92	32.22	.01156	.9231	86.50	1.083	37.28	71.85	109.13	.0734	.1928	142
144	48.35	33.65	.01159	.8970	86.32	1.115	37.71	71.64	109.35	.0741	.1928	144
146	49.81	35.11	.01161	.8719	86.14	1.147	38.15	71.43	109.58	.0748	.1928	146
148	51.31	36.61	.01163	.8476	85.96	1.180	38.59	71.21	109.80	.0755	.1927	148
150	52.85	38.15	0.01166	0.8240	85.78	1.214	39.02	71.00	110.02	0.0763	0.1927	150
152	54.42	39.71	.01168	.8014	85.60	1.248	39.46	70.78	110.24	.0770	.1927	152
154	56.01	41.31	.01171	.7794	85.41	1.283	39.91	70.56	110.47	.0777	.1927	154
156	57.65	42.95	.01173	.7581	85.23	1.319	40.35	70.34	110.69	.0784	.1927	156
158	59.32	44.62	.01176	.7376	85.04	1.356	40.79	70.12	110.90	.0791	.1926	158
160	61.04	46.34	0.01179	0.7176	84.85	1.394	41.23	69.89	111.12	0.0798	0.1926	160

† Standard ton temperature.

TABLE A-15. REFRIGERANT 12, DICHLORODIFLUOROMETHANE (CCl₂F₂)
PROPERTIES OF SATURATED VAPOR

Temp.	Pressure		Volume		Density		Heat content from − 40°			Entropy from − 40°		Temp.
°F	Abs. lb./in.²	Gage lb./in.²	Liquid ft.³/lb.	Vapor ft.³/lb.	Liquid lb./ft.³	Vapor lb./ft.³	Liquid Btu./lb.	Latent Btu./lb.	Vapor Btu./lb.	Liquid Btu./lb.°F	Vapor Btu./lb.°F	°F
t	p	p_d	v_f	v_g	$1/v_f$	$1/v_g$	h_f	h	h_g	s_f	s_g	t
−40	9.32	10.92*	0.0106	3.911	94.58	0.2557	0	73.50	73.50	0	0.17517	−40
−38	9.82	9.91*	.0106	3.727	94.39	.2683	0.40	73.34	73.74	0.00094	.17490	−38
−36	10.34	8.87*	.0106	3.553	94.20	.2815	0.81	73.17	73.98	.00188	.17463	−36
−34	10.87	7.80*	.0106	3.389	93.99	.2951	1.21	73.01	74.22	.00282	.17438	−34
−32	11.43	6.66*	.0107	3.234	93.79	.3092	1.62	72.84	74.46	.00376	.17412	−32
−30	12.02	5.45*	0.0107	3.088	93.59	0.3238	2.03	72.67	74.70	0.00471	0.17387	−30
−28	12.62	4.23*	.0107	2.950	93.39	.3390	2.44	72.50	74.94	.00565	.17364	−28
−26	13.26	2.93*	.0107	2.820	93.18	.3546	2.85	72.33	75.18	.00659	.17340	−26
−24	13.90	1.63*	.0108	2.698	92.98	.3706	3.25	72.16	75.41	.00753	.17317	−24
−22	14.58	0.24*	.0108	2.583	92.78	.3871	3.66	71.98	75.64	.00846	.17296	−22
−20	15.28	0.58	0.0108	2.474	92.58	0.4042	4.07	71.80	75.87	0.00940	0.17275	−20
−18	16.01	1.31	.0108	2.370	92.38	.4219	4.48	71.63	76.11	.01033	.17253	−18
−16	16.77	2.07	.0108	2.271	92.18	.4403	4.89	71.45	76.34	.01126	.17232	−16
−14	17.55	2.85	.0109	2.177	91.97	.4593	5.30	71.27	76.57	.01218	.17212	−14
−12	18.37	3.67	.0109	2.088	91.77	.4789	5.72	71.09	76.81	.01310	.17194	−12
−10	19.20	4.50	0.0109	2.003	91.57	0.4993	6.14	70.91	77.05	0.01403	0.17175	−10
−8	20.08	5.38	.0109	1.922	91.35	.5203	6.57	70.72	77.29	.01496	.17158	−8
−6	20.98	6.28	.0110	1.845	91.14	.5420	6.99	70.53	77.52	.01589	.17140	−6
−4	21.91	7.21	.0110	1.772	90.93	.5644	7.41	70.34	77.75	.01682	.17123	−4
−2	22.87	8.17	.0110	1.703	90.72	.5872	7.83	70.15	77.98	.01775	.17107	−2
0	23.87	9.17	0.0110	1.637	90.52	0.6109	8.25	69.96	78.21	0.01869	0.17091	0
2	24.89	10.19	.0110	1.574	90.31	.6352	8.67	69.77	78.44	.01961	.17075	2
4	25.96	11.26	.0111	1.514	90.11	.6606	9.10	69.57	78.67	.02052	.17060	4
5†	26.51	11.81	.0111	1.485	90.00	.6735	9.32	69.47	78.79	.02097	.17052	5†
6	27.05	12.35	.0111	1.457	89.88	.6864	9.53	69.37	78.90	.02143	.17045	6
8	28.18	13.48	.0111	1.403	89.68	.7129	9.96	69.17	79.13	.02235	.17030	8
10	29.35	14.65	0.0112	1.351	89.45	0.7402	10.39	68.97	79.36	0.02328	0.17015	10
12	30.56	15.86	.0112	1.301	89.24	.7687	10.82	68.77	79.59	.02419	.17001	12
14	31.80	17.10	.0112	1.253	89.03	.7981	11.26	68.56	79.82	.02510	.16987	14
16	33.08	18.38	.0112	1.207	88.81	.8288	11.70	68.35	80.05	.02601	.16974	16
18	34.40	19.70	.0113	1.163	88.58	.8598	12.12	68.15	80.27	.02692	.16961	18
20	35.75	21.05	0.0113	1.121	88.37	0.8921	12.55	67.94	80.49	0.02783	0.16949	20
22	37.15	22.45	.0113	1.081	88.13	.9251	13.00	67.72	80.72	.02873	.16938	22
24	38.58	23.88	.0113	1.043	87.91	.9588	13.44	67.51	80.95	.02963	.16926	24
26	40.07	25.37	.0114	1.007	87.68	.9930	13.88	67.29	81.17	.03053	.16913	26
28	41.59	26.89	.0114	0.973	87.47	1.028	14.32	67.07	81.39	.03143	.16900	28
30	43.16	28.46	0.0115	0.939	87.24	1.065	14.76	66.85	81.61	0.03233	0.16887	30
32	44.77	30.07	.0115	.908	87.02	1.102	15.21	66.62	81.83	.03323	.16876	32
34	46.42	31.72	.0115	.877	86.78	1.140	15.65	66.40	82.05	.03413	.16865	34
36	48.13	33.43	.0116	.848	86.55	1.180	16.10	66.17	82.27	.03502	.16854	36
38	49.88	35.18	.0116	.819	86.33	1.221	16.55	65.94	82.49	.03591	.16843	38
40	51.68	36.98	0.0116	0.792	86.10	1.263	17.00	65.71	82.71	0.03680	0.16833	40
42	53.51	38.81	.0116	.767	85.88	1.304	17.46	65.47	82.93	.03770	.16823	42
44	55.40	40.70	.0117	.742	85.66	1.349	17.91	65.24	83.15	.03859	.16813	44
46	57.35	42.65	.0117	.718	85.43	1.393	18.36	65.00	83.36	.03948	.16803	46
48	59.35	44.65	.0117	.695	85.19	1.438	18.82	64.74	83.57	.04037	.16794	48
50	61.39	46.69	0.0118	0.673	84.94	1.485	19.27	64.51	83.78	0.04126	0.16785	50
52	63.49	48.79	.0118	.652	84.71	1.534	19.72	64.27	83.99	.04215	.16776	52
54	65.63	50.93	.0118	.632	84.50	1.583	20.18	64.02	84.20	.04304	.16767	54
56	67.84	53.14	.0119	.612	84.28	1.633	20.64	63.77	84.41	.04392	.16758	56
58	70.10	55.40	.0119	.593	84.04	1.686	21.11	63.51	84.62	.04480	.16749	58
60	72.41	57.71	0.0119	0.575	83.78	1.740	21.57	63.25	84.82	0.04568	0.16741	60
62	74.77	60.07	.0120	.557	83.57	1.795	22.03	62.99	85.02	.04657	.16733	62
64	77.20	62.50	.0120	.540	83.34	1.851	22.49	62.73	85.22	.04745	.16725	64
66	79.67	64.97	.0120	.524	83.10	1.909	22.95	62.47	85.42	.04833	.16717	66
68	82.24	67.54	.0121	.508	82.86	1.968	23.42	62.20	85.62	.04921	.16709	68
70	84.82	70.12	0.0121	0.493	82.60	2.028	23.90	61.92	85.82	0.05009	0.16701	70
72	87.50	72.80	.0121	.479	82.37	2.090	24.37	61.65	86.02	.05097	.16693	72
74	90.20	75.50	.0122	.464	82.12	2.153	24.84	61.38	86.22	.05185	.16685	74
76	93.00	78.30	.0122	.451	81.87	2.218	25.32	61.10	86.42	.05272	.16677	76
78	95.85	81.15	.0123	.438	81.62	2.284	25.80	60.81	86.61	.05359	.16669	78
80	98.76	84.06	0.0123	0.425	81.39	2.353	26.28	60.52	86.80	0.05446	0.16662	80

* Inches of mercury below one atmosphere.
† Standard ton temperatures.

TABLE A-15. REFRIGERANT-12, DICHLORODIFLUOROMETHANE (CCl$_2$F$_2$)
PROPERTIES OF SATURATED VAPOR

Temp.	Pressure		Volume		Density		Heat content from −40°			Entropy from −40°		Temp.
°F	Abs. lb./in.²	Gage lb./in.²	Liquid ft.³/lb.	Vapor ft.³/lb.	Liquid lb./ft.³	Vapor lb./ft.³	Liquid Btu./lb.	Latent Btu./lb.	Vapor Btu./lb.	Liquid Btu./lb.°F	Vapor Btu./lb.°F	°F
t	p	p_d	v_f	v_g	$1/v_f$	$1/v_g$	h_f	h	h_g	s_f	s_g	t
80	98.76	84.06	0.0123	0.425	81.39	2.353	26.28	60.52	86.80	0.05446	0.16662	80
82	101.7	87.00	.0123	.413	81.12	2.423	26.76	60.23	86.99	.05534	.16655	82
84	104.8	90.1	.0124	.401	80.87	2.495	27.24	59.94	87.18	.05621	.16648	84
86†	107.9	93.2	.0124	.389	80.63	2.569	27.72	59.65	87.37	.05708	.16640	86†
88	111.1	96.4	.0124	.378	80.37	2.645	28.21	59.35	87.56	.05795	16632	88
90	114.3	99.6	0.0125	0.368	80.11	2.721	28.70	59.04	87.74	0.05882	0.16624	90
92	117.7	103.0	.0125	.357	79.86	2.799	29.19	58.73	87.92	.05969	.16616	92
94	121.0	106.3	.0126	.347	79.60	2.880	29.68	58.42	88.10	.06056	.16608	94
96	124.5	109.8	.0126	.338	79.32	2.963	30.18	58.10	88.28	.06143	.16600	96
98	128.0	113.3	.0126	.328	79.06	3.048	30.67	57.78	88.45	.06230	.16592	98
100	131.6	116.9	0.0127	0.319	78.80	3.135	31.16	57.46	88.62	0.06316	0.16584	100
102	135.3	120.6	.0127	.310	78.54	3.224	31.65	57.14	88.79	.06403	.16576	102
104	139.0	124.3	.0128	.302	78.27	3.316	32.15	56.80	88.95	.06490	.16568	104
106	142.8	128.1	.0128	.293	78.00	3.411	32.65	56.46	89.11	.06577	.16560	106
108	146.8	132.1	.0129	.285	77.73	3.509	33.15	56.12	89.27	.06663	.16551	108
110	150.7	136.0	0.0129	0.277	77.46	3.610	33.65	55.78	89.43	0.06749	0.16542	110
112	154.8	140.1	.0130	.269	77.18	3.714	34.15	55.43	89.58	.06836	.16533	112
114	158.9	144.2	.0130	.262	76.89	3.823	34.65	55.08	89.73	.06922	.16524	114
116	163.1	148.4	.0131	.254	76.60	3.934	35.15	54.72	89.87	.07008	.16515	116
118	167.4	152.7	0131	.247	76.32	4.049	35.65	54.36	90.01	.07094	.16505	118
120	171.8	157.1	0.0132	0.240	76.02	4.167	36.16	53.99	90.15	0.07180	0.16495	120
122	176.2	161.5	.0132	.233	75.72	4.288	36.66	53.62	90.28	.07266	.16484	122
124	180.8	166.1	.0133	.277	75.40	4.413	37.16	53.24	90.40	.07352	.16473	124
126	185.4	170.7	.0133	.220	75.10	4.541	37.67	52.85	90.52	.07437	.16462	126
128	190.1	175.4	.0134	.214	74.78	4.673	38.18	52.46	90.64	.07522	.16450	128
130	194.9	180.2	0.0134	0.208	74.46	4.808	38.69	52.07	90.76	0.07607	0.16438	130
132	199.8	185.1	.0135	.202	74.13	4.948	39.19	51.67	90.86	.07691	.16425	132
134	204.8	190.1	.0135	.196	73.81	5.094	39.70	51.26	90.96	.07775	.16411	134
136	209.9	195.2	.0136	.191	73.46	5.247	40.21	50.85	91.06	.07858	.16396	136
138	215.0	200.3	.0137	.185	73.10	5.405	40.72	50.43	91.15	.07941	.16380	138
140	220.2	205.5	0.0138	0.180	72.73	5.571	41.24	50.00	91.24	0.08024	0.16363	140

TABLE A-15. REFRIGERANT-12, DICHLORODIFLUOROMETHANE (CCl₂F₂) PROPERTIES OF SUPERHEATED VAPOR

Temp. °F.	Abs. Pressure 8 lb./in.² Gage Pressure 13.6 in. vac. (Sat'n. Temp.—45.8° F.)			Abs. Pressure 9 lb./in.² Gage Pressure 11.6 in. vac. (Sat'n. Temp.—41.4° F.)			Abs. Pressure 10 lb./in.² Gage Pressure 9.6 in. vac. (Sat'n. Temp.—37.3° F.)			Abs. Pressure 11 lb./in.² Gage Pressure 7.5 in. vac. (Sat'n. Temp.—33.5° F.)		
t	V	H	S	V	H	S	V	H	S	V	H	S
(at sat'n)	(4.502)	(73.80)	(0.17596)	(4.056)	(73.52)	(0.17555)	(3.652)	(73.80)	(0.17480)	(3.356)	(74.27)	(0.17452)
−40	4.569	73.56	0.17777	4.050	73.51	0.17576						
−30	4.684	74.87	.18085	4.152	74.83	17884	3 728	74.77	0.17704	3.383	74.73	0.17540
−20	4.799	76.20	.18390	4.255	76.15	18188	3 821	76.11	18008	3.467	76.06	.17845
−10	4.914	77.54	.18691	4.357	77.49	18490	3.913	77 46	18310	3.551	77 40	18146
0	5.028	78.89	0.18991	4.460	78.84	0 18791	4 006	78 81	0 18611	3 635	78.75	0.18448
10	5.142	80.26	.19284	4.562	80.20	19084	4 098	80 18	18905	3.719	80 12	18742
20	5.257	81.64	.19574	4.663	81.58	19374	4 189	81 56	.19194	3.802	81.50	19032
30	5.370	83.02	.19860	4.766	82.98	19661	4 280	82 94	19482	3.887	82.90	.19320
40	5.484	84.43	.20143	4.867	84 39	19945	4 371	84 35	19766	3.971	84 31	19605
50	5.598	85.85	0.20425	4.969	85 80	0 20227	4 463	85 77	0 20047	4 055	85.73	0.19887
60	5.711	87.27	.20703	5.071	87.24	20505	4 556	87 19	20326	4 138	87 16	.20165
70	5.824	88.72	.20977	5.171	88.68	20779	4 648	88 64	20601	4 221	88 61	20440
80	5.938	90.18	.21250	5.272	90 13	21051	4 740	90.11	20874	4 304	90.07	20713
90	6.051	91 64	.21519	5.374	91 60	21321	4 832	91 58	21144	4 388	91 54	20984
100	6.165	93.13	0.21786	5.475	93.09	0 21588	4 923	93.05	0 21411	4 471	93 03	0 21251
110	6.278	94.63	.22051	5.576	94.59	21853	5 015	94.56	21676	4 553	94 52	21515
120	6.391	96.13	.22314	5.677	96.10	22116	5 107	96 07	.21940	4 636	96 03	21778
130	6.504	97.64	.22573	5.778	97.63	22375	5.198	97.59	.22199	4 718	97 56	22037
140	6.617	99.18	.22831	5.879	99 16	22634	5 289	99.14	22458	4.800	99 09	22296
150	6.730	100.73	0.23087	5.979	100.70	0 22889	5 379	100.66	0.22713	4 882	100 63	0.22551
160	6.843	102.29	.23340	6.080	102.26	23143	5 470	102.24	.22967	4 965	102.20	22805
170	6.955	103.87	.23591	6.180	103.84	23394	5.560	103.81	23218	5 047	103 78	23057
180	7.068	105.44	.23842	6.280	105.43	23645	5.650	105 40	23469	5.130	105 37	23308
190	7.181	107.05	.24090	6.380	107.03	23893	5 740	107 00	.23717	5 214	106 97	23557
200	7.294	108.67	0.24337	6.481	108.64	0.24140	5.831	108.63	0 23963	5.297	108.58	0.23804
210	7.407	110.28	.24581	6.581	110.26	24384	5.921	110.25	.24208	5.379	110.21	.24049
220	7.520	111.93	.24825	6.682	111.90	24628	6.011	111 88	24451	5.462	111.85	.24291
230	7.633	113.57	.25066	6.782	113.55	.24868	6.101	113.53	24692	5.544	113.50	.24532
240										5 626	115.18	24773

Temp. °F.	Abs. Pressure 12 lb./in.² Gage Pressure 5.5 in vac. (Sat'n. Temp.—30.0° F.)			Abs. Pressure 13 lb./in.² Gage Pressure 3.5 in. vac. (Sat'n. Temp.—26.8° F.)			Abs. Pressure 14 lb./in.² Gage Pressure 1.4 in. vac (Sat'n. Temp.—23.7° F.)			Abs Pressure 15 lb./in.² Gage Pressure 0.3 lb in.² (Sat'n. Temp —20.8° F)		
t	V	H	S	V	H	S	V	H	S	V	H	S
(at sat'n)	(3.095)	(74.69)	(0.17589)	(2.875)	(75.08)	(0.17350)	(2.677)	(75.45)	(0.17314)	(2.518)	(75.78)	(0 17282)
−30	3.093	74.69	0.17389									
−20	3.172	76.02	.17695	2.920	75.98	0.17556	2.706	75 94	0.17427	2.521	75 89	0 17307
−10	3.250	77.37	.17998	2.992	77.32	.17859	2 773	77 28	.17731	2 583	77 23	17611
0	3.328	78.73	0.18299	3.064	78.69	0.18160	2.841	78.64	0 18032	2.646	78.59	0 17913
10	3.405	80.10	.18594	3 136	80.05	.18455	2.908	80.01	18328	2.708	79.97	18208
20	3.483	81.48	.18884	3 207	81.43	18746	2.974	81 40	18618	2.771	81.37	18499
30	3.560	82 87	.19173	3 278	82.83	19034	3.041	82.80	18907	2.833	82 77	18788
40	3.637	84.28	19458	3 349	84.23	.19319	3.107	84 21	19192	2.895	84 18	19074
50	3.714	85.71	0.19739	3 420	85 66	0.19601	3 173	85 63	0.19475	2.957	85.60	0 19357
60	3.790	87.14	.20018	3.491	87.10	19880	3 239	87 06	.19753	3.019	87 03	.19635
70	3.867	88.59	.20293	3.562	88 54	20156	3 303	88 51	20028	3.081	88 48	19911
80	3.943	90 05	.20566	3.632	90 01	20428	3 369	89 97	.20302	3 143	89.94	20185
90	4.019	91 52	.20836	3.703	91 48	20699	3 435	91 44	20572	3 204	91.41	20455
100	4.095	93 00	0 21104	3.774	92 96	0 20967	3 501	92.93	0 20841	3 266	92 91	0.20723
110	4.170	94.50	.21367	3.844	94.47	21231	3 567	94 43	21106	3.327	94.41	.20989
120	4.246	96.01	.21631	3.915	95 98	.21495	3.633	95 95	21369	3 388	95.91	21252
130	4.323	97.53	.21891	3.986	97 50	.21755	3.699	97 48	21630	3.450	97.44	.21513
140	4.400	99.07	.22151	4 056	99 04	.22014	3.763	99 01	21889	3.510	98 98	21772
150	4.474	100.62	0.22406	4.126	100.59	0 22270	3.828	100 56	0 22144	3.571	100 53	0.22028
160	4.549	102.18	.22659	4.196	102 16	.22524	3.894	102.13	.22400	3.632	102.10	.22282
170	4.624	103.75	.22911	4.266	103.73	.22775	3.960	103 71	.22651	3.694	103.68	.22535
180	4.700	105.34	.23162	4.337	105 32	.23027	4 025	105 30	.22902	3.755	105.27	.22786
190	4.774	106.94	.23409	4.408	106.92	.23276	4.090	106.90	.23150	3.816	106.87	.23034
200	4.850	108.55	0.23656	4.478	108.55	0.23523	4.155	108.52	0.23398	3.877	108.49	0.23282
210	4.926	110.18	.23901	4.547	110.16	.23767	4.220	110.14	.23643	3.938	110.12	.23527
220	5.000	111.82	.24144	4.617	111 81	.24011	4.285	111.78	.23886	3.998	111.77	.23770
230	5.076	113.47	.24385	4.686	113 45	.24252	4.350	113 44	.24128	4.059	113 42	.24011
240	5.152	115.15	.24626	4.755	115 13	.24492	4.414	115.11	.24368	4.120	115 10	.24253
250							4.479	116.79	0 24607	4.181	116.78	0 24491

TABLE A-15. REFRIGERANT-12, DICHLORODIFLUOROMETHANE (CCl₂F₂)
PROPERTIES OF SATURATED VAPOR

Temp. °F.	Abs. Pressure 16 lb./in.² Gage Pressure 1.3 lb./in.² (Sat'n. Temp.—18.0° F.)			Abs. Pressure 17 lb./in.² Gage Pressure 2.3 lb./in.² (Sat'n. Temp.—15.4° F.)			Abs. Pressure 18 lb./in.² Gage Pressure 3.3 lb./in.² (Sat'n. Temp.—12.9° F.)			Abs. Pressure 19 lb./in.² Gage Pressure 4.3 lb./in.² (Sat'n. Temp.—10.5° F.)		
t	V	H	S	V	H	S	V	H	S	V	H	S
(at sat'n)	(2.570)	(76.11)	(0.17254)	(2.240)	(76.41)	(0.17226)	(2.183)	(76.70)	(0.17202)	(2.019)	(76.99)	(0.17180)
−10	2.417	77.20	0.17498	2.268	77.15	0.17390	2.137	77.09	0.17289	2.022	77.05	0.17195
0	2.476	78.56	0.17800	2.325	78.52	0.17693	2.191	78.47	0.17592	2.072	78.42	0.17497
10	2.535	79.94	.18095	2.382	79.90	.17990	2.244	79.85	.17889	2.122	79.80	.17794
20	2.594	81.33	.18387	2.438	81.29	.18283	2.297	81.24	.18181	2.172	81.19	.18087
30	2.652	82.73	.18676	2.493	82.69	.18571	2.350	82.65	.18471	2.222	82.60	.18376
40	2.710	84.13	.18962	2.548	84.10	.18857	2.402	84.06	.18757	2.272	84.02	.18663
50	2.768	85.55	0.19244	2.603	85.52	0.19140	2.454	85.49	0.19041	2.321	85.45	0.18946
60	2.827	86.99	.19524	2.658	86.96	.19420	2.506	86.93	.19321	2.371	86.90	.19226
70	2.886	88.45	.19800	2.712	88.41	.19696	2.558	88.38	.19597	2.420	88.35	.19503
80	2.944	89.91	.20075	2.767	89.88	.19969	2.610	89.84	.19872	2.469	89.81	19777
90	3.002	91.39	.20345	2.822	91.36	.20241	2.662	91.32	.20142	2.518	91 29	.20047
100	3.059	92.88	0.20613	2.876	92.85	0.20510	2.713	92.81	0.20411	2.567	92.78	0.20317
110	3.117	94.38	.20879	2.930	94.35	.20774	2.764	94.32	.20676	2.616	94.28	.20583
120	3.175	95.89	.21143	2.984	95.86	.21038	2.815	95.83	.20941	2.665	95.80	.20847
130	3.232	97.42	.21403	3.038	97.39	.21298	2 867	97.36	.21201	2.714	97.33	.21108
140	3.290	98.95	.21662	3.092	98.93	.21558	2 918	98.90	.21462	2 763	98.88	.21368
150	3.347	100.50	0.21917	3.147	100.48	0.21814	2.969	100 45	0.21717	2.812	100.43	0 21625
160	3.404	102.07	.22172	3.201	102.05	.22070	3.020	102.02	.21971	2.861	102.00	.21880
170	3.461	103.65	.22425	3.256	103.63	.22323	3.072	103.60	.22223	2.910	103.59	.22133
180	3.519	105.24	.22677	3.310	105.22	.22554	3.124	105.19	.22477	2.958	105.18	.22384
190	3.576	106.85	.22925	3.364	106.82	.22822	3.175	106.80	.22725	3.006	106 78	.22633
200	3.633	108.47	0.23173	3.417	108.44	0.23070	3.226	108.42	0.22973	3 054	108.39	0.22880
210	3.690	110.10	.23418	3.470	110.07	.23315	3.277	110.05	.23219	3.102	110 02	.23126
220	3.747	111.74	.23662	3.524	111.71	.23558	3.327	111.69	.23461	3.150	111.66	.23369
230	3.803	113.40	.23903	3.578	113.37	.23800	3.378	113.34	.23703	3.198	113.31	.23612
240	3.860	115.07	.24143	3.632	115.04	.24041	3.428	115.00	.23944	3.246	114.99	.23852
250	3.917	116.76	0.24382	3.686	116.72	0.24279	3.478	116.68	0.24182	3.294	116.68	0.24091
260				3.739	118.41	.24517	3.528	118.36	.24420	3.342	118.37	.24327

Temp. °F.	Abs. Pressure 20 lb./in.² Gage Pressure 5.3 lb./in.² (Sat'n. Temp.—8.2° F.)			Abs. Pressure 22 lb./in.² Gage Pressure 7.3 lb./in.² (Sat'n. Temp.—3.8° F.)			Abs. Pressure 24 lb./in.² Gage Pressure 9.3 lb./in.² (Sat'n. Temp. 0.3° F.)			Abs. Pressure 26 lb./in.² Gage Pressure 11.3 lb./in.² (Sat'n. Temp. 4.1° F.)		
(at sat'n)	(1.925)	(77.27)	(0.17160)	(1.768)	(77.77)	(0.17131)	(1.623)	(78.24)	(0.17089)	(1.510)	(78.68)	(0.17059)
0	1.965	78.39	0.17407	1.779	78.30	0.17237						
10	2.013	79.76	.17704	1.823	79.68	.17534	1.664	79.59	0.17378	1.530	79.50	0.17233
20	2.060	81.14	.17996	1.866	81.07	.17827	1.705	80.99	17673	1.568	80.90	.17529
30	2.107	82.55	.18286	1.909	82.48	.18118	1.745	82.40	.17964	1.606	82.31	17821
40	2.155	83.97	.18573	1.953	83.90	.18405	1.785	83.82	18251	1.643	83 74	.18109
50	2.203	85.40	0.18858	1.997	85.33	0.18691	1.825	85.26	0.18536	1.680	85.19	0 18395
60	2.250	86.85	.19138	2.040	86.78	.18971	1.865	86.71	18817	1.716	86.64	18675
70	2.297	88.31	.19415	2.083	88.25	.19248	1.905	88 17	.19096	1.754	88.10	18954
80	2.343	89.78	.19688	2.125	89.71	.19522	1.944	89 64	19371	1.790	89.57	19229
90	2.390	91.26	.19959	2.168	91.19	.19794	1.984	91 13	19643	1 826	91.05	19501
100	2.437	92.75	0.20229	2.211	92.68	0.20064	2.023	92.63	0 19912	1.863	92.55	0 19772
110	2.483	94.26	.20494	2.253	94.19	.20330	2.062	94.13	20179	1.900	94.06	20039
120	2.530	95.78	.20759	2.296	95.71	.20595	2.101	95.64	.20444	1.936	95.58	.20305
130	2.577	97.31	.21020	2.339	97.25	.20856	2.140	97.17	.20704	1.972	97.12	.20565
140	2.623	98.85	.21280	2.381	98.80	.21116	2.179	98.72	.20966	2.008	98.67	.20827
150	2.669	100.40	0.21537	2.423	100.35	0.21373	2.218	100.28	0.21223	2.045	100.23	0 21085
160	2.716	101.97	.21792	2.465	101.92	.21628	2.257	101.86	.21479	2.082	101.80	.21341
170	2.762	103.56	.22045	2.507	103.50	.21881	2.296	103.45	.21732	2.117	103.39	.21594
180	2.808	105.15	.22297	2.550	105.10	.22133	2.335	105.05	.21984	2 153	104.99	.21547
190	2.854	106.76	.22545	2.592	106.71	.22382	2.373	106 66	.22233	2.189	106.60	.22096
200	2.901	108.38	0.22794	2.634	108.33	0 22630	2.412	108.28	0 22481	2.224	108.23	0.22344
210	2.947	110.01	.23039	2.676	109.96	.22876	2.450	109.92	.22727	2.259	109.86	.22589
220	2.992	111.65	.23283	2.717	111.60	.23120	2.489	111.57	.22972	2.295	111.51	.22834
230	3.038	113.31	.23524	2.758	113.26	.23361	2.528	113.23	.23214	2.331	113.17	.23076
240	3.084	114.98	.23766	2.800	114.94	.23603	2.566	114.90	.23455	2.366	114.85	.23318
250	3.130	116.67	0.24005	2.842	116.62	0.23843	2.605	116.58	0.23695	2.402	116.54	0.23557
260	3.177	118.36	.24242	2.884	118.32	.24080	2.644	118.28	.23933	2.438	118.24	.23796
270	3.223	120.07	.24477	2.926	120.04	.24316	2.682	120.00	24169	2.474	119.95	.24033
280										2.510	121.68	.24267

TABLE A-15. REFRIGERANT-12, DICHLORODIFLUOROMETHANE (CC1₂F₂)
PROPERTIES OF SUPERHEATED VAPOR

Temp. °F.	Abs. Pressure 28 lb./in.² Gage Pressure 13.3 lb./in.² (Sat'n. Temp. 7.7° F.)			Abs. Pressure 30 lb./in.² Gage Pressure 15.3 lb./in.² (Sat'n. Temp. 11.1° F.)			Abs. Pressure 32 lb./in.² Gage Pressure 17.3 lb./in.² (Sat'n. Temp. 14.3° F.)			Abs. Pressure 34 lb./in.² Gage Pressure 19.3 lb./in.² (Sat'n. Temp. 17.4° F.)		
t	V	H	S	V	H	S	V	H	S	V	H	S
(at sat'n)	(1.409)	(79.10)	(0.17053)	(1.325)	(79.47)	(0.17008)	(1.245)	(79.84)	(0.16985)	(1.175)	(80.20)	(0.16965)
10	1.415	79.41	0.17099									
20	1.450	80.81	.17393	1.350	80.73	0.17269	1.262	80.67	0.17152	1.183	80.58	0.17040
30	1.485	82.23	.17685	1.383	82.15	.17562	1.293	82.08	.17445	1.212	82.00	.17333
40	1.520	83.66	.17975	1.415	83.58	.17851	1.323	83.51	.17734	1.241	83.44	.17623
50	1.555	85.11	0.18261	1.448	85.03	0.18138	1.354	84.96	0.18022	1.270	84.88	0.17910
60	1.590	86.56	.18544	1.480	86.48	.18420	1.384	86.41	.18304	1.299	86.34	.18194
70	1.625	88.03	.18823	1.512	87.95	.18699	1.414	87.88	.18583	1.328	87.81	.18474
80	1.659	89.51	.19097	1.544	89.43	.18974	1.444	89.36	.18860	1.356	89.29	.18750
90	1.693	90.99	.19371	1.576	90.91	.19249	1.474	90.85	.19133	1.385	90.78	.19025
100	1.727	92.49	0.19642	1.608	92.41	0.19519	1.504	92.35	0.19404	1.413	92.29	0.19295
110	1.761	94.01	.19909	1.640	93.93	.19787	1.535	93.87	.19673	1.441	93.81	.19563
120	1.795	95.53	.20174	1.672	95.46	.20053	1.565	95.40	.19940	1.470	95.34	.19831
130	1.828	97.07	.20436	1.703	97.00	.20315	1.595	96.94	.20202	1.498	96.88	.20094
140	1.862	98.62	.20698	1.735	98.54	.20577	1.624	98.50	.20463	1.526	98.43	.20356
150	1.896	100.18	0.20956	1.767	100.11	0.20836	1.654	100.06	0.20721	1.554	100.00	0.20614
160	1.930	101.75	.21212	1.799	101.69	.21092	1.683	101.64	.20977	1.582	101.58	.20871
170	1.963	103.33	.21466	1.829	103.28	.21344	1.713	103.23	.21232	1.610	103.17	.21125
180	1.997	104.93	.21719	1.860	104.88	.21597	1.743	104.83	.21486	1.638	104.78	.21379
190	2.030	106.55	.21967	1.891	106.49	.21846	1.772	106.45	.21735	1.666	106.40	.21629
200	2.063	108.17	0.22216	1.923	108.12	0.22096	1.802	108.08	0.21985	1.693	108.03	0.21878
210	2.096	109.81	.22462	1.954	109.76	.22342	1.831	109.72	.22231	1.721	109.67	.22125
220	2.129	111.46	.22706	1.986	111.41	.22588	1.860	111.36	.22476	1.749	111.32	.22370
230	2.163	113.12	.22949	2.017	113.08	.22830	1.889	113.03	.22718	1.776	112.98	.22613
240	2.196	114.80	.23191	2.048	114.75	.23072	1.918	114.72	.22960	1.804	114.66	.22856
250	2.229	116.49	0.23430	2.079	116.44	0.23312	1.948	116.41	0.23200	1.833	116.35	0.23097
260	2.262	118.19	.23669	2.110	118.15	.23550	1.977	118.11	.23439	1.860	118.06	.24335
270	2.295	119.91	.23905	2.141	119.87	.23787	2.006	119.83	.23676	1.888	119.79	.23573
280	2.329	121.65	.24141	2.172	121.60	.24023	2.035	121.55	.23912	1.916	121.54	.23809
290	......	......	......	......	......	......	2.065	123.30	.24146	1.944	123.31	.24043

Temp. °F.	Abs. Pressure 36 lb./in.² Gage Pressure 21.3 lb./in.² (Sat'n. Temp. 20.4° F.)			Abs. Pressure 38 lb./in.² Gage Pressure 23.3 lb./in.² (Sat'n. Temp. 23.2° F.)			Abs. Pressure 40 lb./in.² Gage Pressure 25.3 lb./in.² (Sat'n. Temp. 25.9° F.)			Abs. Pressure 42 lb./in.² Gage Pressure 27.3 lb./in.² (Sat'n. Temp. 28.5° F.)		
(at sat'n)	(1.113)	(80.54)	(0.16947)	(1.058)	(80.88)	(0.16931)	(1.009)	(81.16)	(0.16914)	(0.963)	(81.44)	(0.16897)
30	1.140	81.90	0.17227	1.076	81.82	0.17126	1.019	81.76	0.17030	0.967	81.65	0.16939
40	1.168	83.35	.17518	1.103	83.27	.17418	1.044	83.20	.17322	0.991	83.10	.17231
50	1.196	84.81	0.17806	1.129	84.72	0.17706	1.070	84.65	0.17612	1.016	84.56	0.17521
60	1.223	86.27	.18089	1.156	86.19	.17991	1.095	86.11	.17896	1.040	86.03	.17806
70	1.250	87.74	.18369	1.182	87.67	.18272	1.120	87.60	.18178	1.063	87.51	.18086
80	1.278	89.22	.18647	1.208	89.16	.18551	1.144	89.09	.18455	1.087	89.00	.18365
90	1.305	90.71	.18921	1.234	90.66	.18826	1.169	90.58	.18731	1.110	90.50	.18640
100	1.332	92.22	0.19193	1.260	92.17	0.19096	1.194	92.10	0.19004	1.134	92.01	0.18913
110	1.359	93.75	.19462	1.285	93.69	.19365	1.218	93.62	.19272	1.158	93.54	.19184
120	1.386	95.28	.19729	1.310	95.22	.19631	1.242	95.15	.19538	1.181	95.09	.19451
130	1.412	96.82	.19991	1.336	96.76	.19895	1.267	96.70	.19803	1.204	96.64	.19714
140	1.439	98.37	.20254	1.361	98.32	.20157	1.291	98.26	.20066	1.227	98.20	.19979
150	1.465	99.93	0.20512	1.387	99.89	0.20416	1.315	99.83	0.20325	1.250	99.77	0.20237
160	1.492	101.51	.20770	1.412	101.47	.20673	1.340	101.42	.20583	1.274	101.36	.20496
170	1.518	103.11	.21024	1.437	103.07	.20929	1.364	103.02	.20838	1.297	102.96	.20751
180	1.545	104.72	.21278	1.462	104.67	.21183	1.388	104.63	.21092	1.320	104.57	.21005
190	1.571	106.34	.21528	1.487	106.29	.21433	1.412	106.25	.21343	1.343	106.19	.21256
200	1.597	107.97	0.21778	1.512	107.93	0.21681	1.435	107.82	0.21592	1.365	107.82	0.21505
210	1.623	109.61	.22024	1.537	109.57	.21928	1.459	109.52	.21840	1.388	109.47	.21754
220	1.650	111.27	.22270	1.562	111.22	.22176	1.482	111.17	.22085	1.411	111.12	.22000
230	1.676	112.94	.22513	1.587	112.89	.22419	1.506	112.84	.22329	1.434	112.80	.22244
240	1.702	114.62	.22756	1.612	114.58	.22662	1.530	114.52	.22572	1.457	114.49	.22486
250	1.728	116.31	0.22996	1.637	116.28	0.22903	1.554	116.21	0.22813	1.480	116.19	0.22728
260	1.754	118.02	.23235	1.662	117.99	.23142	1.577	117.91	.23052	1.502	117.90	.22967
270	1.780	119.74	.23472	1.687	119.71	.23379	1.601	119.65	.23289	1.524	119.62	.23204
280	1.807	121.47	.23708	1.712	121.45	.23616	1.625	121.40	.23526	1.547	121.36	.23441
290	1.833	123.22	.23942	1.737	123.20	.23850	1.649	123.15	.23760	1.570	123.11	.23675
300	......	......	......	1.762	124.95	0.24083	1.673	124.92	0.23994	1.592	124.87	0.23909

TABLE A-15. REFRIGERANT-12, DICHLORODIFLUOROMETHANE (CCl₂F₂)
PROPERTIES OF SATURATED VAPOR

Temp. °F.	Abs. Pressure 44 lb./in.² Gage Pressure 29.3 lb./in.² (Sat'n. Temp. 31.0° F.)			Abs. Pressure 46 lb./in.² Gage Pressure 31.3 lb./in.² (Sat'n. Temp. 33.5° F.)			Abs. Pressure 48 lb./in.² Gage Pressure 33.13 lb./in² (Sat'n. Temp. 35.8° F.)			Abs. Pressure 50 lb./in.² Gage Pressure 35.3 lb./in.² (Sat'n. Temp. 38.3° F.)		
t	V	H	S	V	H	S	V	H	S	V	H	S
(at sat'n)	(0.922)	(81.72)	(0.16882)	(0.885)	(82.00)	(0.16867)	(0.849)	(82.25)	(0.16855)	(0.817)	(82.52)	(0.16841)
40	0.943	83.03	0.17142	0.899	82.94	0.17057	0.858	82.85	0.16974	0.821	82.76	0.16895
50	0.966	84.48	0.17432	0.921	84.40	0.17347	0.880	84.32	0.17266	0.842	84.24	0.17187
60	0.989	85.96	17717	0.943	85.88	.17633	0.902	85.80	.17554	0.863	85.72	.17475
70	1.012	87.45	.18000	0.965	87.37	17916	0.923	87.29	.17837	0.884	87.22	.17760
80	1.035	88.94	.18279	0.988	88.88	.18198	0.944	88.79	.18117	0.904	88.72	.18040
90	1.058	90.44	.18556	1.010	90.39	.18474	0.965	90.30	.18394	0.924	90.23	.18317
100	1.080	91.95	0.18828	1.031	91.90	0.18746	0.986	91.82	0.18668	0.944	91.75	0.18591
110	1.103	93.48	.19099	1.053	93.43	.19016	1.007	93.35	.18939	0.964	93.29	.18862
120	1.125	95.02	.19367	1.074	94.96	.19285	1.028	94.89	.19208	0.984	94.83	.19132
130	1.147	96.57	.19630	1.096	96.51	.19551	1.048	96.44	.19472	1.004	96.39	.19397
140	1.170	98.14	19895	1.117	98.08	.19814	1.069	98.01	.19737	1.024	97.96	.19662
150	1.192	99.72	0.20154	1.139	99.66	0.20075	1.089	99.59	0.19997	1.044	99.54	0.19923
160	1.214	101.31	.20412	1.160	101.25	.20333	1.110	101.18	.20256	1.064	101.14	.20182
170	1.236	102.91	.20667	1.181	102.85	.20588	1.130	102.79	.20513	1.084	102.75	.20439
180	1.258	104.52	20922	1.202	104.46	.20843	1.150	104.40	.20766	1.103	104.36	.20694
190	1.280	106.14	21173	1.223	106.09	.21094	1.170	106.02	.21017	1.123	105.98	.20946
200	1.302	107.78	0.21424	1.244	107.73	0.21344	1.191	107.66	0.21269	1.142	107.62	0.21196
210	1.324	109.42	.21672	1.265	109.38	.21592	1.211	109.31	.21517	1.162	109.28	.21444
220	1.346	111.08	21918	1.286	111.04	.21839	1.231	110.98	.21763	1.181	110.95	.21691
230	1.367	112.75	.22161	1.307	112.71	.22083	1.251	112.66	.22007	1.200	112.62	.21935
240	1.389	114.44	22405	1.327	114.39	.22326	1.271	114.35	.22251	1.220	114.31	.22179
250	1.411	116.14	0.22646	1.348	116.09	0.22567	1.291	116.05	0.22492	1.239	116.00	0.22419
260	1.432	117.85	.22885	1.369	117.81	.22806	1.311	117.77	.22731	1.258	117.71	.22660
270	1.454	119.57	.23123	1.390	119.54	.23044	1.331	119.49	.22970	1.277	119.44	.22898
280	1.475	121.31	.23359	1.410	121.27	.23281	1.351	121.23	.23207	1.296	121.18	.23134
290	1.496	123.06	.23592	1.431	123.02	.23515	1.370	122.98	.23440	1.314	122.93	.23367
300	1.518	124.82	.23826	1.452	124.79	0.23749	1.390	124.75	0.23674	1.332	124.69	0.23600
310	1.539	126.59	.24058	1.472	126.57	.23981	1.410	126.53	.23907	1.350	126.45	.23831

Temp. °F.	Abs. Pressure 52 lb./in.² Gage Pressure 37.3 lb./in.² (Sat'n. Temp. 40.4° F.)			Abs. Pressure 54 lb./in.² Gage Pressure 39.3 lb./in.² (Sat'n. Temp. 42.5° F.)			Abs. Pressure 56 lb./in.² Gage Pressure 41.3 lb./in.² (Sat'n. Temp. 44.6° F.)			Abs. Pressure 58 lb./in.² Gage Pressure 43.3 lb./in.² (Sat'n. Temp. 46.7° F.)		
(at sat'n)	(0.788)	(82.75)	(0.16851)	(0.769)	(82.98)	(0.16820)	(0.734)	(83.22)	(0.16810)	(0.710)	(83.44)	(0.16800)
50	0.808	84.17	0.17114	0.774	84.07	0.17036	0.744	83.99	0.16965	0.716	83.91	0.16896
60	0.827	85.65	.17400	0.794	85.56	.17326	0.763	85.48	.17255	0.734	85.40	.17185
70	0.847	87.14	.17684	0.814	87.06	.17612	0.782	86.98	.17541	0.752	86.90	.17471
80	0.867	88.64	.17966	0.833	88.57	.17894	0.801	88.49	.17824	0.770	88.41	.17753
90	0.886	90.15	.18244	0.852	90.08	.18172	0.819	90.01	.18102	0.788	89.93	.18033
100	0.906	91.68	0.18518	0.871	91.61	0.18446	0.837	91.54	0.18377	0.806	91.46	0.18309
110	0.925	93.22	.18789	0.890	93.16	.18718	0.856	93.08	.18651	0.824	93.00	.18583
120	0.945	94.77	.19059	0.908	94.71	.18989	0.874	94.63	.18921	0.842	94.55	.18854
130	0.964	96.33	.19325	0.927	96.27	.19255	0.892	96.19	.19188	0.860	96.11	.19122
140	0.983	97.90	.19590	0.945	97.84	.19520	0.910	97.77	.19453	0.877	97.68	.19387
150	1.002	99.48	0.19850	0.964	99.43	0.19782	0.928	99.36	0.19715	0.894	99.26	0.19648
160	1.021	101.07	.20109	0.982	101.03	.20043	0.946	100.96	.19975	0.912	100.86	.19908
170	1.040	102.68	.20365	1.001	102.64	.20299	0.964	102.57	.20232	0.929	102.47	.20166
180	1.059	104.30	.20621	1.019	104.25	.20554	0.981	104.19	.20487	0.946	104.09	.20423
190	1.078	105.93	.20873	1.037	105.88	.20806	0.999	105.83	.20739	0.963	105.72	.20676
200	1.097	107.58	0.21125	1.055	107.52	0.21057	1.016	107.48	0.20991	0.980	107.36	0.20927
210	1.116	109.23	.21374	1.073	109.17	.21305	1.034	109.14	.21241	0.997	109.02	.21177
220	1.134	110.89	.21620	1.091	110.84	.21553	1.051	110.81	.21487	1.014	110.70	.21424
230	1.153	112.56	.21865	1.109	112.51	.21797	1.068	112.49	.21731	1.031	112.39	.21669
240	1.172	114.26	.22110	1.127	114.20	.22042	1.086	114.18	.21977	1.048	114.10	.21914
250	1.190	115.96	0.22352	1.145	115.91	0.22283	1.103	115.88	0.22218	1.064	115.82	0.22155
260	1.208	117.67	.22591	1.163	117.63	.22523	1.120	117.59	.22458	1.081	117.55	.22396
270	1.227	119.40	.22829	1.181	119.37	.22762	1.138	119.31	.22698	1.098	119.29	.22635
280	1.245	121.14	.23065	1.199	121.11	.22999	1.155	121.05	.22934	1.114	121.04	.22871
290	1.263	122.90	.23299	1.216	122.86	.23233	1.172	122.80	.23169	1.130	122.80	.23105
300	1.281	124.66	0.23532	1.234	124.63	0.23467	1.189	124.57	0.23403	1.147	124.57	0.23340
310	1.298	126.42	.23763	1.251	126.40	.23699	1.206	126.36	.23635	1.164	126.35	.23574
320	......			......			1.223	128.17	.23867	1.180	128.14	.23806

TABLE A-15. REFRIGERANT-12, DICHLORODIFLUOROMETHANE (CCl_2F_2) PROPERTIES OF SUPERHEATED VAPOR

Temp. °F.	Abs. Pressure 60 lb./in.² Gage Pressure 45.3 lb./in.² (Sat'n. Temp. 48.7° F.)			Abs. Pressure 70 lb./in.² Gage Pressure 55.3 lb./in.² (Sat'n. Temp. 57.9° F.)			Abs. Pressure 80 lb./in.² Gage Pressure 65.3 lb./in.² (Sat'n. Temp. 66 3° F.)			Abs. Pressure 90 lb./in.² Gage Pressure 75.3 lb./in.² (Sat'n. Temp. 73 9° F.)		
t	V	H	S	V	H	S	V	H	S	V	H	S
(at sat'n)	(0.688)	(83.66)	(0.16791)	(0.592)	(84.61)	(0.16749)	(0.521)	(85.45)	(0.16716)	(0.465)	(86.21)	(0.16685)
50	0 690	83.83	0.16829									
60	0.708	85.33	.17120	0.597	84.94	1 6810						
70	0.726	86.84	.17407	0.612	86.44	.17097	0 526	86 01	0.16819			
80	0.743	88.35	.17689	0.628	87.96	.17382	0 540	87 56	.17108	0 473	87.18	0 16862
90	0.760	89.87	.17968	0.643	89.49	.17665	0 554	89 12	.17394	0.486	88.74	.17149
100	0.778	91.41	0.18246	0.658	91 03	0 17943	0 568	90.68	0.17675	0.499	90 31	0.17433
110	0.795	92.96	.18519	0.673	92 59	18219	0 582	92 26	.17954	0.511	91.89	17713
120	0.812	94.51	.18789	0.689	94 16	.18493	0 596	93 84	.18229	0.523	93 48	.17990
130	0 829	96 07	19056	0.704	95 75	.18763	0 609	95 43	.18500	0.535	95 08	.18262
140	0.846	97 65	.19323	0.719	97 34	.19030	0 623	97 03	.18771	0.547	96 69	.18533
150	0.863	99 24	0.19585	0.733	98 94	0 19293	0 636	98 64	0.19035	0.559	98 31	0 18799
160	0.880	100 84	.19846	0.748	100 54	19555	0 649	100 26	.19298	0 571	99 94	.19065
170	0.897	102 45	.20104	0.763	102 16	.19814	0 662	101 88	.19558	0.584	101 58	19327
180	0 913	104 07	.20360	0.777	103 80	20071	0 675	103 52	.19817	0.596	103 23	19588
190	0.930	105.71	.20613	0.792	105 45	.20325	0 688	105 18	.20073	0 607	104.89	.19845
200	0.946	107.36	0 20865	0.806	107 10	0 20579	0 701	106 84	0 20328	0.619	106 56	0 20101
210	0.962	109.02	.21113	0 820	108 76	20829	0 714	108 51	.20580	0.630	108 24	20353
220	0.979	110.69	.21361	0.835	110 43	21079	0 726	110 19	.20828	0 642	109 93	20603
230	0.995	112.37	.21607	0.849	112 13	21325	0 739	111 88	.21076	0 653	111 63	20852
240	1.012	114.06	.21853	0 863	113 83	21570	0 751	113 58	.21321	0 665	113 35	21100
250	1.028	115.77	0.22094	0.878	115 55	0 21815	0 764	115 30	0.21566	0.676	115 08	0 21345
260	1.044	117.49	.22334	0 892	117 28	22057	0 777	117 03	.21809	0 688	116 82	21589
270	1.060	119.23	.22573	0.906	119 02	22296	0 789	118.78	.22049	0 699	118 57	21831
280	1.076	120.97	.22810	0 920	120 76	22534	0 802	120 54	.22289	0 710	120 33	22070
290	1·092	122.73	.23045	0 934	122 52	22770	0.814	122 30	.22525	0 721	122 10	22306
300	1.108	124 50	0.23280	0 948	124 29	0 23006	0 826	124 08	0 22760	0 732	123 88	0 22542
310	1.124	126.28	.23513	0 961	126 07	.23239	0 839	125 88	.22995	0 743	125 67	22776
320	1.140	128 07	.23745	0 975	127 88	23471	0 851	127 70	.23229	0 754	127 48	23008
330				0 989	129 70	23702	0 864	129 52	.23461	0 765	129 31	23240

Temp. °F.	Abs. Pressure 100 lb./in.² Gage Pressure 85.3 lb./in.² (Sat'n. Temp. 80.9° F.)			Abs. Pressure 110 lb./in.² Gage Pressure 95.3 lb./in.² (Sat'n. Temp 87 3°F.)			Abs. Pressure 120 lb./in.² Gage Pressure 105.3 lb./in.² (Sat'n. Temp. 93 4° F.)			Abs. Pressure 130 lb./in.² Gage Pressure 115.3 lb./in.² (Sat'n Temp 99 1° F.)		
(at sat'n)	(0.419)	(86.89)	(0.16659)	(0.382)	(87.50)	(0.16635)	(0 350)	(88 05)	(0.16610)	(0.323)	(88 547)	(0 16588)
90	0.430	88.32	0.16926	0.385	87 91	0.16711						
100	0.442	89.93	0.17210	0 396	89 51	0 17001	0 357	89 13	0.16803	0 324	88 69	0 16615
110	0.454	91.54	.17493	0 407	91 12	17287	0 367	90 75	.17090	0.333	90 33	16905
120	0.465	93.15	.17773	0 417	92 74	17568	0 377	92 38	.17374	0 343	91 98	17193
130	0.477	94.76	.18049	0 428	94 37	17845	0 387	94 01	.17654	0 353	93 64	17476
140	0.488	96.37	.18321	0.438	96 01	18122	0 397	95 65	.17932	0 362	95 30	17756
150	0.499	97.99	0.18590	0.449	97 66	0.18394	0 407	97.30	0 18207	0 371	96.97	0 18030
160	0.510	99.63	.18856	0.459	99 31	.18660	0 417	98 96	.18474	0 380	98 65	18302
170	0.521	101 28	.19120	0.469	100 97	.18924	0 426	100 63	.18743	0 389	100 34	18571
180	0.531	102.94	.19381	0.479	102 64	.19187	0 436	102 31	.19011	0 398	102 04	.18839
190	0.542	104.61	.19638	0.489	104 32	.19447	0 445	104 00	.19271	0 407	103 74	19102
200	0 553	106.29	0.19894	0.499	106 01	0.19706	0 454	105 70	0.19529	0.416	105 45	0.19762
210	0.563	107.98	.20148	0.509	107 71	.19962	0 463	107 41	.19785	0 424	107 16	.19620
220	0.574	109.68	.20401	0.519	109 42	20216	0 472	109 13	.20041	0 433	108 89	19877
230	0.585	111.39	.20650	0.528	111 14	.20464	0 482	110 86	.20294	0 442	110 62	20130
240	0.595	113.11	.20899	0 538	112 87	.20712	0 491	112 60	.20545	0 450	112.36	.20382
250	0.606	114.84	0.21145	0.548	114 61	0.20959	0 500	114.35	0.20792	0 458	114.11	0.20629
260	0.616	116.58	.21389	0 557	116 36	.21205	0 508	116 11	.21035	0 467	115 87	20876
270	0.626	118.33	.21631	0.567	118 12	.21448	0 517	117 88	.21279	0 475	117 64	21122
280	0.636	120.10	.21870	0.576	119 89	21690	0 526	119 66	.21521	0 483	119 42	21364
290	0.646	121.88	.22108	0.586	121 68	21930	0 534	121 45	.21760	0 492	121.21	21605
300	0.657	123.67	0.22347	0.595	123 48	0.22167	0 543	123 25	0.22000	0 500	123.01	0.21846
310	0.667	125.47	.22553	0.605	125 29	22405	0 552	125 07	.22238	0 508	124 82	22084
320	0.677	127.28	.22817	0.614	127.11	.22639	0 560	126 90	.22472	0 516	126.64	22320
330	0.687	129.10	.23050	0 623	128 94	.22872	0 569	128.74	.22707	0 524	128 47	22554
340	0.697	130.94	.23251	0 632	130 78	.23103	0 578	130 59	.22940	0 531	130 31	227s6
350	0.707	132.80	0.23510	0.641	132 63	0 23333	0 586	132 45	0.23171	0 539	132.17	0.23016
360	0.718	134.68	.23738	0.651	134 50	.23562	0 595	134 32	.23400	0.547	134 05	23246
370										0.555	135.94	.23475

TABLE A-15. R-12, DICHLORODIFLUOROMETHANE (CCl_2F_2) PROPERTIES OF SUPERHEATED VAPOR

Temp. °F	Abs. Press. 140 lb/in.² Gage Press. 125.3 lb/in.² (Sat'n. Temp. 104.5°F.)			Abs. Press. 160 lb/in.² Gage Press. 145.3 lb/in.² (Sat'n. Temp. 114.5°F.)			Abs. Press. 180 lb/in.² Gage Press. 165.3 lb/in.² (Sat'n. Temp. 123.7°F.)			Abs. Press. 200 lb/in.² Gage Press. 185.3 lb/in.² (Sat'n. Temp. 132.1°F.)			Abs. Press. 220 lb/in.² Gage Press. 205.3 lb/in.² (Sat'n. Temp. 139.9°F.)		
t	V	H	S	V	H	S	V	H	S	V	H	S	V	H	S
(at sat'n)	(0.298)	(88.99)	(0.16560)	(0.259)	(89.77)	(0.16558)	(0.228)	(90.58)	(0.16476)	(0.208)	(90.86)	(0.16444)	(0.189)	(91.60)	(0.16375)
100															
110	0.304	89.92	0.16725												
120	0.314	91.60	0.17021	0.264	90.68	0.16682									
130	0.323	93.28	0.17306	0.273	92.40	0.16977	0.233	91.47	0.16665						
140	0.332	94.96	0.17590	0.282	94.12	0.17269	0.241	93.23	0.16964	0.203	92.30	0.16661	0.181	91.52	0.16378
150	0.341	96.65	0.17888	0.290	95.84	0.17553	0.249	94.99	0.17254	0.216	94.10	0.16966	0.188	93.32	0.16685
160	0.350	98.34	0.18142	0.298	97.57	0.17832	0.257	96.75	0.17541	0.224	95.90	0.17262	0.195	95.13	0.16986
170	0.358	100.03	0.18412	0.306	99.31	0.18106	0.265	98.52	0.17823	0.231	97.70	0.17551	0.202	96.94	0.17282
180	0.366	101.72	0.18678	0.313	101.05	0.18377	0.272	100.29	0.18102	0.238	99.51	0.17838	0.209	98.75	0.17576
190	0.374	103.42	0.18941	0.321	102.80	0.18646	0.280	102.07	0.18377	0.245	101.32	0.18115	0.216	100.57	0.17861
200	0.383	105.14	0.19205	0.329	104.55	0.18913	0.287	103.85	0.18648	0.252	103.13	0.18388	0.223	102.39	0.18142
210	0.391	106.86	0.19466	0.336	106.31	0.19175	0.294	105.63	0.18912	0.258	104.94	0.18669	0.229	104.22	0.18420
220	0.399	108.59	0.19724	0.344	108.07	0.19435	0.301	107.42	0.19174	0.265	106.76	0.18927	0.236	106.05	0.18694
230	0.407	110.33	0.19976	0.351	109.83	0.19693	0.307	109.21	0.19433	0.272	108.58	0.19192	0.242	107.89	0.18962
240	0.415	112.09	0.20229	0.358	111.60	0.19949	0.314	111.01	0.19693	0.278	110.40	0.19455	0.248	109.74	0.19226
250	0.423	113.85	0.20479	0.366	113.38	0.20203	0.321	112.81	0.19947	0.284	112.23	0.19713	0.254	111.59	0.19487
260	0.431	115.63	0.20728	0.373	115.17	0.20453	0.327	114.62	0.20199	0.290	114.06	0.19967	0.259	113.44	0.19745
270	0.439	117.42	0.20974	0.380	116.97	0.20700	0.334	116.44	0.20449	0.296	115.89	0.20217	0.265	115.30	0.20001
280	0.447	119.22	0.21219	0.387	118.78	0.20946	0.340	118.26	0.20698	0.302	117.73	0.20467	0.271	117.16	0.20255
290	0.455	121.03	0.21461	0.394	120.60	0.21189	0.347	120.09	0.20944	0.308	119.58	0.20715	0.277	119.03	0.20504
300	0.462	122.55	0.21701	0.401	122.43	0.21432	0.353	121.92	0.21187	0.314	121.44	0.20961	0.282	120.91	0.20753
310	0.470	124.67	0.21939	0.408	124.27	0.21672	0.359	123.76	0.21428	0.320	123.31	0.21204	0.288	122.80	0.21002
320	0.477	126.50	0.22174	0.414	126.12	0.21909	0.365	125.61	0.21665	0.326	125.19	0.21445	0.293	124.70	0.21214
330	0.485	128.33	0.22411	0.421	127.98	0.22145	0.371	127.47	0.21904	0.331	127.08	0.21685	0.299	126.60	0.21485
340	0.492	130.17	0.22646	0.428	129.85	0.22381	0.377	129.34	0.22140	0.337	128.98	0.21923	0.304	128.51	0.21724
350	0.500	132.02	0.22880	0.435	131.73	0.22616	0.383	131.23	0.22374	0.343	130.89	0.22159	0.309	130.42	0.21960
360	0.507	133.89	0.23109	0.442	133.63	0.22849	0.390	133.13	0.22608	0.348	132.81	0.22392	0.314	132.34	0.22195
370	0.515	135.78	0.23336	0.448	135.55	0.23079	0.396	135.05	0.22840	0.354	134.74	0.22624	0.320	134.27	0.22430
380							0.402	136.98	0.23072	0.360	136.68	0.22856	0.325	136.21	0.22665
390							0.408	138.91	0.23301	0.365	138.63	0.23085	0.330	138.16	0.22895
400							0.414	140.85	0.23529	0.370	140.59	0.23314	0.335	140.12	0.23124

TABLE A-15. PROPERTIES OF REFRIGERANT-22 (CHClF₂) (LIQUID AND SATURATED VAPOR)

Temp. °F t	Pressure #/sq. in. abs. p	Pressure gauge	Volume cu. ft./lb. Liquid vf	Volume Vapor vg	Density #/cu. ft. Liquid 1/vf	Density Vapor 1/vg	Heat Content Btu./# Liquid hf	Heat Content Latent h	Heat Content Vapor hg	Entropy Btu./# °F Liquid sf	Entropy Vapor sg
−155	.199	*29.51	.0102	188.13	97.67	.0053156	−29.05	115.85	86.80	−0.08075	0.29958
−150	.260	*29.39	.0103	146.06	97.33	.0068467	−27.77	115.15	87.38	−.07670	.29523
−145	.338	*29.23	.0103	114.51	96.99	.0087329	−26.50	114.46	87.96	−.07265	.29118
−140	.433	*29.04	.0103	90.613	96.63	.011036	−25.23	113.78	88.55	−.06865	.28736
−135	.551	*28.80	.0104	72.465	96.27	.013799	−23.98	113.10	89.12	−.06471	.28375
−130	.695	*28.51	.0104	58.214	95.91	.017178	−22.71	112.43	89.72	−.06085	.28026
−125	.869	*28.15	.0105	47.226	95.53	.021175	−21.45	111.76	90.31	−.05706	.27695
−120	1.079	*27.72	.0105	38.600	95.15	.025507	−20.20	111.10	90.90	−.05335	.27380
−115	1.329	*27.21	.0106	31.773	94.76	.031473	−18.96	110.45	91.49	−.04970	.27082
−110	1.626	*26.61	.0106	26.329	94.37	.037981	−17.71	109.80	92.09	−.04609	.26798
−105	1.976	*25.90	.0106	21.960	93.97	.045538	−16.46	109.15	92.69	−.04254	.26527
−100	2.386	*25.06	.0107	18.426	93.56	.054272	−15.21	108.50	93.29	−.03903	.26269
−95	2.865	*24.09	.0107	15.544	93.14	.064333	−13.96	107.85	93.89	−.03557	.26023
−90	3.417	*22.96	.0108	13.196	92.72	.075783	−12.71	107.20	94.49	−.03216	.25788
−85	4.055	*21.67	.0108	11.256	92.29	.088843	−11.45	106.55	95.10	−.02881	.25563
−80	4.787	*20.18	.0109	9.6497	91.85	.10363	−10.20	105.90	95.70	−.02551	.25347
−78	5.13	*19.48	.0109	9.0510	91.67	.11049	−9.69	105.63	95.94	−.02419	.25252
−76	5.48	*18.77	.0109	8.5045	91.49	.11758	−9.19	105.37	96.18	−.02288	.25179
−74	5.83	*18.05	.0109	8.0115	91.31	.12482	−8.68	105.10	96.42	−.02158	.25098
−72	6.20	*17.31	.0110	7.5641	91.13	.13220	−8.18	104.82	96.66	−.02028	.25020
−70	6.57	*16.55	.0110	7.1555	90.95	.13975	−7.67	104.57	96.90	−.01899	.24943
−68	6.97	*15.74	.0110	6.7806	90.77	.14747	−7.16	104.30	97.14	−.01770	.24868
−66	7.40	*14.87	.0110	6.4178	90.58	.15581	−6.66	104.04	97.38	−.01641	.24795
−64	7.84	*13.96	.0111	6.0750	90.39	.16460	−6.15	103.81	97.62	−.01512	.24722
−62	8.33	*12.97	.0111	5.7526	90.21	.17383	−5.65	103.51	97.86	−.01384	.24650
−60	8.86	*11.89	.0111	5.4520	90.03	.18342	−5.14	103.24	98.10	−.01256	.24580
−58	9.41	*10.78	.0111	5.1701	89.84	.19342	−4.62	102.96	98.34	−.01129	.24512

—56	9.98	* 9.62	.0112	4.9039	89.65	.20392	—	4.11	102.69	98.58	—	.01002	.24445
—54	10.56	* 8.44	.0112	4.6536	89.46	.21489	—	3.59	102.41	98.82	—	.00875	.24378
—52	11.15	* 7.24	.0112	4.4172	89.27	.22639	—	3.08	102.14	99.06	—	.00749	.24311
—50	11.74	* 6.02	.0112	4.1948	89.08	.23839	—	2.56	101.86	99.30	—	.00623	.24245
—48	12.39	* 4.70	.0112	3.9872	88.88	.25080	—	2.04	101.58	99.54	—	.00498	.24181
—46	13.07	* 3.33	.0113	3.7936	88.68	.26360	—	1.52	101.30	99.78	—	.00373	.24119
—44	13.78	* 1.38	.0113	3.6114	88.49	.27690	—	1.00	101.02	100.02	—	.00248	.24059
—42	14.52	* 0.36	.0113	3.4399	88.30	.29070	—	.48	100.74	100.26	—	.00124	.24000
—40	15.31	0.609	.0114	3.2787	88.10	.30500		.04	100.46	100.50		0	.23942
—38	16.16	1.459	.0114	3.1250	87.90	.32000		.57	100.17	100.74		.00124	.23884
—36	17.02	2.319	.0114	2.9828	87.70	.33525		1.11	99.86	100.97		.00247	.23827
—34	17.90	3.199	.0114	2.8491	87.50	.35100		1.66	99.54	101.20		.00370	.23771
—32	18.79	4.089	.0115	2.7223	87.29	.36733		2.21	99.22	101.43		.00493	.23717
—30	19.69	4.989	.0115	2.5934	87.09	.38559		2.75	98.91	101.66		.00616	.23663
—28	20.71	6.014	.0115	2.4712	86.89	.40466		3.30	98.59	101.89		.00730	.23609
—26	21.76	7.064	.0116	2.3594	86.69	.42383		3.86	98.26	102.12		.00844	.23556
—24	22.83	8.125	.0116	2.2568	86.48	.44310		4.40	97.95	102.35		.00958	.23505
—22	23.90	9.200	.0116	2.1622	86.27	.46249		4.96	97.62	102.58		.01072	.23455
—20	24.99	10.292	.0116	2.0748	86.06	.48197		5.51	97.30	102.81		.01186	.23406
—18	26.16	11.462	.0117	1.9854	85.85	.50367		6.07	96.97	103.04		.01300	.23358
—16	27.38	12.682	.0117	1.9016	85.64	.52587		6.61	96.65	103.26		.01414	.23311
—14	28.65	13.953	.0117	1.8227	85.43	.54863		7.17	96.32	103.49		.01530	.23264
—12	29.97	15.273	.0117	1.7488	85.21	.57191		7.67	96.04	103.71		.01643	.23217
—10	31.34	16.644	.0118	1.6781	84.99	.59591		8.21	95.67	103.88		.01757	.23168
—8	32.78	18.084	.0118	1.6086	84.78	.62165		8.71	95.33	104.04		.01871	.23120
—6	34.26	19.557	.0118	1.5434	84.56	.64792		9.20	95.01	104.21		.01985	.23074
—4	35.76	21.057	.0119	1.4821	84.34	.67471		9.70	94.67	104.37		.02099	.23029
—2	37.30	22.597	.0119	1.4245	84.12	.70201		10.19	94.35	104.54		.02213	.22985
0	38.87	24.170	.0119	1.3702	83.90	.72980		10.74	94.01	104.75		.02327	.22941
2	40.55	25.85	.0119	1.3193	83.68	.7580		11.28	93.68	104.96		.02442	.22896
4	42.25	27.55	.0120	1.2690	83.46	.7880		11.82	93.36	105.18		.02556	.22852
5†	**43.12**	**28.42**	**.0120**	**1.2421**	**83.34**	**.8051**		**12.09**	**93.20**	**105.29**		**.02613**	**.22830**
6	44.01	29.31	.0120	1.2195	83.12	.8200		12.36	93.03	105.39		.02670	.22807

*Inches mercury below one atmosphere.

†Standard ton temperature

TABLE A-15. PROPERTIES OF REFRIGERANT-22 (CHClF$_2$) (LIQUID AND SATURATED VAPOR)

Temp. °F t	Pressure #/sq. in.		Volume cu. ft./lb.		Density #/cu. ft.		Heat Content Btu/#			Entropy Btu./#°F	
	abs. p	gauge	Liquid v_f	Vapor v_g	Liquid $1/v_f$	Vapor $1/v_g$	Liquid h_f	Latent h	Vapor h_g	Liquid s_f	Vapor s_g
8	45.84	31.14	.0121	1.1733	82.90	.8523	12.90	92.71	105.61	.02784	.22763
10	47.66	32.96	.01208	1.1295	82.78	.88532	13.44	92.38	105.82	.02898	.22720
12	49.65	34.95	.01212	1.0872	82.55	.9198	13.98	92.05	106.03	.03012	.22677
14	51.68	36.98	.01215	1.0473	82.32	.9548	14.52	91.72	106.24	.03126	.22635
16	53.74	39.04	.01218	1.0080	82.09	.9920	15.06	91.40	106.46	.03240	.22593
18	55.85	41.15	.01222	0.97087	81.86	1.0300	15.60	91.07	106.67	.03354	.22551
20	58.00	43.30	.01225	0.93555	81.63	1.0688	16.16	90.73	106.89	.03468	.22509
22	60.30	45.60	.01229	.90278	81.39	1.1076	16.70	90.41	107.11	.03585	.22468
24	62.64	47.94	.01233	.87053	81.16	1.1487	17.24	90.09	107.33	.03702	.22428
26	65.03	50.33	.01237	.83899	80.92	1.1919	17.80	89.76	107.56	.03820	.22389
28	67.37	52.77	.01239	.80997	80.69	1.2346	18.33	89.43	107.76	.03937	.22350
30	69.97	55.27	.01243	.78094	80.45	1.2805	18.85	89.10	107.95	.04054	.22314
32	72.52	57.82	.01247	.75283	80.21	1.3283	19.38	88.77	108.15	.04172	.22278
34	75.19	60.47	.01251	.72640	79.97	1.3766	19.91	88.43	108.34	.04289	.22242
36	77.92	63.22	.01254	.70153	79.93	1.4254	20.44	88.09	108.53	.04407	.22206
38	80.77	66.07	.01258	.67809	79.49	1.4747	20.98	87.74	108.72	.04524	.22170
40	83.72	69.02	.01262	.65591	79.25	1.5246	21.52	87.39	108.91	.04642	.22134
42	86.77	72.07	.01266	.63339	79.00	1.5788	22.12	86.97	109.09	.04761	.22100
44	89.85	75.15	.01270	.61199	78.76	1.6340	22.72	86.55	109.27	.04879	.22066
46	92.97	78.27	.01274	.59161	78.51	1.6903	23.33	86.12	109.45	.04998	.22032
48	96.15	81.45	.01277	.57221	78.27	1.7476	23.94	85.69	109.63	.05116	.21998
50	99.40	84.70	.01282	.55371	78.02	1.8060	24.55	85.25	109.80	.05235	.21964
52	102.76	88.06	.01286	.53547	77.77	1.8675	25.17	84.79	109.96	.05355	.21931
54	106.22	91.52	.01290	.51794	77.51	1.9307	25.79	84.33	110.12	.05475	.21897
56	109.78	95.08	.01293	.50112	77.26	1.9955	26.41	83.87	110.28	.05594	.21864
58	113.44	98.74	.01298	.48498	77.01	2.0619	27.03	83.41	110.44	.05713	.21830

50	117.2	102.5	.01303	.46951	76.75	2.1299	27.65	82.95	110.60	.05833	.21797
60	121.14	106.34	.01307	.45435	76.49	2.2009	28.28	82.46	110.74	.05954	.21765
64	124.95	110.25	.01312	.43987	76.23	2.2734	28.91	81.97	110.88	.06074	.21733
66	128.94	114.24	.01316	.42600	75.98	2.3474	29.54	81.48	111.02	.06195	.21700
68	133.02	118.32	.01321	.41272	75.72	2.4229	30.17	80.99	111.16	.06315	.21669
70	137.2	122.5	.01325	.40000	75.46	2.5000	30.81	80.50	111.31	.06436	.21636
72	141.5	126.8	.01330	.38734	75.20	2.5817	31.47	79.97	111.44	.06556	.21603
74	145.9	131.2	.01335	.37519	74.94	2.6653	32.12	79.45	111.57	.06676	.21570
76	150.4	135.7	.01339	.36354	74.68	2.7507	32.78	78.92	111.70	.06796	.21537
78	155.0	140.3	.01344	.35239	74.42	2.8377	33.43	78.40	111.83	.06916	.21503
80	159.7	145.0	.01349	.34174	74.15	2.9262	34.09	77.86	111.95	.07035	.21469
82	164.5	149.8	.01353	.33146	73.88	3.0169	34.76	77.30	112.06	.07154	.21432
84	169.4	154.7	.01358	.32143	73.61	3.1111	35.43	76.74	112.17	.07273	.21394
86†	174.4	159.7	.01363	.31165	73.34	3.2087	36.09	76.19	112.28	.07392	.21356
88	179.5	164.8	.01368	.30212	73.07	3.3099	36.76	75.63	112.39	.07511	.21318
90	184.8	170.1	.01374	.29284	72.81	3.4148	37.43	75.06	112.49	.07630	.21281
92	190.1	175.4	.01380	.28407	72.52	3.5202	38.10	74.47	112.57	.07749	.21245
94	195.5	180.8	.01384	.27560	72.23	3.6285	38.78	73.87	112.65	.07867	.21209
96	201.1	186.4	.01389	.26733	71.94	3.7406	39.45	73.28	112.73	.07985	.21173
98	206.8	192.1	.01395	.25936	71.65	3.8556	40.13	72.68	112.81	.08103	.21137
100	212.6	197.9	.01402	.25169	71.35	3.9731	40.80	72.08	112.88	.08221	.21102
102	218.5	203.8	.01408	.24429	71.04	4.0935	41.47	71.45	112.92	.08338	.21064
104	224.5	209.8	.01414	.23710	70.73	4.2176	42.15	70.81	112.96	.08456	.21026
106	230.7	216.0	.01420	.23011	70.42	4.3457	42.82	70.19	113.01	.08574	.20988
108	237.0	222.3	.01426	.22332	70.10	4.4778	43.50	69.56	113.06	.08692	.20950
110	243.4	228.7	.01433	.21673	69.78	4.6140	44.17	68.94	113.11	.08810	.20913
112	249.9	235.2	.01440	.21057	69.45	4.7490	44.87	68.28	113.15	.08928	.20876
114	256.6	241.9	.01447	.20453	69.12	4.8893	45.57	67.62	113.19	.09046	.20839
116	263.4	248.7	.01454	.19861	68.78	5.0349	46.27	66.97	113.24	.09164	.20802
118	270.3	255.6	.01461	.19280	68.44	5.1867	46.97	66.32	113.29	.09281	.20765
120	277.3	262.6	.01469	.18709	68.10	5.3451	47.67	65.67	113.34	.09398	.20728

*Inches mercury below one atmosphere.
†Standard ton temperature

TABLE A-15. SATURATED CARBON DIOXIDE (CO_2)

Temp.	Pressure	Volume		Total heat from $-40°$			Entropy from $32°$ plus 1	
°F.	Abs., lb./in.²	Liquid, ft.³/lb.	Vapor, ft.³/lb.	Liquid, Btu./lb.	Latent, Btu./lb.	Vapor, Btu./lb.	Liquid, Btu./lb.°F.	Vapor, Btu./lb.°F.
t	p	v_f	v_g	h_f	h	h_g	s_f	s_g
-10	257.3	0.01532	0.3472	13.9	124.8	138.7	.9532	1.2303
-8	266.5	0.01540	0.3349	14.9	123.9	138.8	.9552	1.2297
-6	275.9	0.01547	0.3231	15.9	122.9	138.8	.9573	1.2284
-4	285.4	0.01555	0.3118	16.9	122.0	138.9	.9594	1.2272
-2	295.3	0.01563	0.3009	17.9	121.0	138.9	.9614	1.2259
0	305.5	0.01570	0.2904	18.8	120.1	138.9	.9636	1.2247
2	315.9	0.01579	0.2803	19.8	119.0	138.8	.9657	1.2235
4	326.5	0.01588	0.2707	20.8	118.0	138.8	.9679	1.2224
6	337.4	0.01596	0.2614	21.8	116.9	138.7	.9701	1.2212
8	348.7	0.01605	0.2526	22.9	115.8	138.7	.9722	1.2199
10	360.2	0.01614	0.2437	24.0	114.7	138.7	.9744	1.2188
12	371.9	0.01623	0.2354	25.0	113.6	138.6	.9765	1.2175
14	383.9	0.01632	0.2274	26.1	112.5	138.6	.9787	1.2163
16	396.2	0.01642	0.2197	27.2	111.3	138.5	.9810	1.2151
18	408.9	0.01652	0.2121	28.3	110.1	138.4	.9833	1.2139
20	421.8	0.01663	0.2049	29.4	108.9	138.3	.9856	1.2127
22	434.0	0.01673	0.1979	30.5	107.7	138.2	.9879	1.2115
24	448.4	0.01684	0.1912	31.7	106.4	138.1	.9902	1.2103
26	462.2	0.01695	0.1846	32.9	105.1	138.0	.9927	1.2091
28	476.3	0.01707	0.1783	34.1	103.8	137.9	.9951	1.2079
30	490.8	0.01719	0.1722	35.4	102.4	137.8	.9976	1.2067
32	505.5	0.01731	0.1663	36.7	101.0	137.7	1.0000	1.2055
34	522.6	0.01744	0.1603	37.9	99.5	137.4	1.0023	1.2038
36	536.0	0.01759	0.1550	39.1	98.1	137.2	1.0046	1.2024
38	551.7	0.01773	0.1496	40.4	96.5	136.9	1.0071	1.2009
40	567.8	0.01787	0.1444	41.7	95.0	136.7	1.0092	1.1994
42	584.3	0.01801	0.1393	42.9	93.4	136.3	1.0115	1.1979
44	601.1	0.01817	0.1344	44.3	91.8	136.1	1.0140	1.1964
46	618.2	0.01834	0.1297	45.6	90.1	135.7	1.0166	1.1949
48	635.7	0.01851	0.1250	47.0	88.4	135.4	1.0194	1.1933
50	653.6	0.01868	0.1205	48.4	86.6	135.0	1.0218	1.1917
52	671.9	0.01887	0.1161	49.8	84.7	134.5	1.0254	1.1901
54	690.6	0.01906	0.1117	51.2	82.7	133.9	1.0272	1.1882
56	709.5	0.01927	0.1075	52.6	80.8	133.4	1.0283	1.1865
58	728.8	0.01948	0.1034	54.0	78.7	132.7	1.0312	1.1846
60	748.6	0.01970	0.0994	55.5	76.6	132.1	1.0353	1.1826
64	789.4	0.02020	0.0918	58.6	72.0	130.6	1.0410	1.1803
66	810.3	0.02048	0.0880	60.2	69.5	129.7	1.0438	1.1780
68	831.6	0.02079	0.08422	61.9	66.8	128.7	1.0468	1.1754
70	853.4	0.02112	0.08040	63.7	63.8	127.5	1.0500	1.1724
74	898.2	0.02192	0.07269	67.3	57.2	124.5	1.0568	1.1690
76	921.3	0.02242	0.06875	69.4	53.4	122.8	1.0607	1.1655
78	944.8	0.02300	0.06473	71.6	49.3	120.9	1.0649	1.1605
80	968.7	0.02370	0.06064	73.9	44.8	118.7	1.0694	1.1555
82	993.0	0.02456	0.05648	76.4	40.2	116.6	1.0740	1.1505
84	1017.7	0.02553	0.05223	79.4	34.5	113.9	1.0790	1.1455
86	1043.0	0.02686	0.04789	83.3	27.1	110.4	1.0854	1.1381
87.8	1069.4	0.03454	0.03454	97.0	0.0	97.0	1.1098	1.1098

TABLE A-16—HEAT LOSS FROM BARE AND INSULATED PIPE

Pipe Size Inches	Heat Loss Btu Per Deg. Fahr. Diff. in Temperature			
	Per Lin. Foot		Per sq. Foot	
	Per 1 Hour	Per 24 Hours	Per 1 Hour	Per 24 Hours
¼	0.340	8.2	2.405	57.72
⅜	0.406	9.75	2.297	57.13
½	0.485	11.6	2.205	52.92
¾	0.581	14.0	2.113	50.71
1	0.698	16.7	2.027	48.65
1¼	0.856	20.5	1.969	47.26
1½	0.960	23.0	1.929	46.30
2	1.16	28.0	1.865	44.76
2½	1.39	33.3	1.846	44.30
3	1.66	40.0	1.811	43.46
3½	1.86	44.6	1.774	42.58
4	2.06	49.5	1.747	41.93
4½	2.29	54.5	1.747	41.93
5	2.49	59.8	1.708	40.99
6	2.90	69.6	1.670	40.08
7	3.33	79.6	1.665	39.96
8	3.74	89.7	1.653	39.67
9	4.16	100.0	1.647	39.53
10	4.63	111.0	1.644	39.45
12	5.49	132.0	1.642	39.41
14	5.88	141.0	1.605	38.52
16	6.75	162.0	1.613	38.68

HEAT LOSS THROUGH CORK PIPE COVERING—ICE WATER THICKNESS

¼	0.101	2.42	0.714	17.15
⅜	0.114	2.74	0.644	15.48
½	0.132	3.17	0.600	14.40
¾	0.140	3.37	0.509	12.22
1	0.152	3.64	0.442	10.60
1¼	0.173	4.15	0.398	9.56
1½	0.187	4.50	0.376	9.03
2	0.216	5.20	0.347	8.33
2½	0.257	6.17	0.342	8.19
3	0.273	6.55	0.298	7.15
3½	0.292	7.00	0.276	6.62
4	0.311	7.46	0.264	6.33
4½	0.335	8.05	0.255	6.13
5	0.371	8.90	0.254	6.10
6	0.397	9.53	0.229	5.49
7	0.458	11.00	0.229	5.49
8	0.504	12.10	0.223	5.34
9	0.548	13.15	0.217	5.21
10	0.571	13.70	0.203	4.86
12	0.750	18.00	0.224	5.38

—Armstrong Cork Co. Data

TABLE A-16—HEAT LOSS THROUGH CORK PIPE COVERING—BRINE THICKNESS

| Pipe Size Inches | Heat Loss Btu Per Deg. Fahr. Diff. in Temperature | | | |
| | Per Lin. Foot | | Per sq. Foot | |
	Per 1 Hour	Per 24 Hours	Per 1 Hour	Per 24 Hours
¼	0.088	2.12	0.622	14.92
⅜	0.098	2.36	0.554	13.29
½	0.113	2.71	0.513	12.32
¾	0.120	2.87	0.436	10.47
1	0.129	3.11	0.374	8.99
1¼	0.135	3.22	0.311	7.46
1½	0.138	3.32	0.277	6.65
2	0.158	3.80	0.254	6.09
2½	0.175	4.21	0.232	5.57
3	0.187	4.49	0.204	4.89
3½	0.199	4.78	0.190	4.56
4	0.231	5.55	0.196	4.70
4½	0.219	5.26	0.167	4.01
5	0.250	6.05	0.171	4.11
6	0.285	6.85	0.164	3.94
7	0.320	7.68	0.160	3.84
8	0.328	7.88	0.145	3.48
9	0.339	8.15	0.134	3.22
10	0.376	9.02	0.133	3.20
12	0.434	10.40	0.130	3.12
14	0.471	11.30	0.129	3.08
16	0.525	12.60	0.125	3.01

HEAT LOSS THROUGH CORK PIPE COVERING—SPECIAL THICK BRINE

Pipe Size Inches	Per 1 Hour	Per 24 Hours	Per 1 Hour	Per 24 Hours
¼	0.068	1.64	0.481	11.55
⅜	0.077	1.84	0.435	10.45
½	0.089	2.13	0.405	9.71
¾	0.099	2.39	0.360	8.63
1	0.101	2.43	0.293	7.04
1¼	0.112	2.70	0.258	6.18
1½	0.118	2.84	0.237	5.69
2	0.133	3.20	0.215	5.17
2½	0.156	3.75	0.207	4.97
3	0.175	4.21	0.191	4.58
3½	0.167	4.00	0.159	3.83
4	0.187	4.49	0.159	3.83
4½	0.178	4.28	0.136	3.26
5	0.199	4.78	0.137	3.27
6	0.206	4.95	0.119	2.85
7	0.238	5.71	0.119	2.85
8	0.258	6.20	0.114	2.74
9	0.282	6.76	0.112	2.68
10	0.306	7.33	0.109	2.61
12	0.348	8.36	0.104	2.50
14	0.375	9.00	0.102	2.46
16	0.417	10.00	0.099	2.39

—Armstrong Cork Co. Data

CALCULATING OVERALL HEAT LEAKAGE FACTORS

On page 268 a simplified method of calculating heat transfer factors through a composite wall was given. The mathematical method more commonly used is to add the conductances of the various materials in the wall. Conductances are the reciprocals of the heat transfer or k factors. The overall figure obtained is called a U factor. It is calculated by the following formula.

$$U = \frac{1}{\dfrac{x_1}{k_1} + \dfrac{x_2}{k_2} + \dfrac{x_3}{k_3}}$$

where U = overall heat transfer factor for the complete wall thickness in Btu per sq ft per degree per hr.

x_1 = thickness of first material in inches.
x_2 = thickness of second material in inches.
x_3 = thickness of third material in inches.
k_1 = k factor of first material.
k_2 = k factor of second material.
k_3 = k factor of third material.

As many more $\dfrac{x}{k}$ factors as are needed can be added if the wall contains more different materials.

Example A-1.—Work Eample 18-3, page 268, by solving for the U factor.

$$U = \frac{1}{\dfrac{x_1}{k_1} + \dfrac{x_2}{k_2}}$$

$$= \frac{1}{\dfrac{\dfrac{5}{8} + \dfrac{5}{8}}{.80} + \dfrac{3}{.28}} = \frac{1}{1.56 + 10.71}$$

$$= \frac{1}{12.27}$$

= .0815 Btu per sq ft per hour per degree.

This may be checked against the answer of Example 18-3 by solving for the leakage of 3.44 inches of cork.

$$\frac{.28}{3.44} = .0815$$

The total heat loss for the entire wall then could be solved by the following formula:

$$H = A U (t_2 - t_1)$$

Notice this is the same as the formula given on page 267 except that U is substituted for $\dfrac{k}{x}$

The U factor formula is sometimes given more completely as follows:

$$U = \cfrac{1}{\dfrac{1}{f_i} + \dfrac{x_1}{k_1} + \dfrac{x_2}{k_2} + \dfrac{x_3}{k_3} + \dfrac{n}{1.1} + \dfrac{1}{f_o}}$$

where f_i = inside air film = 1.65

This is the estimated insulation effect of the film of air that clings to the surface. The inside air film is for still air. For a box inside a building, this figure is also used for f_o; because the latter is only for a surface exposed to wind.

n = number of separate air spaces between surfaces. The thickness of the air space if more than ¼ inch makes no difference.

f_o = outside air film = 6.5

This figure is used for the outside of the building which is exposed to outside winds. It is not used for the outside surface of a cooler or cabinet enclosed in another building.

Example A-2.—A wall is made up of an 8 inch brick, facing outside, an air space, and 4 inches of cork. What is its U factor?

$$U = \cfrac{1}{\dfrac{1}{f_i} + \dfrac{x_1}{k_1} + \dfrac{x_2}{k_2} + \dfrac{n}{1.1} + \dfrac{1}{f_o}}$$

$$= \cfrac{1}{\dfrac{1}{1.65} + \dfrac{8}{5.0} + \dfrac{4}{.28} + \dfrac{1}{1.1} + \dfrac{1}{6.5}}$$

$$= \cfrac{1}{0.61 + 1.60 + 14.28 + 0.91 + 0.15}$$

$$= 0.0570$$

In common insulation problems, the effect of surface air films is neglected because they are so small. Their effect is of value in the following type of problem.

Example A-3.—Figure the U factor of a double glass door with an air space between the two glasses. Assume each pane of glass is ⅛ inch thick.

$$U = \cfrac{1}{\cfrac{1}{1.65} + \cfrac{1}{1.1} + \cfrac{1}{1.65} + \cfrac{.25}{6.5}}$$

$$= \quad 0.457$$

Compare this answer with the value given for double glass in Table A-9, page 445.

ANSWERS TO PROBLEMS IN QUESTIONS

1- 2. 277 Btu per gal.

1- 3. 40.1 Btu per gal.

1- 4. 8.5 Btu per gal.

1- 5. 1.92 lb; 0.28 lb; 0.06 lb.

1- 6. 1.13 lb; 0.16 lb; 0.03 lb.

2-1a. 77 F; 2-1b. 60 F; 2-1c. 5 F.

14-14. Approximately saturated.

14-15. Very wet but not yet to the slugging point.

14-16. At the slugging point.

14-17. Nearly 50 F superheat in the suction line; entirely too much.

18-1a. 1020 Btu per hour; 18-1b. 1450 Btu per hour.

18-1c. 3705 Btu per hour.

18-2a. 627 Btu per hour. 18-2b. 677 Btu per hour.

18-2c. 1956 Btu per hour. 18-2d. 236 Btu per hour.

18-2e. 180 Btu per hour. 18-2f. 2090 Btu per hour.

18-2g. 2580 Btu per hour. 18-2h. 4300 Btu per hour.

18-3a. 522 Btu per hour. 18-3b. 479 Btu per hour.

18-3c. 1500 Btu per hour.

18-4a. 20,600 Btu per minute. 18-4b. 8.7 F.

18-4c. 148 Btu per sq ft. 18-4d. 75 F. 18-4e. 80 F.

19- 4. RH = 37 percent; DP = 25.5 F; moisture = 1.6 grains per cubic foot.

19- 5. WB = 40 F; DP = 26 F; moisture = 1.65 grains per cubic foot.

19- 6. WB = 47 F; RH = 60 percent; moisture = 2.85 grains per cubic foot.

19- 7. Cools to 54 F saturated; cools to 25 F dropping all but 1.55 grains per cubic foot; reheats to 35 F, RH = 67 percent.

19- 8. Cools to 25 F and 1 grain per cubic foot; reheats to 35 F, RH = 42 percent.

19- 9. 10 F.

20- 5. 17 percent.

20- 8. 75.5 percent.

20- 9. 62 percent.

21- 1. 21.4 tons.

21- 3. 970 rpm.

21- 4. Displacement = 18.5 cfm per ton; power = 2.27 hp per ton.

21- 5. Displacement = 17.9 cfm per ton; power = 2.2 hp per ton.

21- 6. 35 psia or 20.3 psig.

21- 7. 0.969 lb per min per ton of refrigeration in the low temperature evaporator.

21- 8.

	Low pressure	High pressure	Total
Displacement	17.9 cfm	5.63 hp	
Power	1.01 hp	1.19 hp	2.20 hp

21- 9. 1.34 lb per ton of refrigeration under previous conditions.

21-10. Increase capacity to 7.16 cfm.
Increase power to 1.51 hp.

21-11. 33 percent more refrigeration.

22- 1. 25 percent less capacity.

22- 2. 1⅝ in suction; 1⅛ in discharge; ½ in liquid.

22- 3. 3⅛ in suction; 1⅛ in discharge if shorter than 25 ft. equivalent, otherwise use 1⅜ in; ⅞ in liquid line.

22- 4. 4 in standard suction; ¾ in ex-heavy liquid; 2 in ex-heavy discharge.

22- 5. Suction pressure drop, 0.3223 or about ⅓ psi which is too much. A larger line should be installed. Liquid line drop, 2.7 psi. which is O.K. Discharge pressure drop is 1.7 psi which is too much.

25-2a. 13,057 Btu per hr based on average sun effect.

25-2b. 1,960,000 Btu per day for eggs;
240,000 Btu per day for crates.

25-2c. 2740 Btu per hr.

25-2d. 5 in × 5 in at 450 rpm.

25-2e. 8040 lineal ft.

25- 3.

	Condensing Unit	Evaporator
Locker room	5580 Btu at —10 F	319 sq ft surface or 160 sq ft plates
Freezer	4000 Btu at —30 F	24 sq ft plates
Chill room	3114 Btu at 26 F	3114 Btu blower coil at 10 F T.D.

26- 8. 62½ cents.

27-1a. 14.7 psi; 30 inches mercury.

27-1b. 12.9 psi; 26.4 inches mercury.

27-1c. 12.1 psi; 24.8 inches mercury.

27-1d. 10.5 psi; 21.5 inches mercury.

INDEX

A

Absolute,
  humidity, 274
  pressure, 13, 416
Absorber, 421
Absorption,
  cycle, 422
  systems, 421
Accumulator, 77, 79, 81, 84
Adiabatic,
  compression factors, 305
  curve, 307
Aging of meat, 188
Air agitation in ice making, 404
Air bound high side float valve, 58
Air conditioning, 115, 116, 396
Air cooled condenser, 120
Air in system, effect of, 212, 214
Air washer, 399
Altitude effects, 416
Ambient temperature, 248
Ammeter, 246
Ammonia, 20, 32, 36, 40, 43
  compressor, 87, 112
  compressor performance, 304
  valve, 139
Analyzer, 423
Area, copper tube, table, 442
  in pipes, table, 444
Asbestos insulation, 228
Atmospheres of pressure, 244
Atmospheric,
  condenser, 125
  condensers, heat transfer, 447
  pressure, 13, 244
Attemperator coils, 371
Automatic,
  expansion valve, 60, 84, 171
  purger, 143, 196
Auxiliary valves, 376

B

Baudelot cooler, 368
  heat transfer, 447
Back pressure, 23
  control, 148, 158
Bacterial spoilage, 186
Beer cooling, 366
Beverage cooling, 362

Binoc thermometer, 331
Blanching, 188
Booster system, 327, 331
Bourdon tube, 242
Breweries, 369
Brine, 172, 402
  chemistry, 350
  cooler, 76, 73
  heat transfer in, 447
Brine,
  system, 348
  tables, 354, 355
  thickness, pipe covering, 488
British Thermal Unit, 7
Btu, 7
Bypass,
  capacity control, 108
  valve, 106

C

Cabinets, 222
Cabinet construction, 232
Calcium chloride, 352, 355
Calculations, compressor, 283
Capacitor split phase motor, 177
Capacity,
  control, 106, 182, 183
  effect of condensing temperature on, 313
  effect of suction temperature on, 311
  variations, 310
Capillary tube, 59, 83, 154
Carbon dioxide, 32, 36, 40, 45, 366, 367, 372, 409
Carrene-1, 32, 36, 40, 46
Carrene-2, 32, 36, 40
Cascade, 333
Centigrade, 6
Central station air conditioner, 398
Centrifugal compressors, 115
Change of state, 11
Changing refrigerants, 48, 320
Charged water, 367
Charging, refrigerant quantity, table, 448
Checking,
  a thermometer, 241
  a gage, 245
Check valve, 157
Chlorophyll, 188
Chromate, 352
Chromic acid, 352
Circulating water system, 364

Clearance, 306
  pocket, 108
Clear ice, 402
Cloud point, 163
Codes, 428
Coefficient of performance, 28, 294
Coils,
  heat transfer in, table, 447
  refrigerant to charge, 448
Cold storage, 184, 186, 383
  temperature, table, 432
Commercial,
  maintenance, 207
  refrigeration, 15
Compression discharge temperature, 36, 44
Compressor, 22, 87
  calculations, 283, 310
  capacity control, 106
  centrifugal, 115
  clearance, 306
  cooling, 104
  does not run, 216, 217
  drive, 174
  dual effect, 108
  hermetically sealed, 112
  horizontal double acting, 110
  horsepower, 288, 296, 298
  how to test, 218
  indicator diagrams, 303
  lubrication, 103
  manifold, 106
  rotary, 114
  safety head, 99
  shaft seal, 101
  size, 284, 294
  speed, 110
  stuffing box, 101
  valves, 98, 105, 200
  valves, effect of faulty, 212, 214
Condenser, 22, 119, 266, 421
  air cooled, 120
  heat, 267
  heat transfer, 268
  heat transfer, table, 447
  types of, see particular type
  water cooled, 123
  water cost, 195
Condensing unit capacity table, 302
Condensing temperature,
  effect on capacity, 313
  effect on compressor, 194
Conductivity, 250
  tables, 445
Congealing tank, 359
Constant pressure valve, 156, 157
Containers, food, table, 436
Control, 148
  applications, 154
  effect of improper setting, 212
  valve, 148
Convection in evaporators, 82
Conversion equivalents, table, 439
Cooler,
  storage temperatures, table, 432
  usage factors, 446
Cooling tower, 128
Copper tube, 134
  refrigerant to charge, 448
  tables, 442

Core of ice, 404
Cork, 224
Corrosion control, 352
Counterflow, 124
Cubic measure, 440
Cut in point, 149
Cut out point, 149
Cylinders, refrigerant, 51

D

Dairy products, properties of, 435
Dalton's Law of Partial Pressure, 14, 17
Defrost device on control, 151
Defrosting, 207, 220
  methods, 167
Dehumidification, 396
Dehydration of food, 186, 188
Dehydrator, 140
Density of various substances, 431
Design temperature, 248
Desuperheater, heat transfer, 447
Dew point, 278
Dial thermometer, 241
Diesel engine, 183
Differential, 149
Direct current motor, 182
Direct system, 348
Dirty condenser, effect of, 212, 214
Discharge,
  temperature, 201
  valves, 98
Displacement, 295, 298, 299
Domestic refrigeration, 15
Door loss, 261
Door, refrigerator, 231, 233
Double pipe,
  condenser, 124
  condenser, heat transfer, 447
  exchanger, heat transfer, 447
Dry expansion evaporator, 76, 79
Dry ice, 409
  compared to water ice, 412
Drying of food, 186-
Dry vapor, 11
Drier, 140
Dual effect, 333
  compressor, 108

E

Economy of operation, 174
Efficiency, 286, 289
Electric control, 148
Electric,
  drive, 175
  instruments, 246
  loads, thermal, 446
  troubles, 215
Electrolux system, 425
Elevation effects, 416
Energy, 12
  equivalents, 439
Enthalpy, 284
Entropy, 284, 288
Enzymic action, 185, 188
Equivalents,
  conversion, table, 439

pressure, table, 439
Error in gage, 245
Error in thermometer, 236, 240
Ethyl chloride, 34
Ether, 20
Evaporation, 18
Evaporative condenser, 131
  heat transfer, 447
Evaporator, 22, 54, 73, 421
  dry type, 79
  feed device, 53
  flooded, 75, 76, 83
  forced draft, 82, 167
  natural convection, 82
  sizing, 256
  temperature, effect of, 279
Eutectic, 351
  plate, 359
Expansion valve, 22, 53, 148
  automatic, 60, 84, 154
  effect of improper setting, 212
  flooding, 210
  hand, 54, 77
  starved, 211
  thermostatic, 64, 84
External equalizer, 67

F

Fahrenheit, 5, 6
Faulty refrigeration, 216
Felt insulation, 225
Fermentation, 371, 373
Filters, 140
Fish, properties of, table, 435
Fittings, 135, 136, 137
Fittings, pressure drops, 345
Flake-Ice, 406
Flare,
  connections, 135
  fittings, 135
Flash gas, 28, 322, 328
  calculation of, 290
Flash point, 163
Float valve,
  high side, 58
  low side, 55, 84
Flooded evaporator, 75, 76, 84
Foil insulation, 227
Food,
  container sizes, table, 436
  freezing temp., table, 432
  latent heat, table, 432
  preservation, 184
  properties of, table, 432
  storage temp., table, 432
  storage troubles, 217, 219
  water content of, 432
Forced draft evaporator, 82, 167
Foul gas, 196
Freezer,
  burn, 188
  floors, 233
  storage temperatures, 435
Freezing,
  food, 187
  temp. of goods, table, 432
Fruits, properties of, table, 432
Fusible plug, 51, 159

G

Gage, 242
  error, 245
  pressure, 12, 416
Gas engine, 183
Generator, 421
Glass insulation, 226
  thermal conductivity, 446
Glazing, 188
Ground temperature, 260

H

Hand,
  expansion valve, 55
  valves, 138
Handling refrigerants, 50
Hard drawn tubing, 136
Hard solder, 137
HDA compressor, 110
Headers,
  in condensers, 121, 131
  in evaporators, 75, 77, 82, 84
Heat,
  calculations, 248
  cycle, 26
  exchanger, 70, 86, 146, 322, 423
  insulation, 228
  latent, 9
  ioss from pipe, table, 487
  specific, 7, 8
  to condenser, 267
Heat transfer,
  calculations, 489
  in condenser, 268, 447
  in equipment, table, 447
Heater defrost, 172
Hermetic motors, 179
Hermetically sealed compressor, 112
High pressure cutout, 152
High side, 23
  float valve, 58, 84
  float valve, air bound, 58
Hold over, brine, 350
Hops, 373
Horizontal,
  double acting compressor, 110
  S & T condensers, heat transfer, 447
Horsepower per ton, 298
Hot gas defrosting, 168
Humidity, 220, 274, 396
  control, 356
  measurement, 275
Hunting expansion valve, 68

I

Ice cream,
  freezer, 77
  packing, 43
Ice,
  maker, 77
  making, 401
  melting equipment, 10
I M E, 10
Indicator, 88

diagram, 90, 303
Indicators, 352
Indirect system, 348
Induction motor, 175
Industrial refrigeration, 15
Inhibitors, 352
Instruments, 235, 246
Interstate Commerce regulations, 38, 50
Insulation, 208, 222, 265
   thermal conductivity, 445
Intercooling, 327, 331, 333
Intermediate pressure, 329
Intermittent absorption system, 421
Iron pipe, 137
Iron pipe table, 444
Isothermal compression factor, 305

K

King valve, 133
K factor, 222, 255
   conductivity table, 445

L

Latent heat, 9
   of foods, table, 432
   of fusion, 9
   of sublimation, 10
   of vaporization, 9
Leak testing
   ammonia, 45
   methyl chloride, 43, 47
   R-11, 47
   R-12, 47
   water vapor, 42
Liquid,
   indicator, 145
   lift pressure drop, 341
   measure, 441
   receiver, 23, 133
   seal, 133
   valve, 59
   -vapor cycle, 28
Liquor, 422
   pump, 422
Litmus, 353
Load due to product, 260
Locker plants, 386
Log mean temperature difference, 267, 449
Low,
   refrigerant charge, 58, 59, 60, 64
   side, 23, 73
      float valve, 55, 84
   temperature tolerance, 186
   water cutout, 158
Lubrication, 103, 111, 161, 206

M

Magnetic controller, 150
Maintaining temperature, 190
Maintenance, 207
   of insulation, 208
Manifold, 106

Marble ice, 402
Mean temperature difference, 266, 449
Meat, properties of, table, 435
Mechanical efficiency, 289
Metal foil insulation, 277
Methyl chloride, 32, 36, 40, 42
Mercury,
   column, 245
   thermometer, 236
Milk,
   coolers, 368
   cooling, 358
Mineral insulation, 226
Moisture,
   in system, 42, 44, 140, 165
   proofing insulation, 228
   proofing frozen food, 188
Mold, 274
   spoilage, 186
Mollier diagram, 291, 315
Motor speed, 179, 181
Multiple evaporators on one compressor, 154
Multiplexing, 376
Multiplex systems, 154

N

Non-condensable gas, 59, 143, 195

O

Oil, 161
   foaming 162
   lantern, 110
   regenerator, 143
   slugging, 99, 200, 205
   specifications, 166
   trap, 141, 165
Operating, 190
   faults, 212
   troubles, their causes, 216
Overload, effect of, 212, 214
Oxy-acetylene torch, 136

P

Packless valve, 138
Pak-Ice, 407
Parallax, 236
Partial pressure, 14, 17, 426
pH scale, 352
Phenolphthalein, 353
Pipe,
   covering tables, 487
   refrigerant to charge, 448
   table, 444
Piping pressure drops, 339, 343
Piston speed, 110
Plastic insulation, 227
Plugged up system, 211, 212
Pour point, 163
Power compressor, 288, 296
Power equivalents, table, 439
ppm, parts per million, 37
Preservation of food, 184

Pressure, 12
  absolute, 13, 416
  atmospheric, 13
  cycle, 23
  drop in lines, 339, 343
  drop, liquid lift, 341
  effect on boiling temperature, 18, 19
  gage, 12, 242, 416
  heat diagram, 291
  partial, 14, 17
  ratios, table, 439
  relief device, 159
  relief valve, 159
Prest-O-Lite torch, 136
Problem answers, 493
Product load, 260
Psychrometer, 276
Psychrometric chart, 277
Purge, high side float valve, 58
Purger, 143
Purging, 196

Q

Quality of refrigerant, 293
Quick freezing, 187, 188

R

Range, 149
Reaumur, 6
Receiver vent pipe, 134
Recording,
  gage, 245
  thermometer, 242
Rectifier, 423
Reflecting thermometer, 237
Reflective insulation, 227
Refrigerant,
  control device, 53
  cylinders, 51
  excess amount, 198, 212, 214
  feed device, 53
  not enough, 212
  requirements, 31
  shortage, 58, 58, 60, 64
  tables, 283, 450, 486
  to charge system, 448
Refrigerants,
  R-11, 32, 36, 37, 40, 47
  R-12, 32, 36, 37, 40, 47, 49
  R-13, 32, 36, 40, 48
  R-21, 32, 36, 40
  R-22, 32, 36, 40, 48, 49
  R-30, 32, 36, 40, 42, 46, 47
  R-40, 32, 36, 37, 40, 42
  R-113, 32, 36, 40, 48
  R-114, 36, 40, 48
  R-500, 32, 36, 40
  R-717, 32, 36, 37, 40, 41, 43
  R-718, 32, 36, 40, 42
  R-744, 32, 36, 37, 40, 45
  R-764, 32, 36, 37, 40, 42
Refrigerated enclosures, 222
Refrigeration,
  measure table, 441
  faulty, 216

Relative humidity, 274
  food storage, table, 432
Repulsion,
  start induction run motor, 177
  induction motor, 178
Resistance split phase motor, 176
Restrictor tube, 59
Ripening, 185
Rotary compressors, 114
Rupture,
  disk, 159
  member, 159

S

Safety,
  head, 99
  in operating, 198
Salt, 351
Saturated,
  air, 274
  vapor, 11
Saybolt, 163
Self regulation, 190
Service valves, 105
Servicing, 210
Shaft seal, 101
Sharp freezing, 187, 188
Shell and coil condenser, 124, 447
Shell and tube condenser, 125, 447
Short cycling, 150, 211, 214, 215, 216
Shipping bolts, 219
Single phase motor, 175
Sight glass, 144
Silver,
  brazing alloy, 136
  solder, 136
Slugging, 200, 201, 205
Soda water, 367
Sodium,
  chloride, 351, 354
  dichromate, 352
Soft drawn tubing, 134
Solder, 136
  fittings, 136
Solenoid valve, 154, 157
Specific heat, 7, 8
  of foods, table, 432
  various substances, 431
Speed, compressor, 110
Spirit thermometer, 236
Split phase motor, 176
Spoilage of foods, 186
Standard ton conditions, 30, 314
Starting,
  compressor, 199
  relay, 179
  torque, 175
Steam,
  drive, 182
  jet, 42, 117
  power, 371
Stoppage in system, 211, 212
Storage,
  life, foods, table, 432
  troubles, 217, 219
Storage refrigeration, brine or ice, 350
Strainers, 140
Strong liquor, 422

Stuffing box, 101
Subcooled liquid, 291
Subcooling, 315, 317
Suction,
   pressure, effect on compressor, 193
   temperature, effect on capacity, 311
   valves, 98
Sulphur dioxide, 32, 36, 40, 42
Sun effect, 260
Superheat, its effect on thermostatic expansion
   valve, 65
Superheated vapor, 11
Superheating, 315, 316
Surface cooler, 368
Sweat fittings, 136
Synchronous motor, 181

T

Temperature, 5
   ambient, 248
   control, 150
   cycle, 24
   design, 248
   formulas, 6
   ground, 260
   -pressure relationship, 18, 32
   scales, 6
Temperature difference,
   coil to room, 349
   effect on coils, 191
   effect on humidities and food products, 275, 279
Tenderizing meat, 185, 188
Testing compressor, 218
Thermal conductivity, table, 445
Thermal expansion valve, 64
Thermobank defrost system, 170
Thermometer, 235, 276
   errors, 236, 240
   how to check, 241
   locations, 239
   well, 238
Thermon, 36, 40
Thermostat, 242
Thermostatic expansion valve, 64, 84
Thickness of insulation, 265
Three phase motor, 180
Three stage compressor, 410
Tolerance, low temperature, 186
Ton of refrigeration, 10
Torque, 175
Triple point, 409
Tropical foods, 187
Truck refrigeration, 359, 414
Tube, copper,
   refrigerant to charge, 448
   table, 442
Tube-Ice, 407
Tubing, copper, 134
Two stage system, 327, 331

U

Ultra-violet light, use on food, 187
Usage factors, 253
   -cooler, table, 446
U-valve calculations, 489

V

Vacuum, 13
Valves, 138, 148, 200
   check, 157
   pressure relief, 159
   solenoid, 154, 157
   water regulating, 158
Vapor, 11, 12
   saturated, 11
Vegetable fiber insulation, 226
Vegetables, properties of, table, 433
Velocity in lines, 339
Vertical,
   single acting compressor, 87
   S & T condensers, heat transfer, 447
Viscosity, 163
Vital heat, 185
Vitamin changes, 186
Voltage of motors, 178, 181
Voltmeter, 246
Volume,
   liquid per ton, 342
   measures, 440
   discharge vapor, per ton, 343
Volumetric efficiency, 92, 286, 301
VSA compressor, 87

W

Wall heat leakage calculations, 489
Water,
   content, foods, table, 432
   cooled condenser, 123
   cooling, 362
   regulating valve, 158
   spray defrost, 171
   supply, 128
Wattmeter, 246
Wax in oil, 163
Weak liquor, 422
Weights,
   food containers, table, 436
   and measures, table, 440
   various substances, 431
Welding, 137
Wet compression, 318
Wet vapor, 11
Wet-bulb thermometer 276
White ice, 402
Wine making, 373
Wire drawing, 57
Wood, insulating value, table, 445
Wort, 370

Y

Yeast, 373

Z

Zeon, 36, 40